STUDENT SOLUTIONS MANUAL

EDUTORIAL PUBLISHING SERVICES

Third Edition

INTERMEDIATE ALGEBRA

FUNCTIONS &
AUTHENTIC
APPLICATIONS

JAY LEHMANN

PEARSON

Prentice
Hall

Upper Saddle River, NJ 07458

Vice President and Editorial Director, Mathematics: Christine Hoag
Editor-in-Chief: Paul Murphy
Sponsoring Editor: Mary Beckwith
Editorial Assistant: Georgina Brown
Senior Managing Editor: Linda Mihatov Behrens
Associate Managing Editor: Bayani Mendoza de Leon
Project Manager, Production: Traci Douglas
Supplement Cover Manager: Paul Gourhan
Supplement Cover Designer: Victoria Colotta
Operations Specialist: Ilene Kahn
Senior Operations Supervisor: Diane Peirano

© 2008 Pearson Education, Inc.

Pearson Prentice Hall

Pearson Education, Inc.

Upper Saddle River, NJ 07458

The author and publisher of this book have used their best efforts in preparing this book. These efforts include the development, research, and testing of the theories and programs to determine their effectiveness. The author and publisher make no warranty of any kind, expressed or implied, with regard to these programs or the documentation contained in this book. The author and publisher shall not be liable in any event for incidental or consequential damages in connection with, or arising out of, the furnishing, performance, or use of these programs.

Printed in the United States of America

10   9   8   7   6   5   4   3   2   1

ISBN 13: 978-0-13-195351-2 Standalone

ISBN 10:   0-13-195351-6 Standalone

ISBN 13: 978-0-13-195359-8 Component

ISBN 13:   0-13-195359-1 Component

Pearson Education Ltd., *London*
Pearson Education Australia Pty. Ltd., *Sydney*
Pearson Education Singapore, Pte. Ltd.
Pearson Education North Asia Ltd., *Hong Kong*
Pearson Education Canada, Inc., *Toronto*
Pearson Educación de Mexico, S.A. de C.V.
Pearson Education—Japan, *Tokyo*
Pearson Education Malaysia, Pte. Ltd.

Table of Contents

Chapter 1
Linear Equations and Linear Functions

Homework 1.1

1. **a.** d

   b. c

   c. a

   d. b

3. The more tests there are to grade, the more time it takes to grade them. Time to grade (t) is the dependent variable and the number of tests (N) is the independent variable.

5. The hotter the temperature in an oven, the faster a potato will cook. The number of minutes (T) is the dependent variable and the oven temperature (F) is the independent variable.

7. The longer the song, the more time in seconds it takes to download. The number of seconds to download (T) is the dependent variable and the length of a song (L) is the independent variable.

9. The greater income a person earns, the more likely it is that she owns a car. The percentage of Americans who own a car (P) is the dependent variable and the income (I) is the independent variable.

11. The larger the radius of a plate, the more spaghetti it holds. The number of ounces of spaghetti (n) is the dependent variable and the radius of a plate (r) is the independent variable.

13.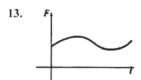

    Temperature (F) is the dependent variable and time (t) is the independent variable. The graph shows that the temperature increases as the sun rises around 6 AM ($t = 0$). It reaches a high in the afternoon and drops slowly as the sun begins to set. Shortly after dawn of the following day, the temperature begins to rise again.

15.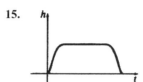

    The dependent variable is altitude (h) and the independent variable is time (t). The graph shows that the altitude of the airplane increased quickly after takeoff, then leveled off for the flight. Near the end of the trip, the plane descended for its landing.

17.

    The dependent variable is the number of people undergoing laser eye surgery (n) and the independent variable is time (t). The graph shows that the number of people having laser eye surgery is increasing steadily as time goes on from 1996.

19.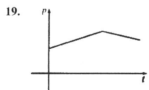

    The dependent variable is the percentage of major firms that perform drug testing (p) and the independent variable is time (t). The graph shows that the percentage of major firms performing drug testing increases over time from 1987 through 1996, and then decreases over time.

21.

    The dependent variable is amount of gas in the tank (g) and the independent variable is time (t) in minutes since the commuter left home. The graph decreases until the commuter purchases gas, rises when the gas is purchased, and then begins to decrease again as the commuter drives to work.

23.

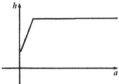

The dependent variable is height (*h*) and the independent variable is age (*a*). The curve shows that a person's height increases from birth and levels off after a number of years. Note that height will never be 0, and that it eventually levels off at a certain age.

25.

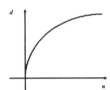

The diameter of a balloon in inches (*d*) is the dependent variable and the number of times a person has blow into the balloon (*n*) is the independent variable. The graph shows that as the number of blows into the balloon increases, the diameter increases (although at an ever slower rate).

27.

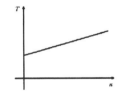

The time it takes to drive from home to school (*T*) is the dependent variable and the average number of cars per mile (*n*) is the independent variable. The graph shows that as the number of cars per mile increases, the time to drive from home to school increases.

29.

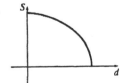

Speed (*S*) is the dependent variable and inches

(*d*) is the independent variable. This graph shows that when the distance between the accelerator and the floor of the car increases, the speed of the car decreases until the car comes to a stop at *S* = 0.

31.

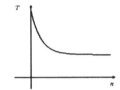

The time it takes a person to make lasagna (*T*) is the dependent variable and the number of times a person has made lasagna (*n*) is the independent variable. The graph shows that as the number of times a person has made lasagna increases, the time to make lasagna decreases.

33.

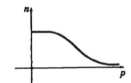

The dependent variable is *n*, the number of people that will buy the Honda Civic® CX, and the independent variable is *p*, the price at which the purchase occurs. The graph shows that more people will buy less expensive Honda Civic® CXs. As the price in dollars increases, fewer people are willing to purchase this car. The curve eventually levels off since there are only so many people who will buy the car no matter what the price.

35.

Area (*A*) is the dependent variable and radius (*r*) is the independent variable. The graph shows a rapid increase in area (*A*) as the circle's radius (*r*) increases. This is because the radius *r* is squared in the formula $A = \pi r^2$.

37. Answers may vary.

    a. Let *y* represent the height of a ball *x* seconds after it was thrown straight up in the air.

b. Let y represent the speed of a snow skier x seconds after skiing off a ramp when competing for the distance jumped.

c. Let y represent the water level of a creek t days after July 10 in Georgia. The water level remained the same during a cloudy week with very little rain and it dropped again steadily as summer passed until it completely dried up.

d. Let y represent the temperature of a building x minutes after the thermostat is adjusted to reach a warmer setting.

Homework 1.2

1.

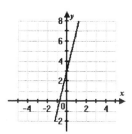

3.

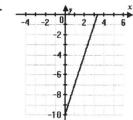

5.

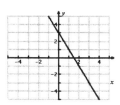

7.

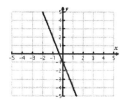

9.

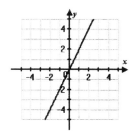

11.

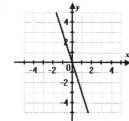

13.

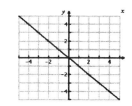

15. $9x - 3y = 0$

$$\frac{-3y}{-3} = \frac{-9x}{-3}$$

$$y = 3x$$

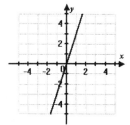

17. $3y - 6x = 12$

$$\frac{3y}{3} = \frac{12 + 6x}{3}$$

$$y = 4 + 2x$$

3

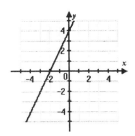

19. $8x - 2y - 10 = 0$
$$8x - 2y = 10$$
$$\frac{-2y}{-2} = \frac{-8x + 10}{-2}$$
$$y = 4x - 5$$

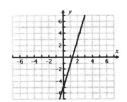

21. $2y - 6x - 14 = -4$
$$2y - 6x = 10$$
$$\frac{2y}{2} = \frac{10 + 6x}{2}$$
$$y = 5 + 3x$$

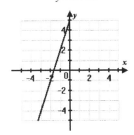

23. $8y - 7x + 3 = -4x + 5y - 9$
$$8y - 5y = -4x + 7x - 12$$
$$\frac{3y}{3} = \frac{3x - 12}{3}$$
$$y = x - 4$$

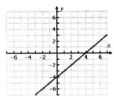

25. $-3(y - 5) = 2(3x - 6)$
$$-3y + 15 = 6x - 12$$
$$\frac{-3y}{-3} = \frac{6x - 27}{-3}$$
$$y = -2x + 9$$

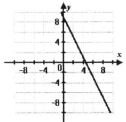

27. $6x - 3(2y - 3) = y - 2(4x - 1)$
$$6x - 6y + 9 = y - 8x + 2$$
$$-6y - y = -8x - 6x - 7$$
$$\frac{-7y}{-7} = \frac{-14x - 7}{-7}$$
$$y = 2x + 1$$

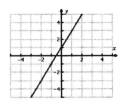

29.

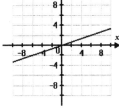

31.

4

33.

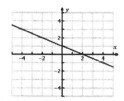

iii.

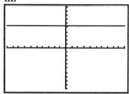

35. a.

Yes, this graph is a line with slope -4.1 and y-intercept 8.7.

b.

Yes, this graph is a horizontal line passing through $(0, 6)$.

c. Answers may vary. One example is as follows.

$$y = 2x + 3$$

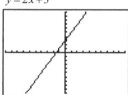

37. a. **i.**

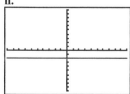

ii.

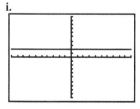

b. An equation of the form $y = b$ is a horizontal line passing through $(0, b)$.

39.

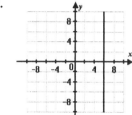

41.

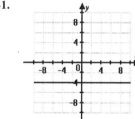

43.

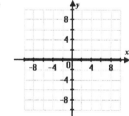

45.

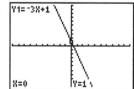

$(0, 1)$ is a point on the line.

$$y = -3x + 1$$

5

$$1 \overset{?}{=} -3(0) + 1$$
$$1 \overset{?}{=} 1$$
True

47. $0.83x = 4.98y - 2$
$$\frac{0.83x + 2}{4.98} = \frac{4.98y}{4.98}$$
$$y = \frac{(0.83x + 2)}{4.98}$$

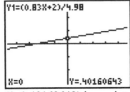

Y1=(0.83X+2)/4.98

X=0   Y=.40160643

$(0, 0.40160643)$ is a point on the line.
$$y = \frac{(0.83x + 2)}{4.98}$$
$$0.40160643 \overset{?}{=} \frac{(0.83(0) + 2)}{4.98}$$
$$0.40160643 \overset{?}{=} \frac{2}{4.98}$$
$$0.40160643 \overset{?}{=} 0.40160643$$
True

49. $x - 1 + 2x = 3x - 9x + 17$
$$3x - 1 = -6x + 17$$
$$\frac{9x}{9} = \frac{18}{9}$$
$$x = 2$$

51. $-2(3w + 5) = 3w - 4$
$$-6w - 10 = 3w - 4$$
$$\frac{-9w}{-9} = \frac{6}{-9}$$
$$w = -\frac{2}{3}$$

53. $4 - 6(2 - 3x) = 2x - (4 - 5x)$
$$4 - 12 + 18x = 2x - 4 + 5x$$
$$-8 + 18x = 7x - 4$$
$$\frac{11x}{11} = \frac{4}{11}$$
$$x = \frac{4}{11}$$

55. $4(r - 2) - 3(r - 1) = 2(r + 6)$
$$4r - 8 - 3r + 3 = 2r + 12$$
$$r - 5 = 2r + 12$$
$$-17 = r$$

57. $\frac{1}{2}x + \frac{1}{3} = \frac{5}{2}$
$$6\left(\frac{1}{2}x + \frac{1}{3}\right) = 6\left(\frac{5}{2}\right)$$
$$3x + 2 = 15$$
$$\frac{3x}{3} = \frac{13}{3}$$
$$x = \frac{13}{3}$$

59. $-\frac{5}{6}b + \frac{3}{4} = \frac{1}{2}b - \frac{2}{3}$
$$12\left(-\frac{5}{6}b + \frac{3}{4}\right) = 12\left(\frac{1}{2}b - \frac{2}{3}\right)$$
$$-10b + 9 = 6b - 8$$
$$\frac{-16b}{-16} = \frac{-17}{-16}$$
$$b = \frac{17}{16}$$

61. $2.75x - 3.95 = -6.21x + 74.92$
$$\frac{8.96x}{8.96} = \frac{78.87}{8.96}$$
$$x \approx 8.80$$

63. $P = 2L + 2W$
$$\frac{P - 2W}{2} = \frac{2L}{2}$$
$$L = \frac{P - 2W}{2}$$

65. $ax + by = c$
$$\frac{by}{b} = \frac{c - ax}{b}$$
$$y = \frac{c - ax}{b}$$

67. $y = 2x + 10$
To find the *x*-intercept, let $y = 0$ and solve for *x*.
$$0 = 2x + 10$$
$$-10 = 2x$$
$$-5 = x$$
The *x*-intercept is $(-5, 0)$. To find the *y*-intercept, let $x = 0$ and solve for *y*.

$$y = 2(0) + 10$$
$$y = 0 + 10$$
$$y = 10$$
The y-intercept is $(0, 10)$.

69. $2x + 3y = 12$
To find the x-intercept, let $y = 0$ and solve for x.
$$2x + 3(0) = 12$$
$$2x + 0 = 12$$
$$2x = 12$$
$$x = 6$$
The x-intercept is $(6, 0)$. To find the
y-intercept, let $x = 0$ and solve for y.
$$2(0) + 3y = 12$$
$$0 + 3y = 12$$
$$3y = 12$$
$$y = 4$$
The y-intercept is $(0, 4)$.

71. $y = 3x$
To find the x-intercept, let $y = 0$ and solve for x.
$$0 = 3x$$
$$0 = x$$
The x-intercept is $(0, 0)$. To find the
y-intercept, let $x = 0$ and solve for y.
$$y = 3(0)$$
$$y = 0$$
The y-intercept is $(0, 0)$.

73. $y = 3$
Since $y = 3$ is a horizontal line, it never intersects
the x-axis. Therefore, there is no x-intercept.
Since the graph passes through $(0, 3)$, this is the
y-intercept.

75. $y = mx + b$
To find the x-intercept, let $y = 0$ and solve for x.
$$0 = mx + b$$
$$-b = mx$$
$$-\frac{b}{m} = x$$
The x-intercept is $\left(-\dfrac{b}{m}, 0\right)$. To find the
y-intercept, let $x = 0$ and solve for y.
$$y = m(0) + b$$
$$y = b$$
The y-intercept is $(0, b)$.

77. $\dfrac{x}{a} + \dfrac{y}{b} = 1$
To find the x-intercept, let $y = 0$ and solve for x.
$$\frac{x}{a} + \frac{0}{b} = 1$$
$$a\left(\frac{x}{a}\right) = a(1)$$
$$x = a$$
The x-intercept is $(a, 0)$. To find the
y-intercept, let $x = 0$ and solve for y.
$$\frac{0}{a} + \frac{y}{b} = 1$$
$$b\left(\frac{y}{b}\right) = b(1)$$
$$y = b$$
The y-intercept is $(0, b)$.

79. Answers may vary.

x	y
-5	4
-3	3
-1	2
1	1
3	0

81. $y = -3$

83. $y \approx 3$

85. $y \approx -2.5$

87. $x \approx 6$

89. $x \approx -2$

91. $x \approx -5$

93. a.

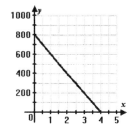

b. To find the y-intercept, let $x = 0$ and solve
for y.

$$y=-200(0)+800$$
$$y=0+800$$
$$y=800$$

The *y*-intercept is (0, 800). This means that before the person begins to lower the balloon, the height is 800 feet.

c. To find the *x*-intercept, let *y* = 0 and solve for *x*.
$$0=-200x+800$$
$$-800=-200x$$
$$4=x$$

The *x*-intercept is (4, 0). This means that after 4 minutes, the balloon will be lowered to the ground (altitude = 0).

95. Substitute for *x* and *y* in the equation and solve for *b*.
$$y=2x+b$$
$$5=2(7)+b$$
$$5=14+b$$
$$-9=b$$

97. The points *B*, *C* and *F* satisfy the equation.

99.
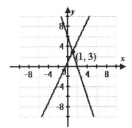

The ordered pair (1, 3) satisfies both equations, since this point lies on the intersection of the lines.

101. To sketch the graph of a linear equation, create a table of ordered pair solutions of the equation by substituting values of one variable and solving for the other variable. Then, plot the ordered pairs from the table and sketch the line that passes through these plotted points. The graph of an equation is all points that satisfy the equation.

Homework 1.3

1. $m_A=\dfrac{120}{4000}=0.03$

$m_B=\dfrac{160}{6500}\approx0.025$

Road A is steeper than road B, since the slope of road A is greater than the slope of road B.

3. $m_A=\dfrac{|-90|}{300}=\dfrac{90}{300}=0.3$

$m_B=\dfrac{|-125|}{450}=\dfrac{125}{450}=0.3125$

Ski run B is steeper than ski run A, since the slope of ski run B is greater than the slope of ski run A. (In determining which is steeper, ignore the sign of the slope by considering the absolute value.)

5. $m=\dfrac{y_2-y_1}{x_2-x_1}=\dfrac{9-3}{5-2}=\dfrac{6}{3}=2$

Since *m* is positive, the line is increasing.

7. $m=\dfrac{y_2-y_1}{x_2-x_1}=\dfrac{7-3}{-5-1}=\dfrac{4}{-6}=-\dfrac{2}{3}$

Since *m* is negative, the line is decreasing.

9. $m=\dfrac{y_2-y_1}{x_2-x_1}=\dfrac{10-(-2)}{-4-2}=\dfrac{10+2}{-6}=\dfrac{12}{-6}=-2$

Since *m* is negative, the line is decreasing.

11. $m=\dfrac{y_2-y_1}{x_2-x_1}=\dfrac{-2-(-4)}{1-7}=\dfrac{2}{-6}=-\dfrac{1}{3}$

Since *m* is negative, the line is decreasing.

13. $m=\dfrac{y_2-y_1}{x_2-x_1}=\dfrac{-8-(-2)}{-5-4}=\dfrac{-6}{-9}=\dfrac{2}{3}$

Since *m* is positive, the line is increasing.

15. $m=\dfrac{y_2-y_1}{x_2-x_1}=\dfrac{-9-(-1)}{-4-(-2)}=\dfrac{-8}{-2}=4$

Since *m* is positive, the line is increasing.

17. $m=\dfrac{y_2-y_1}{x_2-x_1}=\dfrac{1-0}{1-0}=\dfrac{1}{1}=1$

Since *m* is positive, the line is increasing.

19. $m=\dfrac{y_2-y_1}{x_2-x_1}=\dfrac{6-6}{7-2}=\dfrac{0}{5}=0$

Since *m* = 0, the line is horizontal.

21.
$$m = \frac{y_2 - y_1}{x_2 - x_1} = \frac{-2 - 5}{-6 - (-6)} = \frac{-7}{0} = \text{undefined}$$
Since m is undefined, the line is vertical.

23.
$$m = \frac{y_2 - y_1}{x_2 - x_1} = \frac{5.4 - 2.6}{1.2 - 3.9} = \frac{2.8}{-2.7} \approx -1.04$$
Since m is negative, the line is decreasing.

25.
$$m = \frac{y_2 - y_1}{x_2 - x_1} = \frac{-17.94 - (-2.34)}{8.94 - 21.13} = \frac{-15.6}{-12.19} \approx 1.28 \text{ Si}$$
nce m is positive, the line is increasing.

27. a. The slope is defined since it is increasing. The slope is positive.

  b. The slope is defined since it is decreasing. The slope is negative.

  c. The slope is defined since it is a horizontal line. The slope is zero.

  d. The slope of the line is undefined. The line is vertical.

29. The points $(3, 0)$ and $(-2, 2)$ lie on the line.
$$m = \frac{y_2 - y_1}{x_2 - x_1} = \frac{2 - 0}{-2 - 3} = \frac{2}{-5} = -\frac{2}{5}$$
The slope of the line is $-\frac{2}{5}$.

31. Since $m_1 = m_2$, the lines are parallel.

33. The lines are neither parallel nor perpendicular.

35. Since $m_2 = -\dfrac{1}{m_1}$, the lines are perpendicular.

37. The lines are neither parallel nor perpendicular.

39. Since $m_1 = 0$, l_1 is a horizontal line. Since m_2 is undefined, l_2 is a vertical line. From geometry, any horizontal line is perpendicular to any vertical line. Therefore, the lines are perpendicular.

41. No, the lines are not perpendicular because their slopes, $-\dfrac{1}{4}$ and 3, are not opposite reciprocals.

43. Answers may vary.

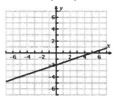

45. Answers may vary.

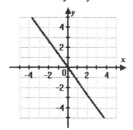

47. Answers may vary.

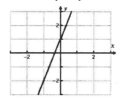

49. Answers may vary.

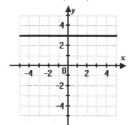

51.

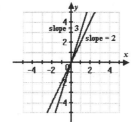

The line with slope 3 is steeper.

53.

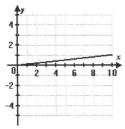

The points $(0, 0)$ and $(10, 1)$ are on the line and can be used to find the slope.

$$m = \frac{y_2 - y_1}{x_2 - x_1} = \frac{1 - 0}{10 - 0} = \frac{1}{10}$$

55.

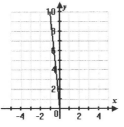

The points $(0, 0)$ and $(-1, 10)$ are on the line and can be used to find the slope.

$$m = \frac{y_2 - y_1}{x_2 - x_1} = \frac{10 - 0}{-1 - 0} = \frac{10}{-1} = -10$$

57.

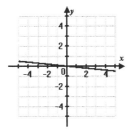

59.

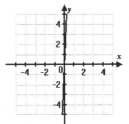

61. The student exchanged the *x*-coordinates with the *y*-coordinates. So, the correct slope is $\frac{3}{2}$ instead

of $\frac{2}{3}$ since $m = \frac{y_2 - y_1}{x_2 - x_1} = \frac{5 - 8}{2 - 4} = \frac{-3}{-2} = \frac{3}{2}$.

63.

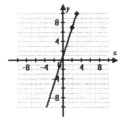

Answers may vary. Three points that lie on the line are $(1, 4)$, $(0, 1)$, and $(-1, -2)$.

65. a. i.

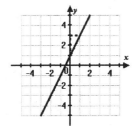

$$\frac{\text{rise}}{\text{run}} = \frac{2}{1} = 2$$

ii.

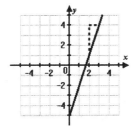

$$\frac{\text{rise}}{\text{run}} = \frac{3}{1} = 3$$

iii.

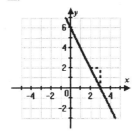

$$\frac{\text{rise}}{\text{run}} = \frac{2}{-1} = -2$$

b. The slope of the line found using $\frac{\text{rise}}{\text{run}}$ is the same as the coefficient of x in each of the corresponding equations.

67. a.

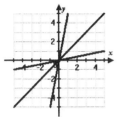

b.

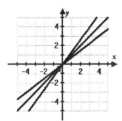

c.

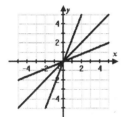

d. The graphs in parts a-c are mirror images of each other across the graph of $y = x$.

e.

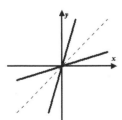

69. The line contains both points, S and Q. The slope is $-\frac{2}{3}$ and can be written $\frac{\text{rise}}{\text{run}} = \frac{-2}{3} = \frac{2}{-3}$. From point P, moving 3 units to the right and 2 units

down is the equivalent of $\frac{\text{rise}}{\text{run}} - \frac{-2}{3}$. From point P, moving 3 units to the left and 2 units up is the equivalent of $\frac{\text{rise}}{\text{run}} = \frac{2}{-3}$.

Homework 1.4

1. Since $y = 6x + 1$ is in the form $y = mx + b$, the slope is $m = 6 = \frac{6}{1} = \frac{\text{rise}}{\text{run}}$, and the y-intercept is (0, 1).

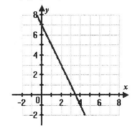

3. Since $y = -2x + 7$ is in the form $y = mx + b$, the slope is $m = -2 = \frac{-2}{1} = \frac{\text{rise}}{\text{run}}$, and the y-intercept is (0, 7).

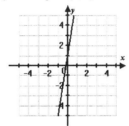

5. Since $y = \frac{5}{4}x - 2$ is in the form $y = mx + b$, the slope is $m = \frac{5}{4} = \frac{\text{rise}}{\text{run}}$, and the y-intercept is (0, −2).

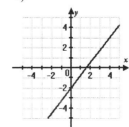

7. Since $y = -\dfrac{3}{7}x + 2$ is in the form $y = mx + b$,

the slope is $m = -\dfrac{3}{7} = \dfrac{-3}{7} = \dfrac{\text{rise}}{\text{run}}$, and the y-intercept is $(0, 2)$.

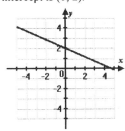

9. Since $y = -\dfrac{5}{3}x - 1$ is in the form $y = mx + b$, the

slope is $m = -\dfrac{5}{3} = \dfrac{-5}{3} = \dfrac{\text{rise}}{\text{run}}$, and the y-intercept is $(0, -1)$.

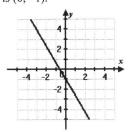

11. First, rewrite $y + x = 5$ in slope-intercept form.
$$y + x = 5$$
$$y = -x + 5$$

The slope is $m = -1 = \dfrac{-1}{1} = \dfrac{\text{rise}}{\text{run}}$, and the y-intercept is $(0, 5)$.

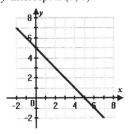

13. First, rewrite $-7x + 2y = 10$ in slope-intercept form.

$$-7x + 2y = 10$$
$$2y = 7x + 10$$
$$y = \dfrac{7}{2}x + 5$$

The slope is $m = \dfrac{7}{2} = \dfrac{\text{rise}}{\text{run}}$, and the y-intercept is $(0, 5)$.

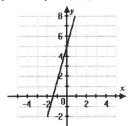

15. First, rewrite $3(x - 2y) = 9$ in slope-intercept form.
$$3(x - 2y) = 9$$
$$3x - 6y = 9$$
$$-6y = -3x + 9$$
$$y = \dfrac{1}{2}x - \dfrac{3}{2}$$

The slope is $m = \dfrac{1}{2} = \dfrac{\text{rise}}{\text{run}}$, and the y-intercept is $\left(0, -\dfrac{3}{2}\right)$.

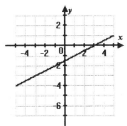

17. First, rewrite $2x - 3y + 9 = 12$ in slope-intercept form.
$$2x - 3y + 9 = 12$$
$$-3y = -2x + 3$$
$$y = \dfrac{2}{3}x - 1$$

The slope is $m = \dfrac{2}{3} = \dfrac{\text{rise}}{\text{run}}$, and the

y-intercept is $(0,-1)$.

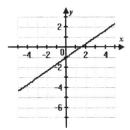

19. First, rewrite $4x-5y+3=2x-2y-3$ in slope-intercept form.

$$4x-5y+3=2x-2y-3$$
$$-3y=-2x-6$$
$$y=\frac{2}{3}x+2$$

The slope is $m=\frac{2}{3}=\frac{\text{rise}}{\text{run}}$, and the y-intercept is $(0,2)$.

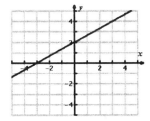

21. First, rewrite $1-3(y-2x)=7+3(x-3y)$ in slope-intercept form.

$$1-3(y-2x)=7+3(x-3y)$$
$$1-3y+6x=7+3x-9y$$
$$6y=-3x+6$$
$$y=-\frac{1}{2}x+1$$

The slope is $m=\frac{-1}{2}=\frac{\text{rise}}{\text{run}}$, and the y-intercept is $(0,1)$.

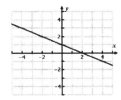

23. Rewrite $y=4x$ as $y=4x+0$ to obtain slope-

intercept form. The slope is $m=4=\frac{4}{1}=\frac{\text{rise}}{\text{run}}$, and the y-intercept is $(0,0)$.

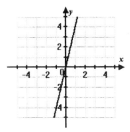

25. Since $y=-1.5x+3$ is in the form $y=mx+b$, the slope is $m=-1.5=\frac{-3}{2}=\frac{\text{rise}}{\text{run}}$, and the y-intercept is $(0, 3)$.

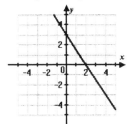

27. Rewrite $y=x$ as $y=1x+0$ to obtain slope-intercept form. The slope is $m=1=\frac{1}{1}=\frac{\text{rise}}{\text{run}}$, and the y-intercept is $(0,0)$.

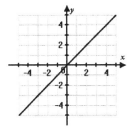

29. The linear equation $y=4$ is a horizontal line. The slope of a horizontal line is $m=0$, and there is no x-intercept.

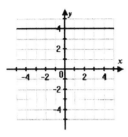

31. Solve for y.

$y + 2 = 0$

$y = -2$

The linear equation $y = -2$ is a horizontal line.

The slope of a horizontal line is $m = 0$, and there is no x-intercept.

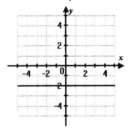

33. Solve for y.

$ax - by = c$

$-by = -ax + c$

$y = \dfrac{a}{b}x - \dfrac{c}{b}$

The slope is $\dfrac{a}{b}$ and the y-intercept is $\left(0, -\dfrac{c}{b}\right)$.

35. Solve for y.

$a(y + b) = x$

$ay + ab = x$

$ay = x - ab$

$y = \dfrac{1}{a}x - b$

The slope is $\dfrac{1}{a}$ and the y-intercept is $(0, -b)$.

37. Solve for y.

$\dfrac{x}{a} + \dfrac{y}{a} = 1$

$x + y = a$

$y = -x + a$

The slope is -1 and the y-intercept is $(0, a)$.

39. Set 1 is not linear. As x increases by 1, y_1 does not change by some consistent value. It is possible that there is a line that comes close to every point since the changes in y_1 are roughly the same.

Set 2 is linear. As x increases by 1, y_2 decreases by -0.3. The slope is $\dfrac{-0.3}{1} = -0.3$.

Set 3 is not linear. The value of x does not change (increase or decrease) consistently, even though y_3 increases by 5.

Set 4 is linear. As x increases by 1, y_4 decreases by 10. The slope is $-\dfrac{10}{1} = -10$.

41.

Values of Four Linear Equations							
Eq. 1		Eq. 2		Eq. 3		Eq. 4	
x	y	x	y	x	y	x	y
1	12	23	69	1	47	30	15
2	15	24	53	2	41	31	24
3	18	25	37	3	35	32	33
4	21	26	21	4	29	33	42
5	24	27	5	5	23	34	51
6	27	28	-11	6	17	35	60

43. a. Since this is a decreasing line, the slope, *m,* is negative ($m < 0$). The line crosses the y-axis above the origin so the y-intercept is positive ($b > 0$).

b. Since this is as increasing line, the slope, *m,* is positive ($m > 0$). The line crosses the y-axis below the origin so the y-intercept is negative ($b < 0$).

c. Since the line is horizontal and crosses the y-axis below the origin, the slope, *m,* is 0 and the y-intercept, *b,* is negative ($b < 0$).

d. Since this is a decreasing line that passes through the origin, the slope, *m,* is negative ($m < 0$), and the y-intercept, *b,* is 0.

45. The slope is $m = \dfrac{\text{rise}}{\text{run}} = \dfrac{-2}{1}$. The y-intercept is $(0, 3)$. The equation of the line is $y = -2x + 3$.

47. Answers may vary. One example is

$y = \dfrac{1}{100}x + 2$. The slope is a small positive number, and the y-intercept is positive.

49. Answers may vary. One example is $y = -700x - 2$. The slope is a large negative number, and the y-intercept is negative.

51. For both lines, the slope is 4. The lines are parallel.

53. The slopes are $\dfrac{3}{8}$ and $\dfrac{8}{3}$. The slopes are reciprocals, but not negative reciprocals. The lines are neither parallel nor perpendicular.

55. Solve each equation for y.

$$2x + 3y = 6 \qquad\qquad 4x + 6y = 7$$
$$3y = -2x + 6 \qquad\qquad 6y = -4x + 7$$
$$y = -\frac{2}{3}x + 2 \qquad\qquad y = -\frac{2}{3}x + \frac{7}{6}$$

Since the slopes are both $m = -\dfrac{2}{3}$, the lines are parallel.

57. Solve each equation for y.

$$5x - 3y = 1 \qquad\qquad 3x + 5y = -2$$
$$-3y = -5x + 1 \qquad\qquad 5y = -3x - 2$$
$$y = \frac{5}{3}x - \frac{1}{3} \qquad\qquad y = -\frac{3}{5}x - \frac{2}{5}$$

Since the slopes are negative reciprocals, the lines are perpendicular.

59. $x = -3$ and $x = 1$ are both vertical lines. All vertical lines are parallel.

61. $x = 0$ and $y = 0$ are the equations for the vertical and horizontal axes, respectively. These lines are perpendicular.

63. **a.** Substitute values for x in the equation $y = -3x + 18$ to solve for y.

When $x = 0$, $y = -3(0) + 18 = 0 + 18 = 18$.

When $x = 1$, $y = -3(1) + 18 = -3 + 18 = 15$.

When $x = 2$, $y = -3(2) + 18 = -6 + 18 = 12$.

When $x = 3$, $y = -3(3) + 18 = -9 + 18 = 9$.

When $x = 4$, $y = -3(4) + 18 = -12 + 18 = 6$.

When $x = 5$, $y = -3(5) + 18 = -15 + 18 = 3$.

When $x = 6$, $y = -3(6) + 18 = -18 + 18 = 0$.

Amount of Gas in a Car's Gas Tank	
Driving Time (hours) x	Amount of Gas (gallons) y
0	18
1	15
2	12
3	9
4	6
5	3
6	0

b. Each hour, the amount of gas in the tank decreases by 3 gallons. The slope of -3 in the equation shows this decrease of 3. As the value of the independent variable (driving time) increases by 1, the value of the dependent variable (amount of gas) decreases by 3 as determined by the slope.

c. Note that in one hour's time, 3 gallons of gas is used. If the person is driving at approximately 60 mph, he or she uses 3 gallons to drive 60 miles. So for 1 gallon of gas, a person can travel 20 miles ($60 \div 3$).

65. **a.** Substitute values for x in the equation $y = 2x + 26$ to solve for y and complete the table.

When $x = 0$, $y = 2(0) + 26 = 0 + 26 = 26$.

When $x = 1$, $y = 2(1) + 26 = 2 + 26 = 28$.

Similar calculations yield the following table.

Salaries	
Time at Company (years) x	Salary (thousands of dollars) y
0	26
1	28
2	30
3	32
4	34

b. Each year the person's salary increases by $2000, which corresponds to the slope of $y = 2x + 26$ with y in thousands of dollars.

As the value of the independent variable (time at company) increases by 1, the value of the dependent variable (salary) increases by 2 as determined by the slope.

67. a.

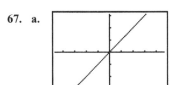

b.

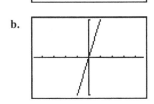

c.

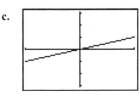

d. The slope of the graph in part b appears to be steeper than the graph in part a. The graph of part c appears to be less steep than the graph in part a.

e. No, you cannot make the sketch of $y = x$ appear to be a decreasing line or cross the y-axis at a point other than $(0, 0)$ by changing the window settings. The line will always appear to be increasing and it will always lie in quadrants one and three, but it may appear to have any steepness within these constraints.

69. Since we have the slope, $m = 2$, and a point on the line, $(0, -3)$, we can substitute in the equation $y = mx + b$ to find the y-intercept, b.

$$y = mx + b$$

$$-3 = 2(0) + b$$

$$-3 = b$$

We can now write the equation of the line in slope-intercept form.

$$y = 2x + (-3)$$

$$y = 2x - 3$$

71. a.

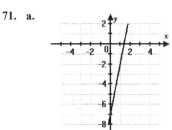

b. From the graph in part a, we see that the y-intercept, b, is -7. Using the slope and the y-intercept, we can write the equation of the line in slope-intercept form.

$$y = 5x + (-7)$$

$$y = 5x - 7$$

c.

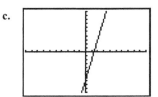

73. a.

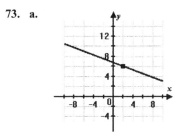

b. From the graph in part a, we see that the y-intercept, b, is approximately $6\frac{1}{2}$. Using the slope and the y-intercept, we can write the equation of the line.

$$y = -\frac{3}{8}x + \frac{13}{2}$$

c.

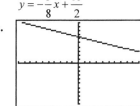

75. a. Each line is a horizontal line with a slope of 0.

b. The slope for the graph for a linear equation of the form $y = k$ is 0 when k is a constant.

77. The coefficient of x is the slope of a line when the equation is written in slope-intercept form. The equation, $2x + 3y = 6$, is not written in slope intercept form. To find the slope, rewrite the equation in slope-intercept form by solving for y.
$$2x + 3y = 6$$
$$3y = -2x + 6$$
$$y = -\frac{2}{3}x + \frac{6}{3}$$
$$y = -\frac{2}{3}x + 2$$

The slope of the line is $-\frac{2}{3}$.

79. Answers may vary.
$$y_1 = mx + b$$
$$y_2 = m(x+1) + b$$
$$y_2 = mx + m + b$$
$$y_2 = y_1 + m$$

Homework 1.5

1. We are given the slope, $m = 3$, and a point on the line, $(5, 2)$. Use $y = mx + b$ to find b.
$$y = mx + b$$
$$2 = 3(5) + b$$
$$2 = 15 + b$$
$$-13 = b$$
Now, substitute for m and b in slope-intercept form to obtain the equation of the line.
$$y = 3x + (-13)$$
$$y = 3x - 13$$

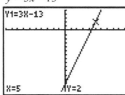

The sign of m (positive) agrees with the increasing line from the graphing calculator screen.

3. We are given the slope, $m = -2$, and a point on the line, $(3, -9)$. Use $y = mx + b$ to find b.
$$y = mx + b$$
$$-9 = -2(3) + b$$
$$-9 = -6 + b$$
$$-3 = b$$
Now, substitute for m and b in slope-intercept form to obtain the equation of the line.
$$y = -2x + (-3)$$
$$y = -2x - 3$$

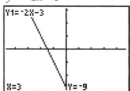

The sign of m (negative) agrees with the decreasing line from the graphing calculator screen.

5. We are given the slope, $m = \frac{3}{5}$, and a point on the line, $(20, 7)$. Use $y = mx + b$ to find b.
$$y = mx + b$$
$$7 = \frac{3}{5}(20) + b$$
$$7 = 12 + b$$
$$-5 = b$$
Now, substitute for m and b in slope-intercept form to obtain the equation of the line.
$$y = \frac{3}{5}x + (-5)$$
$$y = \frac{3}{5}x - 5$$

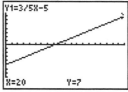

The sign of m (positive) agrees with the increasing line shown on the graphing calculator screen.

7. We are given the slope, $m = -\frac{1}{6}$, and a point on the line, $(2, -3)$. Use $y = mx + b$ to find b.

$$y = mx + b$$

$$-3 = -\frac{1}{6}(2) + b$$

$$-3 = -\frac{1}{3} + b$$

$$-\frac{9}{3} = -\frac{1}{3} + b$$

$$-\frac{8}{3} = b$$

Now, substitute for *m* and *b* in slope-intercept form to obtain the equation of the line.

$$y = -\frac{1}{6}x + \left(-\frac{8}{3}\right)$$

$$y = -\frac{1}{6}x - \frac{8}{3}$$

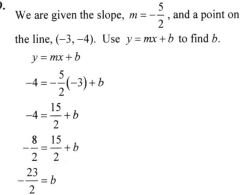

The sign of *m* (negative) agrees with the decreasing line shown on the graphing calculator screen.

9. We are given the slope, $m = -\frac{5}{2}$, and a point on

the line, $(-3, -4)$. Use $y = mx + b$ to find *b*.

$$y = mx + b$$

$$-4 = -\frac{5}{2}(-3) + b$$

$$-4 = \frac{15}{2} + b$$

$$-\frac{8}{2} = \frac{15}{2} + b$$

$$-\frac{23}{2} = b$$

Now, substitute for *m* and *b* in slope-intercept form to obtain the equation of the line.

$$y = -\frac{5}{2}x + \left(-\frac{23}{2}\right)$$

$$y = -\frac{5}{2}x - \frac{23}{2}$$

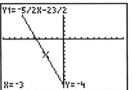

The sign of *m* (negative) agrees with the decreasing line shown on the graphing calculator screen.

11. We are given the slope, $m = 0$, and a point on the line, $(1, 2)$. We know that a line with a slope of 0 is a horizontal line. Horizontal lines are of the form $y = b$. In this example, $y = 2$.

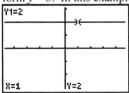

Since *m* is zero, the line is horizontal. This is shown on the graphing calculator screen.

13. We are given that *m* is undefined, and a point on the line is $(3, 7)$. We know that a line with an undefined slope is a vertical line. Vertical lines are of the form $x = a$. In this example, $x = 3$.

Since *m* is undefined, the line is vertical. This is shown on the graphing calculator screen.

15. We are given the slope, $m = 1.6$, and a point on the line, $(2.1, 3.8)$. Use $y = mx + b$ to find *b*.

$$y = mx + b$$

$$3.8 = 1.6(2.1) + b$$

$$3.8 = 3.36 + b$$

$$0.44 = b$$

Now, substitute for *m* and *b* in slope-intercept form to obtain the equation of the line.

$$y = 1.6x + 0.44$$

To check, substitute $(2.1, 3.8)$ into the equation.

$$y = 1.6x + 0.44$$

$$3.8 \overset{?}{=} 1.6(2.1) + 0.44$$

$$3.8 \overset{?}{=} 3.8$$

True

17. We are given the slope, $m = -3.24$, and a point on the line, $(-5.28, 1.93)$. Use $y = mx + b$ to find b.

$$y = mx + b$$
$$1.93 = -3.24(-5.28) + b$$
$$1.93 = 17.1072 + b$$
$$-15.18 \approx b$$

Substitute m and b in slope-intercept form to obtain the equation of the line.
$$y = -3.24x - 15.18$$

To check, substitute $(-5.28, 1.93)$ into the equation.
$$y = -3.24x - 15.18$$
$$1.93 \overset{?}{=} -3.24(-5.28) - 15.18$$
$$1.93 \overset{?}{=} 1.93$$
True

19. First, find the slope.
$$m = \frac{5-3}{4-2} = \frac{2}{2} = 1$$
So, $y = 1x + b$. Since the line contains (2, 3), substitute 2 for x and 3 for y and solve for b.
$$3 = 1(2) + b$$
$$3 = 2 + b$$
$$1 = b$$
So, the equation is $y = x + 1$.

21. First, find the slope.
$$m = \frac{6-(-4)}{-2-3} = \frac{6+4}{-5} = \frac{10}{-5} = -2$$
So, $y = -2x + b$. Since the line contains (−2, 6), substitute −2 for x and 6 for y and solve for b.
$$6 = -2(-2) + b$$
$$6 = 4 + b$$
$$2 = b$$
So, the equation is $y = -2x + 2$.

23. First, find the slope.
$$m = \frac{-6-(-14)}{-8-(-4)} = \frac{-6+14}{-8+4} = \frac{8}{-4} = -2$$
So, $y = -2x + b$. Since the line contains (−8, −6), substitute −8 for x and −6 for y and solve for b.
$$-6 = -2(-8) + b$$
$$-6 = 16 + b$$
$$-22 = b$$

So, the equation is $y = -2x - 22$.

25. First, find the slope.
$$m = \frac{1-0}{1-0} = \frac{1}{1} = 1$$
So, $y = 1x + b$. Since the line contains (0, 0) substitute 0 for x and 0 for y to solve for b.
$$0 = 1(0) + b$$
$$0 = 0 + b$$
$$0 = b$$
So, the equation is $y = x$.

27. First, find the slope.
$$m = \frac{5-1}{7-2} = \frac{4}{5}$$
So, $y = \frac{4}{5}x + b$. Since the line passes through $(2,1)$, substitute 2 for x and 1 for y to solve for b.
$$1 = \frac{4}{5}(2) + b$$
$$1 = \frac{8}{5} + b$$
$$\frac{5}{5} = \frac{8}{5} + b$$
$$-\frac{3}{5} = b$$

So, the equation is $y = \frac{4}{5}x - \frac{3}{5}$.

29. First, find the slope.
$$m = \frac{2-(-5)}{-4-2} = \frac{2+5}{-6} = \frac{7}{-6} = -\frac{7}{6}$$
So, $y = -\frac{7}{6}x + b$. Since the line passes through (−4, 2), substitute −4 for x and 2 for y to solve for b.
$$2 = -\frac{7}{6}(-4) + b$$
$$2 = \frac{14}{3} + b$$
$$\frac{6}{3} = \frac{14}{3} + b$$
$$-\frac{8}{3} = b$$

So, the equation is $y = -\frac{7}{6}x - \frac{8}{3}$.

31. First, find the slope.

$$m = \frac{-7-(-2)}{-5-(-3)} = \frac{-7+2}{-5+3} = \frac{-5}{-2} = \frac{5}{2}$$

So, $y = \frac{5}{2}x + b$. Since the line passes through

$(-5, -7)$, substitute -5 for x and -7 for y to solve for b.

$$-7 = \frac{5}{2}(-5) + b$$

$$-7 = -\frac{25}{2} + b$$

$$-\frac{14}{2} = -\frac{25}{2} + b$$

$$\frac{11}{2} = b$$

So, the equation is $y = \frac{5}{2}x + \frac{11}{2}$.

33. First, find the slope.

$$m = \frac{5-5}{4-2} = \frac{0}{2} = 0$$

So, $y = 0x + b$ or $y = b$. Since this is a horizontal line passing through (2, 5), the equation is $y = 5$.

35. First, find the slope.

$$m = \frac{-4-6}{-3-(-3)} = \frac{-10}{0} \text{ undefined}$$

The slope is undefined. This is a vertical line passing through $(-3, -4)$, so the equation is $x = -3$.

37. First, find the slope.

$$m = \frac{-3.9-2.2}{-5.1-7.4} = \frac{-6.1}{-12.5} \approx -0.49$$

So, $y = 0.49x + b$. Since the line contains (7.4, 2.2), substitute 7.4 for x and 2.2 for y to solve for b.

$$2.2 = 0.49(7.4) + b$$
$$2.2 = 3.626 + b$$
$$-1.45 \approx b$$

So, the equation is $y = 0.49x - 1.45$.

39. First, find the slope.

$$m = \frac{-6.24-(-4.05)}{-5.97-(-1.25)} = \frac{-2.19}{-4.72} \approx 0.46$$

So, $y = 0.46x + b$. Since the line passes through $(-5.97, -6.24)$, substitute -5.97 for x and -6.24

for y to solve for b.

$$-6.24 = 0.46(-5.97) + b$$
$$-6.24 = -2.7462 + b$$
$$-3.49 \approx b$$

So, the equation is $y = 0.46x - 3.49$.

41. The slope of the given line is 3. A line parallel to the given line also has a slope of 3 and an equation $y = 3x + b$. Since the point (4, 5) lies on the parallel line, substitute 4 for x and 5 for y to solve or b.

$$5 = 3(4) + b$$
$$5 = 12 + b$$
$$-7 = b$$

The parallel line's equation is $y = 3x - 7$.

43. The slope of the given line is -2. A line parallel to this has a slope of -2 and an equation $y = -2x + b$. Substitute -3 for x and 8 for y to solve for b since the parallel line contains $(-3, 8)$.

$$8 = -2(-3) + b$$
$$8 = 6 + b$$
$$2 = b$$

The parallel line's equation is $y = -2x + 2$.

45. The slope of the given line is $\frac{1}{2}$. A line parallel to this has a slope of $\frac{1}{2}$ and an equation $y = \frac{1}{2}x + b$. Substitute 4 for x and 1 for y to solve for b since the parallel line contains (4, 1).

$$1 = \frac{1}{2}(4) + b$$
$$1 = 2 + b$$
$$-1 = b$$

The parallel line's equation is $y = \frac{1}{2}x - 1$ or $y = 0.5x - 1$.

47. To find the slope, isolate y.

$$3x - 4y = 12$$
$$-4y = -3x + 12$$
$$y = \frac{3}{4}x - 3$$

The slope is $\frac{3}{4}$. A line parallel to this has the

same slope and an equation $y = \frac{3}{4}x + b$.

Substitute 3 for x and 4 for y to solve for b since the parallel line contains (3, 4).

$$4 = \frac{3}{4}(3) + b$$

$$4 = \frac{9}{4} + b$$

$$\frac{16}{4} = \frac{9}{4} + b$$

$$\frac{7}{4} = b$$

The parallel line's equation $y = \frac{3}{4}x + \frac{7}{4}$ or

$y = 0.75x + 1.75$.

49. To find the slope, isolate y.
$$6y - x = -7$$
$$6y = x - 7$$
$$y = \frac{1}{6}x - \frac{7}{6}$$

The slope is $\frac{1}{6}$. A line parallel to this has the

same slope and an equation $y = \frac{1}{6}x + b$.

Substitute -3 for x and -2 for y to solve for b since the parallel line contains $(-3, -2)$.

$$-2 = \frac{1}{6}(-3) + b$$

$$-2 = -\frac{1}{2} + b$$

$$-\frac{4}{2} = -\frac{1}{2} + b$$

$$-\frac{3}{2} = b$$

The parallel line's equation is $y = \frac{1}{6}x - \frac{3}{2}$.

51. The line $y = 6$ is horizontal and has a slope of 0.
A line parallel to $y = 6$ is also horizontal. Since the parallel line contains (2, 3) and horizontal lines are of the form
$y = b$, the equation of the line is $y = 3$.

The line $x = 2$ is vertical and has undefined slope.

53. A line parallel to $x = 2$ is also vertical. Since vertical lines are of the form $x = a$, and the parallel line contains (−5, 4), the equation of the line is $x = -5$.

55. The slope of the given line is 2. A line perpendicular to the given line must then have a

slope of $-\frac{1}{2}$ and an equation $y = -\frac{1}{2}x + b$.

Substitute 3 for x and 8 for y to solve for b since the line contains (3, 8).

$$8 = -\frac{1}{2}(3) + b$$

$$8 = -\frac{3}{2} + b$$

$$\frac{16}{2} = -\frac{3}{2} + b$$

$$\frac{19}{2} = b$$

The equation of the line is $y = -\frac{1}{2}x + \frac{19}{2}$ or

$y = -0.5x + 9.5$.

57. The slope of the given line is −3. A line perpendicular to the given line must then have a

slope of $\frac{1}{3}$ and an equation $y = \frac{1}{3}x + b$.

Substitute −1 for x and 7 for y to solve for b since the line contains (−1, 7).

$$7 = \frac{1}{3}(-1) + b$$

$$7 = -\frac{1}{3} + b$$

$$\frac{21}{3} = -\frac{1}{3} + b$$

$$\frac{22}{3} = b$$

The equation of the line is $y = \frac{1}{3}x + \frac{22}{3}$.

59.
The slope of the given line is $-\frac{2}{5}$. A line

perpendicular to the given line must then have a

slope of $\frac{5}{2}$ and an equation $y = \frac{5}{2}x + b$.

Substitute 2 for x and 7 for y to solve for b since the line contains (2, 7).

$7 = \frac{5}{2}(2) + b$

$7 = 5 + b$

$2 = b$

The equation of the line is $y = \frac{5}{2}x + 2$ or

$y = 2.5x + 2$.

61. To find the slope of the given line, isolate y.

$4x - 5y = 7$

$-5y = -4x + 7$

$y = \frac{4}{5}x - \frac{7}{5}$

The slope of this line is $\frac{4}{5}$. A line perpendicular

to this line must have a slope of $-\frac{5}{4}$ and an

equation $y = -\frac{5}{4}x + b$. Substitute 10 for x and 3

for y to solve for b since the line contains $(10,2)$.

$3 = -\frac{5}{4}(10) + b$

$3 = -\frac{25}{2} + b$

$\frac{6}{2} = -\frac{25}{2} + b$

$\frac{31}{2} = b$

The equation of the line is $y = -\frac{5}{4}x + \frac{31}{2}$ or

$y = -1.25x + 15.5$.

63. To find the slope of the given line, isolate y.

$-2x + y = 5$

$y = 2x + 5$

The slope of the line is 2. A line perpendicular to

this line must have a slope of $-\frac{1}{2}$ and an

equation $y = -\frac{1}{2}x + b$. Substitute -3 for x and

-1 for y to solve for b since the line contains

$(-3,-1)$.

$-1 = -\frac{1}{2}(-3) + b$

$-1 = \frac{3}{2} + b$

$-\frac{2}{2} = \frac{3}{2} + b$

The equation of the line is $y = -\frac{1}{2}x - \frac{5}{2}$ or

$y = -0.5x - 2.5$.

65. The slope of the equation $x = 5$ is undefined. The graph of the equation is a vertical line. A line perpendicular to $x = 5$ is a horizontal line with a slope of 0. Since this perpendicular line contains $(2, 3)$ and the y-value at this point is 3, the equation of the line is $y = 3$.

67. The slope of the equation $y = -3$ is 0. The graph of the equation is a horizontal line. A line perpendicular to $y = -3$ is a vertical line with an undefined slope. Since this perpendicular line contains $(2,8)$ and the x-value at this point is 2, the equation of the line is $x = 2$.

69. Choose any two points to find the slope.

$m = \frac{17 - 19}{1 - 0} = \frac{-2}{1} = -2$

So, $y = -2x + b$. Since the point $(0, 19)$ is a solution to the equation, substitute 0 for x and 19 for y to solve for b.

$19 = -2(0) + b$

$19 = 0 + b$

$19 = b$

The equation describing the relationship between x and y is $y = -2x + 19$.

71. Find the slope by choosing two points on the line, such as $(2, 0)$ and $(5, 1)$.

$m = \frac{1 - 0}{5 - 2} = \frac{1}{3}$

So, $y = \frac{1}{3}x + b$. Since the line contains

$(2, 0)$, substitute 2 for x and 0 for y to solve for b.

$0 = \frac{1}{3}(2) + b$

$0 = \frac{2}{3} + b$

$-\frac{2}{3} = b$

The equation for the line is $y = \frac{1}{3}x - \frac{2}{3}$.

73. Choose two points on the line to find the slope, such as (3, 3) and (5, 0).

$$m = \frac{3-0}{3-5} = \frac{3}{-2} = -\frac{3}{2}$$

So, $y = -\frac{3}{2}x + b$. Since the line contains (3, 3), substitute 3 for x and 3 for y to solve for b.

$$3 = -\frac{3}{2}(3) + b$$

$$\frac{6}{2} = -\frac{9}{2} + b$$

$$\frac{15}{2} = b$$

The equation for the line is $y = -\frac{3}{2}x + \frac{15}{2}$.

75. a. It is possible for a line to have no
x-intercepts. Horizontal lines of the form
$y = b$ (where b is a constant not equal to 0)
have no x-intercepts.

b. It is possible for a line to have exactly one
x-intercept. One example is $y = x + 1$, where
the x-intercept is (−1, 0). Other lines of the
form $y = mx + b$ have one x-intercept, as long
as $m \neq 0$.

c. It is not possible for a line to have exactly
two x-intercepts. A line can never intersect
the x-axis at exactly two points.

d. It is possible for a line to have an infinite
number of x-intercepts. The line $y = 0$ lies
on the x–axis and therefore, intersects the
x-axis at an infinite number of points.

77. Yes, a line contains all these points. Using
$(-4, 15)$ and $(-1, 9)$, note that the slope is −2.

So, $y = -2x + b$. Substitute −4 for x and 15 for y
to solve for b since the line contains (−4, 15).

$$15 = -2(-4) + b$$

$$15 = 8 + b$$

$$7 = b$$

The equation of the line is $y = -2x + 7$. When
each of the other points is substituted into this
equation, we see that the line contains all of the
given points.

79. a. Answers may vary. Consider the following
example.

Table for
$y = 3x - 6$

x	y
0	−6
1	−3
2	0
3	3
4	6
5	9
6	12

b. Answers may vary. Consider the following
example.

Table of
Points Lying
Close to
$y = 3x - 6$

x	y
0	−5
1	−4
2	1
3	2
4	7
5	10
6	13

c. Answers may vary.

81. a. Any equation of the form $y = -4x + b$,
where $x \neq 0$ and/or $y \neq 0$, will have a slope
of −4. One example is $y = -4x + 1$

b. Any equation of the form $y = mx + \frac{3}{7}$ where
$y \neq 0$, will have a y-intercept of $\left(0, \frac{3}{7}\right)$.

c. Since the line must contain the point (−2, 8),
substitute −2 for x and 8 for y to find an
equation.

$$y = mx + b$$

$$8 = m(-2) + b$$

$$8 = -2m + b$$

Choose any slope and then solve for b, the
y-intercept. Then, use the slope and b to
write the equation of the line. Choose $m = 2$,
for example.

$$8 = 2(-2) + b$$

$$8 = -4 + b$$

$$12 = b$$

An equation of a line that passes through the point $(-2, 8)$ is $y = -2x + 12$. Use TRACE to verify your equation.

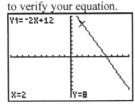

d. The line that has a slope of -4 and y-intercept $\left(0, \dfrac{3}{7}\right)$ is $y = -4x + \dfrac{3}{7}$. Check to see if the point $(-2, 8)$ satisfies this equation.

$$8 = -4(-2) + \dfrac{3}{7}$$

$$8 = 8 + \dfrac{3}{7}$$

$$0 \neq \dfrac{3}{7}$$

This is false. There is no such equation.

83. The student is partially correct. In the $y = mx + b$ form of a line, the slope m is 2 and the y-intercept b is the point where the line crosses the y-axis, or $(0, b)$. Thus, the given point $(3, 5)$ is not the y-intercept. You can be use $(3, 5)$ to find b by substituting it into $y = 2x + b$ and solving for b.

85. Answers may vary. One possible answer follows. First, use the two points to find the slope of the line. Next, use one of the points to find b, by substituting in the equation $y = mx + b$. Finally, substitute for m and b in the equation $y = mx + b$. To verify that the equation contains the two points, substitute the values of x and y for each point to see if a true statement results.

Homework 1.6

1. Relation 1 is not a function. The input $x = 3$ yields *two* outputs $y = 5$ and $y = 7$.
   Relation 2 could possibly be a function since each input yields only one output.

Relation 3 could possibly be a function since each input yields only one output.
Relation 4 is not a function. The input $x = 8$ yields *two* outputs $y = 40$ and $y = 50$.

3. No, the relation is not a function since an input yields more than one output.

5. Yes, it is possible that the relation is a function. Two inputs can yield the same output, but one input cannot yield two outputs.

7. This graph is a function since it passes the vertical line test.

9. This graph is not a function since a vertical line can intersect the graph at more than one point.

11. This graph is not a function since a vertical line can intersect the graph at more than one point.

13. This graph is a function since it passes the vertical line test.

15. The relation $y = 5x - 1$ is function since it can be put into the form $y = mx + b$ which defines a linear function.

17. First, isolate y.
$$2x - 5y = 10$$
$$-5y = -2x + 10$$
$$y = \dfrac{2}{5}x - 2$$
This relation is a function since it can be put into the form $y = mx + b$ which defines a linear function.

19. $y = 4$ is a horizontal line. Because every horizontal line passes the vertical line test, $y = 4$ is a function.

21. $x = -3$ is a vertical line and does not pass the vertical line test. This is not a function.

23. First, isolate y.

$$7x - 2y = 21 + 3(y - 5x)$$
$$7x - 2y = 21 + 3y - 15x$$
$$-2y - 3y = -7x - 15x + 21$$
$$\frac{-5y}{-5} = \frac{22x + 21}{-5}$$
$$y = -\frac{22}{5}x - \frac{21}{5}$$

This relation is a function since it can be put into the form $y = mx + b$ which defines a linear function.

25. Yes, any nonvertical line is a function since it passes the vertical line test.

27. No, a circle is not the graph of a function since a vertical line may intersect the circle at more than one point.

29. **a.** Answers may vary.

x	y
0	$3(0) - 2 = -2$
1	$3(1) - 2 = 1$
2	$3(2) - 2 = 4$
3	$3(3) - 2 = 7$
4	$3(4) - 2 = 10$

b.
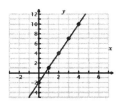

c. For each input-output pair, the output is 2 less than 3 times the input.

31. The domain is $-4 \le x \le 5$ and the range is $-2 \le y \le 3$.

33. The domain is $-5 \le x \le 4$ and the range is $-2 \le y \le 3$. The highest point on the graph appears to include a y-value of 3.

35. The domain is $-4 \le x \le 4$ and the range is $-2 \le y \le 2$. The lowest point on the graph appears to include a y-value of -2 and the highest point appears to include a y-value of 2.

37. The domain is $0 \le x \le 4$ and the range is

$0 \le y \le 2$.

39. The domain is all real numbers and the range is $y \le 4$.

41. The domain is $x \ge 0$ and the range is $y \ge 0$.

43. Answers may vary.
$y = 2^x$ is a function expressed as an equation.

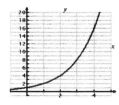

x	y
0	1
1	2
2	4
3	8
4	16

For each input-output pair, the output is 2 raised to the power of the input.

45. Answers may vary. One example follows. Suppose that when $x = 2$, $y = -1$ and $y = 4$. Then suppose when $x = 6$, $y = 0$. Sketch these points.

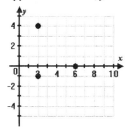

This relation is not a function since it does not pass the vertical line test.

47. Answers may vary.

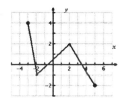

49. Answers may vary.

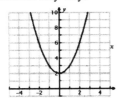

51. The relation $y = \sqrt{x}$ is a function since it passes the vertical line test.

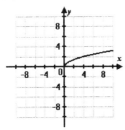

53. Consider the input $x = 16$. Substitute 16 for x and solve for y.

$$y^4 = 16$$

$$y = \pm 2$$

Since the input $x = 16$ yields *two* outputs, the relation, $y^4 = x$, is not a function.

55. No, the student's conclusion is not correct. In a function, *two* inputs can yield the same output, but one input cannot yield *two* outputs.

Chapter 1 Review Exercises

1. The amount of time it takes to read and reply to emails depends on the number of emails that a person receives. The amount of time to read and reply (t) is the dependent variable and the number of emails (n) is the independent variable.

2. The length of the candle (L) is the dependent variable and minutes (t) is the independent variable.

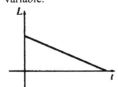

3. The amount of time (T) to cook a marshmallow is the dependent variable and the distance (d) from the campfire is the independent variable.

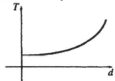

4. $3(2x - 4) - 2 = 5x - (3 - 4x)$

$$6x - 12 - 2 = 5x - 3 + 4x$$

$$6x - 14 = 9x - 3$$

$$\frac{-3x}{-3} = \frac{11}{-3}$$

$$x = -\frac{11}{3}$$

5. $\dfrac{2}{3}w - \dfrac{1}{2} = \dfrac{5}{6}w + \dfrac{4}{3}$

$$6\left(\frac{2}{3}w - \frac{1}{2}\right) = 6\left(\frac{5}{6}w + \frac{4}{3}\right)$$

$$4w - 3 = 5w + 8$$

$$-11 = w$$

6. $a(x - c) = d$

$$x - c = \frac{d}{a}$$

$$x = \frac{d}{a} + c$$

7. To find the x-intercept, substitute 0 for y.

$$3x - 5y = 17$$

$$3x - 5(0) = 17$$

$$\frac{3x}{3x} = \frac{17}{3}$$

$$x = \frac{17}{3}$$

The x-intercept is $\left(\dfrac{17}{3}, 0\right)$.

To find the y-intercept, substitute 0 for x.

$$3x - 5y = 17$$

$$3(0) - 5y = 17$$

$$\frac{-5y}{-5} = \frac{17}{-5}$$

$$y = -\frac{17}{5}$$

The x-intercept is $\left(0, -\dfrac{17}{5}\right)$.

8. To find the *x*-intercept, substitute 0 for *y*.
$$ax + b - cy$$
$$ax + b = (0)y$$
$$\frac{ax}{a} = \frac{-b}{a}$$
$$x = -\frac{b}{a}$$
The *x*-intercept is $\left(-\frac{b}{a}, 0\right)$.

To find the *y*-intercept, substitute 0 for
$$ax + b = cy$$
$$a(0) + b = cy$$
$$\frac{b}{c} = y$$
The *x*-intercept is $\left(0, \frac{b}{c}\right)$.

9. $y = -4$

10. $y \approx -\frac{3}{4}$.

11. $x = -4$

12. $x = -1$

13. $m = \frac{-2 - (-5)}{-3 - 2} = \frac{3}{-5} = -\frac{3}{5}$
The slope is negative, so the line is decreasing.

14. $m = \frac{-7 - (-3)}{-9 - (-1)} = \frac{-4}{-8} = \frac{1}{2}$
The slope is positive, so the line is increasing.

15. $m = \frac{-1 - 3}{4 - 4} = \frac{-4}{0}$ undefined
The slope is undefined, so the line is vertical.

16. $m = \frac{2.99 - (-8.48)}{-5.27 - 3.54} = \frac{11.47}{-8.81} \approx -1.30$
The slope is negative, so the line is decreasing.

17. Use the slope, -3, and the *y*-intercept, 10, to graph the equation.

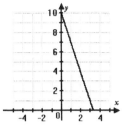

18. First, isolate *y*.
$$y + 2x = 0$$
$$y = -2x$$
Use the slope, -2, and the *y*-intercept, 0, to graph the equation.

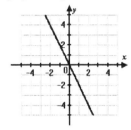

19. $y = 7$ is a horizontal line with a *y*-intercept of 7.

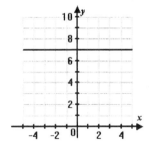

20. First, isolate *y*.
$$3x - 2y = 12$$
$$-2y = -3x + 12$$
$$y = \frac{3}{2}x - 6$$
Use the slope, $\frac{3}{2}$, and the *y*-intercept, -6, to graph the equation.

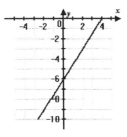

21. First, isolate y.

$$-3(y+2) = 2x+9$$
$$-3y-6 = 2x+9$$
$$-3y = 2x+15$$
$$y = -\frac{2}{3}x-5$$

Use the slope, $-\frac{2}{3}$, and the y-intercept, -5, to graph the equation.

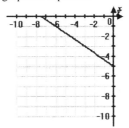

22. First, isolate y.

$$3x-2(2y-1) = 8x-3(x+2)$$
$$3x-4y+2 = 8x-3x-6$$
$$\frac{-4y}{-4} = \frac{2x-8}{-4}$$
$$y = -\frac{1}{2}x+2$$

Use the slope, $-\frac{1}{2}$, and the y-intercept, 2, to graph the equation.

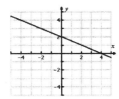

23. First, isolate y.

$$a(x-y) = c$$
$$x-y = \frac{c}{a}$$
$$-y = -x + \frac{c}{a}$$
$$y = x - \frac{c}{a}$$

The slope is 1 and the y-intercept is $\left(0, -\frac{c}{a}\right)$.

24. Solve the first equation for y to find the slope.

$$2x+5y = 7$$
$$5y = -2x+7$$
$$y = -\frac{2}{5}x + \frac{7}{5}$$

The slopes are $-\frac{2}{5}$ and $\frac{2}{5}$. They are reciprocals, but not negative reciprocals. The lines are neither parallel nor perpendicular.

25. Solve each equation for y to find the slope.

$$3x-8y = 7 \qquad\qquad -6x+16y = 5$$
$$\frac{-8y}{-8} = \frac{-3x+7}{-8} \qquad \frac{16y}{16} = \frac{6x+5}{16}$$
$$y = \frac{3}{8}x - \frac{7}{8} \qquad\quad y = \frac{3}{8}x + \frac{5}{16}$$

The slopes are $\frac{3}{8}$ and $\frac{3}{8}$. The lines are parallel.

26. We are given the slope, $m = -4$, and a point on the line, $(-3, 7)$. Use $y = mx + b$ to find b.

$$y = mx + b$$
$$7 = -4(-3) + b$$
$$7 = 12 + b$$
$$-5 = b$$

Now, substitute for m and b in slope-intercept form to obtain the equation of the line.

$$y = -4x + (-5)$$
$$y = -4x - 5$$

27. We are given the slope, $m = -\frac{2}{3}$, and a point on the line, $(5, -4)$. Use $y = mx + b$ to find b.

$$y = mx + b$$

$$-4 = -\frac{2}{3}(5) + b$$

$$-4 = -\frac{10}{3} + b$$

$$-\frac{12}{3} = -\frac{10}{3} + b$$

$$-\frac{2}{3} = b$$

Now, substitute for m and b in slope-intercept form to obtain the equation of the line.

$$y = -\frac{2}{3}x + \left(-\frac{2}{3}\right)$$

$$y = -\frac{2}{3}x - \frac{2}{3}$$

28. First, find the slope.

$$m = \frac{6 - (-2)}{2 - (-3)} = \frac{8}{5}$$

So, $y = \frac{8}{5}x + b$. Since the line contains (2, 6),

substitute 2 for x and 6 for y and solve for b.

$$6 = \frac{8}{5}(2) + b$$

$$6 = \frac{16}{5} + b$$

$$\frac{30}{5} = \frac{16}{5} + b$$

$$\frac{14}{5} = b$$

So, the equation is $y = \frac{8}{5}x + \frac{14}{5}$.

29. First, find the slope.

$$m = \frac{6 - (-2)}{-4 - 2} = \frac{8}{-6} = -\frac{4}{3}$$

So, $y = -\frac{4}{3}x + b$. Since the line contains

$(2, -2)$, substitute 2 for x and -2 for y and solve for b.

$$-2 = -\frac{4}{3}(2) + b$$

$$-\frac{6}{3} = -\frac{8}{3} + b$$

$$\frac{2}{3} = b$$

So, the equation is $y = -\frac{4}{3}x + \frac{2}{3}$.

30. First, find the slope.

$$m = \frac{5 - (-2)}{3 - 3} = \frac{7}{0} = \text{undefined}$$

A line with undefined slope is a vertical line of the form $x = a$. Since (3, 5) is a point on the line and the value of x is 3 at that point, the equation of the line is $x = 3$.

31. First, find the slope.

$$m = \frac{-8.79 - (-6.38)}{-3.62 - 2.51} = \frac{-2.41}{-6.13} \approx 0.39$$

So, $y = 0.39x + b$. Since the line contains $(-3.62, -8.79)$, substitute -3.62 for x and -8.79 for y and solve for b.

$$y = 0.39x + b$$

$$-8.79 = 0.39(-3.62) + b$$

$$-8.79 = -1.4232 + b$$

$$7.37 \approx b$$

So, the equation is $y \approx 0.39x + 7.37$.

32. Line 1: Two points on line 1 are $(1, -2)$ and $(-1, 2)$. Use these points to find the slope.

$$m = \frac{2 - (-2)}{-1 - 1} = \frac{4}{-2} = -2$$

So, $y = -2x + b$. We can see from the graph that the y-intercept is 0. So, the equation of the line is $y = -2x + 0 = -2x$.

Line 2: Two points on line 1 are $(-1, 0)$ and $(0, 2)$. Use these points to find the slope.

$$m = \frac{2 - 0}{0 - (-1)} = \frac{2}{1} = 2$$

So, $y = 2x + b$. We can see from the graph that the y-intercept is 2. So, the equation of the line is $y = 2x + 2$.

Line 3: Since line 3 is a horizontal line, it is of the form $y = b$. Since the y-intercept is -3, the equation of the line is $y = -3$.

33. Find the slope of the line to determine the rate of change.

Points on a Line	
x	y
2	20
3	16
4	12
5	8
6	4
7	0

34. Line 1 is parallel to $y = 0.5x + 6$. Since parallel lines have the same slope, the slope of line 1 is 0.5. The equation of line 1 is $y = 0.5x + b$.
Line 1 has the same y-intercept as the line $y = -1.5x + 3$. The y-intercept is $b = 3$. The equation of line 1 is $y = 0.5x + 3$.

35. a. B, C and F

b. C and E

c. C

d. A and D

36. Since the line is parallel to the line $3x - y = 6$, or $y = 3x - 6$, it will have a slope of 3. Use the slope, 3, and the point on the line, $(-2, 5)$, to find the y-intercept.
$5 = 3(-2) + b$
$5 = -6 + b$
$11 = b$
The equation of the line is $y = 3x + 11$.

37. A line with an infinite number of x-intercepts is the line that lies on the x-axis. This is the horizontal line $y = 0$.

38. Relations 1 and 3 could possibly be functions, since there is only one output for each input. Relations 2 and 4 could not possibly be functions, since there are two or more outputs for a single input.

39. The graph is not a function because a vertical line can intersect the graph more than once.

40. First, isolate y.
$5x - 6y = 3$
$$\frac{-6y}{-6} = \frac{-5x + 3}{-6}$$
$$y = \frac{5}{6}x - \frac{1}{2}$$
This relation is a function since it can be put into the form $y = mx + b$ which defines a linear function.

41. $x = 9$ is a vertical line. It does not pass the vertical line test and is not a function.

42. Sketch the graph of $y^2 = x$.

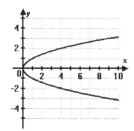

Note that this graph does not pass the vertical line test. Therefore, $y^2 = x$ is not a function.

43. The domain is all real numbers and the range is $y \leq 4$.

Chapter 1 Test

1. The value in dollars of gold depends on the weight of a gold bar. The value (v) is the dependent variable and the weight (w) is the independent variable.

2. Answers may vary. One example is as follows.

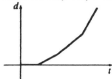

3. Answers may vary.
The diameter of a balloon in inches (y) is the dependent variable and the number of minutes after the knot of the balloon was untied (x) is the independent variable.

4. $5 - 3(4x - 2) = 8 - (7x + 1)$

$5 - 12x + 6 = 8 - 7x - 1$

$-12x + 11 = -7x + 7$

$\dfrac{-5x}{-5} = \dfrac{-4}{-5}$

$x = \dfrac{4}{5}$

5. Line 1: Two points on line 1 are (4, 0) and (2, 5). Use these points to find the slope.

$m = \dfrac{5-0}{2-4} = \dfrac{5}{-2} = -\dfrac{5}{2}$

So, $y = -\dfrac{5}{2}x + b$. Use the slope, $-\dfrac{5}{2}$, and a point on the line to find the y-intercept.

$y = mx + b$

$0 = -\dfrac{5}{2}(4) + b$

$0 = -10 + b$

$10 = b$

The equation of line 1 is $y = -\dfrac{5}{2}x + 10$.

Line 2: Two points on line 1 are (0, 2) and (−3, 0). Use these points to find the slope.

$m = \dfrac{0-2}{-3-0} = \dfrac{-2}{-3} = \dfrac{2}{3}$

So, $y = \dfrac{2}{3}x + b$. We can see from the graph that the y-intercept is 2. So, the equation of the line is $y = \dfrac{2}{3}x + 2$.

Line 3: Since line 3 is a vertical line, it is of the form $x = a$. Since the x-intercept is −3, the equation of the line is $x = -3$.

6. a. $k > m$, since the line $y = kx + c$ is steeper than the line $y = mx + b$.

b. $b > c$, since the y-intercept of the line $y = kx + c$ is greater than the y-intercept of the line $y = mx + b$.

7. $m_A = \dfrac{|-85|}{270} = \dfrac{85}{270} \approx 0.31$

$m_B = \dfrac{|-140|}{475} = \dfrac{140}{475} \approx 0.29$

Ski run A is steeper than ski run B, since the slope of ski run A is greater than the slope of ski run B. (In determining which is steeper, ignore the sign of the slope by considering the absolute value.)

8. The table is completed as follows.

Points on a Line	
x	y
4	25
5	29
6	33
7	37
8	41
9	45

9. Use the slope, $-\dfrac{1}{5}$, and the y-intercept, 4, to graph the line.

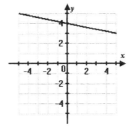

10. First, isolate y.

$2(2x - y) = 2x + 9 + y$

$4x - 2y = 2x + 9 + y$

$-2y - y = 2x - 4x + 9$

$\dfrac{-3y}{-3} = \dfrac{-2x+9}{-3}$

$y = \dfrac{2}{3}x - 3$

Use the slope, $\dfrac{2}{3}$, and the y-intercept, −3, to graph the line.

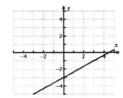

11. $m = \dfrac{2-(-8)}{-3-5} = \dfrac{10}{-8} = -\dfrac{5}{4}$

12. First, find the slope.
$m = \dfrac{8-6}{2-5} = \dfrac{2}{-3} = -\dfrac{2}{3}$
Use the slope and a point on the line, (2, 8), to find b.
$y = mx + b$
$8 = -\dfrac{2}{3}(2) + b$
$8 = -\dfrac{4}{3} + b$
$\dfrac{24}{3} = -\dfrac{4}{3} + b$
$\dfrac{28}{3} = b$

The equation of the line is $y = -\dfrac{2}{3}x + \dfrac{28}{3}$. To
find points on the line, substitute values for x to
find y. For example, let $x = 8$.
$y = -\dfrac{2}{3}(8) + \dfrac{28}{3} = -\dfrac{16}{3} + \dfrac{28}{3} = \dfrac{12}{3} = 4$
The point, (8, 4) is on the line. Similar
calculations will show that (11, 2) and (14, 0),
among others, also lie on the line.

13. Use the slope, $-\dfrac{3}{7}$, and the point $(-2, 5)$, to find
the y-intercept, b.
$y = mx + b$
$5 = -\dfrac{3}{7}(-2) + b$
$5 = \dfrac{6}{7} + b$
$\dfrac{35}{7} - \dfrac{6}{7} = b$
$\dfrac{29}{7} = b$

The equation of the line is $y = -\dfrac{3}{7}x + \dfrac{29}{7}$.

14. First, find the slope.
$m = \dfrac{7-(-5)}{-3-2} = -\dfrac{12}{5}$
Use the slope and a point on the line, $(2, -5)$, to
find b.

$y = mx + b$
$-5 = -\dfrac{12}{5}(2) + b$
$-\dfrac{25}{5} = -\dfrac{24}{5} + b$
$-\dfrac{1}{5} = b$

The equation of the line is $y = -\dfrac{12}{5}x - \dfrac{1}{5}$.

15. All of the points except (0, 2) lie on a line.
Choose two of the points to find the slope.
$m = \dfrac{5-(-3)}{-2-2} = \dfrac{8}{-4} = -2$
Use the slope and a point on the line to find the
y-intercept, b.
$y = mx + b$
$5 = -2(-2) + b$
$5 = 4 + b$
$1 = b$
The equation of the line is $y = -2x + 1$.

16. First, find the slope of the given line by isolating
y.
$3x - 5y = 20$
$-5y = -3x + 20$
$y = \dfrac{3}{5}x - 4$

The slope of the line is $\dfrac{3}{5}$. The slope of a line

perpendicular to this line is $-\dfrac{5}{3}$. Use the slope,

$-\dfrac{5}{3}$, and a point on the line, $(4, -1)$, to find the
y-intercept.
$y = mx + b$
$-1 = -\dfrac{5}{3}(4) + b$
$-1 = -\dfrac{20}{3} + b$
$-\dfrac{3}{3} = -\dfrac{20}{3} + b$
$\dfrac{17}{3} = b$

The equation of the line is $y = -\dfrac{5}{3}x + \dfrac{17}{3}$.

17. To find the *x*-intercept, set *y* = 0 and solve for *x*.

$$2(0) + 5 = 4(x - 1) + 3$$
$$0 + 5 = 4x - 4 + 3$$
$$6 = 4x$$
$$\frac{6}{4} = x$$
$$\frac{3}{2} = x$$

To find the *y*-intercept, set *x* = 0 and solve for *y*.

$$2y + 5 = 4(0 - 1) + 3$$
$$2y + 5 = -4 + 3$$
$$2y = -6$$
$$y = -3$$

The *x*-intercept is $\left(\frac{3}{2}, 0\right)$. The *y*-intercept is $(0, -3)$.

18. a. Answers may vary.

x	*y*
0	2(0) − 4 = −4
1	2(1) − 4 = −2
2	2(2) − 4 = 0
3	2(3) − 4 = 2
4	2(4) − 4 = 4

b.

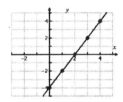

c. For each input-output pair, the output is 4 less than 2 times the input.

19. Answers may vary. Any graph that does not pass the vertical line test is not a function.

20. Sketch the graph of $y = \pm\sqrt{x}$.

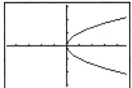

Note that this graph does not pass the vertical line test. Therefore, $y = \pm\sqrt{x}$ is not a function.

21. The graph of $y = -2x + 5$ is a nonvertical line. Any nonvertical line is a function since it passes the vertical line test.

22. The domain is $-3 \le x \le 5$ and the range is $-3 \le y \le 4$. The relation is a function since the graph can be intersected by any vertical line only once.

Chapter 2
Modeling with Linear Functions

Homework 2.1

1. a.

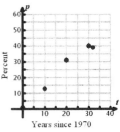

Years since 1970

b.

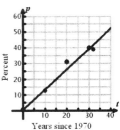

Years since 1970

c. In 2010, 52.5% of dentistry degrees will be earned by women.

d. In 1985, about 20% of dentistry degrees will be earned by women.

3. a.

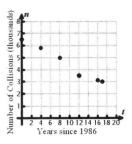

Years since 1986

b.

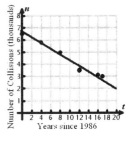

Years since 1986

c. In 1997, there were about 4.2 thousand collisions. We performed interpolation because we used a part of the model whose *t*-coordinates are between the *t*-coordinates of two data points.

d. If the graph is extended, there will be 1.0 thousand collisions in 2011. We performed extrapolation because we used a part of the model whose *t*-coordinates are not between the *t*-coordinates of two data points.

e. If the graph is extended, the *n*-intercept of the model occurs when *t* = 36. This means that there will be no collisions in 2016.

f. The *t*-intercept of the model is when *n* = 7.9. This means that in 1980, there were 7.9 thousand collisions.

5. a.

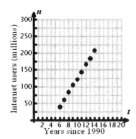

Years since 1990

b.

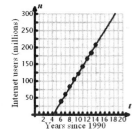

Years since 1990

c. The *t*-intercept is the year 1994. This means that there were no Internet users in the United States in 1994. We performed extrapolation because we used a part of the model whose *t*-coordinates are not between the *t*-coordinates of two data points.

d. The number of Internet users is increasing by

20 million people per year.

e. In 2008 the model predicts that everyone in the U.S. will be an Internet user. We performed extrapolation because we used a part of the model whose t-coordinates are not between the t-coordinates of two data points.

7. a.

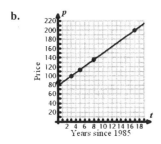

b.

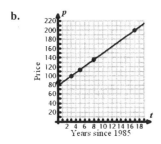

c. In 1999 the model predicts that the price will be about $178. The model overestimated by $28.

d. In 2001 the model predicts that the price will be about $190. The model overestimated by $30.

e. After Michael Jordan returned from retirement the Air Jordans would be more popular and therefore could be sold at higher price. Including this price in the data would cause a model breakdown for the shoes releases during his years of retirement.

f.

9. a.

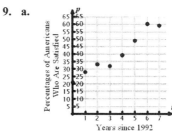

b.

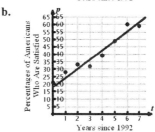

c. If the graph is extended, about 90% of Americans will be satisfied in 2004.

d.

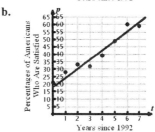

e. The error is 47 percentage points. Up to 2000 the percent of Americans who were satisfied was steadily increasing. After 2000 the percent of Americans who are satisfied was steadily decreasing.

11. a. To find the t-intercept, estimate the number of years since 1990 when $D = 0$. This estimate is approximately $(7, 0)$. This point represents that in 1997 $(t = 7)$, the percentages of sound recording sales for both pop and rap/hip-hop were the same.

b. To find the D-intercept, estimate when $t = 0$. This estimate is approximately $(0, 5.2)$. This point represents a 5.2% difference in the percentage of sales between pop and rap/hip-hop. In 1990, pop sound recordings outsold rap/hip-hop sound recordings by approximately 5.2%.

13. Answers may vary. A linear model is a linear function that describes the relationship between two quantities for an authentic. Every linear model is a linear function. However, not every linear function is a linear model. Functions are used both to describe situations and to describe certain mathematical relationships between two variables.

15. Answers may vary. The linear model that comes closest to all data points is the most accurate model, and allows for the best estimates and predictions based on the given data.

Homework 2.2

1. Use the points $(1, 8.7)$ and $(4, 15.6)$ to write the equation of the line. First find the slope.

$$m = \frac{15.6 - 8.7}{4 - 1}$$

$$= 2.3$$

So, $n = 2.3t + b$. Substitute 1 for t and 8.7 for n since the line contains $(1, 8.7)$ and then solve for b.

$$n = mt + b$$

$$8.7 = 2.3(1) + b$$

$$8.7 = 2.3 + b$$

$$6.4 = b$$

The equation of the line is $y = 2.3t + 6.4$.

3. Use $(2, 1175)$ and $(5, 1880)$ to write the equation of the line. First, find the slope.

$$m = \frac{1880 - 1175}{5 - 2}$$

$$= 235$$

So, $r = 235t + b$. Substitute 2 for x and 1175 for y since the line contains $(2, 1175)$ and then solve for b.

$$r = mt + b$$

$$1175 = 235(2) + b$$

$$1175 = 470 + b$$

$$705 = b$$

The equation of the line is $r = 235t + 705$.

5. Use the points $(1, 440)$ and $(4, 206.33)$ to write the equation of the line. First find the slope.

$$m = \frac{440 - 206.33}{1 - 4}$$

$$= -77.89$$

So, $b = -77.89t + B$. Substitute 1 for t and 440 for b since the line contains $(1, 440)$ and then solve

for B.

$$b = mt + B$$

$$440 = -77.89(1) + B$$

$$440 = -77.89 + B$$

$$517.89 = B$$

The equation of the line is $b = -77.89t + 517.89$.

7. Use the points $(6, 27)$ and $(20, 54.5)$ to find the equation of the line.

$$m = \frac{54.5 - 27}{20 - 6}$$

$$\approx 1.96$$

So, $L = 2.18a + b$. Substitute 6 for a and 27 for L since the line contains $(6, 27)$ and then solve for b.

$$L = ma + b$$

$$27 = 1.96(6) + b$$

$$27 = 11.76 + b$$

$$15.24 = b$$

The equation of the line is $L = 1.96a + 15.24$.

9.

In this model, m will be the same as the original model. However, the value of b will increase.

11. Use $(3, 5)$ and $(7, 15)$ to write the equation of the line. First, find the slope.

$$m = \frac{15 - 5}{7 - 3}$$

$$= 2.5$$

So $y = 2.5x + b$. Substitute 3 for x and 5 for y since the line contains $(3, 5)$ and then solve for b.

$$y = mx + b$$

$$5 = 2.5(3) + b$$

$$5 = 7.5 + b$$

$$-2.5 = b$$

The equation of the line is $y = 2.5x - 2.5$. (Your equation may be slightly different if you chose different points.) Use the graphing calculator to check your results.

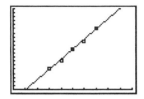

13. Student B made the best choice of points. The graph that best fits all the points goes though the points (3, 9.0) and (4, 11.0).

15. a.

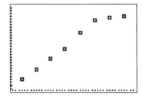

b. Use the points (80, 18.4) and (100, 33.2) to write the equation of the line. First find the slope.

$$m = \frac{33.2 - 18.4}{100 - 80}$$

$$= 0.74$$

So, $p = 0.74t + b$. Substitute 80 for t and 18.4 for p, since the line contains (80, 18.4) and then solve for b.

$$p = mt + b$$

$$18.4 = 0.74(80) + b$$

$$18.4 = 59.2 + b$$

$$-40.8 = b$$

The equation of the line is $p = 0.74t - 40.8$. (Your equation may be slightly different if you chose different points.)

c.

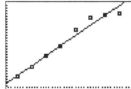

Notice that the points (80, 18.4) and (100, 33.2) are filled in, showing that the line goes through these points.

17. a.

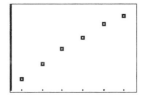

b. Use the points (2, 30) and (4, 56) to find the equation of the line.

$$m = \frac{56 - 30}{4 - 2}$$

$$= 13$$

So, $p = 13n + b$. Substitute 2 for n and 30 for p since the line contains (2, 30) and then solve for b.

$$p = mn + b$$

$$30 = 13(2) + b$$

$$30 = 26 + b$$

$$4 = b$$

The equation of the line is $y = 13x + 4$. (Your equation may be slightly different if you chose different points.)

c.

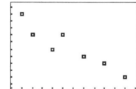

Notice that the points (2, 30) and (4, 56) are filled in, showing that the line goes through these points.

19. a.

b. Use the points (10, 13) and (14, 10) to find the equation of the line.

$$m = \frac{13 - 10}{10 - 14}$$

$$= -0.75$$

So, $p = -0.75t + b$. Substitute 10 for t and 13 for p since the line contains (10, 13) and then solve for b.

$$p = mt + b$$

$$13 = -0.75(10) + b$$

$$13 = -7.5 + b$$

$$20.5 = b$$

The equation of the line is $y = -0.75t + 20.5$. (Your equation may be slightly different if you chose different points.)

c.

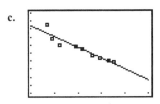

21. a.

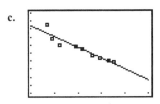

b. Use the points (69, 51.7) and (83, 47.99) to find the equation of the line.

$$m = \frac{47.99 - 51.7}{83 - 69}$$

$$\approx -0.27$$

So, $r = -0.27t + b$. Substitute 69 for t and 51.7 for r since the line contains (69, 51.7) and then solve for b.

$$r = mt + b$$

$$51.7 = -0.27(69) + b$$

$$51.7 = -18.63 + b$$

$$70.33 = b$$

The equation of the line is $r = -0.27t + 70.33$. (Your equation may be slightly different if you chose different points.)

c.

23. a.

b. Yes, the model predicts that the women's record time will equal the men's record time.

This will happen in the year 2003 with a record time of approximately 42.6 seconds

c. Yes, the model predicts that the women's record time will be less than the men's record time in years 2004 and after.

25. a.

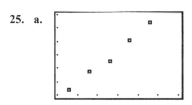

b. Use the points (23, 34) and (43, 84) to find the equation of the line.

$$m = \frac{84 - 34}{43 - 23}$$

$$= 2.5$$

So, $y = 2.5x + b$. Substitute 23 for x and 34 for y since the line contains (23, 34) and then solve for b.

$$p = mx + b$$

$$34 = 2.5(23) + b$$

$$34 = 57.5 + b$$

$$-23.5 = b$$

The equation of the line is $y = 2.5x - 23.5$. (Your equation may be slightly different if you chose different points.)

c.

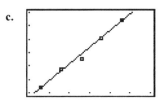

27. To find an equation of a linear model, first make a scatter gram of the points. Then determine if there is a line that comes close to all the data points. If so, choose two points (not necessarily data points) that you can use to find the equation of a linear model. Find an equation of the line between the two points you found. To verify that the linear function models the situation well, use a graphing calculator to verify that the graph of your equation comes close to the points of the scatter gram.

Homework 2.3

1. Substituting 5 whenever there is an x in $f(x)$:

$$f(5) = 6(5) - 4$$
$$= 30 - 4$$
$$f(5) = 26$$

3. Substituting $\dfrac{2}{3}$ wherever there is an x in $f(x)$:

$$f\left(\dfrac{2}{3}\right) = 6\left(\dfrac{2}{3}\right) - 4$$
$$= 4 - 4$$
$$f\left(\dfrac{2}{3}\right) = 0$$

5. Substituting $a + 2$ wherever there is an x in $f(x)$:
$$f(a+2) = 6(a+2) - 4$$
$$= 6a + 12 - 4$$
$$f(a+2) = 6a + 8$$

7. Substituting 2 wherever there is an x in $g(x)$:
$$g(2) = 2(2)^2 - 5(2)$$
$$= 2(4) - 10$$
$$= 8 - 10$$
$$g(2) = -2$$

9. Substituting -3 wherever there is an x in $g(x)$:
$$g(-3) = 2(-3)^2 - 5(-3)$$
$$= 2(9) + 15$$
$$= 18 + 15$$
$$g(-3) = 33$$

11. Substituting 2 wherever there is an x in $h(x)$:

$$h(2) = \dfrac{3(2) - 4}{5(2) + 2}$$
$$= \dfrac{6 - 4}{10 + 2}$$
$$= \dfrac{2}{12}$$
$$h(2) = \dfrac{1}{6}$$

13. Substituting $a - 3$ wherever there is an x in $h(x)$:

$$h(a-3) = \dfrac{3(a-3) - 4}{5(a-3) + 2}$$
$$= \dfrac{3a - 9 - 4}{5a - 15 + 2}$$
$$h(a-3) = \dfrac{3a - 13}{5a - 13}$$

15. Substituting -2 wherever there is an x in $g(x)$:
$$g(-2) = -3(-2)^2 + 2(-2)$$
$$= -3(4) - 4$$
$$= -12 - 4$$
$$g(-2) = -16$$

17. Substituting 5 wherever there is an x in $f(x)$:
$$f(5) = -2(5) + 7$$
$$= -10 + 7$$
$$f(5) = -3$$

19. Since $h(x) = -4$, for all x, $h(7) = -4$.

21. Substituting $5a$ wherever there is an x in $f(x)$:
$$f(5a) = -4(5a) - 7$$
$$f(5a) = -20a - 7$$

23. Substituting $\dfrac{a}{2}$ wherever there is an x in $f(x)$:

$$f\left(\dfrac{a}{2}\right) = -4\left(\dfrac{a}{2}\right) - 7$$
$$f\left(\dfrac{a}{2}\right) = -2a - 7$$

25. Substituting $a + 4$ wherever there is an x in $f(x)$:
$$f(a+4) = -4(a+4) - 7$$
$$= -4a - 16 - 7$$
$$f(a+4) = -4a - 23$$

27. Substituting $a + h$ wherever there is an x in $f(x)$:
$$f(a+h) = -4(a+h) - 7$$
$$f(a+h) = -4a - 4h - 7$$

29. To find x when $f(x) = 6$, substitute 6 for $f(x)$ and solve for x.
$$6 = -3x + 7$$
$$3x = 1$$
$$x = \dfrac{1}{3}$$

31.
To find x when $f(x) = \dfrac{5}{2}$, substitute $\dfrac{5}{2}$ for $f(x)$ and solve for x.

$$\frac{5}{2} = -3x + 7$$

$$\frac{-9}{2} = -3x$$

$$\frac{3}{2} = x$$

$$x = \frac{3}{2}$$

33. To find x when $f(x) = a$, substitute a for $f(x)$ and solve for x.

$$a = -3x + 7$$

$$a - 7 = -3x$$

$$\frac{7 - a}{3} = x$$

$$x = \frac{7 - a}{3}$$

35. Substituting 10.91 wherever there is an x in $f(x)$:

$$f(10.91) = -5.95(10.91) + 183.22$$

$$= -64.91 + 183.22$$

$$\approx 118.31$$

37. To find x when $f(x) = 99.34$, substitute 99.34 for $f(x)$ and solve for x.

$$99.34 = -5.95x + 183.22$$

$$-83.88 = -5.95x$$

$$14.10 \approx x$$

$$x = 14.10$$

39. The student mistakenly substituted 5 for x and solved for $f(x)$. The student should have substituted 5 for $f(x)$ and solved for x.

$$5 = x + 2$$

$$3 = x$$

$$x = 3$$

41. **a.** To find $f(3)$, $f(5)$ and $f(8)$, substitute the correct value for x in $f(x)$:

$$f(3) = 4(3)$$

$$= 12$$

$$f(5) = 4(5)$$

$$= 20$$

$$f(8) = 4(8)$$

$$= 32$$

To check $f(3 + 5) = f(3) + f(5)$, substitute for the above values:

$$f(3+5) = f(3) + f(5)$$

$$f(8) = 12 + 20$$

$$32 = 32$$

This is a true statement, so $f(3 + 5) = f(3) + f(5)$ is a true statement.

b. To find $f(2)$, $f(3)$ and $f(5)$, substitute the correct value for x in $f(x)$:

$$f(2) = (2)^2$$

$$= 4$$

$$f(3) = (3)^2$$

$$= 9$$

$$f(5) = (5)^2$$

$$= 25$$

To check $f(2 + 3) = f(2) + f(3)$, substitute for the above values:

$$f(2+3) = f(2) + f(3)$$

$$f(5) = 4 + 9$$

$$25 = 13$$

This is not a true statement, so $f(2 + 3) = f(2) + f(3)$ is not a true statement.

c. To find $f(9)$, $f(16)$ and $f(25)$, substitute the correct value for x in $f(x)$:

$$f(9) = \sqrt{9}$$

$$= 3$$

$$f(16) = \sqrt{16}$$

$$= 4$$

$$f(25) = \sqrt{25}$$

$$= 5$$

To check $f(9 + 16) = f(9) + f(16)$, substitute for the above values:

$$f(9+16) = f(9) + f(16)$$

$$f(25) = 3 + 4$$

$$5 = 7$$

This is not a true statement, so $f(9 + 16) = f(9) + f(16)$ is not a true statement.

d. It is not true that $f(a + b) = f(a) + f(b)$ for every function f as shown by two of these three equations.

43. The second row of the chart indicates that $f(2) = 4$.

45. The second row of the chart indicates that $f(x) = 2$ when $x = 1$ or $x = 3$.

47. Since the line includes the point $(-6, 4)$, $f(-6) = 4$.

49. Since the line includes the point $(2.5, 1.2)$, $f(2.5) = 1.2$.

51. Since the line includes the point $(6, 0)$, $x = 6$ when $f(x)$ or $y = 0$.

53. Since the line includes the point $(-3, 3)$, $x = -3$ when $f(x)$ or $y = 3$.

55. Since the line includes the point $(4.5, \frac{1}{2})$, $x = 4.5$ when $f(x)$ or $y = \frac{1}{2}$.

57. The domain of f is all the x-coordinates of the points in the graph. In this case f has a domain of all real numbers.

59. Sine the curve includes the point $(-2, 1)$, $x = -2$ when $g(x)$ or $y = 1$.

61. The domain of g is all of the x-coordinates of the points in the graph. In this case g has a domain of $-4 \le x \le 5$.

63. Since the curve includes the point $(1, -3)$, $x = 1$ when $h(x)$ or $y = -3$.

65. The domain of h is all of the x-coordinates of the points in the graph. In this case h has a domain of $-5 \le x \le 4$.

67. $f(x)$ or $y = 5x - 8$
To find the y-intercept, set $x = 0$ and solve for y.
$y = 5(0) - 8$
$y = 0 - 8$
$y = -8$

To find the x-intercept, set $y = 0$ and solve for x.
$0 = 5x - 8$
$8 = 5x$
$\frac{8}{5} = x$
$x = \frac{8}{5}$

69. $f(x)$ or $y = 3x$
To find the y-intercept, set $x = 0$ and solve for y.
$y = 3(0)$
$y = 0$
To find the x-intercept, set $y = 0$ and solve for x.
$0 = 3x$
$0 = x$
$x = 0$

71. $f(x)$ or $y = 5$ is the equation of a horizontal line. The y-intercept of the line will be $y = 5$. There is no x-intercept.

73. $f(x)$ or $y = \frac{1}{2}x - 3$
To find the y-intercept, set $x = 0$ and solve for y.
$y = \frac{1}{2}(0) - 3$
$y = -3$
To find the x-intercept, set $y = 0$ and solve for x.
$0 = \frac{1}{2}x - 3$
$3 = \frac{1}{2}x$
$6 = x$
$x = 6$

75. $f(x)$ or $y = 2.58x - 45.21$
To find the y-intercept, set $x = 0$ and solve for y.
$y = 2.58(0) - 45.21$
$y = -45.21$
To find the x-intercept, set $y = 0$ and solve for x.
$0 = 2.58x - 45.21$
$45.21 = 2.58x$
$17.52 = x$
$x = 17.52$

77. a.

x	$g(x)$
-2	10
-1	7
0	4
1	1
2	-2

b.

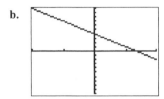

c. Multiply the input by –3 and add 4 to find the output.

79. a. $f(t) = 0.77t - 42.90$

b. $f(110) = 0.77(110) - 42.90$
$$= 84.7 - 42.90$$
$$= 41.8$$
When $t = 110$, $p = 41.8$. This means that in the year $1900 + 110 = 2010$, the percentage of births out of wedlock will be 41.8%.

c. $44 = 0.77t - 42.9$
$$86.9 = 0.77t$$
$$t \approx 113$$
When $p = 44$, $t \approx 113$. This means that the percentage of out of wedlock births will hit 44% in the year $1900 + 113 = 2013$.

d. $100 = 0.77t - 42.9$
$$142.9 = 0.77t$$
$$t \approx 186$$
In the year $1900 + 180 = 2086$, all births will be out of wedlock according to this model.

e. Find p, when $t = 1997 - 1900 = 97$.
$$f(97) = 0.77(97) - 42.9$$
$$= 74.69 - 42.9 = 31.79$$
This means that in the year 1997, the percentage of births out of wedlock will be 31.79%. Since the actual percentage was 32.4%, the error was $31.79\% - 32.4\% = -0.61\%$.

81. a. $f(t) = -0.77t + 20.86$

b. $f(6) = -0.77(6) + 20.86$
$$= -4.62 + 20.86$$
$$= 16.24$$
When $t = 6$, $p = 16.24$. This means that in $1990 + 6 = 1996$, baseball is the favorite sport of 16.24 percent of Americans.

c. $6 = -0.77t + 20.86$
$$-14.86 = -0.77t$$
$$t \approx 19$$
This means that in $1990 + 19 = 2009$, baseball will be the favorite sport of 6 percent of Americans.

d. To find the p-intercept of the model, we must find p when $t = 0$.
$$p = -0.77(0) + 20.86$$
$$= 20.86$$
This means that in $1990 + 0 = 1990$, baseball is the favorite sport of 20.86 percent of Americans.

e. To find the t-intercept of the model, we must find t when $p = 0$.
$$0 = -0.77t + 20.86$$
$$-20.86 = -0.77t$$
$$t \approx 27$$
This means that in $1990 + 27 = 2017$, baseball will be the favorite sport of 0 percent of Americans.

83. a. $f(n) = 12.74n + 4.40$

b. To find the p-intercept of the model, we must find p when $n = 0$.
$$p = -12.74(0) + 4.40$$
$$= 4.40$$
This means the cost of a ski rental packafe for 0 days is $4.40.

c. To find the cost for seven days, we must find $f(n)$ when $n = 7$.
$$f(7) = 12.74(7) + 4.40$$
$$= 89.18 + 4.40$$
$$= 93.58$$

d.

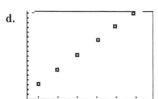

As *p* increases by 1, p increases by 12.74. This is equal to the slope of the equation.

e.
$$g(1) = \frac{12.74(1) + 4.40}{1} = 17.14$$

$$g(2) = \frac{12.74(2) + 4.40}{2} = 14.94$$

$$g(3) = \frac{12.74(3) + 4.40}{3} \approx 14.21$$

$$g(4) = \frac{12.74(4) + 4.40}{4} = 13.84$$

$$g(5) = \frac{12.74(5) + 4.40}{5} = 13.62$$

$$g(6) = \frac{12.74(6) + 4.40}{6} \approx 13.47$$

$g(6)$ is the least value. This represents the cost per day for a six day ski rental package.

f. The cost per day will reach its lowest value for packages over 6 days.

85. a.

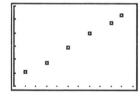

b. Use the points (1, 452) and (10, 666) to find the equation of the line.
$$m = \frac{666 - 452}{10 - 1}$$
$$= \frac{214}{9}$$
$$\approx 23.8$$
So, $y = 23.8x + b$. Substitute 1 for *x* and 452 for *y* since the line contains (1, 452) and then solve for *b*.
$$y = mx + b$$
$$452 = 23.8(1) + b$$
$$452 = 23.8 + b$$
$$428.2 = b$$
The equation of the line is $y = 23.8x + 428.2$.

(Your equation may be slightly different if you chose different points.)

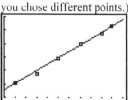

Graphing the line with the scatterplot, we see that the model fits the data very well.

c. Since 2001 – 1990 = 11, find $f(11)$.
$$f(11) = 23.8(11) + 428.2$$
$$= 261.8 + 428.2 = 690$$
According to the model, 690 million boardings were made in 2001. The actual number of boardings was 622 million. This is an error of 68 million boardings.

d. 68 million boardings is equivalent to $\frac{68}{4} = 17$ million round trips. If on average each round trip is $340, the airlines lost $17 \cdot \$340 = \$5780$ million or $5.78 billion.

87. a.

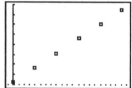

The data points lie close to the line that passes through (0, 32) and (100, 212). To find the equation for *f*, start by finding the slope using these points.
$$m = \frac{212 - 32}{100 - 0}$$
$$= \frac{180}{100}$$
$$= 1.8$$
So, $f(c) = 1.8c + b$. To solve for *b*, substitute 0 for *C* and 32 for $f(c)$ since the line contains (0, 32).
$$32 = 1.8(0) + b$$
$$32 = b$$
The equation for *f* is $f(c) = 1.8c + 32$. This is also the linear regression equation. This model fits the extremely well.

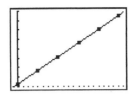

b. $f(25) = 1.8(25) + 32 = 45 + 32 = 77$
If it is $25°C$, it is $77°F$.

c. $40 = 1.8c + 32$
$8 = 1.8c$
$\dfrac{8}{1.8} = c$
$c \approx 4.4$
If it is $40°F$, the it is $4.4°C$.

89. a. $f(x) = 2.48x - 23.64$

b. $100 = 2.48x - 23.64$
$123.64 = 2.48x$
$x \approx 50$
This means that the cutoff score would have to be 50 (out of 50) to ensure that all students succeed in the intermediate algebra course.

c. $0 = 2.48x - 23.64$
$23.64 = 2.48x$
$x \approx 10$
This means that for scores 10 and under, no students would succeed in the intermediate algebra course.

d. For the $16 - 20$ range, we use a score of 18 to represent the group. Find the percentage for $x = 18$.
$p = 2.48(18) - 23.64$
$= 44.64 - 23.64 = 21$
This means that 21% of the students who score in the $16 - 20$ range pass the intermediate algebra course. If 145 students scored in this range, we could expect 21% or $0.21 \cdot 145 \approx 31$ students to pass.
It would not make sense for CSM to lower the placement score cutoff to 16. While 21% of student might pass, based on the model, the vast majority, 79%, would not pass.

e. First calculate the percentages for each of the score groups. Use the average score in each range to represent group.

$p = 2.48(23) - 23.64 = 33.4$
$p = 2.48(28) - 23.64 = 45.8$
$p = 2.48(33) - 23.64 = 58.2$
$p = 2.48(38) - 23.64 = 70.6$
$p = 2.48(43) - 23.64 = 83$
$p = 2.48(48) - 23.64 = 95.4$

Next, multiply each of the percentages by the number of students in that category.
$0.334 \cdot 94 = 31.4$ students
$0.458 \cdot 44 = 20.2$ students
$0.582 \cdot 19 = 11.1$ students
$0.706 \cdot 12 = 8.5$ students
$0.83 \cdot 9 = 7.5$ students
$0.954 \cdot 4 = 3.8$ students
Add these results to obtain the total number of students, 82.5. This means that of students who scored at least 21 points on the placement test, approximately 83 students will pass the class.

91. If we let t be the number of years after 1980, and E the public school per-student expenditures we can make a linear model of the given information. To start, we can use the two points $(1, 5.2)$ and $(22, 9)$ to find the slope of the model:
$m = \dfrac{9 - 5.2}{22 - 1} \approx 0.18$
So $E = 0.18t + b$. To solve for b, substitute 1 for t and 5.2 for E, since the line contains $(1, 5.2)$
$5.2 = 0.18(1) + b$
$5.2 = 0.18 + b$
$5.02 = b$
The equation for E is $E = 0.18t + 5.02$.
To find E for 2011, or when $t = 31$, substitute 31 for t and solve for E.
$E = 0.18(31) + 5.02$
$= 5.58 + 5.02$
$= 10.6$
According to the model, in 2011 the public school per-student expenditures will be $10.6 thousand.

93. If we let *t* be the number of years after 1970, and *p* the percentage of male workers who prefer a female boss over a male boss, we can make a linear model of the given information. To start, we can use the two points (5, 4) and (32, 13) to find the slope of the model:

$$m = \frac{13-4}{32-5} \approx 0.33$$

So $p = 0.33t + b$. To solve for *b* substitute 5 for *t* and 4 for *p* since the line contains (5, 4).

$$4 = 0.33(5) + b$$
$$4 = 1.65 + b$$
$$2.35 = b$$

The equation for *p* is $p = 0.33t + 2.35$.
To find the year when 16% of male workers will prefer a female boss, we must substitute 16 for *p* and solve for *t* in the equation.

$$16 = 0.33t + 2.35$$
$$13.65 = 0.33t$$
$$t \approx 41$$

According to the model in 1970 + 41 = 2011, 16% of male workers will prefer a female boss.

95. a. If we let *t* be the number of years after 1990, and *p* the percentage of large or medium-sized companies paying 100% of their employees' health care premiums, we can make a linear model of the given information. To start, we can use the two points (9, 33) and (14, 17) to find the slop of the model:

$$m = \frac{33-17}{9-14} = -3.2$$

So $p = -3.2t + b$. To solve for *b* substitute 9 for *t* and 33 for *p* since the line contains (9, 33).

$$33 = -3.2(9) + b$$
$$33 = -28.8 + b$$
$$61.8 = b$$

The equation for *p* is $p = -3.2t + 61.8$.
To find the year when no large or medium-sized companies are paying 100% of their employees' health care premiums, we can substitute 0 for *p* and solve for *t*.

$$0 = -3.2t + 61.8$$
$$-61.8 = -3.2t$$
$$t \approx 19$$

According to the model in 1990 + 19 = 2009, no large or medium-sized companies will be paying their employees' health care premiums.

b. To find the percent of large or medium-sized companies who are paying 100% of their employees' health care premiums in 2006, substitute 2006 − 1990 = 16 for *t* and solve for *p*.

$$p = -3.2(16) + 61.8$$
$$= -51.2 + 61.8$$
$$= 10.6$$

According to the model in 2006, 10.6 percent large or medium-sized companies were paying their employees' health care premiums.

97. If we let *t* be the amount of time a forth-grader studies history a week and *s* be the average score of a fourth-grader gets on the National Assessment of Educational Progress test in U.S. history, we can make a linear model of the given information. To start, we can use the two points (45, 195) and (150, 211) to find the slope of the model:

$$m = \frac{211-195}{150-45}$$
$$\approx 0.15$$

So $s = 0.15t + b$. To solve for *b* substitute 45 for *t* and 195 for *s* since the line contains (45, 195).

$$195 = 0.15(45) + b$$
$$195 = 6.75 + b$$
$$188.25 = b$$

The equation for *s* is $s = 0.15t + 188.25$.
To find the average score for fourth graders who study history about 200 minutes per week, we must substitute 200 for *t* and solve for *s* in the equation.

$$s = 0.15(200) + 188.25$$
$$= 30 + 188.25$$
$$s = 218.25$$

According to the model, when a fourth grader studies history for about 200 minutes per week, they will score 218.25.

99. a. From the information given, we have the data points (0, 640) and (4, 0). Use these points to find the slope of the equation for *f*.

$$m = \frac{640 - 0}{0 - 4} = \frac{640}{-4} = -160$$

So, $f(t) = -160t + b$. To solve for *b*, substitute 0 for *t* and 640 for $f(t)$ since the line contains (0, 640).

$$640 = -160(0) + b$$
$$640 = b$$

The equation for *f* is $f(t) = -160t + 640$.

b.

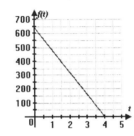

c. Since it takes 4 hours to pump out the water, the domain is $0 \le t \le 4$. Since the water level is at 640 cubic feet before starting to pump, the range is $0 \le f(t) \le 640$.

101. When $f(3) = 5$, the input for *f* is 3 and the output is 5. Possible equations for *f* will vary. Sample equations are as follows.

$$f(x) = 2x - 1$$
$$f(x) = \frac{1}{3}x + 4$$
$$f(x) = \frac{5}{3}x$$

Homework 2.4

1. The average rate of change of the number of shredder models the company makes per year between 1990 and 2005 is given by dividing the change in the number of models offered by the change in years.

$$m = \frac{\text{change in models}}{\text{change in years}}$$
$$= \frac{30 - 2}{2005 - 1990}$$
$$\approx 1.87$$

This says that the average rate of change of the number of shredder models was 1.87 shredder models per year.

3. The average rate of change of employment per year in oil companies is given by dividing the change in oil company employment by the change in the year.

$$m = \frac{\text{change in employment}}{\text{change in year}}$$
$$= \frac{0.5 - 1.6}{2004 - 1982}$$
$$= -0.05$$

This says that the average rate of change of employment per year in oil companies was –0.05 million employees per year, or a decrease of 0.05 million employees per year.

5. The average rate of change of the percentage of Americans who have trust in newspapers per year is given by dividing the change in the percent of Americans who have trust in newspapers by the change in years.

$$m = \frac{\text{change in percentage}}{\text{change in years}}$$
$$= \frac{28 - 37}{2005 - 2000}$$
$$= -1.8$$

This says that the average rate of change of the percentage of Americans who have trust in newspapers per year is –1.8, or a decrease of 1.8 percent per year.

7. The average rate of change of the cost per credit hour of classes is given by dividing the change in cost by the change in credits.

$$m = \frac{\text{change in cost}}{\text{change in credits}}$$
$$= \frac{672 - 504}{12 - 9}$$
$$= 56$$

This says that the average cost of a credit hour at Triton College is $56.

9. a. Yes, there is a linear relationship between *t* and *d*. For every hour that passes, the car has gone 70 miles. The slope of the graph is 70miles per hour, the speed of the car.

b. $d = 70t$

11. a. Yes there is a linear relationship between *t* and *n*; the rate of increase is constant. The slope of the model is 6.7, the rate of increase of U.S. households that pay bills online per year.

b. The n-intercept of the model is 18.9. This means that at $t = 0$, or 2003, the number of U.S. households that paid bills online was 18.9 million.

c. $n = 6.7t + 18.9$

d.
$$\text{households} = \frac{\text{households}}{\text{year}} \text{year} + \text{households}$$
$$= \text{households} + \text{households}$$
$$= \text{households}$$
This unit analysis shows that this model uses the correct units.

e. Since $2011 - 2003 = 8$, the year 2011 corresponds to $t = 8$.
$$n = 6.7(8) + 18.9$$
$$= 53.6 + 18.9$$
$$= 72.5$$
The model predicts that 72.5 million households will pay their bills online in 2011

13. a. The slope of the graph is –3.8, or a decrease of 3.8 minutes per year.

b. $g(t) = -3.8t + 166$

c. Since $2010 - 2003 = 7$, 2010 corresponds to $t = 7$.
$$g(7) = -3.8(7) + 166$$
$$= -26.6 + 166$$
$$= 139.4$$

d. Since 2.5 hours is the same as 150 minutes we can substitute 150 for $g(t)$ and solve for t to find the year at which the average baseball game is 2.5 hours long;
$$150 = -3.8t + 166$$
$$-16 = -3.8t$$
$$4 \approx t \text{ or } t \approx 4$$
So in $2003 + 4 = 2007$, the average baseball game should be 2.5 hours long.

e. The t-intercept of the model is given by solving for t when $g(t) = 0$;

$$0 = -3.8t + 166$$
$$-166 = -3.8t$$
$$44 \approx t \text{ or } t \approx 44$$
The models predicts that the average major league baseball game last 0 minutes in 2003 $+ 44 = 2047$.

15. a. The slope of the graph is 25, or $25 per course a student is taking.

b. $f(n) = 25n + 1585.5$

c.
$$\text{dollars} = \frac{\text{dollars}}{\text{course}} \text{course} + \text{dollars}$$
$$= \text{dollars} + \text{dollars}$$
$$= \text{dollars}$$
This unit analysis shows that this model uses the correct units.

d. $f(4) = 25(4) + 1585.5$
$$= 100 + 1585.5$$
$$= 1685.5$$
$f(4)$ corresponds to the cost of taking 4 courses, or $1685.50.

e. $1710.5 = 25n + 1585.5$
$$125 = 25n$$
$$5 = n \text{ or } n = 5$$
This says that a student who takes 5 courses will pay $1710.5.

17. a. Since 0.05 gallons of gas are being used each mile, the slope is –0.05. This means that for every mile that is driven, the amount of gas in the tank decreases by 0.05 gallons.

b. An equation for g is in the form $g(x) = mx + b$. Since at the beginning of the trip, there are 15.3 gallons of gas in the tank, when $x = 0$, $b = 15.3$. So, $f(t) = -0.05t + 15.3$.

c. To find the x-intercept, let $g(x) = 0$ and solve for x.
$$0 = -0.05x + 15.3$$
$$-15.3 = -0.05x$$
$$306 = x$$
The x-intercept is $(306, 0)$. This means that when 306 miles have been driven, the gas tank will be empty.

d. Since the car can be driven between 0 and 306 miles on the 15.3-gallon tank of gas, the domain is $0 \le x \le 306$. Since the gas tank is filled with 15.3 gallons and empty with 0 gallons, the range is $0 \le y \le 15.3$.

e. Find x when $g(x) = 1$.
$$1 = -0.05x + 15.3$$
$$-14.3 = -0.05x$$
$$286 = x$$
The car can be driven 286 miles before refueling.

19. The model will relate the year, t, and the percentage of materials that were recycled in the U.S., p. The slope of the model is 0.86, or an increase of 0.86 percentage points per year. If we let $t = 0$ in 2001, the t-intercept is 30, or 30% of materials that were recycled in the U.S. The equation is $p = 0.86t + 30$. If $p = 40$ we can solve for t;
$$40 = 0.86t + 30$$
$$10 = 0.86t$$
$$12 \approx t \text{ or } t \approx 12$$
The model predicts that in 2001 + 12 = 2013, 40% of materials in the U.S. will be recycled.

21. The model will relate the time of a call, t, and the cost of the call, c. The slope is 1.25, or $1.25 per minute. If we let $t = 0$ be a call that is 0 minutes long, the c-intercept is 1.75, or $1.75 per-call. The equation is $c = 1.25t + 1.75$. If $c = 48$ we can solve for t;
$$48 = 1.25t + 1.75$$
$$46.25 = 1.25t$$
$$37 = t \text{ or } t = 37$$
The model predicts that a 37 minute call will cost $48.

23. The slope of this model is 1.71. This means that each year after 1900 the average salary of professors at four-year public colleges and universities increases by 1.71 thousand dollars.

25. The slope of this model is –0.27. This means that each year after 1900 the record time for the women's 400-meter run decreases by 0.27 seconds.

27. The slope of this model is 1.8. This means that a 1 degree Celsius change corresponds to a 1.8 degree Fahrenheit change.

29. a. Create a scattergram using the data in the table.

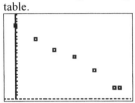

Use the first and last data points, (0, 70) and (53, 52) to find the slope.
$$m = \frac{70 - 52}{0 - 53}$$
$$= \frac{18}{-53}$$
$$\approx -0.34$$
So, the equation is of the form $f(t) = -0.34t + b$. Substitute 0 for t and 70 for $f(t)$ and solve for b.
$$70 = -0.34(0) + b$$
$$70 = 0 + b$$
$$70 = b$$
The equation is $f(t) = -0.34t + 70$.

Graphing the equation on the same graph as the scattergram, we see that the equation fits the data fairly well.

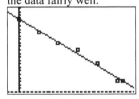

b. The slope of f is –0.34. This means that the percentage of the world's population that lives in rural areas decreases by 0.34 of one percent each year.

c.
$$f(56) = -0.34(56) + 70$$
$$= -19.04 + 70$$
$$= 50.96$$
In 2006, about 51 percent of the world's population lived in rural areas. If the population was 6.6 billion in 2006, then about 6.6 (0.51) = 3.4 billion people lived in rural areas.

d. Half of the world population will live in rural areas when $f(t) - 50$.

$$50 = -0.34(t) + 70$$

$$= -19.04 + 70$$

$$\approx 59$$

So 50 percent of the world's population will live in rural areas in $1950 + 59 = 2009$.

e. The t-intercept is the value of t when $f(t) = 0$.

$$0 = -0.34t + 70$$

$$-70 = -0.34t$$

$$206 \approx t$$

This means that in the year $1950 + 206 = 2156$, no one in the world will live in a rural area. It is highly improbable that there will ever be a time that no one lives in a rural area. Also, it is highly unlikely that a mathematical model will be valid for a span of nearly 200 years.

31. a. Create a scattergram using the data in the table.

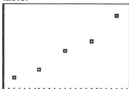

Use the first and last data points, (4, 2074) and (24, 4694) to find the slope.

$$m = \frac{4694 - 2074}{24 - 4}$$

$$= 131$$

So, the equation is of the form $f(t) = 131t + b$. Substitute 4 for t and 2074 for $f(t)$ and solve for b.

$$2074 = 131(4) + b$$

$$2074 = 524 + b$$

$$1550 = b$$

The equation is $f(t) = 131t + 1550$.

Graphing the equation on the same graph as the scattergram, we see that the equation fits the data fairly well.

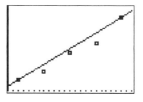

b. Create a scattergram using the data in the table.

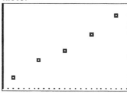

Use the first and last data points, (4, 9202) and (24, 19710) to find the slope.

$$m = \frac{19710 - 9202}{24 - 4} = 525.4$$

So, the equation is of the form $g(t) = 525.4t + b$. Substitute 4 for t and 9202 for $g(t)$ and solve for b.

$$9202 = 525.4(4) + b$$

$$9202 = 2101.6 + b$$

$$7100 = b$$

The equation is $g(t) = 525.4t + 7100$.

Graphing the equation on the same graph as the scattergram, we see that the equation fits the data very well.

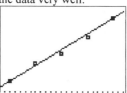

c. The slope of f is \$131 and the slope of g is \$525.4. This tells us that the tuition at private schools is increasing more rapidly that the tuition at public schools.

d. Calculate the tuition for each of the 4 years. Since t is in years since 1980, calculate $f(30)$, $f(31)$, $f(32)$ and $f(33)$, as well as, $g(30)$, $g(31)$, $g(32)$ and $g(33)$.
We can use the table feature of the graphing calculator to determine these values.

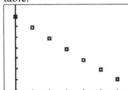

So, for public colleges, the cost of a four-year program will be $5480 + $5611 + $5742 + $5873 = $22,706. Similarly, for private colleges, the cost of a four-year program will be $22,862 + $23,387 + $23,913 + $24,438 = $94,600.

33. a. Create a scattergram using the data in the table.

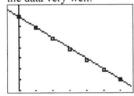

Use the first and last data points, (0, 29.92) and (6, 23.98) to find the slope.

$$m = \frac{29.92 - 23.98}{0 - 6} = -0.99$$

So the equation is of the form $f(a) = -0.99a + b$. Substitute 0 for a and 29.92 for $f(a)$ and solve for b.

$$29.92 = -0.99(0) + b$$

$$29.92 = b$$

The equation is $f(a) = -0.99a + 29.92$. Graphing the equation on the same graph as the scattergram, we see that the equation fits the data very well.

b. The slope of the model is –0.99. This means that for every increase of one thousand feet above sea level, the pressure measured in inches of mercury will decrease by 0.99 inches.

c. i. To find the rate of change in pressure between 1 thousand feet to 4 thousand feet, divide the differences in the pressures by the differences in the elevation.

$$m = \frac{25.84 - 28.86}{4 - 1} = -1.01$$

This is a steeper rate of change than we found in part **b**.

ii. To find the rate of change in pressure between 2 thousand feet to 5 thousand feet, divide the differences in the pressures by the differences in the elevation.

$$m = \frac{24.89 - 27.82}{5 - 2} = -0.98$$

This is a shallower rate of change than we found in part **b**.

iii. Since we used the points (0, 29.92) and (6, 23.98), we have already found this rate of change to be –0.99.

d. To find the pressure at 14,440 feet we can substitute 14.44 for $f(a)$ and solve for a.

$$14.44 = -0.99a + 29.92$$

$$-15.48 = -0.99a$$

$$15.64 \approx a$$

This says that at 14,440 feet the pressure is 15.64 inches of mercury.

35. a.

t	$f(t)$
0	0
1	500
2	1000
3	1500
4	1900
5	2300

b.

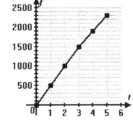

c. Answers may vary. No, it will take some amount of time to decelerate from 500 mph to 400 mph. The given speeds represent average speeds over a time interval.

d. The constant rate of change property does not apply in this exercise. Since the rate is

500 miles per hour for the first few hours and 400 miles per hour for the next 2 hours, the rate of change is not constant. Since we do not have a constant rate of change, we cannot say that the relationship between the variables is linear.

37. Answers may vary. One example is as follows.

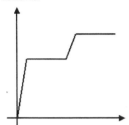

39. Answers may vary. One example is as follows.

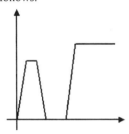

41. Answers may vary. Slope is a measurement of how much the dependent variable changes when the independent variable changes per unit.

Chapter 2 Review Exercises

1. $f(3) = 3(3)^2 - 7$
$= 3(9) - 7$
$= 27 - 7$
$= 20$

2. $f(-3) = 3(-3)^2 - 7$
$= 3(9) - 7$
$= 27 - 7$
$= 20$

3. $g(2) = \dfrac{2(2) + 5}{3(2) + 6}$
$= \dfrac{4 + 5}{6 + 6}$
$= \dfrac{9}{12}$
$= \dfrac{3}{4}$

4. $h\left(\dfrac{3}{5}\right) = -10\left(\dfrac{3}{5}\right) - 3$
$= -2(3) - 3$
$= -6 - 3$
$= -9$

5. $h(a + 3) = -10(a + 3) - 3$
$= -10a - 30 - 3$
$= -10a - 33$

6. $-6 = 2x + 3$
$-6 - 3 = 2x + 3 - 3$
$-9 = 2x$
$\dfrac{-9}{2} = x \quad \text{or} \quad x = \dfrac{-9}{2}$

7. $\dfrac{2}{3} = 2x + 3$
$\dfrac{2}{3} - 3 = 2x + 3 - 3$
$\dfrac{-7}{3} = 2x$
$\dfrac{1}{2}\left(\dfrac{-7}{3}\right) = \dfrac{1}{2}(2x)$
$\dfrac{-7}{6} = x \quad \text{or} \quad x = \dfrac{-7}{6}$

8. $a + 7 = 2x + 3$
$a + 7 - 3 = 2x + 3 - 3$
$a + 4 = 2x$
$\dfrac{a + 4}{2} = \dfrac{2x}{2}$
$\dfrac{a}{2} + 2 = x \quad \text{or} \quad x = 2 + \dfrac{a}{2}$

9. Since the graph includes the point (2, 0), $f(2) = 0$.

10. Since the graph includes the point $(0, 1)$, $f(0) = 1$.

11. Since the graph includes the point $(-3, 3.5)$, $f(-3) = 3.5$.

12. Since the graph includes the point $(-2, 3)$, $f(-2) = 3$.

13. Since the graph includes the point $(2, 0)$, $f(2) = 0$.

14. Since the graph includes the point $(4, -1)$, $f(4) = -1$

15. The domain of f is $-5 \le x \le 6$.

16. The range of f is $-2 \le y \le 4$.

17. Since x is 0 when $f(x) = 1$, $f(0) = 1$.

18. Since x is 1 when $f(x) = 2$, $f(2) = 1$.

19. When $f(x) = 0$, $x = 4$.

20. When $f(x) = 2$, $x = 1$.

21. $f(x)$ or $y = -7x + 3$

    To find the x-intercept, set $y = 0$ and solve for x.
    $$0 = -7x + 3$$
    $$-3 = -7x$$
    $$x = \frac{-3}{-7} = \frac{3}{7}$$
    To find the y-intercept, set $x = 0$ and solve for y.
    $$y = -7(0) + 3$$
    $$y = 0 + 3$$
    $$y = 3$$

22. $f(x)$ or $y = 4$ is the equation of a horizontal line. The y-intercept of the line will be $y = 4$. There is no x-intercept.

23.
    $$f(x) \text{ or } y = -\frac{4}{7}x + 2$$
    To find the y-intercept, set $x = 0$ and solve for y.
    $$y = -\frac{4}{7}(0) + 2$$
    $$y = 0 + 2$$
    $$y = 2$$

To find the x-intercept, set $y = 0$ and solve for x.
$$0 = -\frac{4}{7}x + 2$$
$$-2 = -\frac{4}{7}x$$
$$-2\left(-\frac{7}{4}\right) = x$$
$$-2\left(-\frac{7}{4}\right) = x$$
$$x = \frac{7}{2}$$

24. To find the x-intercept, set y equal to zero and solve for x;
    $$2.56x - 9.41(0) = 78.25$$
    $$2.56x = 78.25$$
    $$x \approx 30.57$$

    To find the y-intercept, set x equal to zero and solve for y;
    $$2.56(0) - 9.41y = 78.25$$
    $$-9.41y = 78.25$$
    $$y \approx -8.32$$

25.

    The "New line" has an increased slope since it is steeper than the "Model." The y-intercept is lower in the "New line" equation as it intersects the y-axis at a lower point than the "Model."

26. a. The student's car has 13 gallons of gas in the tank when no hours have been driven, so when $t = 0$, $b = 13$. Since the car uses 1.8 gallons of gas per hour, the slope is -1.8. An equation for f is $f(t) = -1.8t + 13$.

    b. The slope of f is -1.8. This means that the amount of gasoline decreases at a constant rate of 1.8 gallons per hour of driving.

c. To find the *A*-intercept of *f,* let $t - 0$.
$$A = f(t) = -1.8(0) + 13 = 0 + 13 = 13$$
The *A*-intercept is (0, 13). This represents the amount of gas in a full tank before any time has been spent driving ($t = 0$). At that time, the car has 13 gallons of gas in the tank.

d.
$$\text{gallons} = \text{gallons} - \frac{\text{gallons}}{\text{hour}} \text{hour}$$
$$= \text{gallons} - \text{gallons}$$
$$= \text{gallons}$$
This unit analysis shows that this model uses the correct units.

e. To find the *t*-intercept of *f,* let $f(t) = 0$.
$$0 = -1.8t + 13$$
$$1.8t = 13$$
$$t = \frac{13}{1.8}$$
$$t \approx 7.22$$
The *t*-intercept is (7.22, 0). This means that the student can drive for 7.22 hours before running out of gas.

f. Since the car can be driven for 7.22 hours before running out of gas, the domain is $0 \le t \le 7.22$. Since the gas tank has between 0 and 13 gallons of gas, the range is $0 \le f \le 13$.

27. a. Since the average household income increases by \$962 per year, the slope of *g* is 962.

b. In 2004, $t = 0$ and the average household income was \$32,937. Therefore, $b = 32,937$. Since the slope is 962, the equation for *g* is $g(t) = 962t + 32,937$.

c. To find $g(6)$, substitute 6 for *t*.
$$g(6) = 32,937 + 962(6)$$
$$= 32,937 + 5772$$
$$= 38,709$$
For this model $g(6) = 38,709$, is the average U.S. personal income in $2004 + 6 = 2010$.

d. Substitute 40,000 for $g(t)$ and solve for *t*.

$$40,000 = 962t + 32,937$$
$$7,063 = 962t$$
$$7 \approx t \text{ or } t \approx 7$$
The average household income will be \$40,000 in the year $2004 + 7 = 2011$.

28. The rate of change in the number of times President George W. Bush used the word "economy" in the State of the Union addresses per year is given by the difference in the usage of the word divided by the difference in years.
$$m = \frac{\text{change in usage}}{\text{change in years}} = \frac{16 - 4}{2006 - 2002} = 3$$

29. If we let *t* be the number of years after 1980, and *s* the sales at duty-free shops worldwide we can make a linear model of the given information. To start, we can use the two points (0, 2) and (25, 25) to find the slop of the model:
$$m = \frac{25 - 2}{25 - 0} = 0.92$$
So $s = 0.92t + b$. To solve for *b* substitute 0 for *t* and 2 for *s* since the line contains (0, 2).
$$2 = 0.92(0) + b$$
$$2 = b$$
The equation for *s* is $s = 0.92t + 2$.
To find the year when sales at duty-free shops worldwide reach \$31 billion, we can substitute 31 for *s* and solve for *t*.
$$31 = 0.92t + 2$$
$$29 = 0.92t$$
$$32 \approx t$$
According to the model in $1980 + 32 = 2012$, sales at duty-free shops worldwide will reach \$31 billion.

30. a.

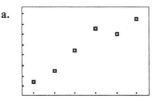

The data points lie close to the line that passes through (9, 31.4) and (14, 37.5). To find the equation for *f,* start by finding the slope using these points.
$$m = \frac{37.5 - 31.4}{14 - 9}$$
$$= 1.22$$

So, $f(t) = 1.22t + b$. To solve for b, substitute 9 for t and 31.4 for f(t) since the line contains (9, 31.4).

$$31.4 = 1.22(9) + b$$

$$31.4 = 10.98 + b$$

$$20.42 = b$$

The equation for f is $f(t) = 1.22t + 20.42$. Graphing the equation on the same graph as the scattergram, we see that the equation fits the data very well.

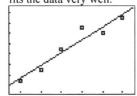

b. The slope of the model is 1.22. This means that for every year between 1999 and 2004, the standard mileage rate increases by 1.22 cents per mile.

c. The M-intercept is given by letting t equal zero and solving for M.
$$M = 1.22(0) + 20.42$$
$$M = 20.42$$
This means that during 1990 the standard mileage rate was 20.42 cents per mile.

d. To predict when the standard mileage rate will be 45 cents per mile, substitute 45 for M and solve for t.
$$45 = 1.22t + 20.42$$
$$24.58 = 1.22t$$
$$20 \approx t$$
The model predicts that the standard mileage rate will be about 45 cents per mile in $1990 + 20 = 2010$.

e. 2012 corresponds to $t = 22$.
$$M = 1.22(22) + 20.42$$
$$M = 26.84 + 20.42$$
$$M = 47.26$$
The model predicts that the standard mileage rate in 2012 will be 47.26 cents per mile.
If someone will drive 12,500 miles in 2012 their deduction will be given by the standard mileage rate times the distance they traveled;
$$12,500(47.26) = 590,750$$

This person will be able to deduct $5,907.50 since the standard mileage rate is in cents per mile.

f. The estimate of 31.4 is calculated when each standard mileage rate is weighted by the number of months it was used.
$$\frac{3(32.5) + 9(31)}{12} = \frac{376.5}{12}$$
$$\approx 31.4$$

31. a.

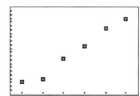

The data points lie close to the line that passes through (10, 28.3) and (13, 38.9). To find the equation for f, start by finding the slope using these points.
$$m = \frac{38.9 - 28.3}{13 - 10}$$
$$\approx 3.53$$
So, $f(t) = 3.53t + b$. To solve for b, substitute 10 for t and 28.3 for f(t) since the line contains (10, 28.3).
$$28.3 = 3.53(10) + b$$
$$28.3 = 35.3 + b$$
$$-7 = b$$
The equation for f is $f(t) = 3.53t - 7$. Graphing the equation on the same graph as the scattergram, we see that the equation fits the data very well.

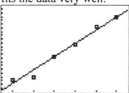

b. The slope is 3.53. This means that for every year that passes between 1998 to 2003 lobbying expenditures by Fortune 500 technology companies increased by $3.53 million.

c. To find the t-intercept, set $f(t)$ equal to zero and solve for t.

$$0 = 3.53x - 7$$

$$7 = 3.53x$$

$$1.98 \approx x$$

According to the model, in 1990 there were $1.98 million in lobbying expenditures by Fortune 500 technology companies.

d. $f(20) = 3.53(20) - 7$

$$= 70.6 - 7$$

$$= 63.6$$

The model predicts that in 1990 + 20 = 2010, lobbying expenditures by Fortune 500 technology companies will reach $63.6 million.

e. $20 = 3.53t - 7$

$$27 = 3.53t$$

$$8 \approx t$$

According to the model, in 1990 + 8 = 1998, there was $20 million in lobbying expenditures by Fortune 500 technology companies.

f. $72 = 3.53t - 7$

$$79 = 3.53t$$

$$22 \approx t$$

According to the model, in 1990 + 22 = 2012, lobbying expenditures by Fortune 500 technology companies will reach $79 million.

Chapter 2 Test

1. Since the line includes the point $(-3, -2)$, $f(-3) = -2$.

2. Since the line includes the point $(3, 0)$, $f(3) = 0$.

3. Since the line includes the point $(0, -1)$, $f(0) = -1$.

4.
Since the line includes the point $\left(-5, \dfrac{-8}{3}\right)$,

$f(-5) = -\dfrac{8}{3}$ or approximately -2.7.

5. Since the line includes the point $(-6, -3)$, $x = -6$ when $f(x) = -3$.

6. Since the line includes the point $(-3, -2)$, $x = -3$ when $f(x) = -2$.

7. Since the line includes the point $(3, 0)$, $x = 3$ when $f(x) = 0$.

8. Since the line includes the point $(4.5, 0.5)$, $x = 4.5$ when $f(x) = 0.5$.

9. The domain of f is all the x-coordinates of the points in the graph. In this case f has a domain of $-6 \le x \le 6$.

10. The range of f is all the y-coordinates of the points in the graph. In this case f has a range of $-3 \le y \le 1$.

11. To find $f(-3)$, substitute -3 for x.

$$f(-3) = -4(-3) + 7$$

$$= 12 + 7$$

$$= 19$$

12. To find $f(a - 5)$, substitute $a - 5$ for x.

$$f(a - 5) = -4(a - 5) + 7$$

$$= -4a + 20 + 7$$

$$= -4a + 27$$

13. To find x when $f(x) = 2$, substitute a for $f(x)$.

$$2 = -4x + 7$$

$$-5 = -4x$$

$$\dfrac{-5}{-4} = x$$

$$x = \dfrac{5}{4}$$

14. To find x when $f(x) = a$, substitute 2 for $f(x)$.

$$a = -4x + 7$$

$$a - 7 = -4x$$

$$\dfrac{a - 7}{-4} = x \quad \text{or} \quad x = \dfrac{-a + 7}{4}$$

15. To find the x-intercept, let $f(x) = 0$ and solve for x.

$0 = 3x - 7$

$7 = 3x$

$\dfrac{7}{3} = x$

$x = \dfrac{7}{3}$

The x-intercept is $\left(\dfrac{7}{3}, 0\right)$.

To find the y-intercept, let $x = 0$ and solve for y or $f(x)$ since $y = f(x)$.

$y = 3(0) - 7$

$y = -7$

The y-intercept is $(0, -7)$.

16. To find the x-intercept, let $g(x) = 0$ and solve for x.

$0 = -2x$

$0 = x$

$x = 0$

The x-intercept is $(0, 0)$.

To find the y-intercept, let $x = 0$ and solve for y or $g(x)$ since $y = g(x)$.

$y = -2(0)$

$y = 0$

The y-intercept is $(0, 0)$.

17. To find the x-intercept, let $k(x) = 0$ and solve for x.

$0 = \dfrac{1}{3}x - 8$

$8 = \dfrac{1}{3}x$

$24 = x$

$x = 24$

The x-intercept is $(24, 0)$.

To find the y-intercept, let $x = 0$ and solve for y or $k(x)$ since $y = k(x)$.

$y = \dfrac{1}{3}(0) - 8$

$y = -8$

The y-intercept is $(0, -8)$.

18. a. Use the first three steps of the modeling process to find the equation. Begin by creating a scattergram using the data in the table.

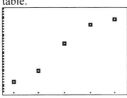

A line close to the data points passes through (16, 56.8) and (20, 81.8). Use those points to find the slope of the line.

$m = \dfrac{56.8 - 81.8}{16 - 20} = 6.25$

So $f(a) = 6.25a + b$. To solve for b, substitute 16 for a and 68.8 for $f(a)$ since the line contains (16, 56.8).

$56.8 = 6.25(16) + b$

$56.8 = 100 + b$

$-43.2 = b$

The equation for f is $f(a) = 6.25a - 43.2$. Your equation may be slightly different if you chose 2 other points. The graph of the model fits the data well.

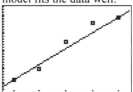

b. The slope of the model is 6.25. This means that the percentage of teens with driver's licenses increases by about 6.25 every year after their 16th birthday.

c. $0 = 6.25a - 43.2$

$43.2 = 6.25a$

$7 \approx a$

According to the model, 0% of 7 year olds have a drivers license. While this might be true, it implies that some percentage of 8 though 15 year olds do have a driver's license, something that probably doesn't happen.

d. Let $a = 21$ and solve for $f(a)$.

$f(21) = 6.25(21) - 43.2$

$= 131.25 - 43.2$

$= 88.05$

This means that 88.05 percent of 21-year-old adults have a driver's license.

e. Let $f(a) = 100$ and solve for a.

$100 = 6.25a - 43.2$

$143.2 = 6.25a$

$23 \approx a$

This means that 100 percent of 23-year-old

adults have a driver's license.

19. a. Use the first three steps of the modeling process to find the equation. Begin by creating a scattergram using the data in the table.

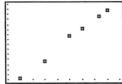

A line close to the data points passes through (65, 1.2) and (90, 11.1). Use those points to find the slope of the line.

$$m = \frac{11.1 - 1.2}{90 - 65}$$

$$= \frac{9.9}{25}$$

$$= 0.396$$

So $f(t) = 0.396t + b$. To solve for b, substitute 65 for t and 1.2 for $f(t)$ since the line contains (65, 1.2).

$$1.2 = 0.396(65) + b$$

$$11.2 = 25.74 + b$$

$$-24.54 = b$$

$$b = -24.54$$

The equation for f is $f(t) = 0.396t - 24.54$. (Your equation may be slightly different if you chose 2 other points. The linear regression equation is $f(t) = 0.40t - 24.82$. This equation will be used for f in parts b–e.) The graph of the model fits the data well.

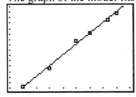

b. The slope of the model is 0.40. This means that the percentage of the military who are women is increasing by 0.40% each year.

c. $f(100) = 0.40(100) - 24.82$
$$= 15.18$$
This means that 15.2 percent of the military will be women in the year 2000 ($t = 100$).

d. Let $f(t) = 100$ and solve for t.

$$100 = 0.40t - 24.82$$

$$124.82$$

$$\frac{124.82}{0.40} = t$$

$$t = 312.05$$

This means that 100 percent of the military will be women in the year $1900 + 312 = 2212$.

e. Model breakdown occurs for certain when the percent is below 0 or above 100. Find t when $f(t) = 0$.

$$0 = 0.40t - 24.82$$

$$24.82 = 0.40t$$

$$\frac{24.82}{0.40} = t$$

$$t = 62.05$$

Therefore, model breakdown occurs in years before $1900 + 62 = 1962$, since it is not possible for a percent to be negative in this context. We know that, according to the model, 100 percent of the military will be women in 2212. Therefore, model breakdown is occurring in years after 2212. Therefore, model breakdown occurs when $t < 62.05$ and $t > 312.05$.

20. Use the first three steps of the modeling process to find the equation. Use those points (1, 311.2) and (5, 467.7) to find the slope of the line.

$$m = \frac{467.7 - 311.2}{5 - 1}$$

$$\approx 39.13$$

So $f(t) = 39.13t + b$. To solve for b, substitute 1 for t and 311.2 for $f(t)$ since the line contains (1, 311.2).

$$311.2 = 39.13(1) + b$$

$$311.2 = 39.13 + b$$

$$272.07 = b$$

The equation for f is $f(t) = 39.13t + 272.07$.

Predicting for 2010 using this equation, let $t = 10$ for $f(t)$.

$$f(10) = 39.13(10) + 272.07$$

$$= 391.3 + 272.07$$

$$= 663.37$$

This means that in 2010, total ad spending for the NCAA basketball tournament can be predicted to be $663.37 million.

21. a. Yes, the rate of increase has remained constant, showing a linear relationship. The slope in this case is 6.8, or an increase in 6.8 percentage points per year.

   b. The *p*-intercept is the *p* value when $t = 0$, or during 2001. In 2001, $p = 41$, or 41% of community banks offered Internet banking in 2001.

   c. Based on the first two parts, the equation of the model is $f(t) = 6.8t + 41$.

   d. Since $2008 - 2001 = 7$, $t = 7$ corresponds to 2008.
$$f(7) = 6.8(7) + 41$$
$$= 47.6 + 41$$
$$= 88.6$$
   The model predicts that in 2008, 88.6 percent of community banks will offer Internet banking.

   e. To find when all community banks will offer Internet banking, substitute 100 for *p*, and solve for *t*.
$$100 = 6.8t + 41$$
$$59 = 6.8t$$
$$9 \approx t$$
   The model predicts that in 2010 all community banks will offer Internet banking.

22. Answers may vary.

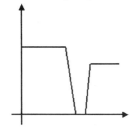

58

Chapter 3
Systems of Linear Equations

Homework 3.1

1.

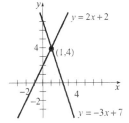

Verify that $(1,4)$ satisfies both equations.

$y = 2x+2$ $y = -3x+7$

$4 = 2(1)+2$ $4 = -3(1)+7$

$4 = 2+2$ $4 = -3+7$

$4 = 4$ true $4 = 4$ true

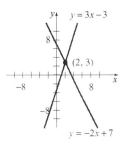

Verify that $(2,3)$ satisfies both equations.

$y = 3(x-1)$ $y = -2x+7$

$3 = 3(2-1)$ $3 = -2(2)+7$

$3 = 3(1)$ $3 = -4+7$

$3 = 3$ true $3 = 3$ true

3.

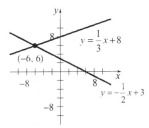

Verify that $(-6,6)$ satisfies both equations.

$y = -\dfrac{1}{2}x+3$ $y = \dfrac{1}{3}x+8$

$6 = -\dfrac{1}{2}(-6)+3$ $6 = \dfrac{1}{3}(-6)+8$

$6 = 3+3 \cdot$ $6 = -2+8$

$6 = 6$ true $6 = 6$ true

5. Write $y = 3(x-1)$ in slope-intercept form.

$y = 3(x-1)$

$y = 3x-3$

7. Write both equations in slope-intercept form.

$x+4y = 20$ $2x-4y = -8$

$4y = 20-x$ $-4y = -8-2x$

$y = 5-\dfrac{1}{4}x$ $y = 2+\dfrac{1}{2}x$

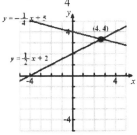

Verify that $(4,4)$ satisfies both equations.

$x+4y = 20$ $2x-4y = -8$

$(4)+4(4) = 20$ $2(4)-4(4) = -8$

$8+16 = 20$ $8-16 = -8$

$20 = 20$ true $-8 = -8$ true

9. Write both equations in slope-intercept form.

$5(y-2) = 21-2(x+3)$ $y = 3(x-1)+8$

$5y-10 = 21-2x-6$ $y = 3x-3+8$

$5y = -2x+25$ $y = 3x+5$

$y = -\dfrac{2}{5}x+5$

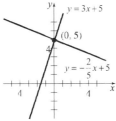

Verify that $(0,5)$ satisfies both equations.

$$5(y-2)=21-2(x+3) \quad y=3(x-1)+8$$
$$5(5-2)=21-2(0+3) \quad 5=3(0-1)+8$$
$$5(3)=21-2(3) \quad 5=3(-1)+8$$
$$15=15 \quad \text{true} \quad 5=5 \quad \text{true}$$

11. Write $4y-12=-8x$ in slope-intercept form.
$$4y-12=-8x$$
$$4y=-8x+12$$
$$y=-2x+3$$

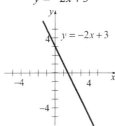

The system is dependent. The solution set is the set of numbers represented by points on the line.

13. Write both equations in slope-intercept form.

$$4x-6y=24 \qquad\qquad 6x-9y=18$$
$$-6y=-4x+24 \qquad -9y=-6x+18$$
$$y=\frac{2}{3}x-4 \qquad\qquad y=\frac{2}{3}x-2$$

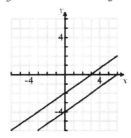

The system is inconsistent. There is no solution. The solution set is the empty set.

15. Write both equations in slope-intercept form.

$$\frac{1}{2}x-\frac{1}{2}y=1 \qquad\qquad \frac{1}{4}x+\frac{1}{2}y=2$$
$$x-y=2 \qquad\qquad x+2y=8$$
$$-y=-x+2 \qquad\qquad 2y=-x+8$$
$$y=x-2 \qquad\qquad y=-\frac{1}{2}x+4$$

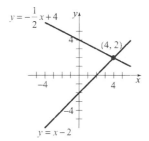

Verify that $(4,2)$ satisfies both equations.

$$\frac{1}{2}x-\frac{1}{2}y=1 \qquad\qquad \frac{1}{4}x+\frac{1}{2}y=2$$
$$\frac{1}{2}(4)-\frac{1}{2}(2)=1 \qquad \frac{1}{4}(4)+\frac{1}{2}(2)=2$$
$$2-1=1 \qquad\qquad 1+1=2$$
$$1=1 \quad \text{true} \qquad\qquad 2=2 \quad \text{true}$$

17.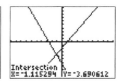

The solution is roughly $(-1.12, -3.69)$.

19. Write both equations in slope-intercept form.

$$2x+5y=7 \qquad\qquad 3x-4y=-13$$
$$5y=7-2x \qquad\qquad -4y=-3x-13$$
$$y=\frac{7}{5}-\frac{2}{5}x \qquad\qquad y=\frac{3}{4}x+\frac{13}{4}$$

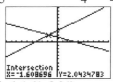

The solution is roughly $(-1.61, 2.04)$.

21. Write $2(2x-y)=2$ in slope-intercept form.

$$2(2x - y) = 2$$
$$4x - 2y = 2$$
$$-2y = -4x + 2$$
$$y = 2x - 1$$

The equations are identical.

The system is dependent. The solution set contains all ordered pairs (x, y) such that $y = 2x - 1$.

23. Write $0.2y - x = 1$ in slope-intercept form.
$$0.2y - x = 1$$
$$0.2y = x + 1$$
$$y = 5x + 5$$

The system is inconsistent. The solution set is the empty set.

25. Write both equations in slope-intercept form.

$$\frac{1}{2}x - \frac{1}{2}y = 1 \qquad \frac{1}{3}x + \frac{2}{3}y = 2$$
$$x - y = 2 \qquad x + 2y = 6$$
$$-y = -x + 2 \qquad 2y = -x + 6$$
$$y = x - 2 \qquad y = -\frac{1}{2}x + 3$$

The solution is roughly $(3.33, 1.33)$.

27. a. In 2002, $t = 32$.
$$W(36) = -0.172(36) + 43.44$$
$$= 37.25$$
$$M(36) = -0.147(36) + 39.80$$
$$= 34.51$$
The women's time is 37.25 seconds and the men's time is 34.51 seconds. The error for

the women's time estimate is 1.04 seconds and the error for the men's time estimate is 0.37 seconds.

b. The absolute value of the slope of W is more than the absolute value of the slope of M. This shows that the winning times of women decrease at a greater rate than the winning times of men.

c. Since the winning time for women is decreasing at a faster rate than for men, the winning time for men may equal the winning time for women in an upcoming year since these times are only a few seconds apart in the year 2006 and they are getting closer as each year passes.

d.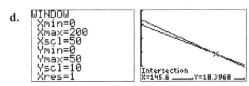

Men and women will have a winning time of 18.40 seconds in the year 2116.

29. a. Start by plotting the data. Then find the regression lines for the data.

Women

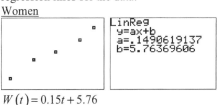

$$W(t) = 0.15t + 5.76$$

Men

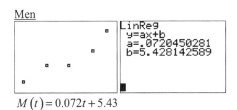

$$M(t) = 0.072t + 5.43$$

b.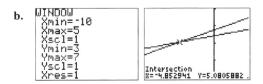

The enrollment for men and women were

equal in 1975 with roughly 5.1 million each.

c. In 2011, $t = 41$.

$$W(31) = 0.15(31) + 5.76$$
$$\approx 10.4$$
$$M(31) = 0.072(31) + 5.43$$
$$\approx 7.7$$

The total enrollment will be roughly $10.4 + 7.7 = 18.1$ million students.

31. a. Start by plotting the data. Then find the regression lines for the data.

Landline

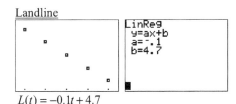

$$L(t) = -0.1t + 4.7$$

Wireless

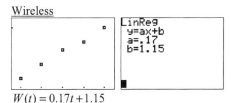

$$W(t) = 0.17t + 1.15$$

b.

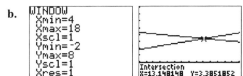

The number of land line 411 calls will be equal to the number of wireless 411 calls during 2013, at about 3.4 billion calls.

c. In 2006, $t = 6$.

$$L(6) = -0.1(6) + 4.7$$
$$= -0.6 + 4.7$$
$$= 4.1$$
$$W(6) = 0.17(6) + 1.15$$
$$= 1.02 + 1.15$$
$$= 2.17$$

The total amount of money collected from landline and wireless 411 calls in 2006 was $4.1(1.25) + 2.17(1.50) = 8.38$, or $8.38 billion.

33. a. Points B and E satisfy $y = ax + b$ since these points lie on the graph of this equation.

b. Points E and F satisfy $y = cx + d$ since these points lie on the graph of this equation.

c. Point E satisfies both equations because it lies at the intersection of the graphs of the two equations.

d. Points A, C, and D do not satisfy either equation because they do not lie on the graph of either equation.

35. The solution of this system is estimated to be $(-1.9, -2.8)$.

37. To estimate the solution, identify the slopes of each line to extend the graphs until they intersect. The blue line has a slope of $-\dfrac{1}{2}$, while the red line has a slope of $\dfrac{1}{4}$. The blue line goes through the point (6, 1), while the red line goes through the point (6, –2). If both lines are extended, they intersect at (–1, 10).

39. Using the tables of each line, notice that when $x = 3$, both equations are equal to –4. The intersection of these two lines is the point (3, –4).

41. Using the tables of each function notice that f has a slope of –3 and g has a slope of 5. Every time x increases by one, f decreases by 3 and g increases by 5. Using the table you can see that $f(3) = 21$, $f(4) = 18$, $g(3) = 17$ and $g(4) = 22$. This shows that f and g intersect between $x = 3$ and $x = 4$, or approximately at $x = 3.5$.

43. $f(-4) = 0$.

45. $f(x) = 3$ when $x = 5$.

47. $f(x) = g(x)$ when $x = -1$.

49. a. Answers may vary. Possible answers:

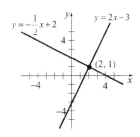

b.

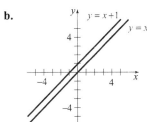

c. $y = \dfrac{3}{2}x$

$y = \dfrac{1}{2}(3x+2)-1$

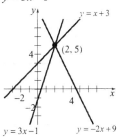

51. Graph the equations.
$y = x+3$
$y = -2x+9$
$y = 3x-1$

The solution of the system is $(2,5)$.

53. Answers may vary.

$y = \dfrac{3}{4}x$

$y = x+7$

$y = -2x-5$

55. The student did not check whether (1,2) satisfies $y = -2x + 9$, which it does not. The student should examine the graph of the lines for their point of intersection. The common point to both graphs is (2, 5).

57. Written response. Answers may vary.
The three types of systems are *one-solution systems*, *inconsistent systems*, and *dependent systems*.

Homework 3.2

1. Substitute $x-5$ for y in $x+y=9$.
$x+(x-5)=9$
$2x-5=9$
$2x=14$
$x=7$
Let $x=7$ in $y=x-5$.
$y=7-5$
$=2$
The solution is $(7,2)$.

3. Substitute $4y+7$ for x in $2x-3y=-1$.
$2(4y+7)-3y=-1$
$8y+14-3y=-1$
$5y+14=-1$
$5y=-15$
$y=-3$
Let $y=-3$ in $x=4y+7$.

$x = 4(-3) + 7$

$\quad = -12 + 7$

$\quad = -5$

The solution is $(-5, -3)$.

5. Substitute $2(x-5)$ for y in $3x - 5y - 29 = 0$.

$3x - 5(2(x-5)) - 29 = 0$

$\quad 3x - 5(2x - 10) = 29$

$\quad 3x - 10x + 50 = 29$

$\quad\quad\quad\quad -7x = -21$

$\quad\quad\quad\quad\quad x = 3$

Let $x = 3$ in $y = 2(x-5)$.

$y = 2(3-5)$

$\quad = 2(-2)$

$\quad = -4$

The solution is $(3, -4)$.

7. Substitute $99x$ for y in $y = 100x$.

$99x = 100x$

$\quad -x = 0$

$\quad\quad x = 0$

Let $x = 0$ in $y = 99x$.

$y = 99(0)$

$\quad = 0$

The solution is $(0, 0)$.

9. Substitute $4x + 5$ for y in $y = 2x - 1$.

$(4x + 5) = 2x - 1$

$\quad 2x + 5 = -1$

$\quad\quad 2x = -6$

$\quad\quad\quad x = -3$

Let $x = -3$ in $y = 2x - 1$.

$y = 2(-3) - 1$

$\quad = -6 - 1$

$\quad = -7$

The solution is $(-3, -7)$.

11. Substitute $0.2x + 0.6$ for y in $2y - 3x = -4$.

$2(0.2x + 0.6) - 3x = -4$

$\quad 0.4x + 1.2 - 3x = -4$

$\quad\quad\quad\quad -2.6x = -5.2$

$\quad\quad\quad\quad\quad\quad x = 2$

Let $x = 2$ in $y = 0.2x + 0.6$.

$y = 0.2(2) + 0.6$

$\quad = 0.4 + 0.6$

$\quad = 1$

The solution is $(2, 1)$.

13. First solve $4x + 3y = 2$ for y.

$4x + 3y = 2$

$\quad 3y = -4x + 2$

$\quad y = -\dfrac{4}{3}x + \dfrac{2}{3}$

Now substitute $-\dfrac{4}{3}x + \dfrac{2}{3}$ for y in $2x - y = -4$.

$2x - \left(-\dfrac{4}{3}x + \dfrac{2}{3}\right) = -4$

$\quad 2x + \dfrac{4}{3}x - \dfrac{2}{3} = -4$

$\quad\quad \dfrac{10}{3}x - \dfrac{2}{3} = -4$

$\quad\quad\quad \dfrac{10}{3}x = -\dfrac{10}{3}$

$\quad\quad\quad\quad x = -1$

Let $x = -1$ in $2x - y = -4$

$2(-1) - y = -4$

$\quad -2 - y = -4$

$\quad\quad -y = -2$

$\quad\quad\quad y = 2$

The solution is $(1, 2)$

15. Substitute $\dfrac{1}{2}x - 5$ for y in $2x + 3y = -1$.

$2x + 3\left(\dfrac{1}{2}x - 5\right) = -1$

$\quad 2x + \dfrac{3}{2}x - 15 = -1$

$\quad\quad\quad \dfrac{7}{2}x = 14$

$\quad\quad\quad\quad x = 4$

Let $x = 4$ in $y = \dfrac{1}{2}x - 5$.

$y = \dfrac{1}{2}(4) - 5$

$ = 2 - 5$

$ = -3$

The solution is $(4, -3)$.

17. Add the two equations.

$-x + 3y = -25$

$\underline{x - 5y = 39}$

$-2y = 14$

$y = -7$

Substitute $y = -7$ into $x - 5y = 39$.

$x - 5(-7) = 39$

$x + 35 = 39$

$x = 4$

The solution is $(4, -7)$.

19. Multiply the first equation by -1 and add the equations.

$-3x + 4y = 6$

$\underline{5x - 4y = -2}$

$2x = 4$

$x = 2$

Substitute $x = 2$ into $5x - 4y = -2$ and solve for y.

$5(2) - 4y = -2$

$10 - 4y = -2$

$-4y = -12$

$y = 3$

The solution is $(2, 3)$.

21. Multiply the first equation by 2 and add the equations.

$4x + 2y = 4$

$\underline{5x - 2y = -13}$

$9x = -9$

$x = -1$

Substitute $x = -1$ into $5x - 2y = -13$ and solve for y.

$5(-1) - 2y = -13$

$-5 - 2y = -13$

$-2y = -8$

$y = 4$

The solution is $(-1, 4)$.

23. Multiply the first equation by 2 and add the equations.

$6x - 4y = 14$

$\underline{-6x - 5y = 4}$

$-9y = 18$

$y = -2$

Substitute $y = -2$ into $3x - 2y = 7$ and solve for x.

$3x - 2(-2) = 7$

$3x + 4 = 7$

$3x = 3$

$x = 1$

The solution is $(1, -2)$.

25. Multiply the first equation by 2 and the second equation by 5, and then add the equations.

$6x + 10y = 6$

$\underline{35x - 10y = -170}$

$41x = -164$

$x = -4$

Substitute $x = -4$ into $3x + 5y = 3$ and solve for y.

$3(-4) + 5y = 3$

$-12 + 5y = 3$

$5y = 15$

$y = 3$

The solution is $(-4, 3)$.

27. Multiply the first equation by -3 and the second equation by 2, and then add the equations.

$-24x + 27y = 129$

$\underline{24x + 30y = 42}$

$57y = 171$

$y = 3$

Substitute $y = 3$ into $8x - 9y = -43$ and solve for x.

$$8x-9(3)=-43$$
$$8x-27=-43$$
$$8x=-16$$
$$x=-2$$

The solution is $(-2,3)$.

29. Multiply the first equation by 5 and the second equation by 4, and then add the equations.

$$20x-35y=-145$$
$$\underline{-20x-8y=16}$$
$$-43y=-129$$
$$y=3$$

Substitute $y=3$ into $4x-7y=-29$ and solve for x.

$$4x-7(3)=-29$$
$$4x-21=-29$$
$$4x=-8$$
$$x=-2$$

The solution is $(-2, 3)$.

31. Write the first equation in standard form. Multiply the first equation by 4 and the second equation by 3, and then add the equations.

$$-8x+12y=-24$$
$$\underline{15x-12y=3}$$
$$7x=-21$$
$$x=-3$$

Substitute $x=-3$ into $3y=2x-6$ and solve for y.

$$3y=2(-3)-6$$
$$3y=-6-6$$
$$3y=-12$$
$$y=-4$$

The solution is $(-3,-4)$.

33. Multiply the second equation by 2 and add the equations.

$$0.9x+0.4y=1.9$$
$$\underline{0.6x-0.4y=2.6}$$
$$1.5x=4.5$$
$$x=3$$

Substitute $x=3$ into $0.9x+0.4y=1.9$ and solve for y.

$$0.9(3)+0.4y=1.9$$
$$2.7+0.4y=1.9$$
$$0.4y=-0.8$$
$$y=-2$$

The solution is $(3,-2)$.

35. Use the distributive property to simplify both equations.

$$3(2x-1)+4(y-3)=1$$
$$6x-3+4y-12=1$$
$$6x+4y=16$$
$$4(x+5)-2(4y+1)=18$$
$$4x+20-8y-2=18$$
$$4x-8y=0$$

The system can be rewritten as
$$6x+4y=16$$
$$4x-8y=0$$

Multiply the first equation by 2, and then add the equations.

$$12x+8y=32$$
$$\underline{4x-8y=0}$$
$$16x=32$$
$$x=2$$

Substitute $x=2$ into $4x-8y=0$ and solve for y.

$$4(2)-8y=0$$
$$8-8y=0$$
$$-8y=-8$$
$$y=1$$

The solution is $(2,1)$.

37. Multiply the first equation by 3 and add the equations.

$$\frac{3}{5}x+\frac{9}{2}y=21$$
$$\underline{\frac{2}{5}x-\frac{9}{2}y=-16}$$
$$x=5$$

Substitute $x=5$ into $\frac{1}{5}x+\frac{3}{2}y=7$ and solve for y.

66

$$\frac{1}{5}(5)+\frac{3}{2}y=7$$

$$1+\frac{3}{2}y=7$$

$$\frac{3}{2}y=6$$

$$y=4$$

The solution is $(5,4)$.

39. Multiply the first equation by 3 and the second equation by -4, then add the equations.

$$2x+\frac{3}{2}y=\frac{1}{2}$$

$$\underline{-2x-5y=-11}$$

$$-\frac{7}{2}y=-\frac{21}{2}$$

$$y=3$$

Substitute $y=3$ into $\frac{2}{3}x+\frac{1}{2}y=\frac{1}{6}$ and solve

for x.

$$\frac{2}{3}x+\frac{1}{2}(3)=\frac{1}{6}$$

$$\frac{2}{3}x+\frac{3}{2}=\frac{1}{6}$$

$$\frac{2}{3}x=-\frac{4}{3}$$

$$x=-2$$

The solution is $(-2,3)$.

41. Substitute $2x+5$ for y in $6x-3y=-3$.

$$6x-3(2x+5)=-3$$

$$6x-6x-15=-3$$

$$-15=-3 \quad \text{false}$$

This is a contradiction. The system is inconsistent. The lines are parallel so the solution set is the empty set.

43. Multiply the first equation by 3 and the second equation by 2, then add the equations.

$$39x+30y=-21$$

$$\underline{34x-30y=94}$$

$$73x=73$$

$$x=1$$

Substitute $x=1$ into $13x+10y=-7$ and solve for y.

$$13(1)+10y=-7$$

$$13+10y=-7$$

$$10y=-20$$

$$y=-2$$

The solution is $(1,-2)$.

45. Multiply the first equation by 3 and add the equations.

$$12x-15y=9$$

$$\underline{-12x+15y=-9}$$

$$0=0 \quad \text{true}$$

This is an identity. The system is dependent. The solution set is the set of ordered pairs (x,y) such that $4x-5y=3$.

47. Multiply the first equation by 5 and add the equations.

$$20x-15y=5$$

$$\underline{-20x+15y=-3}$$

$$0=-2 \quad \text{false}$$

This is a false statement, the system is inconsistent. There is not solution to this system.

49. Substitute $-2x+4$ for y in $y=-4x+10$ and solve for x.

$$(-2x+4)=-4x+10$$

$$-2x=-4x+6$$

$$2x=6$$

$$x=3$$

Substitute $x=3$ into $y=-2x+4$ and solve for y.

$$y=-2(3)+4$$

$$=-6+4$$

$$=-2$$

The solution is $(3,-2)$

51. Use the distributive property to simplify both equations.

$$2(x+3)-(y+5)=-6$$

$$2x+6-y-5=-6$$

$$2x-y=-7$$

$$5(x-2)+3(y-4)=-34$$

$$5x-10+3y-12=-34$$

$$5x+3y=-12$$

The system can be rewritten as

$2x - y = -7$

$5x + 3y = -12$

Multiply the first equation by 3, then add the two equations.

$6x - 3y = -21$

$\underline{5x + 3y = -12}$

$11x = -33$

$x = -3$

Substitute $x = -3$ into $2x - y = -7$

$2(-3) - y = -7$

$-6 - y = -7$

$-y = -1$

$y = 1$

The solution is $(-3, 1)$.

53. Substitute $\frac{1}{2}x + 3$ for y in $2y - x = 6$.

$2\left(\frac{1}{2}x + 3\right) - x = 6$

$x + 6 - x = 6$

$6 = 6$ true

This is an identity. The system is dependent. The solution set is the set of ordered pairs (x, y) such that $y = \frac{1}{2}x + 3$.

55. Multiply the first equation by 2 and the second equation by 5, then add the equations.

$\frac{5}{3}x + \frac{1}{2}y = 6$

$\underline{-\frac{5}{3}x + \frac{25}{2}y = 20}$

$13y = 26$

$y = 2$

Substitute $y = 2$ into $\frac{5}{6}x + \frac{1}{4}y = 3$ and solve for x.

$\frac{5}{6}x + \frac{1}{4}(2) = 3$

$\frac{5}{6}x + \frac{1}{2} = 3$

$\frac{5}{6}x = \frac{5}{2}$

$x = 3$

The solution is $(3, 2)$.

57. First simplify the equations by multiplying by their LCD.

$2(x + 2y) - 3(x - y) = 13$

$2x + 4y - 3x + 3y = 13$

$-x + 7y = 13$

$2(x + 3y) + (x + y) = 17$

$2x + 6y + x + y = 17$

$3x + 7y = 17$

The system can be rewritten as

$-x + 7y = 13$

$3x + 7y = 17$

Multiply the first equation by -1 and add both equations.

$x - 7y = -13$

$3x + 7y = 17$

$4x = 4$

$x = 1$

Substitute $x = 1$ into $3x + 7y = 17$ and solve for y.

$3(1) + 7y = 17$

$3 + 7y = 17$

$7y = 14$

$y = 2$

The solution is $(1, 2)$.

59. Substitute $2.58x - 8.31$ for y into $y = -3.25x + 7.86$ and solve for x.

$(2.58x - 8.31) = -3.25x + 7.86$

$2.58x = -3.25x + 16.17$

$5.83x = 16.17$

$x \approx 2.77$

Substitute $x = 2.77$ into $y = 2.58x - 8.31$ and solve for y.

$y = 2.58(2.77) - 8.31$

$\approx 7.15 - 8.31$

≈ -1.16

The solution is approximately $(2.77, -1.16)$.

61. Multiply the first equation by -3 and add the equations.

$$-3y = 2.31x - 14.52$$
$$\underline{y = -2.31x - 1.49}$$
$$-2y = -16.01$$
$$y \approx 8.01$$

Substitute $y = 8.01$ into $y = -0.77x + 4.84$ and solve for y.
$$8.01 = -0.77x + 4.84$$
$$3.17 = -0.77x$$
$$-4.12 \approx x$$

The solution is approximately $(-4.12, 8.01)$.

63. Elimination
Rewrite the second equation so the variables are on the left side of the equation.
$$3x + y = 11$$
$$2x + y = 9$$

Multiply the second equation by -1 and add the equations.
$$3x + y = 11$$
$$\underline{-2x - y = -9}$$
$$x = 2$$

Substitute $x = 2$ into $y = -2x + 9$ and solve for y.
$$y = -2(2) + 9$$
$$= 5$$

The solution is $(2, 5)$.

Substitution
Substitute $-2x + 9$ for y in the first equation.
$$3x + (-2x + 9) = 11$$
$$3x - 2x + 9 = 11$$
$$x = 2$$

Substitute $x = 2$ into $y = -2x + 9$ and solve for y.
$$y = -2(2) + 9$$
$$= -4 + 9$$
$$= 5$$

The solution is $(2, 5)$.

Graphing

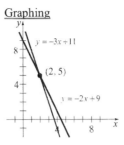

65. a. Multiply the first equation by 3 and the second equation by -2, then add the equations.
$$6x + 12y = 30$$
$$\underline{-6x + 14y = -4}$$
$$26y = 26$$
$$y = 1$$

Substitute $y = 1$ into $2x + 4y = 10$
$$2x + 4(1) = 10$$
$$2x + 4 = 10$$
$$2x = 6$$
$$x = 3$$

The solution is $(3, 1)$.

b. Multiply the first equation by 7 and the second equation by 4, then add the equations.
$$14x + 28y = 70$$
$$\underline{12x - 28y = 8}$$
$$26x = 78$$
$$x = 3$$

Substitute $x = 3$ into $2x + 4y = 10$
$$2(3) + 4y = 10$$
$$6 + 4y = 10$$
$$4y = 4$$
$$y = 1$$

c. The results are the same if the x terms or the y terms are eliminated. It doesn't matter which variable you choose to eliminate first.

67. The graph show that $y = \dfrac{1}{2}x + \dfrac{5}{2}$ and $y = 2x + 7$ intersect at the point $(-3, 1)$. So the solution of the given equation is $x = -3$.

69. The graph show that $y = \frac{1}{2}x + \frac{5}{2}$ and $y = 3$ intersect as the point $(1, 3)$. So the solution of the given equation is $x = 1$.

71. The graph show that $y = 2x + 7$ and $y = -3$ intersect at the point $(-5, -3)$. So the solution of the given equation is $x = -5$.

73. The graph show that $y = \frac{1}{3}x + \frac{5}{3}$ and $y = x - 1$ intersect at the point $(4, 3)$. So the solution of the given equation is $x = 4$.

75. The graph show that $y = \frac{1}{3}x + \frac{5}{2}$ and $y = 2$ intersect at the point $(1, 2)$. So the solution to the given equation is $x = 1$.

77. The graph shows that $y = \frac{1}{3}x + \frac{5}{3}$ and $y = -3x - 5$ intersect at the point $(-2, 1)$. So the solution to the given system of equations is $(-2, 1)$.

79.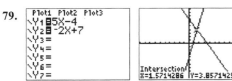
The solution to the equation is approximately $x \approx 1.57$

81.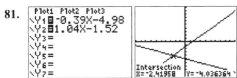
The solution to the equation is approximately $x \approx -2.42$.

83.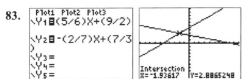
The solution to the equation is approximately $x \approx -1.94$

85. Notice that for $y = \frac{1}{2}x + \frac{7}{2}$ and $y = \frac{4}{5}x + 2$ when

$x = 5$ they are both equal to 6. So the solution to the given equation is $x = 5$.

87. Notice that for $y = \frac{11}{10}x + \frac{17}{10}$ and $y = 5$ when $x = 3$ they are both equal to 5. So the solution to the given equation is $x = 5$.

89. Notice that for $y = \frac{4}{5}x + 2$ and $y = \frac{11}{10}x + \frac{17}{10}$ when $x = 1$ they are both equal to 2.8. So the solution to the given system of equations is $(1, 2.8)$.

91. The function f has a slope of 4 and an f-intercept of $(0, 3)$. Therefore, $f(x) = 4x + 3$. The function g has a slope of -6 and a g-intercept of $(0, 50)$. Therefore, $g(x) = -6x + 50$. Write the system that describes the functions f and g.

$y = 4x + 3$
$y = -6x + 50$

Solve using substitution.
Substitute $4x + 3$ for y in $y = -6x + 50$ and solve for x.

$4x + 3 = -6x + 50$
$10x = 47$
$x = 4.7$

Substitute $x = 4.7$ into $y = 4x + 3$ and solve for y.

$y = 4(4.7) + 3$
$= 18.8 + 3$
$= 21.8$

The solution is $(4.7, 21.8)$.

93. The student is not correct. A system is inconsistent (i.e. the solution set is the empty set) when the lines are parallel. Parallel lines must have the same slope. The slopes are different yet they are close enough to where the lines look parallel around the origin. To find the correct solution, substitute $2x + 3$ for y in $y = 2.01x + 1$ and solve for x.

$2x + 3 = 2.01x + 1$
$-0.01x = -2$
$x = 200$

Substitute $x = 200$ into $y = 2x + 3$ and solve

for y.

$y = 2(200) + 3$

$\quad = 403$

The solution is $(200, 403)$.

95. The coordinates for A are $(0,0)$ since it lies at the origin. The coordinates for B are the same as the coordinates of the y-intercept of l_1, which is $(0,3)$. The coordinates for C are the same as the point of intersection of l_1 and l_2. Solve the following system.

$l_1 : y = 2x + 3$

$l_2 : 3y + x = 30$

Substitute $2x + 3$ for y in the second equation.

$3(2x + 3) + x = 30$

$\quad 6x + 9 + x = 30$

$\qquad\qquad 7x = 21$

$\qquad\qquad x = 3$

Substitute $x = 3$ into the first equation and solve for y.

$y = 2(3) + 3$

$\quad = 6 + 3$

$\quad = 9$

The solution is $(3, 9)$ so the coordinates of C are $(3, 9)$. The coordinates for D are the same as the coordinates of the point of intersection of l_2 and l_3. Solve the following system.

$l_2 : 3y + x = 30$

$l_3 : y + 3x = 26$

Multiply the second equation by -3 and add the equations.

$\quad 3y + x = 30$

$\underline{-3y - 9x = -78}$

$\qquad -8x = -48$

$\qquad\quad x = 6$

Substitute $x = 6$ into $3y + x = 30$ and solve for y.

$3y + (6) = 30$

$\quad 3y = 24$

$\quad y = 8$

The solution is $(6, 8)$ so the coordinates of D are $(6, 8)$. The coordinates for E are the same as the

coordinates of the point of intersection of l_3 and l_4. Solve the following system.

$l_3 : y + 3x = 26$

$l_4 : y = 2x - 10$

Substitute $2x - 10$ in for y in $y + 3x = 26$.

$2x - 10 + 3x = 26$

$\qquad\quad 5x = 36$

$\qquad\quad x = 7.2$

Substitute $x = 7.2$ into $y = 2x - 10$ and solve for x.

$y = 2(7.2) - 10$

$\quad = 4.4$

The solution is $(7.2, 4.4)$ so the coordinates of E are $(7.2, 4.4)$. The coordinates of F are the same as the coordinates of the x-intercept of l_4. Let $y = 0$ in l_4 and solve for x.

$y = 2x - 10$

$0 = 2x - 10$

$2x = 10$

$x = 5$

The coordinates of F are $(5, 0)$.

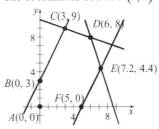

97. a. You may use more than one method to solve the system. For example, you may use substitution as follows.

Solve the first equation for y.

$ax + by = c$

$\quad by = -ax + c$

$\quad y = \dfrac{-ax + c}{b}$

Substitute this result for y in the second equation and solve for x.

$$kx + p\left(\frac{-ax + c}{b}\right) = d$$

$$kx - \frac{apx}{b} + \frac{cp}{b} = d$$

$$bkx - apx + cp = bd$$

$$(bk - ap)x + cp = bd$$

$$(kd - ap)x = bd - cp$$

$$x = \frac{bd - cp}{bk - ap} \quad \text{or} \quad \frac{cp - bd}{ap - bk}$$

Substitute this result for x in $ax + by = c$ and solve for y.

$$a\left(\frac{cp - bd}{ap - bk}\right) + by = c$$

$$\frac{acp - abd}{ap - bk} + by = c$$

$$by = c - \frac{acp - abd}{ap - bk}$$

$$by = \frac{acp - bck}{ap - bk} - \frac{acp - abd}{ap - bk}$$

$$by = \frac{-bck + abd}{ap - bk}$$

$$by = \frac{abd - bck}{ap - bk}$$

$$y = \frac{ad - ck}{ap - bk} \quad \text{or} \quad y = \frac{ck - ad}{bk - ap}$$

Therefore, the solution is

$$\left(\frac{cp - bd}{ap - bk}, \frac{ad - ck}{ap - bk}\right), \text{ assuming } ae - bd \neq 0.$$

b. Substitute 3 for a, 5 for b, 2 for c, 4 for k, 3 for p, and 4 for d in the solution from part **a**.

$$x = \frac{2(3) - 5(4)}{3(3) - 5(4)} = \frac{-14}{-11} = \frac{14}{11}$$

$$y = \frac{3(4) - 2(4)}{3(3) - 5(4)} = \frac{4}{-11} = -\frac{4}{11}$$

The solution is $\left(\frac{14}{11}, -\frac{4}{11}\right)$.

99. Written response. Answers may vary.

Homework 3.3

1. Solve the system
$$y = -0.172t + 43.44$$
$$y = -0.147t + 39.80$$

Substitute $-0.172t + 43.44$ for y in the second equation and solve for t.
$$-0.172t + 43.44 = -0.147t + 39.80$$
$$-0.025t = -3.64$$
$$t \approx 145.6$$
Substitute this result into the first equation and solve for y.
$$y = -0.172(145.6) + 43.44$$
$$\approx 18.40$$
According to the models, the winning times for women and men will both be 18.40 seconds in the year 2116.

3. Solve the system
$$W(t) = 0.15t + 5.76$$
$$M(t) = 0.072t + 5.43$$
Substitute $0.15t + 5.76$ for M in the second equation and solve for t.
$$0.15t + 5.76 = 0.072t + 5.43$$
$$0.078t = -0.33$$
$$t \approx -4.23$$
Substitute this result into the first equation and solve for W.
$$E = 0.15(-4.23) + 5.76 \approx 5.13$$

According to the models, the enrollments for men and women were approximately equal in 1976 (roughly 5.13 million).

5. a. Milk

$$M(t) = -0.28t + 35.64$$

Soft Drinks

$$S(t) = 0.86t + 8.30$$

b. Substitute the $M(t)$ for $S(t)$ and solve for t.
$$-0.28t + 35.64 = 0.86t + 8.3$$
$$27.34 = 1.14t$$
$$24 \approx t$$
During 1974 the per-person milk and soft

drink consumptions were the same.

$M(23.98) = -0.28(23.98) + 35.64$

$\qquad = -6.71 + 35.64$

$\qquad \approx 28.9$

$S(23.98) = 0.86(23.98) + 8.3$

$\qquad = 20.62 + 8.3$

$\qquad \approx 28.9$

The annual consumption per-person in 1974 was about 28.9 gallons.

c.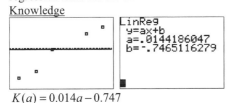

7. a. Start by plotting the data. Then find the regression lines for the data.

Knowledge

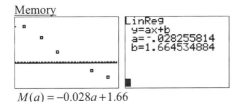

$K(a) = 0.014a - 0.747$

Memory

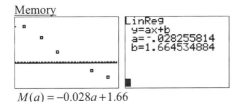

$M(a) = -0.028a + 1.66$

b. Solve the system

$K(a) = 0.014a - 0.747$

$M(a) = -0.028a + 1.66$

Substitute $0.014a - 0.747$ in for $M(a)$ in the second equation and solve for a.

$0.014a - 0.747 = -0.028a + 1.66$

$0.042a = 2.407$

$a \approx 57.31$

The scores will be roughly equal when a person is 57 years old.

c. Find the intersection point using a graphing utility.

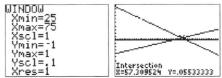

This confirms our original solution of 57 years old.

9. a. Solve the system

$y = 13.5t + 229$

$y = -5t + 365$

Substitute $13.5t + 229$ for y in the second equation and solve for t.

$13.5t + 229 = -5t + 365$

$18.5t = 136$

$t \approx 7.35$

Substitute this result into the first equation and solve for y.

$y = 13.5(7.35) + 229$

$\qquad \approx 328.24$

According to the models, the two newspapers had equal circulations of roughly 328 thousand in 1997.

b. Since the circulations were roughly equal in 1997, competition heated up as each newspaper tried to overtake the other.

c. $D(10) = 13.5(10) + 229$

$\qquad = 135 + 229$

$\qquad = 364$

$R(10) = -5(10) + 365$

$\qquad = -50 + 365$

$\qquad = 315$

$826 - (364 + 315) = 826 - 679 = 147$

According to the models, the combined increase due to bonus copies was roughly 147 thousand bonus copies.

d. $D(11) = 13.5(11) + 229$

$\qquad = 377.5$

$R(11) = -5(11) + 365$

$\qquad = 310$

$377.5 + 310 = 687.5$

According to the models, the combined circulation from the two newspapers was roughly 688 thousand copies in 2001.

e. The estimate in part d. was an overestimate. After joining revenue streams, the competition for subscribers ceased (or, at least, reduced if there were other competitors). The end of bonus copies, or just the merger in general, may have caused some subscribers to cancel subscriptions.

11. a. For both $T(t)$ and $E(t)$ we are given the T and E intercepts and the slope in terms of the price of the cars in 2005 and their depreciation rates, respectively.

$T(t) = -1725t + 12281$

$E(t) = -1424t + 10952$

b. Substitute $-1725t + 12281$ for E in $E(t) = -1424t + 10952$ and solve for t.

$-1725t + 12281 = -1424t + 10952$

$-301t = -1329$

$t \approx 4.42$

So both cars will have the same value around 2009. To find that value substitute $t = 4.41$ into $T(t)$.

$T(4.42) = -1725(4.42) + 12281$

≈ 4665

So in 2009 they will be roughly $4,665.

c. Find the intersection point using a graphing utility.

This confirms our original solution (4.41, 4673.75)

13. a. Since Jenny Craig's program fees increase by a constant $72 each week, the function J is linear and its slope is 72. The J-intercept is $(0, 19)$, since the start-up fee is $19 at $t = 0$.

So, an equation for $J(t)$ is $J(t) = 72t + 19$.

Since Weight Watchers' program fees increase by a constant $77 each week ($17 fee + $60 food), the function W is linear and its slope is 77. The W-intercept is $(0, 0)$ since there is no start-up fee at $t = 0$. An

equation for $W(t)$ is $W(t) = 77t$.

b. $J(t) = 72t + 19$

$\text{dollars} = \dfrac{\text{dollars}}{\text{weeks}} \text{weeks} + \text{dollars}$

$\text{dollars} = \text{dollars} + \text{dollars}$

$\text{dollars} = \text{dollars}$

The units of $J(t)$ are correct.

$W(t) = 77t$

$\text{dollars} = \dfrac{\text{dollars}}{\text{weeks}} \text{weeks}$

$\text{dollars} = \text{dollars}$

The units of $W(t)$ are correct.

c. Solve the system

$y = 72t + 19$

$y = 77t$

Substitute $72t + 19$ for y into the second equation.

$72t + 19 = 77t$

$5t = 19$

$t = 3.8$

Substitute this result into the first equation and solve for y.

$y = 72(3.8) + 19$

$= 292.6$

The total cost at both Jenny Craig and Weight Watchers is approximately $293 in 4 weeks.

d. Find the intersection point using a graphing utility.

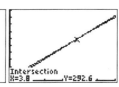

15. For both large/midsize and small SUVs we are given the initial sales in 2002 and the rates of change per year. Using this information we can write two equations of the SUV sales in terms of t, the years after 2002.

$L(t) = -7t + 281$

$S(t) = 33t + 140$

To find when the sales of each kind of SUV were the same we can substitute $-7t + 281$ for S in $S(t)$ $= 33t + 140$.

$-7t + 281 = 33t + 140$

$-40t = -141$

$t = 3.525$

During 2005 the sales of large and midsize SUVs were the same as small SUVs.

17. **a.** For each state we are given the personal incomes in 1998 and the personal incomes in 2003. Since the personal income in both states increased linearly we can write a linear model. To do this we first need to find the rate of increase for both states.

$$m_f = \frac{22629 - 20656}{2003 - 1998} = 394.6$$

$$m_g = \frac{26530 - 26017}{2003 - 1998} = 102.6$$

So $f(t) = 394.6t + b$ and $g(t) = 102.6t + b$. Since t is the years since 1998, $f(0) = 20656$ and $g(0) = 26017$. These equations can be written in slope-intercept form.

$$f(t) = 394.6t + 20656$$

$$g(t) = 102.6t + 26017$$

b. Substitute 394.6t + 20656 for $g(t)$ in $g(t) = 102.6t + 26017$ and solve for t.

$394.6t + 20656 = 102.6t + 26017$

$292t = 5361$

$t = 18.36$

So during 2016, personal income in New Mexico will equal the personal income in Ohio.

c. Find the intersection point using a graphing utility.

 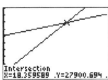

19. First find the slope of Toyota's market share, $T(t)$, and then find the slope of Ford's market share, $F(t)$.

$$m_T = \frac{12 - 10}{2004 - 1999} = 0.4$$

$$m_F = \frac{19 - 25}{2004 - 1999} = -1.2$$

If we let t be the years after 1999, $T(0) = 10$ and $F(0) = 25$ we find that

$T(t) = 0.4t + 10$

$F(t) = -1.2t + 25$

Substitute $0.4t + 10$ for $F(t)$ in $F(t) = -1.2t + 25$ and solve for t.

$0.4t + 10 = -1.2t + 25$

$1.6t = 15$

$t = 9.375$

So their market share will be equal during 2008. To find the market share substitute $t = 9.375$ in $T(t)$.

$T(9.375) = -1.2(9.375) + 25$

$= -11.25 + 25$

$= 13.75$

So Toyota and Ford will both have a market share of about 13.75% during 2008.

21. **a.** Due to rounding, it is not exact. In the following graph, notice that the intersection is not at an integer value of t.

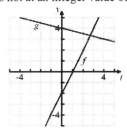

b. $f(I)$ will be larger than $g(I)$. Notice in the previous graph the slope of f is larger than the slope of g.

Homework 3.4

1. The total number of seats is 5000. To find the total revenue multiply the number of each type of seat by how much they cost and add these numbers together. Let the $27 seats be x and the $40 seats be y. This gives the following system of equations.

$x + y = 5000$

$27x + 40y = 150,600$

Substitute $5000 - x$ for y in the second equation and solve for x.

$$27x + 40(5000 - x) = 150,600$$
$$27x + 200,000 - 40x = 150,600$$
$$-13x + 200,000 = 150,600$$
$$-13x = -49400$$
$$x = 3800$$

So about 3800 $27 tickets should be sold and 1200 $40 tickets should be sold.

3. Let the number of CDs sold be represented by x and the number of EPs sold be represented by y. This gives the following system of equations.
$$x + y = 836$$
$$12.96x + 9.99y = 10,475.19$$

Substitute $836 - x$ for y in the second equation and solve x.
$$12.96x + 9.99(836 - x) = 10,475.19$$
$$12.96x + 8351.64 - 9.99x = 10,475.19$$
$$2.97x = 2123.55$$
$$x = 715$$

So about 715 CDs were sold and 121 EPs were sold.

5. Let the price of main-level seats be p and let the price of the balcony seats be m. These two prices are related by $m = p - 15$. This gives the following system of equations.
$$m = p - 15$$
$$500m + 1800p = 84,500$$

Substitute $p - 15$ for m in the second equation and solve for p.
$$500(p - 15) + 1800p = 84,500$$
$$500p - 7,500 + 1800p = 84,500$$
$$2300p = 92,000$$
$$p = 40$$

So the main-level seats should cost $40 and the auditorium should cost $25.

7. A system of equations can be written based on the given information: there will be three times as many full-time students as part-time students, each full-time student takes 14 units, each part-time student takes 3 units, and each unit costs $13.
$$3p = f$$
$$13(14f + 3p) = 877,500$$

Substitute $3p$ for f in the second equation and solve for p.

$$13(14(3p) + 3p) = 877,500$$
$$13(42p + 3p) = 877,500$$
$$13(45p) = 877,500$$
$$585p = 877,500$$
$$p = 1500$$

There needs to be 1500 part-time students and 4500 full-time students in order for the revenue to be $877,500.

9. **a.** The total revenue will be given by multiplying the number of tickets by their respective price, and adding these amounts. The total number of tickets will be 20,000 so $x + y = 20,000$. We only want R to be in terms of x so $y = 20,000 - x$.
$$f(x) = 50x + 75(20,000 - x).$$

b.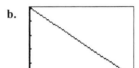

The slope of the graph is –25. This represents the fact that as more $50 tickets are sold, the revenue decreases by $25 compared to selling only $75 tickets.

c.
$$f(16,000) = 50(16,000) + 75(20,000 - 16,000)$$
$$= 800,000 + 75(4,000)$$
$$= 800,000 + 300,000$$
$$= 1,100,000$$

$f(16,000)$ represents the amount of revenue made when 16,000 $50 tickets are sold.

d. The total revenue must cover the $475,000 production cost and make $600,000 in profit. This means that the total revenue must be $1,075,000.

$$1,075,000 = 50x + 75(20,000 - x)$$
$$1,075,000 = 50x + 1,500,000 - 75x$$
$$1,075,000 = -25x + 1,500,000$$
$$-425,000 = -25x$$
$$17,000 = x$$

So 17,000 of the $50 tickets and 3,000 of the $75 tickets must be sold.

11. **a.** The total revenue will be given by multiplying the number of tickets by their

respective prices, and adding these amounts. The total number of tickets will be 12,000 so $x + y = 12,000$. We only want R to be in terms of x so $y = 12,000 - x$.
$$f(x) = 45x + 70(12,000 - x)$$
$$= 45x + 840,000 - 70x$$
$$= -25x + 840,000$$

b.

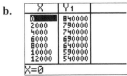

In each case $f(x)$ means that x of the $45 tickets were sold.

c. The possible revenues from the concert range from $540,000 to $840,000.

d. $602,500 = -25x + 840,000$
$$-237,500 = -25x$$
$$9500 = x$$
So 9,500 of the $45 tickets and 2,500 of the $75 tickets should be sold.

13. a. Since a first-class ticket is $242 more than a coach ticket, $y = 242 + x$. To find the total revenue of a single flight, multiply the number of tickets sold by their respective prices, and then add these amounts.
$$R = 8y + 126x$$
$$f(x) = 8(242 + x) + 126x$$
$$= 1936 + 8x + 126x$$
$$= 134x + 1936$$

b. The slope of the graph of f is 134. As the price of a coach ticket increases by a dollar, the total revenue increases by $134 on a full plane.

c. $14,130 = 134x + 1936$
$$12,194 = 134x$$
$$91 = x$$
United Airlines should charge $91 for a coach ticket, and $333 for a first-class ticket.

15. Let x be the amount of money put into the American Funds New Perspective F account, and y be the amount of money put into the Oppenheimer Global Y account. Both amounts

of money add to $15,000, and their interest after one year will be $1410.
$$x + y = 15,000$$
$$0.09x + 0.11y = 1410$$
Substitute $15,000 - y$ for x in the second equation and solve for y.
$$0.09(15,000 - y) + 0.11y = 1410$$
$$1350 - 0.09y + 0.11y = 1410$$
$$1350 + 0.02y = 1410$$
$$0.02y = 60$$
$$y = 3000$$
So $3,000 should go into the Oppenheimer Global Y account and $12,000 should go into the American Funds New Perspective F account.

17. Let x be the amount of money put into the GMO Growth III account, and y be the amount of money put into the Gartmore Destinations Mod Agg Svc account. Both amounts of money add to $8,500, and their interest after one year will be $303.
$$x + y = 8,500$$
$$0.023x + 0.066y = 303$$
Substitute $5,500 - y$ for x in the second equation and solve for y.
$$0.023(5,500 - y) + 0.066y = 303$$
$$126.5 - 0.023y + 0.066y = 303$$
$$0.043y = 176.5$$
$$y \approx 4104.65$$
So about $4,104.64 should go into the Gartmore Destinations Mod Agg Svc account and about $4,395.35 should go into the GMO Growth III account.

19. Let x be the amount of money put into the Lord Abbett Developing Growth B account, and y be the amount of money put into the Bridge Micro-Cap Limited account. The problem states that $x = 2y$. The interest for any account is the amount deposited into the account multiplied by its interest rate in decimal form.
$$I = 0.082x + 0.215y$$
$$f(y) = 0.082(2y) + 0.215y$$
$$= 0.164y + 0.215y$$
$$= 0.379y$$
$$758 = 0.379y$$
$$2000 = y$$
So $2,000 should be invested in the Bridge

Micro-Cap Limited account and $4,000 in the Lord Abbett Developing Growth B account.

21. Let x be the amount of money put into the Dreyfus Premier Worldwide Growth R account, and y be the amount of money put into the Oppenheimer Global Opportunities Y account. Both amounts of money add to $15,000, and their interest after one year will be $1410.

$$x = 3y$$
$$0.045x + 0.149y = 426$$

Substitute $3y$ for x in the second equation and solve for y.
$$0.045(3y) + 0.149y = 426$$
$$0.135y + 0.149y = 426$$
$$0.284y = 426$$
$$y = 1500$$

So $1,500 should go into the Oppenheimer Global Opportunities Y account and $4,500 Dreyfus Premier Worldwide Growth R account.

23. a. Since the total amount of money to be invested is $10,000, the sum of x and y must be $10,000. The interest for any account is the amount deposited into the account, multiplied by its return as a decimal.
$$x + y = 10000$$
$$I = 0.0287x + 0.081y$$
$$f(x) = 0.0287x + 0.081(10,000 - x)$$
$$= 0.0287x + 810 - 0.081x$$
$$= -0.0523x + 810$$

b.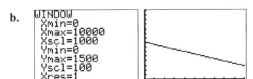

The slope is -0.0523, this is the decrease in the total amount of interest for every dollar put into the Charter One Bank CD. The more money put into the mutual fund, the higher the interest. The more money put into the CD the lower the interest.

c. $$400 = -0.0523x + 810$$
$$-410 = -0.0523x$$
$$7839.34 = x$$

So about $7,839.34 should go into the CD, while about $2,160.66 should go into the

mutual fund to earn a total of $400 in one year.

25. a. Since the total amount of money to be invested is $9,000, the sum of x and y must be $9,000. The interest for any account is the product of the amount deposited into the account and its interest rate in decimal form.
$$x + y = 9000$$
$$I = 0.025x + 0.0945y$$
$$f(x) = 0.025x + 0.0945(9,000 - x)$$
$$= 0.025x + 850.5 - 0.0945x$$
$$= -0.695x + 850.5$$

b. When $x = 500$, this means that $500 has been invested in the CD. $f(500)$ is the amount of interest earned per year when $500 has been invested in the CD, and the rest has been invested in the mutual fund.
$$f(500) = -0.0695(500) + 850.5$$
$$= -34.75 + 850.5$$
$$= 815.75$$

c. $f(x) = 500$ is when x amount of dollars has been invested into the CD, and both investments return $800 in interest per year .
$$500 = -0.0695x + 850.5$$
$$-350.5 = -0.0695x$$
$$5043.17 = x$$

So about $5043.17 should be invested in the CD, and about $3,956.83 should be invested in the mutual fund.

d. When $x = 10,000$, this means that $10,000 has been invested in the CD. $f(10,000)$ is the amount of interest earned per year when $10,000 has been invested in the CD, and nothing has been invested in the mutual fund.
$$f(10,000) = -0.0695(10,000) + 850.5$$
$$= -695 + 850.5$$
$$= 155.5$$

Since $9,000 is invested initially, you would have to borrow $1,000 to invest $10,000. This is shown by the above since $9,000(0.025) = \$225$, and not the $155.5 above.

27. a. Since the total amount of money to be

invested is $8,000, the sum of x and y must be $8,000. The interest for any account is the product of the amount deposited into the account and its interest rate in decimal form.

$x + y = 8000$

$I = 0.015x + 0.116y$

$f(x) = 0.015x + 0.116(8,000 - x)$

$= 0.015x + 928 - 0.116x$

$= -0.101x + 928$

b. The minimum principal of $2,500, relates to the function above by restricting the domain. Now $2,500 \le x \le 8,000$, and so

$f(2,500) = -0.101(2,500) + 928$

$= -252.5 + 928$

$= 675.5$

$f(8,000) = -0.101(8,000) + 928$

$= -808 + 928$

$= 120$

So the interest is between $675.5 and $120.

c. $400 = -0.101x + 928$

$-528 = -0.101x$

$5227.72 = x$

So about $5,227.72 should be invested in the CD, and $2,772.28 should be invested in the mutual fund.

29. a. Since the total amount of money to be invested is $6,000, the sum of x and y must be $6,000. The interest for any account is the product of the amount deposited into the account and its interest rate in decimal form.

$x + y = 6000$

$I = 0.0285x + 0.09y$

$f(x) = 0.0285x + 0.09(6,000 - x)$

$= 0.0285x + 540 - 0.09x$

$= -0.0615x + 540$

b. The I-intercept of the model is when $x = 0$, or when no money has been invested in the CD and all of it is invested in the mutual fund.

$I = -0.0615(0) + 540$

$= 540$

This means that if no money was invested in the CD, the interest per year would be $540.

c. The x-intercept is when $I = 0$, or when there is no interest being made.

$0 = -0.0651x + 540$

$-540 = -0.0651x$

$8,294.93 = x$

So $6,000 would be invested in the CD, and an extra $2,294.93 would have to be borrowed and invested into the CD.

d. The slope is -0.0615, or a decrease in 0.0615 of interest for every dollar invested in the CD.

31. Let x be the amount of 10% alcohol solution and y be the amount of 30% alcohol solution. Both amounts need to be 10 ounces, and make a mixture of 22% alcohol.

$x + y = 10$

$0.10x + 0.30y = 0.22(10)$

Substitute $10 - y$ for x in the second equation and solve for y.

$0.10(10 - y) + 0.30y = 0.22(10)$

$1 - 0.10y + 0.30y = 2.2$

$0.20y = 1.2$

$y = 6$

So 6 ounces of the 30% solution need to be added, while 4 ounces of the 10% solution need to be added.

33. Let x be the amount of 5% antifreeze solution and y be the amount of 20% antifreeze solution. Both amounts need to be 3 gallons, and make a 15% antifreeze solution.

$x + y = 3$

$0.05x + 0.20y = 0.15(3)$

Substitute $3 - y$ for x in the second equation and solve for y.

$0.05(3 - y) + 0.20y = 0.15(3)$

$0.15 - 0.05y + 0.20y = 0.45$

$0.15 + 0.15y = 0.45$

$0.15y = 0.30$

$y = 2$

So 2 gallons of the 20% solution need to be added, while 1 gallon of the 5% solution need to be added.

35. Let x be the amount of 10% acid solution and y be the amount of 25% acid solution. Both amounts need to be 4 gallons, and make a 15%

antifreeze solution.

$$x + y = 4$$

$$0.1x + 0.25y = 0.15(6)$$

Substitute $4 - x$ for y in the second equation, and solve for x.

$$0.1x + 0.25(4 - x) = 0.15(6)$$

$$0.1x + 1 - 0.25x = 0.9$$

$$-0.15x + 1 = 0.9$$

$$-0.15x = -0.1$$

$$x = 0.67$$

So 0.67 gallons of the 10% solution need be added, while 3.33 gallons of the 25% solution need to be added.

37. Let x be the amount of water and y be the amount of 25% alcohol solution. Both amounts total 5 liters and make a 20% alcohol solution. Assume that water is a 0% alcohol solution.

$$x + y = 5$$

$$0x + 0.25y = 0.2(5)$$

$$0.25y = 1$$

$$y = 4$$

So 4 liters of the 25% alcohol solution need to be added, while 1 liter of water needs to be added.

39. Answers will vary. A 30-seat political fundraiser has two types of admission, a $2,500 diner and a $9,500 meet-and-greet. The organizers need to make $579,000. How many of each type of admission do they sell?
Substitute the first equation into the second, and solve for y.

$$9500(y - 30) + 2500y = 579,000$$

$$9500y - 285,000 + 2500y = 579,000$$

$$12,000y = 864,000$$

$$y = 72$$

They need to sell 72 of the $9,500 meet-and-greet admission, something they cannot do for a 30-seat fundraiser.

41. Answers will vary. To have a correct balance of investments, a banker wants to put three times as much money in Fund X than in Fund Y. Fund X has an annual return of 5%, while Fund Y has an annual return of 12%. If the banker wants $135 in interest, how much money do they need to put into each fund?
Substitute the first equation into the second equation and solve for y.

$$0.015(3y) + 0.12y = 135$$

$$0.045y + 0.12y = 135$$

$$0.165y = 135$$

$$y \approx 818.18$$

So about $818.18 needs to be put into Fund Y and about $2,454.54 needs to be put into Fund X.

Homework 3.5

1.

Words	Inequality Notation	Graph	Interval Notation
Numbers greater than 3	$x > 3$		$(3, \bullet\,)$
Numbers less than or equal to –4	$x \leq -4$		$(-\bullet, -4]$
Numbers less than 5	$x < 5$		$(-\bullet, 5)$
Numbers greater than or equal to -1	$x \geq -1$		$[-1, \bullet\,)$

3. $x + 2 \geq 5$

$x + 2 - 2 \geq 5 - 2$

$x \geq 3$

Interval: $[3, \bullet\,)$

5. $-4x \geq 12$

$\dfrac{-4x}{-4} \leq \dfrac{12}{-4}$

$x \geq -3$

Interval: $(-\bullet, -3]$

7. $2x + 7 < 11$

$2x + 7 - 7 < 11 - 7$

$2x < 4$

$\dfrac{2x}{2} < \dfrac{4}{2}$

$x < 2$

Interval: $(-\bullet, 2)$

9. $9x < 4 + 5x$

$9x - 5x < 4 + 5x - 5x$

$4x < 4$

$\dfrac{4x}{4} < \dfrac{4}{4}$

$x < 1$

Interval: $(-\bullet, 1)$

11. $2.1x - 7.4 \leq 4.36$

$2.1x - 7.4 + 7.4 \leq 4.36 + 7.4$

$2.1x \leq 11.76$

$\dfrac{2.1x}{2.1} \leq \dfrac{11.76}{2.1}$

$x \leq 5.6$

Interval: $(-\bullet, 5.6]$

13. $2b - 3 > 7b + 22$

$2b - 3 + 3 > 7b + 22 + 3$

$2b > 7b + 25$

$2b - 7b > 7b + 25 - 7b$

$-5b > 25$

$\dfrac{-5b}{-5} < \dfrac{25}{-5}$

$b < -5$

Interval: $(-\bullet, -5)$

15. $3 - 2(x - 4) > 4x + 1$

$3 - 2x + 8 > 4x + 1$

$-2x + 11 > 4x + 1$

$-2x + 11 - 11 > 4x + 1 - 11$

$-2x > 4x - 10$

$-2x - 4x > 4x - 10 - 4x$

$-6x > -10$

$\dfrac{-6x}{-6} < \dfrac{-10}{-6}$

$x < \dfrac{5}{3}$

Interval: $\left(-\bullet, \dfrac{5}{3}\right)$

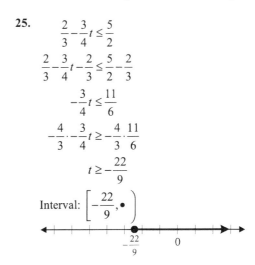

17.
$$6.2a + 61.31 < 5(3.1 - 2.7a) + 0.5$$
$$6.2a + 61.31 < 15.5 - 13.5a + 0.5$$
$$6.2a + 61.31 < 16 - 13.5a$$
$$6.2a + 61.31 - 61.31 < 16 - 13.5a - 61.31$$
$$6.2a < -45.31 - 13.5a$$
$$6.2a + 13.5a < -45.31 - 13.5a + 13.5a$$
$$19.7a < -45.31$$
$$\dfrac{19.7a}{19.7} < \dfrac{-45.31}{19.7}$$
$$a < -2.3$$
Interval: $(-\bullet, -2.3)$

19. $7(x+1) - 8(x-2) \le 0$
$$7x + 7 - 8x + 16 \le 0$$
$$-x + 23 \le 0$$
$$-x \le -23$$
$$\dfrac{-x}{-1} \ge \dfrac{-23}{-1}$$
$$x \ge 23$$
Interval: $[23, \bullet)$

21. $5r - 4(2r-6) - 1 \ge 3(3r-1) + r$
$$5r - 8r + 24 - 1 \ge 9r - 3 + r$$
$$-3r + 23 \ge 10r - 3$$
$$-3r + 23 - 23 \ge 10r - 3 - 23$$
$$-3r \ge 10r - 26$$
$$-3r - 10r \ge 10r - 10r - 26$$
$$-13r \ge -26$$
$$\dfrac{-13r}{-13} \le \dfrac{-26}{-13}$$
$$r \le 2$$
Interval: $(-\bullet, 2]$

23.
$$-\dfrac{2}{3}x > 4$$
$$-\dfrac{3}{2} \cdot -\dfrac{2}{3}x < -\dfrac{3}{2} \cdot 4$$
$$x < -6$$
Interval: $(-\bullet, -6)$

25.
$$\dfrac{2}{3} - \dfrac{3}{4}t \le \dfrac{5}{2}$$
$$\dfrac{2}{3} - \dfrac{3}{4}t - \dfrac{2}{3} \le \dfrac{5}{2} - \dfrac{2}{3}$$
$$-\dfrac{3}{4}t \le \dfrac{11}{6}$$
$$-\dfrac{4}{3} \cdot -\dfrac{3}{4}t \ge -\dfrac{4}{3} \cdot \dfrac{11}{6}$$
$$t \ge -\dfrac{22}{9}$$
Interval: $\left[-\dfrac{22}{9}, \bullet\right)$

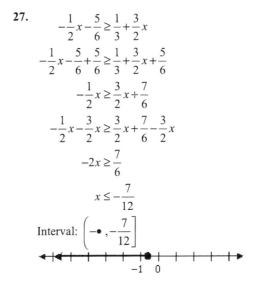

27.
$$-\dfrac{1}{2}x - \dfrac{5}{6} \ge \dfrac{1}{3} + \dfrac{3}{2}x$$
$$-\dfrac{1}{2}x - \dfrac{5}{6} + \dfrac{5}{6} \ge \dfrac{1}{3} + \dfrac{3}{2}x + \dfrac{5}{6}$$
$$-\dfrac{1}{2}x \ge \dfrac{3}{2}x + \dfrac{7}{6}$$
$$-\dfrac{1}{2}x - \dfrac{3}{2}x \ge \dfrac{3}{2}x + \dfrac{7}{6} - \dfrac{3}{2}x$$
$$-2x \ge \dfrac{7}{6}$$
$$x \le -\dfrac{7}{12}$$
Interval: $\left(-\bullet, -\dfrac{7}{12}\right]$

29.
$$\frac{4c-5}{6} \le \frac{3c+7}{4}$$
$$\left(\frac{4c-5}{6}\right)(12) \le \left(\frac{3c+7}{4}\right)(12)$$
$$8c-10 \le 9c+21$$
$$8c-10+10 \le 9c+21+10$$
$$8c \le 9c+31$$
$$8c-9c \le 9c+31-9c$$
$$-c \le 31$$
$$\frac{-c}{-1} \ge \frac{31}{-1}$$
$$c \ge -31$$
Interval: $[-31, \bullet)$

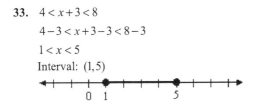

31.
$$\frac{3x+1}{6} - \frac{5x-2}{9} > \frac{2}{3}$$
$$\left(\frac{3x+1}{6} - \frac{5x-2}{9}\right)(18) > \left(\frac{2}{3}\right)(18)$$
$$(3x+1)(3) - (5x-2)(2) > (2)(6)$$
$$9x+3-10x+4 > 12$$
$$-x+7 > 12$$
$$-x+7-7 > 12-7$$
$$-x > 5$$
$$\frac{-x}{-1} < \frac{5}{-1}$$
$$x < -5$$
Interval: $(-\bullet, -5)$

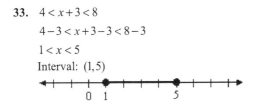

33. $4 < x+3 < 8$
$$4-3 < x+3-3 < 8-3$$
$$1 < x < 5$$
Interval: $(1,5)$

35. $-15 \le 2x-5 \le 7$
$$-15+5 \le 2x-5+5 \le 7+5$$
$$-10 \le 2x \le 12$$
$$\frac{-10}{2} \le \frac{2x}{2} \le \frac{12}{2}$$
$$-5 \le x \le 6$$
Interval: $[-5,6]$

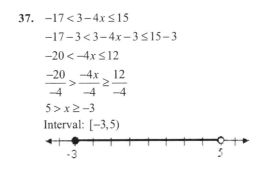

37. $-17 < 3-4x \le 15$
$$-17-3 < 3-4x-3 \le 15-3$$
$$-20 < -4x \le 12$$
$$\frac{-20}{-4} > \frac{-4x}{-4} \ge \frac{12}{-4}$$
$$5 > x \ge -3$$
Interval: $[-3,5)$

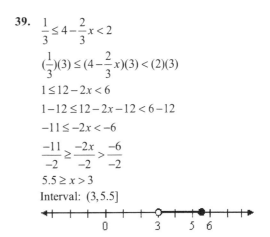

39.
$$\frac{1}{3} \le 4 - \frac{2}{3}x < 2$$
$$(\frac{1}{3})(3) \le (4 - \frac{2}{3}x)(3) < (2)(3)$$
$$1 \le 12-2x < 6$$
$$1-12 \le 12-2x-12 < 6-12$$
$$-11 \le -2x < -6$$
$$\frac{-11}{-2} \ge \frac{-2x}{-2} > \frac{-6}{-2}$$
$$5.5 \ge x > 3$$
Interval: $(3, 5.5]$

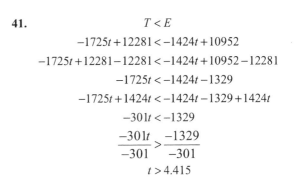

41.
$$T < E$$
$$-1725t+12281 < -1424t+10952$$
$$-1725t+12281-12281 < -1424t+10952-12281$$
$$-1725t < -1424t-1329$$
$$-1725t+1424t < -1424t-1329+1424t$$
$$-301t < -1329$$
$$\frac{-301t}{-301} > \frac{-1329}{-301}$$
$$t > 4.415$$

The value of the Taurus is less than the value of the Focus for years up after mid-2009 ($t > 4$).

43. **a.** Since U-Haul's charge increases at a constant rate of \$0.69 per mile, the equation is linear with slope 0.69. The U-intercept is 19.95 since U-Haul charges a flat fee of \$19.95.

$U(d) = 0.69d + 19.95$.

Using the same method, an equation can be made for Penske's charge.

$P(d) = 0.39d + 29.95$.

b.
$$U < P$$
$$0.69d + 19.95 < 0.39d + 29.95$$
$$0.69d + 19.95 - 19.95 < 0.39d + 29.95 - 19.95$$
$$0.69d < 0.39d + 10$$
$$0.69d - 0.39d < 0.39 + 10 - 0.39d$$
$$0.3d < 10$$
$$\frac{0.3d}{0.3} < \frac{10}{0.3}$$
$$d < \frac{100}{3}$$

U-Haul will be cheaper for miles driven less than $33.\overline{3}$ miles.

45. The number of employees at Northwest Airlines can be modeled by $N(t) = 50.1 - 4.2t$. The number of employees at Continental Airlines can be modeled by $C(t) = 42.1 - 2.4t$.

$$C > N$$
$$42.1 - 2.4t > 50.1 - 4.2t$$
$$42.1 - 2.4t + 4.2t > 50.1 - 4.2t + 4.2t$$
$$42.1 + 1.8t > 50.1$$
$$42.1 + 1.8t - 42.1 > 50.1 - 42.1$$
$$1.8t > 8$$
$$\frac{1.8t}{1.8} > \frac{8}{1.8}$$
$$t > 4.4\overline{4}$$

By this model, there will be more employees at Continental than at Northwest after the year 2005 ($t > 4$).

47. **a.**

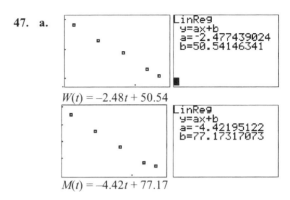

$W(t) = -2.48t + 50.54$

$M(t) = -4.42t + 77.17$

b.
$$W(t) < M(t)$$
$$-2.48t + 50.54 < -4.42t + 77.17$$
$$-2.48t + 50.54 - 77.17 < -4.42t + 77.17 - 77.17$$
$$-2.48t - 26.63 < -4.42t$$
$$-2.48t - 26.63 + 2.48t < -4.42t + 2.48t$$
$$-26.63 < -1.94t$$
$$13.73 > t$$

So the violent victimization rate for women was less than men during 2003.

49. **a.**
$$W(31) = 0.105(31) + 77.53$$
$$= 3.255 + 77.53$$
$$\approx 80.8$$
$$M(31) = 0.203(31) + 69.91$$
$$= 6.293 + 69.91$$
$$\approx 76.2$$
$$80.8 - 76.2 = 4.6$$

Women born in 2011 will live roughly 4.6 years longer, on average, than men born in 2011.

b.
$$W < M$$
$$0.105t + 77.53 < 0.203t + 69.91$$
$$0.105t + 77.53 - 77.53 < 0.203t + 69.91 - 77.53$$
$$0.105t < 0.203t - 7.62$$
$$0.105t - 0.203t < 0.203t - 7.62 - 0.203t$$
$$-0.098t < -7.62$$
$$\frac{-0.098t}{-0.098} > \frac{-7.62}{-0.098}$$
$$t > 77.76$$

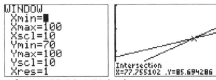

After $t = 77.76$, $M(t)$ is above, or greater than, $W(t)$.

c. **i.** The woman should marry a younger man since the life expectancies increase as year of birth increases.

ii. The woman's average life expectancy is 77.4 years. As time passes t increases, as does the age of the woman. So after t years, she wants to find a man of life expectancy $M(t)$, but she will be t years older.

$$77.4 < M(t) + t$$
$$77.4 < 0.203t + 69.91 + t$$
$$77.4 < 1.203t + 69.91$$
$$7.49 < 1.203t$$
$$6.23 < t$$

She should marry a man born during 1986.

51. The student made a mistake. It is not necessary to switch the direction of the inequality when dividing by a positive number.

$$3x + 7 > 1$$
$$3x + 7 - 7 > 1 - 7$$
$$3x > -6$$
$$\frac{3x}{3} > \frac{-6}{3}$$
$$x > -2$$

53. **a.** Solve the inequality for x.

$$3(x - 2) + 1 \geq 7 - 4x$$
$$3x - 6 + 1 \geq 7 - 4x$$
$$3x - 5 \geq 7 - 4x$$
$$3x - 5 + 5 \geq 7 - 4x + 5$$
$$3x \geq 12 - 4x$$
$$3x + 4x \geq 12 - 4x + 4x$$
$$7x \geq 12$$
$$\frac{7x}{7} \geq \frac{12}{7}$$
$$x \geq \frac{12}{7}$$

Any three numbers that are greater than or equal to $\frac{12}{7}$ are possible solutions.

b. From part a., any number less than $\frac{12}{7}$ is not a solution.

55. Given $mx < c$ and $x > 2$, rearrange the first inequality.

$$mx < c$$
$$\frac{mx}{m} < \frac{c}{m}$$
$$x < \frac{c}{m}$$

Values of c and m are such that $\frac{c}{m} > x > 2$.

Therefore, $c > 2m$.

57. **a.**
$$x + 1 = -2x + 10$$
$$-9 = -3x$$
$$3 = x$$

b.
$$x + 1 < -2x + 10$$
$$-9 < -3x$$
$$3 > x$$

c.
$$x + 1 > -2x + 10$$
$$-9 > -3x$$
$$3 < x$$

d.

The first equation has solution the solid

circle on 3. The second equation has solutions to the left of 3. The third equation has solutions to the right of 3. The solutions to the second and third equations are symmetrical around $x = 3$.

e.

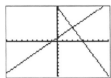

Notice that when x is less than 3 $g(x)$ is above, or larger than, $f(x)$. When x is more than 3, $g(x)$ is below, or smaller than, $f(x)$. When $x = 3$, $g(x) = f(x)$.

59. True. When $x = -4$, the graph of f is above the graph of g.

61. False. When $x = -1$, the graph of f is above the graph of g.

63. The graph of f is above the graph of g for all values of x such that $x < 2.8$. So $f(x) > g(x)$ when $x < 2.8$.

65. Written response. Answers may vary.

Chapter 3 Review Exercises

1.
$$y = -\frac{3}{2}x + 1$$
$$y = \frac{1}{4}x - 6$$

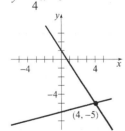

The solution is $(4, -5)$.

2. $3x - 5y = -1 \qquad y = -2(x - 4)$
$-5y = -3x - 1 \qquad = -2x + 8$
$$y = \frac{3}{5}x + \frac{1}{5}$$

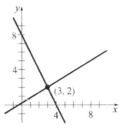

The solution is $(3, 2)$.

3. Solve using elimination.
Multiply the first equation by 3 and the second equation by -4, then add the equations.
$12x - 15y = -66$
$\underline{-12x - 8y = 20}$
$-23y = -46$
$y = 2$
Substitute $y = 2$ into $3x + 2y = -5$ and solve for x.
$3x + 2(2) = -5$
$3x + 4 = -5$
$3x = -9$
$x = -3$
The solution is $(-3, 2)$.

4. Solve using elimination.
Multiply the first equation by -2 and add the equations.
$-6x + 14y = -10$
$\underline{6x - 14y = -1}$
$0 = -11$ false
This is a contradiction. The system is inconsistent. The solution set is the empty set.

5. Solve using elimination.
Rewrite the second equation so all the variables are on the left side of the equation and the constant is on the right side.
$-4x - 5y = 3$
$8x + 10y = -6$
Multiply the first equation by 2 and add the equations.
$-8x - 10y = 6$
$\underline{8x + 10y = -6}$
$0 = 0$ true
This is an identity. The system is dependent. The

solution set contains all ordered pairs (x, y) such that $y = -\dfrac{4}{5}x - \dfrac{3}{5}$.

6. Solve using substitution.
Substitute $4.2x - 7.9$ for y in the second equation.
$$y = -2.8x + 0.5$$
$$4.2x - 7.9 = -2.8x + 0.5$$
$$4.2x - 7.9 + 7.9 = -2.8x + 0.5 + 7.9$$
$$4.2x = -2.8x + 8.4$$
$$4.2x + 2.8x = -2.8x + 8.4 + 2.8x$$
$$7x = 8.4$$
$$x = 1.2$$
Substitute this result into the first equation and solve for y.
$$y = 4.2(1.2) - 7.9$$
$$\approx -2.86$$
The solution is approximately $(1.29, -2.86)$.

7. Solve using substitution.
Substitute $4.9x$ for y in the second equation and solve for x.
$$-3.2y = x$$
$$-3.2(4.9x) = x$$
$$-15.68x = x$$
$$-16.68x = 0$$
$$x = 0$$
Substitute this result into the first equation and solve for y.
$$y = 4.9(0)$$
$$= 0$$
The solution is $(0, 0)$.

8. Solve using substitution.
Substitute $\dfrac{1}{2}x - 4$ for y in the first equation.

$$3x - 5\left(\dfrac{1}{2}x - 4\right) = 21$$
$$3x - \dfrac{5}{2}x + 20 = 21$$
$$\dfrac{1}{2}x + 20 = 21$$
$$\dfrac{1}{2}x = 1$$
$$x = 2$$
Substitute $x = 2$ into the second equation and solve for y.
$$y = \dfrac{1}{2}(2) - 4$$
$$= 1 - 4$$
$$= -3$$
The solution is $(2, -3)$.

9. Solve using elimination. Multiply both sides of the first equation by 2.
$$\dfrac{6}{5}x - \dfrac{4}{3}y = 8$$
$$-\dfrac{6}{5}x + \dfrac{8}{3}y = -4$$
$$\overline{}$$
$$\dfrac{4}{3}y = 4$$
$$y = 3$$
Substitute $y = 3$ into $\dfrac{3}{5}x - \dfrac{2}{3}y = 4$ and solve for x.
$$\dfrac{3}{5}x - \dfrac{2}{3}(3) = 4$$
$$\dfrac{3}{5}x - 2 = 4$$
$$\dfrac{3}{5}x = 6$$
$$x = 10$$
The solution is $(10, 3)$.

10. First use the distributive property to simplify each equation.
$$2(3x - 4) + 3(2y - 1) = -5$$
$$6x - 8 + 6y - 3 = -5$$
$$6x + 6y - 11 = -5$$
$$6x + 6y = 6$$

$$-3(2x+1)+4(y+3)=-7$$
$$-6x-3+4y+12=-7$$
$$-6x+4y+9=-7$$
$$-6x+4y=-16$$

Solve using elimination.
$$6x+6y=6$$
$$-6x+4y=-16$$

Add the two equations together.
$$6x+6y=6$$
$$\underline{-6x+4y=-16}$$
$$10y=-10$$
$$y=-1$$

Substitute $y=-1$ into $6x+6y=6$ and solve for x.
$$6x+6y=6$$
$$6x+6(-1)=6$$
$$6x-6=6$$
$$6x=12$$
$$x=2$$

The solution is $(2,-1)$.

11. Elimination
Rewrite the second equation so that all the variables are on the left side of the equation and the constant is on the right side.
$$2x-5y=15$$
$$2x+y=9$$

Multiply the second equation by -1 and add the equations.
$$2x-5y=15$$
$$\underline{-2x-y=-9}$$
$$-6y=6$$
$$y=-1$$

Substitute $y=-1$ into $2x-5y=15$ and solve for x.
$$2x-5(-1)=15$$
$$2x+5=15$$
$$2x=10$$
$$x=5$$

The solution is $(5,-1)$.

Substitution
Substitute $-2x+9$ for y in the first equation and solve for x.

$$2x-5y=15$$
$$2x-5(-2x+9)=15$$
$$2x+10x-45=15$$
$$12x=60$$
$$x=5$$

Substitute this result into the second equation and solve for y.
$$y=-2x+9$$
$$=-2(5)+9$$
$$=-10+9$$
$$=-1$$

The solution is $(5,-1)$.

Graphically
$$2x-5y=15 \qquad\qquad y=-2x+9$$
$$-5y=-2x+15$$
$$y=\frac{2}{5}x-3$$

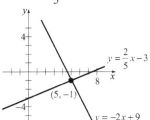

The solution is $(5,-1)$.

12. a. Answers may vary. Possible answers follow.
$$x+2y=4$$
$$3x+6y=12$$
Solving this system yields an identity such as $0=0$. The solution set is the set of ordered pairs (x,y) such that $x+2y=4$.

b. $$x+2y=4$$
$$2x+6y=10$$
Solving this system yields a contradiction such as $0=-2$. The solution set is the empty set.

c. $$x+y=10$$
$$3x-3y=-6$$
The point $(4,6)$ satisfies both equations.

13. The two lines intersect at the point $(1, -2)$.

14. The red line intersects the line $y = 2$ at the point $(-5, 2)$.

15. Answers will vary. Notice that the functions cross between 0 and 1, and between 2 and 3. Approximate solutions may include 0.5 and 2.5.

16. $2(5) + 3(3) = a \quad 6(5) - 4(3) = b$

$\qquad 10 + 9 = a \qquad 30 - 12 = b$

$\qquad 19 = a \qquad\qquad 18 = b$

17. The coordinates of point A are the same as the coordinates of the origin, $(0, 0)$.

The coordinates of point B is the same as the y-intercept of $y = 3x + 4$, $(0, 4)$.

Use substitution to find the intersection of l_1 and l_2.
$3(3x + 4) + 2x = 34$
$9x + 12 + 2x = 34$
$\qquad 11x = 22$
$\qquad x = 2$
Substitute to find the other coordinate.
$y = 3(2) + 4$
$\quad = 10$
C is the point (2, 10).

Substitute $-4x + 28$ into l_2.
$3(-4x + 28) + 2x = 34$
$-12x + 84 + 2x = 34$
$\qquad -10x = -50$
$\qquad x = 5$
Substitute to find the other coordinate.
$y + 4(5) = 28$
$\quad y + 20 = 28$
$\qquad y = 8$
D is the point $(5, 8)$.

Substitute $3x - 14$ for y in l_3.

$(3x - 14) + 4x = 28$
$\qquad 7x - 14 = 28$
$\qquad 7x = 42$
$\qquad x = 6$
$y = 3(6) - 14$
$y = 18 - 14$
$y = 4$
E is the point $(6, 4)$.

Find the x-intercept of l_4.
$\quad 0 = 3x - 14$
$14 = 3x$
$\dfrac{14}{3} = x$
F is the point $\left(\dfrac{14}{3}, 0 \right)$.

18. Graph each of the equations.
$y = -x + 2$
$y = -2x + 7$
$y = 3x - 6$

The three graphs do not share a common point. The solution set is the empty set.

19. $\qquad 3x - 8 \le 13$
$3x - 8 + 8 \le 13 + 8$
$\qquad 3x \le 21$
$\qquad \dfrac{3x}{3} \le \dfrac{21}{3}$
$\qquad x \le 7$
Interval: $(-\infty, 7]$

20.
$$29.19 - 3.6a \geq 3.9(a+2.1)$$
$$29.19 - 3.6a \geq 3.9a + 8.19$$
$$29.19 - 3.6a - 29.19 \geq 3.9a + 8.19 - 29.19$$
$$-3.6a \geq 3.9x - 21$$
$$-3.6x - 3.9x \geq 3.9x - 21 - 3.9x$$
$$-7.5x \geq -21$$
$$\frac{-7.5x}{-7.5} \leq \frac{-21}{-7.5}$$
$$x \leq 2.8$$
Interval: $(-\bullet, 2.8]$

21.
$$-5(2x+3) \geq 2(3x-4)$$
$$-10x - 15 \geq 6x - 8$$
$$-10x - 15 + 15 \geq 6x - 8 + 15$$
$$-10x \geq 6x + 7$$
$$-10x - 6x \geq 6x + 7 - 6x$$
$$-16x \geq 7$$
$$\frac{-16x}{-16} \leq \frac{7}{-16}$$
$$x \leq -\frac{7}{16}$$
Interval: $\left(-\bullet, -\frac{7}{16}\right]$

22.
$$\frac{2x-1}{4} - \frac{4x+3}{6} > \frac{5}{3}$$
$$\left(\frac{2x-1}{4} - \frac{4x+3}{6}\right)(12) > \left(\frac{5}{3}\right)(12)$$
$$3(2x-1) - 2(4x+3) > 5(4)$$
$$6x - 3 - 8x - 6 > 20$$
$$-2x - 9 > 20$$
$$-2x > 29$$
$$x < -\frac{29}{2}$$
Interval: $\left(-\bullet, -\frac{29}{2}\right)$

23.
$$1 \leq 2x + 5 \leq 11$$
$$1 - 5 \leq 2x + 5 - 5 \leq 11 - 5$$
$$-4 \leq 2x \leq 6$$
$$-2 \leq x \leq 3$$
Interval: $[-2, 3]$

24. a. Solve the inequality for *x*.
$$7 - 2(3x+5) < 4x + 1$$
$$7 - 6x - 10 < 4x + 1$$
$$-6x - 3 < 4x + 1$$
$$-6x - 3 + 3 < 4x + 1 + 3$$
$$-6x < 4x + 4$$
$$-6x - 4x < 4x + 4 - 4x$$
$$-10x < 4$$
$$\frac{-10x}{-10} > \frac{4}{-10}$$
$$x > -\frac{2}{5}$$

Any three numbers that are greater than $-\frac{2}{5}$ are possible solutions.

b. From part a., any number less than or equal to $-\frac{2}{5}$ is not a solution.

25. The student's work is incorrect. When dividing both sides of an inequality by a negative number, the direction of the inequality must be switched.

26. $f(4) = 1$

27. $g(x) = 0$ when $x = -5$.

28. $f(x) = g(x)$ when $x = -2$.

29. The graph of $f(x)$ is above the graph of $g(x)$ for values of *x* that are greater than -2. Thus, $f(x) > g(x)$ when $x > -2$.

30. Any values for *a*, *b*, and *c* so that $\frac{c-b}{a} < 5$. For example, $a = -1$, $b = 6$, and $c = 1$ will work.

31. a. Start by plotting the data sets, then find the regression line for each region.

North America

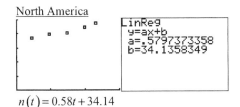

$$n(t) = 0.58t + 34.14$$

Far East

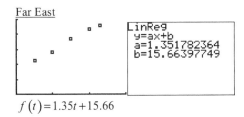

$$f(t) = 1.35t + 15.66$$

b. Both slopes are positive indicating an increase in consumption each year. The slope for the Far East is larger than the slope for North America. The consumption of petroleum is increasing at a faster rate in the Far East than in North America.

c.
$$n(t) = f(t)$$
$$0.58t + 34.14 = 1.35t + 15.66$$
$$0.58t + 34.14 - 34.14 = 1.35t + 15.66 - 34.14$$
$$0.58t = 1.35t - 18.48$$
$$0.58t - 1.35t = 1.35t - 18.48 - 1.35t$$
$$-0.77t = -18.48$$
$$t = 24$$

The consumption of petroleum was the same for the Far East and North America in 2004. $n(24) = 48.1$.

d.
$$n(t) = f(t)$$
$$0.58t + 34.14 < 1.35t + 15.66$$
$$0.58t + 34.14 - 34.14 < 1.35t + 15.66 - 34.14$$
$$0.58t < 1.35t - 18.48$$
$$0.58t - 1.35t < 1.35t - 18.48 - 1.35t$$
$$-0.77t < -18.48$$
$$t > 24$$

The consumption of petroleum in North America will be less than the consumption of petroleum in the Far East for years after 2004.

32. a. Start by plotting the data sets, then find the regression line for each set of ratings.

World Series

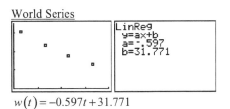

$$w(t) = -0.597t + 31.771$$

Prime Time

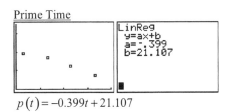

$$p(t) = -0.399t + 21.107$$

b.
$$-0.597t + 31.771 = -0.399t + 21.107$$
$$-0.597t + 31.771 - 31.771 = -0.399t + 21.107 - 31.771$$
$$-0.597t = -0.399t - 10.664$$
$$-0.597t + 0.399t = -0.399t + 0.399t - 10.664$$
$$-0.198t = -10.664$$
$$t = 53.859$$

The ratings will be equal approximately 54 years after 1970, in the year 2024.

33. a. Since U-Haul's charge increases at a constant rate of $0.69 per mile, the equation is linear with slope 0.69. The U-intercept is 29.95 since U-Haul charges a flat fee of $29.95.
$$U(x) = 0.69x + 29.95.$$

Similar work yields an equation for Rent A Wreck's charge.
$$R(x) = 0.22x + 75.00.$$

b.
$$U(x) = R(x)$$
$$0.69x + 29.95 = 0.22x + 75$$
$$0.69x + 29.95 - 29.95 = 0.22x + 75 - 29.95$$
$$0.69x = 0.22x + 45.05$$
$$0.69x - 0.22x = 0.22x + 45.05 - 0.22x$$
$$0.47x = 45.05$$
$$x \approx 95.85$$

The two charges will be the same when the number of miles driven is roughly 95.85 miles.

c.
$$R < U$$
$$0.22x + 75 < 0.69x + 29.95$$
$$0.22x + 75 - 75 < 0.69x + 29.95 - 75$$
$$0.22x < 0.69x - 45.05$$
$$0.22x - 0.69x < 0.69 - 45.05 - 0.69x$$
$$-0.47x < -45.05$$
$$\frac{-0.47x}{-0.47} > \frac{-45.05}{-0.47}$$
$$x > 95.9$$

Rent A Wreck will be cheaper for miles driven more than 95.9 miles.

34. Let $P(t)$ represent the average price (in dollars) of a home in a community and $S(t)$ represent the amount of money (in dollars) a family has saved at t years since 2000.

Since the average price of a home increases at a constant $9000 per year, the function P is linear and its slope is 9000. the P-intercept is $(0, 250000)$ since the price of a home is $250,000 in year $t = 0$.
$P(t) = 9000t + 250000$.

Similar work yields the equation for the function S.
$S(t) = 2760t + 12000$. (The slope of S is 4800 because the family plans to save $230 each month which is $2760 each year.)

In order to predict when the family will be able to pay a 10% down payment on an average-priced house, solve the following system for t.

$$y = 0.1(P(t)) = 0.1(9000t + 250000)$$
$$y = S(t) = 2760t + 12000$$

Substitute $0.1(9000t + 250000)$ for y in the second equation and solve for t.
$$0.1(9000t + 250000) = 2760t + 12000$$
$$900t + 25000 = 2760t + 12000$$
$$-1860t = -13000$$
$$t \approx 6.99$$

The family will be able to pay a 10% down payment in 5 years (2007).

35. Let A represent the number of $55 tickets sold, and B represent the number of $70 tickets sold. There are 20,000 total tickets available, so $A + B = 20000$.
Selling A tickets at $55 and B tickets at $70, the theater wants to make $1,197,500.
$55A + 70B = 1197500$.
Use substitution or elimination to solve for A and B.
$$55(A + B) = 55(20000)$$
$$55A + 70B = 1197500$$
Subtract the second equation from the first.
$$55A + 55B = 1100000$$
$$-(55A + 70B = 1197500)$$
$$-15B = -97500$$
$$B = 6500$$
Now use this information to solve for A.
$$A + B = 20000$$
$$A + 6500 = 20000$$
$$A = 20000 - 6500$$
$$A = 13500$$
The theater must sell 13,500 tickets at $55 and 6,500 tickets at $70 in order to generate a total revenue of $1,197,500.

36. a. To formulate a function $f(x)$ for total interest, substitute $(8000 - x)$ for y.
$$x + y = 8000$$
$$x + y - x = 8000 - x$$
$$y = 8000 - x$$

Write the equation for the total interest earned (in dollars) from investing $8,000 for one year.
$$I = f(x) = 0.068x + 0.13y$$
$$f(x) = 0.068x + 0.13(8000 - x)$$

b. $f(575) = 0.068(575) + 0.13[8000 - (575)]$

$= 1004.35$

This means that if the person invests $575 in the 6.8% interest account (and therefore $7,425 in the 13.0% interest account), they will earn $1,004.35 total interest.

c. $575 = 0.068x + 0.13(8000 - x)$

$575 = 0.068x + 1040 - 0.13x$

$575 = -0.062x + 1040$

$575 - 1040 = -0.062x + 1040 - 1040$

$-465 = -0.062x$

$7500 = x$

This means that by investing $7,500 in the 6.8% interest account and $2,500 in the 13.0% interest account, the person will earn $575.

Chapter 3 Test

1. Solve using substitution.
Substitute $3x - 1$ for y in the second equation and solve for x.

$3x - 2y = -1$

$3x - 2(3x - 1) = -1$

$3x - 6x + 2 = -1$

$-3x + 2 = -1$

$-3x = -3$

$x = 1$

Substitute $x = 1$ into the first equation and solve for y.

$y = 3(1) - 1$

$= 3 - 1$

$= 2$

The solution is $(1, 2)$.

2. Solve using elimination.
First write the second equation so that all the variables are on the left side of the equation and the constant is on the right side.

$2x - 5y = 3$

$6x - 15y = 9$

Multiply the first equation by -3 and add the equations.

$-6x + 15y = -9$

$\underline{6x - 15y = 9}$

$0 = 0$ true

This is an identity. The system is dependent. The solution set is the set of ordered pairs (x, y) such that $2x - 5y = 3$.

3. Solve using elimination.
Multiply the first equation by 3 and the second equation by -2, then add the equations.

$12x - 18y = 15$

$\underline{-12x + 18y = 4}$

$0 = 19$ false

This is a contradiction. The system is inconsistent. The solution set is the empty set.

4. Solve using elimination.
Multiply the second equation by 3 and add the equations.

$\frac{2}{5}x - \frac{3}{4}y = 8$

$\underline{\frac{9}{5}x + \frac{3}{4}y = 3}$

$\frac{11}{5}x = 11$

$x = 5$

Substitute $x = 5$ into $\frac{9}{5}x + \frac{3}{4}y = 3$ and solve for y.

$\frac{3}{5}(5) + \frac{1}{4}y = 1$

$3 + \frac{1}{4}y = 1$

$\frac{1}{4}y = 1 - 3$

$\frac{1}{4}y = -2$

$y = -8$

The solution is $(5, -8)$.

5. First use the distributive property to simplify each equation.

$$-4(x+2)+3(2y-1)=21$$
$$-4x-8+6y-3=21$$
$$-4x+6y-11=21$$
$$-4x+6y=32$$
$$2x-3y=-16$$
$$5(3x-2)-(4y+3)=-59$$
$$15x-10-4y-3=-59$$
$$15x-4y-13=-59$$
$$15x-4y=-46$$

These equations can be written as a system.
$$2x-3y=-16$$
$$15x-4y=-46$$

Solve using elimination.
Multiply the first equation by 4 and the second equation by -3, then add the equations.

$$8x-12y=-64$$
$$\underline{-45x+12y=138}$$
$$-37x=74$$
$$x=-2$$

Substitute $x=-2$ into $2x-3y=-16$ and solve for y.

$$2(-2)-3y=-16$$
$$-4-3y=-16$$
$$-3y=-12$$
$$y=4$$

The solution is $(-2,4)$.

6. Answers may vary. One possible answer:
$$x-2y=1$$
$$3x+y=17$$

7. <u>Elimination</u>
First rewrite the second equation so that all the variables are on the left side and the constant is on the right side.
$$4x-3y=9$$
$$-2x+y=-5$$

Multiply the second equation by 2 and add the equations.

$$4x-3y=9$$
$$\underline{-4x+2y=-10}$$
$$-y=-1$$
$$y=1$$

Substitute $y=1$ into $4x-3y=9$ and solve for x.

$$4x-3(1)=9$$
$$4x-3=9$$
$$4x=12$$
$$x=3$$

The solution is $(3,1)$.

<u>Substitution</u>
Substitute $2x-5$ for y in the first equation.

$$4x-3y=9$$
$$4x-3(2x-5)=9$$
$$4x-6x+15=9$$
$$-2x+15=9$$
$$-2x=-6$$
$$x=3$$

Substitute $x=3$ into $y=2x-5$ and solve for y.

$$y=2(3)-5$$
$$=1$$

The solution is $(3,1)$.

<u>Graphically</u>
$$4x-3y=9 \qquad\qquad y=2x-5$$
$$y=\frac{4}{3}x-3$$

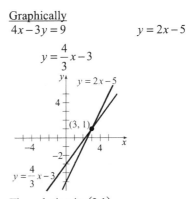

The solution is $(3,1)$.

8. If the solution set is the empty set, the system consists of two parallel lines. Therefore, m in $y=mx+b$ is 5, because this is the slope in $y=5x-13$ and parallel lines have the same slope. The y-intercept in $y=mx+b$ is any number other than -13 since $y=5x-13$ and $y=mx+b$ intersect the y-axis at different points. So $b\neq-13$.

9.
$$2 - 10x \geq 3x + 14$$
$$2 - 10x - 2 \geq 3x + 14 - 2$$
$$-10x \geq 3x + 12$$
$$-10x - 3x \geq 3x + 12 - 3x$$
$$-13x \geq 12$$
$$\frac{-13x}{-13} \leq \frac{12}{-13}$$
$$x \leq -\frac{12}{13}$$
Interval: $\left(-\bullet, -\frac{12}{13}\right]$

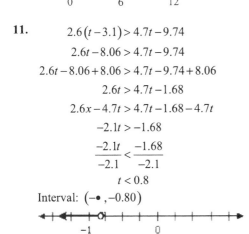

10. $3(x+4) + 1 < 5(x-2)$
$$3x + 12 + 1 < 5x - 10$$
$$3x + 13 < 5x - 10$$
$$3x + 13 - 13 < 5x - 10 - 13$$
$$3x < 5x - 23$$
$$3x - 5x < 5x - 23 - 5x$$
$$-2x < -23$$
$$\frac{-2x}{-2} > \frac{-23}{-2}$$
$$x > \frac{23}{2}$$
Interval: $\left(\frac{23}{2}, \bullet\right)$

11.
$$2.6(t - 3.1) > 4.7t - 9.74$$
$$2.6t - 8.06 > 4.7t - 9.74$$
$$2.6t - 8.06 + 8.06 > 4.7t - 9.74 + 8.06$$
$$2.6t > 4.7t - 1.68$$
$$2.6x - 4.7t > 4.7t - 1.68 - 4.7t$$
$$-2.1t > -1.68$$
$$\frac{-2.1t}{-2.1} < \frac{-1.68}{-2.1}$$
$$t < 0.8$$
Interval: $(-\bullet, -0.80)$

12.
$$-\frac{5}{3}w + \frac{1}{6} \leq \frac{7}{4}w$$
$$-\frac{5}{3}w + \frac{1}{6} + \frac{5}{3}w \leq \frac{7}{4}w + \frac{5}{3}w$$
$$\frac{1}{6} \leq \frac{41}{12}w$$
$$\frac{12}{41} \cdot \frac{1}{6} \leq \frac{12}{41} \cdot \frac{41}{12}x$$
$$\frac{2}{41} \leq x$$
$$x \geq \frac{2}{41}$$
Interval: $\left[\frac{2}{41}, \bullet\right)$

13. $f(5) = 3$

14. $g(x) = 3$ when $x = -4$.

15. $f(x) = g(x)$ when $x = 2$.

16. The graph of *f* is below the graph of *g* for $x < 2$ and the two graphs are equal for $x = 2$. Therefore, $f(x) \leq g(x)$ when $x \leq 2$.

17.

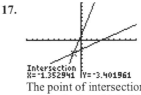

```
Intersection
X=-1.352941   Y=-3.401961
```
The point of intersection is $(-1.35, -3.40)$, so the value of *x* for which this statement is true is -1.35.

18. The graph of *f* is lower than the graph of *g* for all values of *x* that are greater than 13. Thus, $f(x) < g(x)$ for $x > 13$.

19. a. Answers may vary.
Solve the inequality for *x*.

$$3x - 11 < 7 - 6x$$
$$3x - 11 + 11 < 7 - 6x + 11$$
$$3x < 18 - 6x$$
$$3x + 6x < 18 - 6x + 6x$$
$$9x < 18$$
$$\frac{9x}{9} < \frac{18}{9}$$
$$x < 2$$

Any number less than 2 will satisfy the inequality.

b. Answers may vary. From part a., any number greater than or equal to 2 does not satisfy the inequality.

20. a. Start by plotting each set of data, then find the regression lines for the data.

2-Year Colleges:

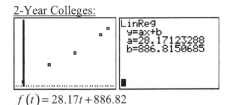

$f(t) = 28.17t + 886.82$

4-Year Colleges

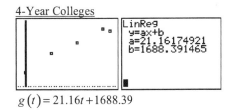

$g(t) = 21.16t + 1688.39$

b. In 2011, $t = 41$.
$$f(41) = 28.17(41) + 886.82$$
$$= 2041.8$$
$$g(41) = 21.16(41) + 1688.39$$
$$= 2555.95$$

The models predict that there will be a total of 4598 two-year and four-year colleges in 2011.

c.
$$f(t) = g(t)$$
$$28.17t + 886.82 = 21.16t + 1688.39$$
$$7.01t = 801.57$$
$$t \approx 114.35$$

So, during 2084 there will be as many four-year colleges as two-year colleges.

d. In 1970 there were over 700 more four-year colleges than two year colleges. The slopes are similar so it will take many years for the number of two-year colleges to overcome the number of four-year colleges.
$(28.17)(114.35) + 886.82 = 4108$.
At that time there will be about 4108 educational institutions

21. a. First, find the equation of $M(t)$.
$$m = \frac{y_2 - y_1}{x_2 - x_1}$$
$$= \frac{25544 - 23596}{2003 - 1998}$$
$$= 389.6$$
Consider 1998 to be year 0.
$M(t) = 389.6t + 23596$.
Find equation of $G(t)$.
$$m = \frac{y_2 - y_1}{x_2 - x_1}$$
$$= \frac{26086 - 25279}{2003 - 1998}$$
$$= 161.4$$
Therefore, $G(t) = 161.4t + 25279$

b. Set $M(t) = G(t)$ and solve for t.
$$389.6t + 23596 = 161.4t + 25279$$
$$389.6t = 161.4t + 1683$$
$$228.2t = 1683$$
$$t \approx 7.4$$
Personal income in Maine will equal personal income in Georgia in 2005, 7.4 years after 1998.
$$M(7.4) = 389.6(7.4) + 23596$$
$$= 2883.04 + 23596$$
$$\approx 26479$$
The income will be $26479.

c. Personal income in Maine was less than personal income in Georgia before 2005.

22. Let x be the number of gallons of the 10% solution, and y be the number of gallons of the 20% solution.

$$x + y = 10$$
$$x(0.10) + y(0.20) = 10(0.16)$$
$$(10 - y)(0.10) + 0.2y = 1.6$$
$$1 - 0.1y + 0.2y = 1.6$$
$$0.1y = 0.6$$
$$y = 6$$

Substitute $y = 6$.
$$x + 6 = 10$$
$$x = 4$$

4 gallons of a 10% antifreeze solution and 6 gallons of a 20% antifreeze solution must be mixed to make 10 gallons of a 16% antifreeze solution.

Cumulative Review of Chapters 1 - 3

1.

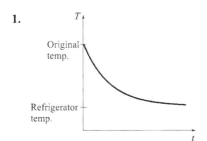

2. $5x - 3y = 15$
$$-3y = -5x + 15$$
$$y = \frac{5}{3}x - 5$$

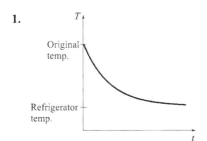

3. $3(x - 4) = -2(y + 5) + 4$
$$3x - 12 = -2y - 10 + 4$$
$$3x - 12 = -2y - 6$$
$$2y = -3x + 6$$
$$y = -\frac{3}{2}x + 3$$

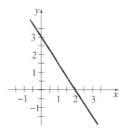

4.
$$m = \frac{y_2 - y_1}{x_2 - x_1}$$
$$= \frac{-1 - 2}{3 - (-4)}$$
$$= \frac{-3}{7}$$
$$= -\frac{3}{7}$$

5.
$$m = -\frac{3}{5}$$
$$y = mx + b$$
$$-3 = -\frac{3}{5}(2) + b$$
$$-3 = -\frac{6}{5} + b$$
$$b = -\frac{9}{5}$$

Write the equation of the line.
$$y = -\frac{3}{5}x - \frac{9}{5} \quad \text{or} \quad y = -0.6x - 1.8$$

6. First find the slope.
$$m = \frac{3 - (-2)}{-2 - (-5)} = \frac{3 + 2}{-2 + 5} = \frac{5}{3}$$

Next use the slope and either point (we will use the first point) to find b.
$$m = \frac{5}{3}; (-5, -2)$$
$$y = mx + b$$
$$-2 = \frac{5}{3}(-5) + b$$
$$-2 = -\frac{25}{3} + b$$
$$b = \frac{19}{3}$$

$$y = \frac{5}{3}x + \frac{19}{3}$$

7. $2x - 5y = 20$

$$-5y = -2x + 20$$

$$y = \frac{2}{5}x - 4$$

Since the slope of the given line is $\frac{2}{5}$, our line

must have slope $-\frac{5}{2}$ since perpendicular lines

have opposite-reciprocal slopes.

$$m = -\frac{5}{2}; (-5, 3)$$

$$y = mx + b$$

$$3 = -\frac{5}{2}(-5) + b$$

$$3 = \frac{25}{2} + b$$

$$b = -\frac{19}{2}$$

Write the equation of the line.

$$y = -\frac{5}{2}x - \frac{19}{2} \text{ or } y = -2.5x - 9.5$$

8. Answers may vary.
   The lines $y = 2x + 3$ and $y = 2x + 3.1$ are parallel. A line between these lines and parallel to both is $y = 2x + 3.05$. We can select any three points on this line. Possible points include $(0, 3.05), (1, 5.05),$ and $(2, 7.05)$.

9. Determine the slopes from the given data and use them to obtain the remaining values.

$f(x):$
$$m = \frac{58 - 97}{3 - 0} = \frac{-39}{3} = -13$$

$g(x):$
$$m = \frac{43 - 4}{9 - 6} = \frac{39}{3} = 13$$

$h(x):$
$$m = \frac{-22 - 23}{6 - 1} = \frac{-45}{5} = -9$$

$k(x):$
$$m = \frac{-16 - (-28)}{14 - 10} = \frac{12}{4} = 3$$

Equation 1		Equation 2		Equation 3		Equation 4	
x	$f(x)$	x	$g(x)$	x	$h(x)$	x	$k(x)$
0	97	4	−22	1	23	10	−28
1	84	5	−9	2	14	11	−25
2	71	6	4	3	5	12	−22
3	58	7	17	4	−4	13	−19
4	45	8	30	5	−13	14	−16
5	32	9	43	6	−22	15	−13

10. $f(5) = 32$

11. $g(x) = 30$ when $x = 8$.

12.
$$f(x) = -\frac{3}{2}x + 7$$
$$f(-4) = -\frac{3}{2}(-4) + 7$$
$$= 6 + 7$$
$$= 13$$

13.
$$f(x) = -\frac{3}{2}x + 7$$
$$\frac{5}{3} = -\frac{3}{2}x + 7$$
$$-\frac{16}{3} = -\frac{3}{2}x$$
$$x = \left(-\frac{16}{3}\right)\left(-\frac{2}{3}\right)$$
$$x = \frac{32}{9}$$

14. The x-intercept is found by solving $f(x) = 0$.
$$0 = -\frac{3}{2}x + 7$$
$$\frac{3}{2}x = 7$$
$$\frac{2}{3} \cdot \frac{3}{2}x = \frac{2}{3} \cdot 7$$
$$x = \frac{14}{3}$$
The x-intercept is $\left(\frac{14}{3}, 0\right)$.

15. Since the equation is in the form $y = mx + b$, the y-intercept is $(0, b)$ or $(0, 7)$.

16.
$$f(x) = -\frac{3}{2}x + 7$$

17. $g(3) = -3$

18. $f(x) - 1$ when $x = 0$.

19. The y-intercept of $f(0,1)$.

20. To find an equation for f, first determine the slope by finding two points on the graph. Two possible points are $(0,1)$ and $(3,3)$. Use the points to find the slope of the line.
$$m = \frac{3-1}{3-0} = \frac{2}{3}$$
Since the y-intercept is $(0,1)$, the equation of the line is $y = \frac{2}{3}x + 1$.

21. $f(x) = g(x)$ when $x = -3$.

22. The graph of f is at or below the graph of g for all values of x that are less than or equal to -3. Therefore, $f(x) \le g(x)$ when $x \le -3$.

23.
$$-5x - 3(2x + 4) = 8 - 2x$$
$$-5x - 6x - 12 = 8 - 2x$$
$$-11x - 12 = 8 - 2x$$
$$-11x - 12 + 12 = 8 - 2x + 12$$
$$-11x = 20 - 2x$$
$$-11x + 2x = 20 - 2x + 2x$$
$$-9x = 20$$
$$x = -\frac{20}{9}$$

24.
$$\frac{7}{8} - \frac{1}{4}b = \frac{1}{2} + \frac{3}{8}b$$
$$\frac{7}{8} - \frac{1}{4}b - \frac{7}{8} = \frac{1}{2} + \frac{3}{8}b - \frac{7}{8}$$
$$-\frac{1}{4}b = \frac{3}{8}b - \frac{3}{8}$$
$$-\frac{1}{4}b - \frac{3}{8}b = \frac{3}{8}b - \frac{3}{8} - \frac{3}{8}b$$
$$-\frac{5}{8}b = -\frac{3}{8}$$
$$b = \frac{3}{5}$$

25.
$$\frac{b}{c} - d = \frac{k}{c}$$
$$\frac{b}{c} - d + d = \frac{k}{c} + d$$
$$\frac{b}{c}(c) = \frac{k}{c}(c) + d(c)$$
$$b = k + cd$$

26. $5x - 3y + 2 = 0$
$$5x - 3y = -2$$
$$-3y = -5x - 2$$
$$y = \frac{5}{3}x + \frac{2}{3}$$

The equation is of the format $y = mx + b$, and so the y-intercept is $\left(0, \frac{2}{3}\right)$.

27. The domain of the relation is $-5 \le x \le 5$.

28. The range of the relation is $-2 \le y \le 3$.

29. Yes, the graph is that of a function. The graph passes the vertical line test.

30.
$$2x + 4y = -8$$
$$2x = -4y - 8$$
$$x = -2y - 4$$
$$5x - 3y = 19$$
$$5(-2y - 4) - 3y = 19$$
$$-10y - 20 - 3y = 19$$
$$-13y = 39$$
$$y = -\frac{39}{13} = -3$$
$$x = -2\left(-\frac{39}{13}\right) - 4$$
$$x = 2$$

31. The system is dependent. The solution set is the set of ordered pairs (x, y) such that $3x - 7y = 14$.

32. The green and blue lines intersect at the point $(-2, -1)$.

33. The green line intersects the line $y = -3$ at the point $(6, -3)$.

34. The red and green lines intersect at the point $(2, -2)$.

35. $-2(4x + 5) \ge 3(x - 7) + 1$
$$-8x - 10 \ge 3x - 21 + 1$$
$$-8x + 10 \ge 3x$$
$$10 \ge 11x$$
$$\frac{10}{11} \ge x$$

Interval: $\left(-\infty, \frac{10}{11}\right]$

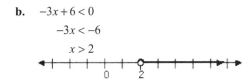

36. a. $-3x + 6 = 0$
$$-3x = -6$$
$$x = 2$$

b. $-3x + 6 < 0$
$$-3x < -6$$
$$x > 2$$

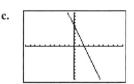

c.

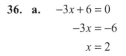

d. $4x - 1 = -3x + 6$
$$7x - 1 = 6$$
$$7x = 7$$
$$x = 1$$
$$y = 4(1) - 1$$
$$y = 3$$

The solution of the system of equations is (1,3).

37. a. Answers may vary. One possibility is $4x = 8$, which has solution $x = 2$.

b. Answers may vary. One possibility is $4x = 8y$, whose solution set is every point

on the line $y = \dfrac{1}{2}x$.

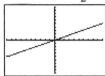

c. Answers may vary.
$4x = 8y$

$y = -2x + 5$

This system has the solution $(2,1)$.

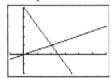

d. Answers may vary. One possible inequality in one variable is $4x < 8$, which has solution interval .

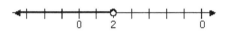

38. a. Start by plotting the data set, and then find the regression line for the data.

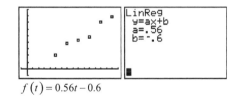

$f(t) = 0.56t - 0.6$

b. $f(10) = 0.56(10) - 0.6$

$= 5.6 - 0.6$

$= 5.0$

This means that the expected number of Chinese children (in thousands) adopted by American families in the year 2000 is 5.

c. $f(t) = 0.56t - 0.6 = 10$

$10 = 0.56t - 0.6$

$10.6 = 0.56t$

$\dfrac{10.6}{0.56} = t$

$18.93 \approx t$

This means that in the year 2009 the expected number of Chinese children (in is about 10.

d. The equation $f(t) = 0.56t - 0.6$ is of the form $y = mx + b$. The slope is 0.56. This means that the increase in expected number of Chinese children (in thousands) adopted by American families is 0.56 per year.

e. $f(1) = 0.56(1) - 0.6$

$= -0.04$

Because the model predicts the expected number of Chinese children adopted by American families in 1991 to be a negative value, model breakdown has occurred.

39. a. At $t = 0$ (2003), the number of bicyclists younger than 16 who were hit and killed by motor vehicles was 142. The slope is -17. These values can be substituted into an equation of the form $y = mx + b$.
$f(t) = -17t + 142$.

b. The slope, -17, means that 17 fewer bicyclists younger than 16 are hit and killed by motor vehicles each year.

c. The n-intercept is 142, which is how many bicyclists younger than 16 hit and killed by motor vehicles in the year 2003 ($t = 0$).

d. $0 = -17t + 142$

$17t = 142$

$t \approx 8$

This means that in the year 2011, it is expected that no bicyclists younger than 16 will be hit and killed by motor vehicles.

e. According to this model, every year after 2011 (2012 and beyond), there will be less than 0 bicyclists younger than 16 hit and killed by motor vehicles, which is unrealistic.

40. a. $A(t) = 1.3t + 9.5$
$B(t) = 1.8t + 5.2$

b.

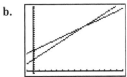

The sales of the companies will be approximately equal during year 8 (2013), when sales will be approximately $20 million.

c. $1.3t + 9.5 = 1.8t + 5.2$
$-0.5t + 9.5 = 5.2$
$-0.5t = -4.3$
$t = 8.6$
$A(8.6) = 1.3(8.6) + 9.5$
$= 20.68$
This means that 8.6 years after 2005, both companies sales will be 20.68 million dollars per year.

d. $1.3t + 9.5 < 1.8t + 5.2$
$1.3t + 9.5 - 1.8t < 1.8t - 1.8t + 5.2$
$1.3t + 9.5 - 1.8t < 1.8t - 1.8t + 5.2$
$-0.5t < -4.3$
$t > 8.6$
This means that after the year 2013, company A's sales will be less than company B's.

41. a. Start by plotting the data sets, then find the regression lines each set of data.

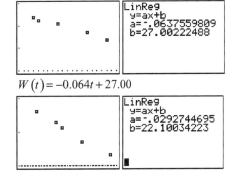

$W(t) = -0.064t + 27.00$

$M(t) = -0.029t + 22.10$

b. $W(111) = -0.064(111) + 27.00$
$= 19.9204$
$M(111) = -0.029(111) + 22.10$
$= 18.88$
This means that in the year 2011, the record time (in seconds) for women will be 19.92, and for men will be 18.88.

c. The slope of women's record times is less than men's. This means that women's times are decreasing at a faster rate than men's.

d. Answers may vary. In general, the record times of men and women will become closer together until women's times are equal to men's.

e. Answers will vary. The record times will be equal about year 2040), at a time of about 18.04 seconds.

f. $-0.064t + 27.00 > -0.029 + 22.10$
$-0.035t + 27.00 > 22.10$
$-0.035t > -4.90$
$t < 140$
This means that until the year 2040, women's record times will be greater than men's.

g. $W(t) = 0$
$-0.064(t) + 27.00 = 0$
$-0.064t = -27.00$
$t = 421.88$
$M(t) = 0$
$-0.029(t) + 22.10 = 0$
$-0.029t = -22.10$
$t = 762.07$
This means that in the year 2322, women's record times are expected to reach zero, and in 2662, men's record times are expected to reach zero. This is an unrealistic feat.

h. Graphs will vary.

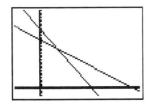

42. Start by setting up a system of equations for U, amount invested in a UBS Global Equity Y account (at 7.2% interest), and F, amount invested in a Fidelity Worldwide account (at 9.4% interest).

$$U = 2F$$

$0.072U + 0.094F = 595$

Now solve for either U or F.

$0.072(2F) + 0.094F = 595$

$0.144F + 0.094F = 595$

$0.238F = 595$

$F = 2500$

Substitute this value into the original equation to solve for the other variable.

$U = 2F$

$U = 2(2500) = 5000$

To earn $595 in one year, the person will have to invest $2500 into the Fidelity Worldwide account, and $5000 into the UBS Global Equity Y account.

Chapter 4
Exponential Functions

1. $2^{-1} = \dfrac{1}{2}$ negative integer exponent

3. $5^0 = 1$

5. $-4^2 = -(4 \cdot 4) = -16$

7. $(-4)^2 = (-4)(-4) = 16$

9. $\left(2^3\right)^2 = 2^6 = 2 \cdot 2 \cdot 2 \cdot 2 \cdot 2 \cdot 2 = 64$

11. $2^{-1} + 3^{-1} = \dfrac{1}{2} + \dfrac{1}{3}$ negative integer exponents
$$= \dfrac{3}{6} + \dfrac{2}{6} = \dfrac{5}{6}$$

13. $\dfrac{7^{902}}{7^{900}} = 7^{902-900} = 7^2 = 49$

15. $13^{500}13^{-500} = 13^{500+(-500)} = 13^0 = 1$

17. $\left(25^3 - 411^5 + 89^2\right)^0 = 1$

19. $b^7 b^{-9} = b^{7-9} = b^{-2} = \dfrac{1}{b^2}$
negative integer exponent

21. $\left(7b^{-3}\right)\left(-2b^{-5}\right) = \left(7(-2)\right)\left(b^{-3}b^{-5}\right)$
$$= -14b^{-3-5} = -14b^{-8}$$
$$= \dfrac{-14}{b^8} \text{ or } -\dfrac{14}{b^8}$$

23. $\left(-9b^{-7}c^5\right)\left(-8b^6c^{-5}\right)$
$$= \left(-9(-8)\right)\left(b^{-7}b^6\right)\left(c^5c^{-5}\right)$$
$$= 72b^{-7+6}c^{5-5} = 72b^{-1}c^0$$
$$= \dfrac{72}{b}$$

25. $\left(3b^2c^4\right)^3\left(2b^3c^5\right)^2 = 3^3 \, b^{2\cdot3}c^{4\cdot3} \, 2^2 \, b^{3\cdot2}c^{5\cdot2}$
$$= 3^3 \, b^6 c^{12} \, 2^2 \, b^6 c^{10}$$
$$= 27(4)b^{6+6}c^{12+10}$$
$$= 108b^{12}c^{22}$$

27. $3\left(b^5c\right)^{-2} = 3b^{5(-2)}c^{-2} = 3b^{-10}c^{-2} = \dfrac{3}{b^{10}c^2}$

29. $\left(2b^4c^{-2}\right)^5\left(3b^{-3}c^{-4}\right)^{-2}$
$$= (2)^5\left(b^4\right)^5\left(c^{-2}\right)^5 (3)^{-2}\left(b^{-3}\right)^{-2}\left(c^{-4}\right)^{-2}$$
$$= 32b^{4\cdot5}c^{-2\cdot5}\dfrac{1}{3^2}b^{-3(-2)}c^{-4(-2)}$$
$$= 32b^{20}c^{-10}\dfrac{1}{9}b^6c^8$$
$$= 32\left(\dfrac{1}{9}\right)b^{20}b^6c^{-10}c^8$$
$$= \dfrac{32b^{26}}{9c^2}$$

31. $\dfrac{b^{-10}}{b^{15}} = b^{-10-15} = b^{-25} = \dfrac{1}{b^{25}}$

33. $\dfrac{2b^{-12}}{5b^{-9}} = \dfrac{2b^{-12-(-9)}}{5} = \dfrac{2b^{-12+9}}{5} = \dfrac{2b^{-3}}{5} = \dfrac{2}{5b^3}$

35. $\dfrac{-12b^{-6}c^5}{14b^4c^5} = \dfrac{-6b^{-6-4}c^{5-5}}{7} = \dfrac{-6b^{-10}c^0}{7} = -\dfrac{6}{7b^{10}}$

37. $\dfrac{15b^{-7}c^{-3}d^8}{-45c^2b^{-6}d^8} = \dfrac{b^{-7-(-6)}c^{-3-2}d^{8-8}}{-3}$
$$= \dfrac{b^{-1}c^{-5}d^0}{-3}$$
$$= \dfrac{1}{-3bc^5}$$

39.
$$\frac{\left(-5b^{-3}c^4\right)\left(4b^{-5}c^{-1}\right)}{80b^2c^{17}} = \frac{-20b^{-3+(-5)}c^{4+(-1)}}{80b^2c^{17}}$$
$$= -\frac{b^{-8}c^3}{4b^2c^{17}}$$
$$= -\frac{b^{-8-2}c^{3-17}}{4}$$
$$= -\frac{b^{-10}c^{-14}}{4}$$
$$= -\frac{1}{4b^{10}c^{14}}$$

41.
$$\frac{\left(24b^3c^{-6}\right)\left(49b^{-1}c^{-2}\right)}{\left(28b^2c^4\right)\left(14b^{-5}c\right)} = \frac{24 \cdot 49b^{3+(-1)}c^{-6+(-2)}}{28 \cdot 14b^{2+(-5)}c^{4+1}}$$
$$= \frac{3b^2c^{-8}}{b^{-3}c^5}$$
$$= 3b^{2-(-3)}c^{-8-5}$$
$$= 3b^5c^{-13}$$
$$= \frac{3b^5}{c^{13}}$$

43.
$$\frac{\left(3b^5c^{-2}\right)^3}{2^{-1}b^{-3}c} = \frac{3^3b^{5\cdot3}c^{-2\cdot3}}{2^{-1}b^{-3}c}$$
$$= \frac{27b^{15}c^{-6}}{2^{-1}b^{-3}c}$$
$$= 27(2)b^{15-(-3)}c^{-6-1}$$
$$= 54b^{18}c^{-7}$$
$$= \frac{54b^{18}}{c^7}$$

45.
$$\frac{\left(2b^{-4}c\right)^{-3}}{\left(2b^2c^{-5}\right)^2} = \frac{2^{-3}b^{-4\cdot-3}c^{-3}}{2^2b^{2\cdot2}c^{-5\cdot2}}$$
$$= \frac{2^{-3}b^{12}c^{-3}}{2^2b^4c^{-10}}$$
$$= \frac{b^{12-4}c^{-3-(-10)}}{8 \cdot 4}$$
$$= \frac{b^8c^7}{32}$$

47.
$$\left(\frac{6b^5c^{-2}}{7b^2c^4}\right)^2 = \frac{6^2b^{5\cdot2}c^{-2\cdot2}}{7^2b^{2\cdot2}c^{4\cdot2}}$$
$$= \frac{36b^{10}c^{-4}}{49b^4c^8}$$
$$= \frac{36b^{10-4}c^{-4-8}}{49}$$
$$= \frac{36b^6c^{-12}}{49}$$
$$= \frac{36b^6}{49c^{12}}$$

49.
$$\left(\frac{5b^4c^{-3}}{15b^{-2}c^{-1}}\right)^{-4} = \left(\frac{b^4c^{-3}}{3b^{-2}c^{-1}}\right)^{-4}$$
$$= \frac{b^{4(-4)}c^{-3(-4)}}{3^{-4}b^{-2(-4)}c^{-1(-4)}}$$
$$= \frac{3^4b^{-16}c^{12}}{b^8c^4}$$
$$= \frac{81c^{12-4}}{b^{16+8}}$$
$$= \frac{81c^8}{b^{24}}$$

51.
$$\left(\frac{7b^4c^{-5}}{14b^7c^{-2}}\right)^0 = 1$$

53.
$$b^{-1}c^{-1} = \frac{1}{bc}$$

55.
$$\frac{1}{b^{-1}} + \frac{1}{c^{-1}} = b + c$$

57.
$$b^{4n}b^{3n} = b^{4n+3n} = b^{7n}$$

59.
$$\frac{b^{7n-1}}{b^{2n+3}} = b^{(7n-1)-(2n+3)} = b^{7n-1-2n-3} = b^{5n-4}$$

61.
$$f(3) = 2(3)^3 = 2(27) = 54$$

63.
$$f(-4) = 2(3)^{-4} = \frac{2}{3^4} = \frac{2}{81}$$

65.
$$g(a+2) = 4^{a+2} = 4^a \cdot 4^2 = 16\left(4^a\right)$$

67.
$$g(2a) = 4^{2a} = \left(4^2\right)^a = 16^a$$

105

69. a.

x	$f(x)$
-3	$f(-3) = 2^{-3} = \dfrac{1}{2^3} = \dfrac{1}{8} = 0.125$
-2	$f(-2) = 2^{-2} = \dfrac{1}{2^2} = \dfrac{1}{4} = 0.25$
-1	$f(-1) = 2^{-1} = \dfrac{1}{2} = 0.5$
0	$f(0) = 2^0 = 1$
1	$f(1) = 2^1 = 2$
2	$f(2) = 2^2 = 4$
3	$f(3) = 2^3 = 8$
4	$f(4) = 2^4 = 16$

b.

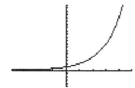

c. $2^{\frac{1}{2}} \approx 1.4$

71. $3.965 \times 10^2 = 3.965 \cdot 100 = 396.5$

73. $2.39 \times 10^{-1} = 2.39 \cdot \dfrac{1}{10} = 0.239$

75. $5.2 \times 10^2 = 5.2 \cdot 100 = 520$

77. $9.113 \times 10^{-5} = 9.113 \cdot \dfrac{1}{100,000} = 0.00009113$

79. $-6.52 \times 10^{-4} = -6.52 \cdot \dfrac{1}{10,000}$
$= -0.000652$

81. $9 \times 10^5 = 9 \cdot 100,000 = 900,000$

83. $-8 \times 10^0 = -8 \cdot 1 = -8$

85. $54,260,000 = 5.426 \times 10,000,000 = 5.426 \times 10^7$

87. $23,587 = 2.3587 \times 10,000 = 2.3587 \times 10^4$

89. $0.00098 = \dfrac{9.8}{10,000} = 9.8 \times 10^{-4}$

91. $0.0000346 = \dfrac{3.46}{100,000} = 3.46 \times 10^{-5}$

93. $-42,215 = -4.2215 \times 10,000 = -4.2215 \times 10^4$

95. $-0.00244 = \dfrac{-2.44}{1000} = -2.44 \times 10^{-3}$

97. $6.3\text{E-}6 = \dfrac{6.3}{1,000,000} = 0.0000063$

$1.3\text{E-}4 = \dfrac{1.3}{10,000} = 0.00013$

$3.2\text{E}6 = 3.2 \cdot 1,000,000 = 3,200,000$

$6.4\text{E}7 = 6.4 \cdot 10,000,000 = 64,000,000$

99. $3.6 \times 10^9 = 3.6 \cdot 1,000,000,000$
$= 3,600,000,000$ years

101. $6.3 \times 10^{-8} = 6.3 \cdot \dfrac{1}{100,000,000}$
$= 0.000000063$ mole per liter

103. $10,080,000 = 1.008 \times 10,000,000$
$= 1.008 \times 10^7$ gallons

105. $0.00000047 = \dfrac{4.7}{10,000,000}$
$= 4.7 \times 10^{-7}$ meter

107. a.

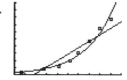

The exponential function $n = 0.29(1.078)^t$ describes the function better.

b. $n = 0.29(1.078)^{52} = 14.407$
The estimated number of bald eagle pairs is 14.4 thousand.

c. $n = 0.18(52) - 1.63 = 9.36 - 1.63 = 7.73$
The estimated number of bald eagle pairs is 7.7 thousand.

109. Student B is correct. Student A did not distribute the -1 exponent to the base 5 correctly. It should have been 5^{-1} and not -5. Student A mistakenly multiplied 5 by -1.

111. The student moved 3 to the denominator with b^{-2}.

$$\frac{3b^{-2}c^4}{d^7} = \frac{3c^4}{b^2d^7}$$

113. $-2^2 = -4$

$2(-1) = -2$

$\left(\frac{1}{2}\right)^2 = \frac{1}{4}$

$\frac{1}{2}$

$2^{-1} = \frac{1}{2}$

$\left(\frac{1}{2}\right)^{-1} = \frac{2}{1} = 2$

$(-2)^2 = 4$

$2^2 = 4$

The "ties" are $2^{-1} = \frac{1}{2}$ and $(-2)^2 = 2^2$.

115. a. $5^0 = 4^0 = 3^0 = 2^0 = 1^0 = 1$

It is reasonable to assume that $0^0 = 1$.

b. $0^5 = 0^4 = 0^3 = 0^2 = 0^1 = 0$

It is reasonable to assume that $0^0 = 0$.

c. Answers may vary. It is a good idea to leave 0^0 meaningless, since depending on the reasoning used, we get different values for 0^0.

117. Answers may vary.

b^m means that the base b is multiplied by itself m times. Also, b^n means that the base b is multiplied by itself n times. So, if we multiply m factors of b by n factors of b, we will have a total of $m + n$ factors of b.

$(b^m)^n$ means that there are n factors of b^m.

Since each b^m has m factors of b, we have a total of $m \cdot n$ or mn factors of b.

119. $f(3) = 2(3) = 6$

121. $g(3) = 2^3 = 8$

123. $y = 3x + 1$

$y = 2x - 4$

$3x + 1 = 2x - 4$

$x = -5$

$y = 3(-5) + 1 = -15 + 1 = -14$

$y = 3x + 1$ and $y = 2x - 4$ form a linear system in two variables.

125. $3x + 1 = 2x - 4$

$x = -5$

$3x + 1 = 2x - 4$ is a linear equation in one variable.

Homework 4.2

1. $16^{1/2} = 4$, since $4^2 = 16$

3. $1000^{1/3} = 10$, since $10^3 = 1000$

5. $49^{1/2} = 7$, since $7^2 = 49$

7. $125^{1/3} = 5$, since $5^3 = 125$

9. $8^{4/3} = \left(8^{1/3}\right)^4 = 2^4 = 16$

11. $9^{3/2} = \left(9^{1/2}\right)^3 = 3^3 = 27$

13. $32^{2/5} = \left(32^{1/5}\right)^2 = 2^2 = 4$

15. $4^{5/2} = \left(4^{1/2}\right)^5 = 2^5 = 32$

17. $27^{-1/3} = \frac{1}{27^{1/3}} = \frac{1}{3}$

19. $-36^{-1/2} = -\frac{1}{36^{1/2}} = -\frac{1}{6}$

21. $4^{-5/2} = \frac{1}{4^{5/2}} = \frac{1}{\left(4^{1/2}\right)^5} = \frac{1}{2^5} = \frac{1}{32}$

23.
$$(-27)^{-4/3} = \frac{1}{(-27)^{4/3}}$$
$$= \frac{1}{\left((-27)^{1/3}\right)^4}$$
$$= \frac{1}{(-3)^4} = \frac{1}{81}$$

25.
$$2^{\frac{1}{4}}2^{\frac{3}{4}} = 2^{\frac{1}{4}+\frac{3}{4}} = 2^{\frac{4}{4}} = 2^1 = 2$$

27.
$$\left(3^{\frac{1}{2}}2^{\frac{3}{2}}\right)^2 = 3^{\left(\frac{1}{2}\right)(2)}2^{\left(\frac{3}{2}\right)(2)} = 3^1 \cdot 2^3 = 3 \cdot 8 = 24$$

29.
$$\frac{7^{\frac{1}{3}}}{7^{-\frac{5}{3}}} = 7^{\frac{1}{3}-\left(-\frac{5}{3}\right)} = 7^{\frac{6}{3}} = 7^2 = 49$$

31.
$$f\left(\frac{3}{4}\right) = 81^{\frac{3}{4}} = \left(81^{\frac{1}{4}}\right)^3 = 3^3 = 27$$

33.
$$g\left(\frac{1}{3}\right) = 4(27)^{\frac{1}{3}} = 4 \cdot 3 = 12$$

35.
$$g\left(-\frac{1}{3}\right) = 4(27)^{-\frac{1}{3}} = \frac{4}{27^{\frac{1}{3}}} = \frac{4}{3}$$

37.
$$h\left(\frac{3}{2}\right) = -2(4)^{\frac{3}{2}} = -2\left(4^{\frac{1}{2}}\right)^3$$
$$= -2(2)^3 = -2 \cdot 8 = -16$$

39.
$$f\left(-\frac{3}{4}\right) = 16^{-\frac{3}{4}} = \frac{1}{16^{\frac{3}{4}}} = \frac{1}{\left(16^{\frac{1}{4}}\right)^3} = \frac{1}{2^3} = \frac{1}{8}$$
$$f\left(-\frac{1}{2}\right) = 16^{-\frac{1}{2}} = \frac{1}{16^{\frac{1}{2}}} = \frac{1}{4}$$
$$f\left(-\frac{1}{4}\right) = 16^{-\frac{1}{4}} = \frac{1}{16^{\frac{1}{4}}} = \frac{1}{2}$$
$$f(0) = 16^0 = 1$$
$$f\left(\frac{1}{4}\right) = 16^{\frac{1}{4}} = 2$$
$$f\left(\frac{1}{2}\right) = 16^{\frac{1}{2}} = 4$$
$$f\left(\frac{3}{4}\right) = 16^{\frac{3}{4}} = \left(16^{\frac{1}{4}}\right)^3 = 2^3 = 8$$
$$f(1) = 16^1 = 16$$

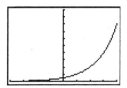

41.
$$b^{\frac{7}{6}}b^{\frac{5}{6}} = b^{\frac{7}{6}+\frac{5}{6}} = b^{\frac{12}{6}} = b^2$$

43.
$$b^{\frac{3}{5}}b^{-\frac{13}{5}} = b^{\frac{3}{5}+\left(-\frac{13}{5}\right)} = b^{-\frac{10}{5}} = b^{-2} = \frac{1}{b^2}$$

45.
$$(16b^8)^{1/4} = (16)^{1/4}(b^8)^{1/4} = 2b^{8\left(\frac{1}{4}\right)} = 2b^2$$

47.
$$4(25b^8c^{14})^{-1/2} = \frac{4}{(25b^8c^{14})^{1/2}}$$
$$= \frac{4}{(25)^{1/2}(b^8)^{1/2}(c^{14})^{1/2}}$$
$$= \frac{4}{5\left(b^{8\left(\frac{1}{2}\right)}\right)\left(c^{14\left(\frac{1}{2}\right)}\right)}$$
$$= \frac{4}{5b^4c^7}$$

49.
$$\left(b^{3/5}c^{-1/4}\right)\left(b^{2/5}c^{-7/4}\right) - b^{\frac{3}{5}+\frac{2}{5}}c^{-\frac{1}{4}+\left(-\frac{7}{4}\right)}$$
$$= b^{\frac{5}{5}}c^{-\frac{8}{4}}$$
$$= b^{1}c^{-2}$$
$$= \frac{b}{c^2}$$

51.
$$\left(5bcd\right)^{1/5}\left(5bcd\right)^{4/5} = \left(5bcd\right)^{\frac{1}{5}+\frac{4}{5}}$$
$$= \left(5bcd\right)^{\frac{5}{5}} = 5bcd$$

53.
$$\left[\left(3b^5\right)^3\left(3b^9c^8\right)\right]^{1/4}$$
$$= \left(3b^5\right)^{3/4}\left(3b^9c^8\right)^{1/4}$$
$$= \left(3\right)^{3/4}\left(b^5\right)^{3/4}\left(3\right)^{1/4}\left(b^9\right)^{1/4}\left(c^8\right)^{1/4}$$
$$= 3^{3/4}b^{15/4}3^{1/4}b^{9/4}c^2$$
$$= 3^{3/4+1/4}b^{15/4+9/4}c^2$$
$$= 3b^6c^2$$

55.
$$\frac{b^{-2/5}c^{11/8}}{b^{18/5}c^{-5/8}} = \frac{c^{11/8-(-5/8)}}{b^{2/5+18/5}} = \frac{c^{16/8}}{b^{20/5}} = \frac{c^2}{b^4}$$

57.
$$\left(\frac{9b^3c^{-2}}{25b^{-5}c^4}\right)^{-1/2} = \left(\frac{9b^3b^5}{25c^2c^4}\right)^{-1/2}$$
$$= \left(\frac{9b^{3+5}}{25c^{2+4}}\right)^{-1/2}$$
$$= \left(\frac{9b^8}{25c^6}\right)^{-1/2}$$
$$= \left(\frac{25c^6}{9b^8}\right)^{1/2}$$
$$= \frac{\left(25\right)^{1/2}\left(c^6\right)^{1/2}}{\left(9\right)^{1/2}\left(b^8\right)^{1/2}} = \frac{5c^3}{3b^4}$$

59. $32^{1/5}b^{3/7}b^{2/5} = 2b^{3/7+2/5} = 2b^{(15+14)/35} = 2b^{29/35}$

61. $\dfrac{b^{5/6}}{b^{1/4}} = b^{\frac{5}{6}-\frac{1}{4}} = b^{\frac{10}{12}-\frac{3}{12}} = b^{7/12}$

63.
$$\frac{\left(9b^5\right)^{3/2}}{\left(27b^4\right)^{2/3}} = \frac{\left(9\right)^{3/2}\left(b^5\right)^{3/2}}{\left(27\right)^{2/3}\left(b^4\right)^{2/3}}$$
$$= \frac{27b^{15/2}}{9b^{8/3}}$$
$$= 3b^{(45-16)/6}$$
$$= 3b^{\frac{29}{6}}$$

65.
$$\left(\frac{8b^{2/3}}{2b^{4/5}}\right)^{3/2} = \left(\frac{4b^{2/3}}{b^{4/5}}\right)^{3/2}$$
$$= \frac{\left(4\right)^{3/2}\left(b^{2/3}\right)^{3/2}}{\left(b^{4/5}\right)^{3/2}}$$
$$= \frac{\left(4^{1/2}\right)^3 b}{b^{6/5}}$$
$$= 2^3 b^{1-\frac{6}{5}}$$
$$= 8b^{-1/5} = \frac{8}{b^{1/5}}$$

67.
$$\frac{\left(8bc^3\right)^{1/3}}{\left(81b^{-5}c^3\right)^{3/4}} = \frac{\left(8\right)^{1/3}b^{1/3}\left(c^3\right)^{1/3}}{\left(81\right)^{3/4}\left(b^{-5}\right)^{3/4}\left(c^3\right)^{3/4}}$$
$$= \frac{2b^{1/3}c}{27b^{-15/4}c^{9/4}}$$
$$= \frac{2b^{\frac{1}{3}+\frac{15}{4}}c^{1-\frac{9}{4}}}{27}$$
$$= \frac{2b^{\frac{4}{12}+\frac{45}{12}}c^{-\frac{5}{4}}}{27}$$
$$= \frac{2b^{49/12}}{27c^{5/4}}$$

69. $b^{2/5}\left(b^{8/5} + b^{3/5}\right) = b^{2/5}b^{8/5} + b^{2/5}b^{3/5}$
$$= b^{\frac{2}{5}+\frac{8}{5}} + b^{\frac{2}{5}+\frac{3}{5}}$$
$$= b^{\frac{10}{5}} + b^{\frac{5}{5}}$$
$$= b^2 + b$$

71. a.

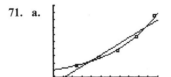

The exponential function $n = 10.1\left(1.02\right)^t$ describes the situation better.

b. $n = 10.1(1.02)^{110} \approx 89.19$

89 countries will participate in the 2010 Winter Olympics.

c.

42 countries participated in the Winter Olympics in 1972.

73. Answers may vary. $5^{1/n}$ may be represented by $\sqrt[n]{5}$. So, when n = 2, $\sqrt[n]{5} = \sqrt[2]{5}$, which is equivalent to $\sqrt{5}$.

75. Answers may vary. For $k = 1$,
$N \times 10^k = N \times 10^1 = N \times 10$, which moves the decimal point of the number N to the right by 1 place. Similarly, for $k = 2$, $N \times 10^2 = N \times 100$, which moves the decimal point of the number N to the right by 2 places, and so on.

77. $f\left(\dfrac{1}{3}\right) = 8 \cdot \dfrac{1}{3} = \dfrac{8}{3}$

79. $g\left(\dfrac{1}{3}\right) = 8^{1/3} = 2$

81. $f\left(-\dfrac{1}{3}\right) = 8 \cdot -\dfrac{1}{3} = -\dfrac{8}{3}$

83. $g\left(-\dfrac{1}{3}\right) = 8^{-1/3} = \dfrac{1}{8^{1/3}} = \dfrac{1}{2}$

85.

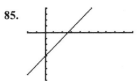

$f(x) = \dfrac{3}{2}x - 4$ is a linear function.

87.
$5 = \dfrac{3}{2}x - 4$
$9 = \dfrac{3}{2}x$
$x = 6$

$f(x) = \dfrac{3}{2}x - 4$ is a linear function.

Homework 4.3

1. $y = 3^x$

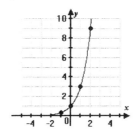

3. $y = 10^x$

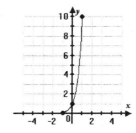

5. $y = 3(2)^x$

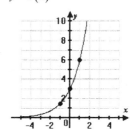

7. $y = 6(3)^x$

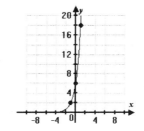

9. $y = 15\left(\dfrac{1}{3}\right)^x$

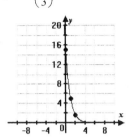

11. $y = 12\left(\dfrac{1}{2}\right)^x$

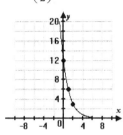

13. $f(x) = 2^x$, $g(x) = -2^x$

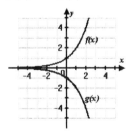

15. $f(x) = 4(3)^x$, $g(x) = -4(3)^x$

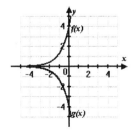

17. $f(x) = 8\left(\dfrac{1}{2}\right)^x$, $g(x) = -8\left(\dfrac{1}{2}\right)^x$

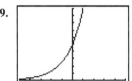

19.

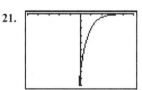

Domain: All real numbers
Range: $y > 0$

21.

Domain: All real numbers
Range: $y < 0$

23. a. $a < 0$ and $b > 1$
negative output and exponential growth

b. $a > 0$ and $b > 1$
positive output and exponential growth

c. $a > 0$ and $0 < b < 1$
positive output and exponential decay

d. $a < 0$ and $0 < b < 1$
negative output and exponential decay

25. Answers may vary. Consider the following example. The family of exponential curves, $f(x) = ab^x$, where $b = \dfrac{1}{2}$ and the coefficient is an integer between -4 and 4, inclusive, excluding 0.

$$f(x) = -4\left(\frac{1}{2}\right)^x \qquad j(x) = 4\left(\frac{1}{2}\right)^x$$

$$g(x) = -3\left(\frac{1}{2}\right)^x \qquad k(x) = 3\left(\frac{1}{2}\right)^x$$

$$h(x) = -2\left(\frac{1}{2}\right)^x \qquad l(x) = 2\left(\frac{1}{2}\right)^x$$

$$i(x) = -1\left(\frac{1}{2}\right)^x \qquad m(x) = 1\left(\frac{1}{2}\right)^x$$

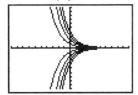

27. Since the *y*-intercept is (0, 3), we know that the equation is of the form $f(x) = 3(b)^x$. Since the point (1, 6) lies on the graph, we know that when *x* is 1, *f*(*x*) is 6. Therefore, $6 = 3b$, and $b = 2$. The equation is $f(x) = 3(2)^x$.

29. Answers may vary. Consider the following example.

$$f(x) = 2\left(\frac{2}{3}\right)^x \qquad h(x) = 2(2)^x$$

$$g(x) = 4\left(\frac{9}{8}\right)^x \qquad k(x) = 3\left(\frac{1}{2}\right)^x$$

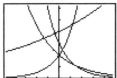

31. a.

x	f(x)
0	4
1	8
2	16
3	32
4	64

b.

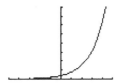

c. For each input–output pair, the output is 4 times 2 raised to the power equal to the input.

33.

x	f(x)	g(x)	h(x)	k(x)
0	162	3	2	800
1	54	12	10	400
2	18	48	50	200
3	6	192	250	100
4	2	768	1250	50

35.

x	f(x)	g(x)	h(x)	k(x)
0	5	160	162	3
1	10	80	54	12
2	20	40	18	48
3	40	20	6	192
4	80	10	2	768

37. $f(-3) = 8$

39. $f(0) = 1$

41. $x = -2$

43. $x = 0$

45. $f(3) = 24$

47. $f(5) = 96$

49. $x = 0$

51. $x = 3$

53. a.

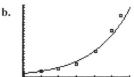

It is better to use an exponential function to model the data as the average ticket price appears to increase at an exponential rate, as opposed to a linear rate.

b.

Yes, the graph of *f* comes close to the data points.

c. $f(60) = 1.22(1.051)^{60} = 24.128082$

The average ticket price in 2010 will be $24.13.

d. The average ticket prices to all major league games will reach $44.56 in 2022.

55. $y = 7^x$

No x-intercept; y-intercept: (0, 1)

57. $y = 3\left(\dfrac{1}{5}\right)^x$

No x-intercept; y-intercept: (0, 3)

59. a. $f(0) = 100$, y-intercept (0, 100)

$g(0) = 5$, y-intercept (0, 5)

b. Since $g(x)$ has a larger base (3 versus 2), $g(x)$ will increase faster than $f(x)$.

c. Eventually $g(x)$ will be much greater than $f(x)$. For every increase in x of one, $g(x)$ increases by a factor of three, while $f(x)$ increases by a factor of two.

d.

X	Y₁	Y₂
0	100	5
1	200	15
2	400	45
3	800	135
4	1600	405
5	3200	1215
6	6400	3645

X=0

61. $f(2) = 2^2 + 3^2 = 4 + 9 = 13$

63. $f(-2) = 2^{-2} + 3^{-2} = \dfrac{1}{4} + \dfrac{1}{9} = \dfrac{9}{36} + \dfrac{4}{36} = \dfrac{13}{36}$

65. $3 = 3^x$

$3^1 = 3^x$

$1 = x$ or $x = 1$

67. $1 = 3^x$

$3^0 = 3^x$

$0 = x$ or $x = 0$

69. $f(x) = 2^{3x}, g(x) = 8^x$

$g(x) = 8^x = \left(2^3\right)^x = 2^{3x} = f(x)$

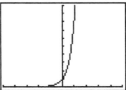

The graphs coincide. f and g are equivalent functions.

71. $f(x) = 2^{x+3}, g(x) = 8(2)^x$

$g(x) = 8(2)^x = 2^3(2)^x = 2^{3+x} = 2^{x+3} = f(x)$

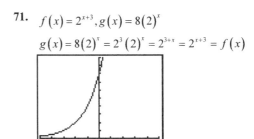

The graphs coincide. f and g are equivalent functions.

73. $f(x) = \dfrac{6^x}{3^x}, g(x) = 2^x$

$g(x) = 2^x = \left(\dfrac{6}{3}\right)^x = \dfrac{6^x}{3^x} = f(x)$

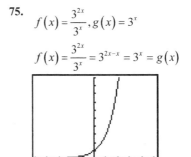

The graphs coincide. f and g are equivalent functions.

75. $f(x) = \dfrac{3^{2x}}{3^x}, g(x) = 3^x$

$f(x) = \dfrac{3^{2x}}{3^x} = 3^{2x-x} = 3^x = g(x)$

The graphs coincide. f and g are equivalent functions.

77. $f(x) = x^{1/2}, g(x) = \sqrt{x}$

$f(x) = x^{1/2} = \sqrt{x} = g(x)$

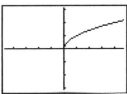

The graphs coincide. *f* and *g* are equivalent functions.

79. $f(x) = 2^x, g(x) = 8^{x/3}$

$g(x) = 8^{x/3} = \left(2^3\right)^{x/3} = 2^{3(x/3)} = 2^x = f(x)$

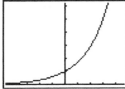

The graphs coincide. *f* and *g* are equivalent functions.

81. a. $f(3+4) = 2^{3+4} = 2^7 = 128$
$f(3) + f(4) = 2^3 + 2^4 = 8 + 16 = 24$
$f(3+4) \neq f(3) + f(4)$
The statement is not true.

b. $f(x+y) = 2^{x+y} = 2^x \cdot 2^y$
$f(x) + f(y) = 2^x + 2^y$
$2^x \cdot 2^y \neq 2^x + 2^y$

The statement is not true.

83. Answers may vary. If $b > 1$, then *f* is increasing because *b* increases as it is multiplied by itself *x* times. If $0 < b < 1$, then *f* is decreasing because *b* decreases toward 0 as it is multiplied by itself *x* times.

85. Answers may vary. If $f(x) = -ab^x$, then $-f(x) = ab^x$. Since $g(x)$ also equals ab^x, $g(x) = -f(x)$. This means that for the same *x*-value, *f* and *g* return opposite *y*-values. Therefore, functions *f* and *g* would reflect each other across the *x*-axis at each *x*.

87.

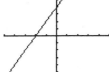

89.

91. $0 = 8 + 4x$
$-8 = 4x$
$x = -2$
$y = 8 + 4(0)$
$y = 8$
The *x*-intercept is (–2, 0) and the *y*-intercept is (0, 8).

93. $f(x) = 13 - 4x$, which is linear.
$g(x) = 4(3)^x$, which is exponential.
$h(x) = 48\left(\dfrac{1}{2}\right)^x$, which is exponential.
$k(x)$ is neither linear nor exponential.

95.

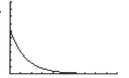

$f(x) = 6\left(\dfrac{1}{2}\right)^x$ is an exponential function.

97. $f(-2) = 6\left(\dfrac{1}{2}\right)^{-2} = 6(2)^2 = 6 \cdot 4 = 24$

$f(x) = 6\left(\dfrac{1}{2}\right)^x$ is an exponential function.

Homework 4.4

1. The *y*-intercept of *f* is (0, 4). As the value of *x* increases by 1, the value of *y* is multiplied by 2. By the base multiplier property, we know that *f* is an exponential function with base 2.
$f(x) = 4(2)^x$
The *y*-intercept of *g* is (0, 36). As *x* increases by 1, the value of *y* is multiplied by $\dfrac{1}{3}$.

$g(x) = 36\left(\dfrac{1}{3}\right)^x$

The *y*-intercept of *h* is (0, 5). As *x* increases by 1, the value of *y* is multiplied by 10.
$h(x) = 5(10)^x$
The *y*-intercept of *k* is (0, 250). As *x* increases by

1, the value of y is multiplied by $\dfrac{1}{5}$.

$$k(x) = 250\left(\dfrac{1}{5}\right)^x$$

3. The y-intercept of f is $(0, 100)$. As x increases by 1, the value of y is multiplied by $\dfrac{1}{2}$. f is exponential with base $\dfrac{1}{2}$.

$$f(x) = 100\left(\dfrac{1}{2}\right)^x$$

The y-intercept of g is $(0, 100)$. As x increases by 1, the value of y decreases by 50. g is linear with slope of -50.
$g(x) = -50x + 100$
The y-intercept of h is $(0, 2)$. As x increases by 1, the value of y increases by 4. h is linear with a slope of 4.
$h(x) = 4x + 2$
The y-intercept of k is $(0, 2)$. As x increases by 1, the value of y is multiplied by 3. k is exponential with base 3.
$k(x) = 2(3)^x$

5. $b^2 = 16$
$b = \pm(16)^{1/2}$
$b = \pm 4$

7. $b^3 = 27$
$b = 27^{1/3}$
$b = 3$

9. $3b^5 = 96$
$b^5 = 32$
$b = 32^{1/5}$
$b = 2$

11. $35b^4 = 15$
$b^4 \approx 0.429$
$b \approx \pm(0.429)^{1/4}$
$b \approx \pm 0.81$

13. $3.6b^3 = 42.5$
$b^3 \approx 11.81$
$b \approx 11.81^{1/3}$
$b \approx 2.28$

15. $32.7b^6 + 8\,1 = 392.8$
$32.7b^6 = 384.7$
$b^6 \approx 11.765$
$b \approx \pm(11.765)^{1/6}$
$b \approx \pm 1.51$

17. $\dfrac{1}{4}b^3 - \dfrac{1}{2} = \dfrac{9}{4}$
$4\left(\dfrac{1}{4}b^3 - \dfrac{1}{2}\right) = 4\left(\dfrac{9}{4}\right)$
$b^3 - 2 = 9$
$b^3 = 11$
$b = 11^{1/3}$
$b \approx 2.22$

19. $\dfrac{b^6}{b^2} = 81$
$b^{6-2} = 81$
$b^4 = 81$
$b = \pm(81)^{1/4}$
$b = \pm 3$

21. $\dfrac{b^8}{b^3} = \dfrac{79}{5}$
$b^{8-3} = \dfrac{79}{5}$
$b^5 = \dfrac{79}{5}$
$b = \left(\dfrac{79}{5}\right)^{1/5}$
$b \approx 1.74$

23. $b^n + k = p$
$b^n = p - k$
$b = (p - k)^{1/n}$

25. $\dfrac{b^n}{a} + k = p$
$\dfrac{b^n}{a} = p - k$
$b^n = a(p - k)$
$b^n = ap - ak$
$b = (ap - ak)^{1/n}$

27. $(0, 4)$ and $(1, 8)$
The y-intercept is $(0, 4)$, and the equation if of the form $y = 4b^x$. Substitute 1 for x and 8 for y.
$8 = 4b^1$

$4b = 8$
$b = 2$
The equation is $y = 4(2)^x$.

29. $(0, 3), (5, 100)$
The y-intercept is $(0, 3)$, and the equation is of the form $y - 3b^x$. Substitute 5 for x and 100 for y to find b.
$100 = 3b^5$
$3b^5 = 100$
$b^5 = \dfrac{100}{3}$
$b = \left(\dfrac{100}{3}\right)^{1/5}$
$b \approx 2.02$
The equation is $y = 3(2.02)^x$.

31. $(0, 87), (6, 14)$
The y-intercept is $(0, 87)$, and the equation is of the form $y = 87b^x$. Substitute 6 for x and 14 for y to find b.
$14 = 87b^6$
$b^6 = \dfrac{14}{87}$
$b = \left(\dfrac{14}{87}\right)^{1/6}$
$b \approx 0.74$
The equation is $y = 87(0.74)^x$.

33. $(0, 7.4), (3, 1.3)$
The y-intercept is $(0, 7.4)$, and the equation is of the form $y = 7.4b^x$. Substitute 3 for x and 1.3 for y to find b.
$1.3 = 7.4b^3$
$7.4b^3 = 1.3$
$b^3 = \dfrac{1.3}{7.4}$
$b = \left(\dfrac{1.3}{7.4}\right)^{1/3}$
$b \approx 0.56$
The equation is $y = 7.4(0.56)^x$.

35. $(0, 5.5), (2, 73.9)$
The y-intercept is $(0, 5.5)$, and the equation is of the form $y = 5.5b^x$. Substitute 2 for x and 73.9 for y to find b.

$73.9 = 5.5b^2$
$5.5b^2 = 73.9$
$b^2 = \dfrac{73.9}{5.5}$
$b = \left(\dfrac{73.9}{5.5}\right)^{1/2}$
$b \approx 3.67$
The equation is $y = 5.5(3.67)^x$.

37. $(0, 39.18), (15, 3.66)$
The y-intercept is $(0, 39.18)$, and the equation is of the form $y = 39.18b^x$. Substitute 15 for x and 3.66 for y to find b.
$3.66 = 39.18b^{15}$
$39.18b^{15} = 3.66$
$b^{15} = \dfrac{3.66}{39.18}$
$b = \left(\dfrac{3.66}{39.18}\right)^{1/15}$
$b \approx 0.85$
The equation is $y = 39.18(0.85)^x$.

39. The points $(0, 4)$ and $(1, 2)$ lie on the graph. Use these points to determine the equation of the exponential curve. The y-intercept is $(0, 4)$, and the equation is of the form $y = 4b^x$. Substitute 1 for x and 2 for y to find b.
$2 = 4b^1$
$4b^1 = 2$
$b = \dfrac{2}{4} = \dfrac{1}{2}$
The equation is $y = 4\left(\dfrac{1}{2}\right)^x$.

41. $(1, 4)$, and $(2, 12)$
We can form a system of equations since both points satisfy $y = a(b)^x$.
$4 = ab^1$
$12 = ab^2$
Combining the two equations yields the following.
$\dfrac{12}{4} = \dfrac{ab^2}{ab^1}$
$3 = b$
Use b and one of the points to solve for a. Substitute 1 for x and 4 for y.

$$4 = a(3)^1$$
$$a(3)^1 = 4$$
$$3a = 4$$
$$a \approx 1.33$$

The equation of the curve is $y = 1.33(3)^x$.

43. (3, 4) and (5, 9)

We can form a system of equations since both points satisfy $y = a(b)^x$.

$$4 = ab^3$$
$$9 = ab^5$$

Combining the two equations yields the following.

$$\frac{9}{4} = \frac{ab^5}{ab^3}$$
$$\frac{9}{4} = b^2$$
$$b = \left(\frac{9}{4}\right)^{1/2}$$
$$b = \frac{3}{2} = 1.5$$

Use b and one of the points to solve for a. Substitute 3 for x and 4 for y.

$$4 = a(1.5)^3$$
$$a = \frac{4}{(1.5)^3}$$
$$a \approx 1.19$$

The equation of the curve is $y = 1.19(1.5)^x$.

45. (10, 329) and (30, 26)

We can form a system of equations since both points satisfy $y = a(b)^x$.

$$329 = ab^{10}$$
$$26 = ab^{30}$$

Combining the two equations yields the following.

$$\frac{26}{329} = \frac{ab^{30}}{ab^{10}}$$
$$\frac{26}{329} = b^{20}$$
$$b = \left(\frac{26}{329}\right)^{1/20}$$
$$b \approx 0.88$$

Use b and one of the points to solve for a. Substitute 10 for x and 329 for y.

$$329 \approx a(0.88)^{10}$$
$$a \approx \frac{329}{(0.88)^{10}}$$
$$a \approx 1170.33$$

The equation of the curve is $y = 1170.33(0.88)^x$.

47. (5, 8.1) and (9, 2.4)

We can form a system of equations since both points satisfy $y = a(b)^x$.

$$8.1 = ab^5$$
$$2.4 = ab^9$$

Combining the two equations yields the following.

$$\frac{2.4}{8.1} = \frac{ab^9}{ab^5}$$
$$\frac{2.4}{8.1} = b^4$$
$$b \approx 0.74$$

Use b and one of the points to solve for a. Substitute 9 for x and 2.4 for y.

$$2.4 \approx a(0.74)^9$$
$$a \approx \frac{2.4}{(0.74)^9}$$
$$a \approx 37.05$$

The equation of the curve is $y = 37.05(0.74)^x$.

49. (2, 73.8) and (7, 13.2)

We can form a system of equations since both points satisfy $y = a(b)^x$.

$$13.2 = ab^7$$
$$73.8 = ab^2$$

Combining the two equations yields the following.

$$\frac{13.2}{73.8} = \frac{ab^7}{ab^2}$$
$$\frac{13.2}{73.8} = b^5$$
$$b \approx 0.71$$

Use b and one of the points to solve for a. Substitute 2 for x and 73.8 for y.

$$73.8 \approx a(0.71)^2$$
$$a \approx \frac{73.8}{(0.71)^2}$$
$$a \approx 146.91$$

The equation of the curve is $y = 146.91(0.71)^x$.

51. $(13, 24.71)$ and $(21, 897.35)$
We can form a system of equations since both
points satisfy $y = a(b)^x$.
$$897.35 = ab^{21}$$
$$24.71 = ab^{13}$$
Combining the two equations yields the
following.
$$\frac{897.35}{24.71} = \frac{ab^{21}}{ab^{13}}$$
$$\frac{897.35}{24.71} = b^8$$
$$b \approx 1.57$$
Use b and one of the points to solve for a.
Substitute 13 for x and 24.71 for y.
$$24.71 \approx a(1.57)^{13}$$
$$a \approx \frac{24.71}{(1.57)^{13}}$$
$$a \approx 0.072$$
The equation of the curve is $y = 0.072(1.57)^x$.

53. The points $(1, 2)$ and $(3, 5)$ lie on the exponential
curve. Use the points to form a system of
equations since both points satisfy the equation
$y = a(b)^x$.
$$5 = ab^3$$
$$2 = ab^1$$
Combining the two equations yields the
following.
$$\frac{5}{2} = \frac{ab^3}{ab^1}$$
$$\frac{5}{2} = b^2$$
$$b \approx 1.58$$
Use b and one of the points to solve for a.
Substitute 1 for x and 2 for y.
$$2 \approx a(1.58)^1$$
$$a \approx \frac{2}{1.58}$$
$$a \approx 1.26$$
The equation of the curve is $y = 1.26(1.58)^x$.

55. Both the exponential equations have the
coefficient 6. Therefore they both have the same
y-intercept $(0, 6)$. Thus, the solution is $(0, 6)$.

57. a. i. Yes. Answers may vary. The equation
$y = 2(2)^x$ contains the point $(0, 2)$.

ii. No. Answers may vary. For $(2, 0)$ to be
a solution to an exponential equation,
the equation must be of the form
$0 = a(b)^2$. However, since $a \neq 0$ and
$b > 0$ in all exponential equations, $(2, 0)$
can never be found on an exponential
curve.

b. No. Answers may vary. Create a system of
equations based on $y = a(b)^x$.
$$1 = ab^3$$
$$-1 = ab^2$$
Combining the two equations yields the
following.
$$\frac{1}{-1} = \frac{ab^3}{ab^2}$$
$$-1 = b$$
Since $b = -1$, the equation is not exponential.

59. Answers may vary. One possible answer is as
follows. The base multiplier property states that
when $y = ab^x$, if the value of x increases by 1, the
value of y is multiplied by the base b. This makes
sense because increasing x by 1 is the same as
multiplying by another factor b, due to the nature
of exponents. For example, if $y = 5(3)^x$, y is 45
when x is 2. If you increase x by 1, y becomes
135, which is the same as the product of 45 and
3.

61. $\dfrac{b^7}{b^2} = b^{7-2} = b^5$

63. $\dfrac{b^7}{b^2} = 76$
$$b^5 = 76$$
$$b = (76)^{1/5}$$
$$b \approx 2.38$$

65. $\dfrac{8b^3}{6b^{-1}} = \dfrac{4b^3}{3b^{-1}} = \dfrac{4b^{3-(-1)}}{3} = \dfrac{4b^4}{3}$

67.
$$\frac{8b^3}{6b^{-1}} = \frac{3}{7}$$
$$\frac{4b^4}{3} = \frac{3}{7}$$
$$b^4 = \frac{9}{28}$$
$$b = \pm\left(\frac{9}{28}\right)^{1/4}$$
$$b \approx \pm 0.75$$

69. L is a linear function of the form $y = mx + b$.
The y-intercept is $(0, 2)$, so $b = 2$ and the equation is of the form $y = mx + 2$.
Substitute 1 for x and 6 for y to find m.
$$6 = m(1) + 2$$
$$6 = m + 2$$
$$4 = m$$
The equation for the linear function is $L(x) = 4x + 2$.
E is an exponential function of the form $y = ab^x$.
The y-intercept is $(0, 2)$, so $a = 2$ and the equation is of the form $y = 2b^x$.
Substitute 1 for x and 6 for y to find b.
$$6 = 2b^1$$
$$\frac{6}{2} = b^1$$
$$3 = b$$
The equation for the exponential function is
$$E(x) = 2(3)^x .$$

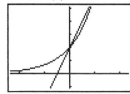

71. A linear function has the form $y = mx + b$.
Substitute for x and y and solve.
$$6 = 7m + b$$
$$3 = 5m + b$$
$$3 = 2m$$
$$m = \frac{3}{2}$$
Solve for b.

$$6 = 7\left(\frac{3}{2}\right) + b$$
$$6 = \frac{21}{2} + b$$
$$b = -\frac{9}{2}$$
The equation for the linear function is
$$y = \frac{3}{2}x - \frac{9}{2} .$$
An exponential function has the form $y = ab^x$.
Substitute for x and y and solve.
$$\frac{6}{3} = \frac{ab^7}{ab^5}$$
$$2 = b^2$$
$$b \approx \pm 1.41$$
Solve for a.
$$6 = a(1.41)^7$$
$$a \approx 0.54$$
The equation for the exponential function is
$$y = 0.54(1.41)^x .$$

So, the function could be either linear or exponential.

73. a. $L(x) = 2x + 100, \ E(x) = 3(2)^x$
To find the y-intercept, set $x = 0$.
$L(0) = 2(0) + 100 = 100$
The y-intercept of L is 100.
$E(0) = 3(2)^0 = 3(1) = 3$
The y-intercept of E is 3.

   b. L is linear. By the slope addition property, when x increases by 1, the value of y increases by 2. E is exponential. By the base multiplier property, when x increases by 1, the value of y is multiplied by 2.

   c. The exponential function, E, will eventually dominate. L increases by a fixed amount for every change in x, while E increases by an increasing amount for every change in x.

   d.

X	Y1	Y2
0	100	3
1	102	6
2	104	12
3	106	24
4	108	48
5	110	96
6	112	192

X=0

75.

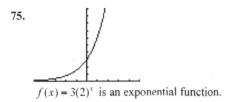

$f(x) = 3(2)^x$ is an exponential function.

77.
$$f(-3) = 3(2)^{-3} = \frac{3}{2^3} = \frac{3}{8} = 0.375$$

$f(x) = 3(2)^x$ is an exponential function.

Homework 4.5

1. a. Complete a table for $f(t)$ based on the assumption that the total number of people triples each day.

t (days)	$f(t)$ (people)
0	40
1	120
2	360
3	1080
4	3240

For every increase of 1 in t, $f(t)$ is multiplied by 3. $f(t)$ is exponential with base 3 and y-intercept 40. The equation is $f(t) = 40(3)^t$.

b. $f(10) = 40(3)^{10} = 2,361,960$ people

c. $f(15) = 40(3)^{15} \approx 574$ million
Model breakdown has occurred, since this is well over the entire population of the United States.

3. a. Complete a table for $f(t)$ based on the assumption that the total number of web pages doubles each year.

t (years)	$f(t)$ (billions of web pages)
0	8
1	16
2	32
3	64
4	128

For every increase in t of 1, $f(t)$ is multiplied by 2. $f(t)$ is exponential with base 2 and y-intercept 8. The equation is $f(t) = 8(2)^t$.

b. Since 2010 is 6 years after 2004, find $f(6)$.

$f(6) = 8(2)^6 = 512$
In the year 2010, 512 billion web pages will be indexed.

c. First convert pages to inches.

$$512,000,000,000 \text{ pages} \cdot \frac{2 \text{ inches}}{500 \text{ pages}}$$
$$= 2,048,000,000 \text{ inches}$$
Now, convert inches to miles.
$$2,048,000,000 \text{ inches} \times \frac{\text{foot}}{12 \text{ inches}} \times \frac{\text{mile}}{5280 \text{ feet}}$$
$$\approx 32,323 \text{ miles}$$

5. a. Complete a table for $h(t)$, assuming that revenue grows by 114% per year.

t (years)	$h(t)$ ($ millions)
0	91
1	$91(2.14) = 194.74$
2	$194.74(2.14) \approx 416.74$
3	$416.74(2.14) \approx 891.82$
4	$891.82(2.14) \approx 1,908.49$

For every increase in t of 1, $h(t)$ is multiplied by 2.14. $h(t)$ is exponential with base 2.14 and y-intercept 91. The equation is $h(t) = 91(2.14)^t$.

b. The r-intercept is the value of a in the equation $h(t) = ab^t$. In this case, the r-intercept is $91 million, which is the revenue from ring tones in 2003, the first year.

c. The base, b, of the model is 2.14. The base minus one is the rate of increase.
$b - 1 = 2.14 - 1 = 1.14 = 114\%$

d. Since 2009 is 6 years after 2003, find $h(6)$.
$h(6) = 91(2.14)^6 = 8740.25$.
If revenue continues at 2.14 times the revenue of the previous year, revenue from ring tones will be $8.74 billion in 2009.

e. No, each year's revenue will not continue to be 2.14 times the revenue of the previous year. According to the model, revenue from ring tones will have passed $724 million by 2006.
Find $h(6)$ when $h = 724$.
$724 = 91b^6$
$b = 1.41$
The base, b, of the model is 1.41. The base minus one is the rate of increase.

$b - 1 = 1.41 - 1 = 0.41 = 41\%$
If revenue from ring tones will be $724 million in 2009, then revenue will grow by 41% per year, which is 1.41 times the previous year's revenue.

7. a. Complete a table for $D(t)$, assuming that the number of subscribers increases by 60% per year.

t (years)	$D(t)$ (thousands of subscribers)
0	194
1	194(1.6) = 310.4
2	310.4(1.6) = 496.64
3	496.64(1.6) ≈ 794.62
4	794.62(1.6) ≈ 1,271.39

For every increase in t of 1, $D(t)$ is multiplied by 1.6. $D(t)$ is exponential with base 1.6 and y-intercept 194. The equation is $D(t) = 194(1.6)^t$.

b. Complete a table for $S(t)$, assuming that the number of subscribers increases by 190% per year.

t (years)	$S(t)$ (thousands of subscribers)
0	15
1	15(2.9) = 43.5
2	43.5(2.9) = 126.15
3	126.15(2.9) ≈ 365.84
4	365.84(2.9) ≈ 1,060.94

For every increase in t of 1, $S(t)$ is multiplied by 2.9. $S(t)$ is exponential with base 2.9 and y-intercept 15. The equation is $S(t) = 15(2.9)^t$.

c.

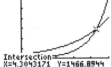

Intersection
X=4.3043171 Y=1466.8944
It means that the number of stand-alone subscribers will pass the number of DirectTV® subscribers in about 4 years, or 2005.

9. a. Complete a table for $f(t)$, assuming 8% interest compounded annually.

t (years)	$f(t)$ ($)

0	3000
1	3000(1.08) = 3240
2	3240(1.08) = 3499.20
3	3499(1.08) ≈ 3799.14

As the value of t increases by 1, the value of $f(t)$ is multiplied by 1.08. $f(t)$ is exponential with base 1.08 and y-intercept 3000. The equation is $f(t) = 3000(1.08)^t$.

b. The base, b, of the model is 1.08. The base minus one is the interest rate.
$b - 1 = 1.08 - 1 = 0.08 = 8\%$

c. The coefficient, a, is the y-intercept. In this model, it is the initial amount invested, $3000.

d. $f(15) = 3000(1.08)^{15} \approx 9516.51$
In 15 years, the account's value will be $9516.51.

11. a. Complete the table for $f(t)$.

t	$f(t)$ ($)
0	4000
6	4000(2) = 4000(2)^1
12	4000(2)(2) = 4000(2)^2
18	4000(2)(2)(2) = 4000(2)^3
t	$4000(2)^{t/6}$

As the value of t increases by 6, the value of $f(t)$ is multiplied by 2. $f(t)$ is exponential with base 2, has a y-intercept of 4000, and an exponent $\dfrac{t}{6}$ which allows t to remain in years even though the doubling occurs every 6 years. The equation is $f(t) = 4000(2)^{t/6}$.

b. $f(20) = 4000(2)^{20/6} \approx 40,317.47$
In 20 years, the investment will be worth $40,317.47.

13. The first 3 years could be modeled using an exponential function with base 1.06 and y-intercept 5000. The equation is $f(t) = 5000(1.06)^t$. After 3 years, there would be $f(3) = 5000(1.06)^3 = \$5955.08$ in the account. Then, all of this money is put into an account earning 8% interest (compounded annually) for 5 years. This can be modeled using an exponential function with base 1.08 and y-intercept 5955.08. The equation is $g(t) = 5955.08(1.08)^t$. After 5 years, there will be $g(5) = 5955.08(1.08)^5 = \$8749.97$. This is the value of the investment after 8 years.

15. **a.** Complete a table for $g(t)$ based on the assumption that the sales are cut in half each year.

t (years)	$g(t)$ (sales)
0	984
1	492
2	246
3	123
4	61.5

When the value of t increases by 1, the value of $g(t)$ is multiplied by 0.5. $g(t)$ is exponential with base 0.5 and y-intercept 984. The equation is $g(t) = 984(0.5)^t$.

b. The coefficient, a, is the s-intercept. In this model, it is the number of new textbooks sold in 2003, which is 984.

c. $g(3) = 984(0.5)^3 = 123$
In this situation, it means that the college bookstore will sell 123 new textbooks in 2006.

d. The half-life of new textbook sales is 1 year, as textbook sales are half of the previous year's sales.

17. **a.** As the value of t increases by 1600, the value of $f(t)$ is multiplied by $\dfrac{1}{2}$. $f(t)$ is exponential with base $\dfrac{1}{2}$, a y-intercept of 100, and an exponent $\dfrac{t}{1600}$ which allows t to remain in years even though the halving occurs every 1600 years. The equation is
$$f(t) = 100\left(\frac{1}{2}\right)^{t/1600}$$

b.
$$f(100) = 100\left(\frac{1}{2}\right)^{100/1600} = 95.76$$
This means that after 100 years, 95.76% of

the radium will remain.

c.
$$f(3200) = 100\left(\frac{1}{2}\right)^{3200/1600} = 25$$

This means that after 3200 years, 25% of the radium will remain. This result can be found without using the equation. We know that after 1600 years, one half of the radium will remain. In an additional 1600 years (for a total of 3200 years), one half of the one half of the radium will remain. We know that
$$\frac{1}{2} \cdot \frac{1}{2} = \frac{1}{4} \text{ or } 25\% \text{ will remain.}$$

19. **a.** As the value of t increases by 7.56, the value of $f(t)$ is multiplied by $\dfrac{1}{2}$. $f(t)$ is exponential with base $\dfrac{1}{2}$, a y-intercept of 100, and an exponent $\dfrac{t}{7.56}$ which allows t to remain in days even though the halving occurs every 7.56 days. The equation is
$$f(t) = 100\left(\frac{1}{2}\right)^{t/7.56}.$$

b.
$$f(3) = 100\left(\frac{1}{2}\right)^{3/7.56} = 75.95$$

This means that after 3 days, 75.95% of the iodine-131 will remain.

c.

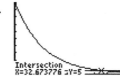

Intersection
X=32.673776 ;Y=5
A patient can safely spend a lot of time near a child after 33 days.

21. As the value of t increases by 6, the value of $f(t)$ is multiplied by $\dfrac{1}{2}$. $f(t)$ is exponential with base $\dfrac{1}{2}$, a y-intercept of 80, and an exponent $\dfrac{t}{6}$. The equation is $f(t) = 80\left(\dfrac{1}{2}\right)^{t/6}$.
$$f(14) = 80\left(\frac{1}{2}\right)^{14/6} = 15.87$$

After 14 hours, 15.87 milligrams of caffeine will remain in the bloodstream.

23. a. The graph passes through $p = 50$ when $t = 10$. So, the half-life of the element is 10 years.

b. $f(t)$ is exponential with base $\frac{1}{2}$, a y-intercept of 100, and an exponent $\frac{t}{10}$. The equation is $f(t) = 100\left(\frac{1}{2}\right)^{t/10}$.

$$f(40) = 100\left(\frac{1}{2}\right)^{40/10} = 6.25$$

After 40 years, 6.25% of the element will remain in the tank.

25. $f(t)$ is exponential with base b, a y-intercept of 0.08, and an exponent t. The equation is $f(t) = 0.08b^t$. When $t = 4$, $f(4) = 1.2$. Solve for b.

$$f(4) = 0.08b^4$$
$$0.08b^4 = 1.2$$
$$b^4 = 15$$
$$b = 1.97$$
$$f(11) = 0.08(1.97)^{11} = 138.75$$

Sales of MP3 players will reach $138.75 billion in 2011.

27. $f(t)$ is exponential with base b, a y-intercept of 1, and an exponent t. The equation is $f(t) = b^t$.

When $t = 23$, $f(23) = 3000$. Solve for b.

$$f(23) = b^{23}$$
$$b^{23} = 3000$$
$$b = 1.42$$
$$f(29) = 1.42^{29} = 26,083.267$$

There will be 26,083 restaurants in 2010.

29. Decrease the base, b, of the model to slow the growth of the function so that it will pass through the middle of the data points.

31. a.

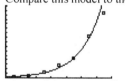

Use an exponential function to describe the data since the data points appear to "bend upwards."

b. Use an exponential regression.

```
ExpReg
 y=a*b^x
 a=1.203536121
 b=1.016213738
```

The equation is $f(t) = 1.20(1.0162)^t$.

c. $a = 1.20$

This is the p-intercept of the function. It corresponds to the world population of 1.20 billion people in the year 1900.

d. $f(110) = 1.20(1.0162)^{110} = 7.029$

This means that the world population will be 7.029 billion in the year 2010.

33. a.

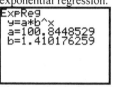

The data points appear to bend upwards, so model with an exponential function. Use an exponential regression.

```
ExpReg
 y=a*b^x
 a=100.8448529
 b=1.410176259
```

The equation is $f(t) = 100.84(1.41)^t$.
Compare this model to the data.

The model appears to fit the data well.

b. The rate of growth is the base, b, minus 1.
$b - 1 = 1.41 - 1 = 0.41$, or 41% growth per year.

c. $f(20) = 100.84(1.41)^{20} = 97,278.102$

There will be 97,278 Starbucks stores in the year 2010.

d.

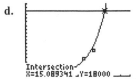

Intersection
X=15.089341 Y=18000

In 2005, there were 18,000 Starbucks stores.

35. a.

The data points appear to bend upwards, so model with an exponential function. Use an exponential regression.

ExpReg
y=a*b^x
a=.6601925687
b=1.095704606

The equation is $g(t) = 0.66(1.096)^t$.

b. $a = 0.66$

This is the g-intercept of the function. It corresponds to the cost of insurance for a newborn child. Model breakdown has occurred,

c. $b = 1.096$

This means that the insurance rate increases by a factor of 1.096 for every year of the faculty member's age.

d. $g(47) = 0.66(1.096)^{47} = 49.05$

It means that a 47-year-old faculty member should pay $49.05 per month in insurance rates.
However, the actual rate, according to the table, is $46.00.

e. Men would pay higher monthly rates because there is a higher likelihood that the man will die at a younger age than a woman.

37. a.

Year	Population	Population Ratio
1790	3.9	
1800	5.3	1.36
1810	7.2	1.36
1820	9.6	1.33
1830	12.9	1.34
1840	17.1	1.33
1850	23.2	1.36
1860	31.4	1.35

b. The ratios stay approximately the same, with the average being about 1.35.

c. It is better to use an exponential model. The populations appear to be increasing by a constant multiplicative factor.

d. As the value of t (years) increases by 10, the value of $f(t)$ (population) is multiplied by approximately 1.35. Thus, the base is about $1.35^{1/10} \approx 1.03$, the y-intercept is 3.94, and the exponent is t. The equation is
$f(t) = 3.94(1.03)^t$.

e.

Year	Population	Population Ratio
1860	31.4	
1870	39.8	1.27
1880	50.2	1.26
1890	62.9	1.25
1900	76.0	1.21

f. It is not likely that f gives reasonable population estimates after 1860. The population ratio changes from approximately 1.35 to 1.25. This indicates that model breakdown may occur in years after 1860.

g. $f(216) = 3.94(1.03)^{216} \approx 2335.3$

The model predicts that the population of the United States was approximately 2335.3 million in the year 2006. The actual population was 298.5 million. The error in the estimate is 2335.3 – 298.5 = 2036.8 million.

39. a. Draw a graph of f.

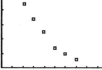

Use a regression model to draw a graph of r.
$r(t) = 113.04(0.96)^t$

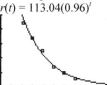

Answers will vary for model f.

b. $r(26) = 113.04(0.96)^{26} = 39.1$
This means that 39.1% of 26-year-old adults will attend a Halloween party this year.

c. $r(42) = 113.04(0.96)^{42} = 20.4$
$4,600,000 \times 0.204 = 938,400$
About 940,000 adults aged 42 years old plan to attend a Halloween party this year.

d. The *p*-intercept is 113.04, which would mean that 113% of newborns would attend a Halloween party this year. Of course, this is not possible.

e. $b = 0.96$
As an adult ages, there is less likelihood that he or she will attend a Halloween party.

41. If $f(t) = ab^t$, where $a > 0$, models a quantity at time *t*, then the percent rate of change is constant. In particular, if $b > 1$, then the quantity grows exponentially at a rate of $b - 1$ percent (in decimal form) per unit of time. If $0 < b < 1$, then the quantity decays exponentially at a rate of $1 - b$ percent (in decimal form) per unit of time.

43. a. $C(t) = 800(1.03)^t$

b. $S(t) = 24t + 800$

c. $C(1) = 800(1.03)^1 = 824$
$C(2) = 800(1.03)^2 = 848.72$
$S(1) = 800(1 + 0.03(1)) = 824$
$S(2) = 800(1 + 0.03(2)) = 848$
$C(1)$ and $S(1)$ are equal because they are both $800(1.03)$. However, $C(2) = 800(1.0609)$, whereas $S(2) = 800(1.06)$.

d. $C(20) = 800(1.03)^{20} = 1444.89$
$S(20) = 800(1 + 0.03(20)) = 1280$
For $C(20)$, interest has compounded for 20 years, whereas for $S(20)$ simple interest has accumulated for 20 years. That is why $C(20)$ is much higher than $S(20)$.

45. a.

A linear function is better as the scattergram shows a relatively straight line.

b. Answers will vary. Choose the first and the

last points and find a linear equation that fits them. The points are (4, 19) and (24, 56), so
$m = \dfrac{56-19}{24-4} = \dfrac{37}{20} = 1.85$. Therefore, $19 = 1.85(4) + b$, so $b = 11.6$. The equation is $f(t) = 1.85t + 11.6$.

c. Answers will vary. $f(31) = 1.85(31) + 11.6 = 68.95$. In 2011, about 69% of prescription drugs will be generic.

d. Answers will vary.
$100 = 1.85t + 11.6$
$t = 47.78$
In 2028, 100% of prescription drugs will be generic. Model breakdown has likely occurred.

47. Answers may vary.
$f(x) = 2(3)^x$
$f(3) = 2(3)^3 = 54$

49. Answers may vary.
$y = 3(2)^x$

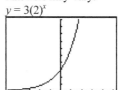

51. Answers may vary.
The growth of a population of frogs is modeled by the exponential expression $85(1.02)^t$. In 8 years, the population of frogs will be $85(1.02)^8 = 99.6$.

Chapter 4 Review Exercises

1. $\dfrac{2^{-400}}{2^{-405}} = 2^{-400-(-405)} = 2^5 = 32$

2. $\dfrac{4b^{-3}c^{12}}{16b^{-4}c^3} = \dfrac{b^{-3-(-4)}c^{12-3}}{4} = \dfrac{bc^9}{4}$

3. $\left(2b^{-5}c^{-2}\right)^3\left(3b^4c^{-6}\right)^{-2} = 2^3b^{-15}c^{-6}\,3^{-2}b^{-8}c^{12}$

$$= \frac{2^3b^{-15+(-8)}c^{-6+12}}{3^2}$$

$$= \frac{8b^{-23}c^6}{9}$$

$$= \frac{8c^6}{9b^{23}}$$

4. $\dfrac{\left(20b^{-2}c^{-9}\right)\left(27b^5c^3\right)}{\left(18b^3c^{-1}\right)\left(30b^{-1}c^{-4}\right)} = \dfrac{20\cdot27b^{-2+5}c^{-9+3}}{18\cdot30b^{3+(-1)}c^{-1+(-4)}}$

$$= \frac{540b^3c^{-6}}{540b^2c^{-5}}$$

$$= b^{3-2}c^{-6-(-5)}$$

$$= bc^{-1}$$

$$= \frac{b}{c}$$

5. $32^{4/5} = \left(32^{1/5}\right)^4 = 2^4 = 16$

6. $16^{-3/4} = \dfrac{1}{16^{3/4}} = \dfrac{1}{\left(16^{1/4}\right)^3} = \dfrac{1}{2^3} = \dfrac{1}{8}$

7. $\dfrac{b^{-1/3}}{b^{4/3}} = b^{-\frac{1}{3}-\frac{4}{3}} = b^{-\frac{5}{3}} = \dfrac{1}{b^{5/3}}$

8. $\dfrac{\left(16b^8c^{-4}\right)^{1/4}}{\left(25b^{-6}c^4\right)^{3/2}} = \dfrac{16^{1/4}b^{8(1/4)}c^{-4(1/4)}}{25^{3/2}b^{-6(3/2)}c^{4(3/2)}}$

$$= \frac{2b^2c^{-1}}{\left(25^{1/2}\right)^3b^{-9}c^6}$$

$$= \frac{2b^{2-(-9)}c^{-1-6}}{5^3}$$

$$= \frac{2b^{11}c^{-7}}{125}$$

$$= \frac{2b^{11}}{125c^7}$$

9. $\left(\dfrac{32b^2c^5}{2b^{-6}c^1}\right)^{1/4} = \left(16b^{2-(-6)}c^{5-1}\right)^{1/4}$

$$= \left(16b^8c^4\right)^{1/4}$$

$$= 16^{1/4}b^{8(1/4)}c^{4(1/4)}$$

$$= 2b^2c$$

10. $\left(8^{2/3}b^{-1/3}c^{3/4}\right)\left(64^{-1/3}b^{1/2}c^{-5/2}\right)$

$$= 8^{2/3}64^{-1/3}b^{-1/3}b^{1/2}c^{3/4}c^{-5/2}$$

$$= \left(8^{1/3}\right)^2\left(64^{1/3}\right)^{-1}b^{-\frac{1}{3}+\frac{1}{2}}c^{\frac{3}{4}+\left(-\frac{5}{2}\right)}$$

$$= 2^2 4^{-1}b^{-\frac{2}{6}+\frac{3}{6}}c^{\frac{3}{4}+\left(-\frac{10}{4}\right)}$$

$$= 4\left(\frac{1}{4}\right)b^{1/6}c^{-7/4}$$

$$= \frac{b^{1/6}}{c^{7/4}}$$

11. $b^{2n-1}b^{4n+3} = b^{(2n-1)+(4n+3)} = b^{2n-1+4n+3} = b^{6n+2}$

12. $\dfrac{b^{n/2}}{b^{n/3}} = b^{\frac{n}{2}-\frac{n}{3}} = b^{\frac{3n}{6}-\frac{2n}{6}} = b^{n/6}$

13. $3^{2x} = \left(3^2\right)^x = 9^x$

14. $f(-2) = 3(5)^{-2} = \dfrac{3}{5^2} = \dfrac{3}{25}$

15. $g(a+2) = 6^{a+2} = 6^a\cdot6^2 = 36\cdot6^a$

16. $f\left(\dfrac{1}{2}\right) = 49^{1/2} = 7$

17. $g\left(-\dfrac{3}{4}\right) = 2(81)^{-3/4} = \dfrac{2}{81^{3/4}} = \dfrac{2}{\left(81^{1/4}\right)^3} = \dfrac{2}{3^3} = \dfrac{2}{27}$

18. $4.4487\times10^7 = 4.4487\cdot10,000,000$
$$= 44,487,000$$

19. $3.85\times10^{-5} = 3.85\cdot\dfrac{1}{100,000}$
$$= 0.0000385$$

20. $54,000,000 = 5.4\times10^7$

21. $-0.00897 = -8.97\times10^{-3}$

22. $f(x) = 2(3)^x$

x	$f(x)$
-1	$\dfrac{2}{3}$
0	2

126

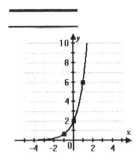

23. $h(x) = -3(2)^x$

x	$h(x)$
-1	-1.5
0	-3
1	-6
2	-12

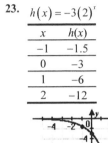

Domain: All real numbers
Range: $y < 0$

24. $g(x) = 12\left(\dfrac{1}{2}\right)^x$

x	$g(x)$
-1	24
0	12
1	6
2	3

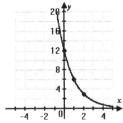

Domain: All real numbers
Range: $y > 0$

25. $3.9b^7 - 283.5$
$b^7 = 72.69$
$b = 72.69^{1/7}$
$b \approx 1.84$

26. $5b^4 - 13 = 67$
$5b^4 = 80$
$b^4 = 16$
$b = \pm(16)^{1/4}$
$b = \pm 2$

27.
$$\frac{1}{3}b^2 - \frac{1}{5} = \frac{2}{3}$$
$$15\left(\frac{1}{3}b^2 - \frac{1}{5}\right) = 15\left(\frac{2}{3}\right)$$
$$5b^2 - 3 = 10$$
$$5b^2 = 13$$
$$b^2 = \frac{13}{5}$$
$$b = \pm\left(\frac{13}{5}\right)^{1/2}$$
$$b \approx \pm 1.61$$

28. $f(x)$ is linear. As x increases by 1, $f(x)$ decreases by 4. The linear equation is $f(x) = -4x + 34$.
$g(x)$ is exponential. As x increases by 1, $g(x)$ is multiplied by 3. The exponential equation is $g(x) = \dfrac{5}{3}(3)^x$.

$h(x)$ does not appear to be linear or exponential.
$k(x)$ is exponential. As x increases by 1, $k(x)$ is multiplied by $\dfrac{1}{2}$. The exponential equation is

$k(x) = 192\left(\dfrac{1}{2}\right)^x$.

29. $f(4) = 18$

30. When $k(x) = 6$, $x = 5$.

31. $(0, 2)$ and $(5, 3)$
The y-intercept is $(0, 2)$, and the equation is of the form $y = 2b^x$. Substitute 5 for x and 3 for y to find b.

$3 = 2b^5$

$b^5 = \dfrac{3}{2}$

$b = \left(\dfrac{3}{2}\right)^{1/5}$

$b \approx 1.08$

The equation is $y = 2(1.08)^x$.

32. (3, 30) and (9, 7)

We can form a system of equations since both points satisfy $y = a(b)^x$.

$30 = ab^3$

$7 = ab^9$

Combining the two equations yields the following.

$\dfrac{7}{30} = \dfrac{ab^9}{ab^3}$

$\dfrac{7}{30} = b^6$

$b = \left(\dfrac{7}{30}\right)^{1/6}$

$b \approx 0.78$

Use b and one of the points to solve for a. Substitute 3 for x and 30 for y.

$30 \approx a(0.78)^3$

$a \approx \dfrac{30}{(0.78)^3}$

$a \approx 62.11$

The equation of the curve is $y = 62.11(0.78)^x$.

33. First, increase the value of the coefficient a to raise the y-intercept until it matches the data point at $t = 0$. Then, decrease the value of the base b to slow the increase of the function until it passes through the middle of the data points.

34. a. For every increase of t by 1, $f(t)$ is multiplied by 1.07. $f(t)$ is exponential with base 1.07. Since \$2000 is the initial investment, $a = 2000$. The equation is $f(t) = 2000(1.07)^t$.

b. $f(5) = 2000(1.07)^5 = 2805.10$

The value of the account after 5 years will be \$2805.10.

35. a. Since sales double every year, $g(t)$ must be exponential with base 2 and exponent t. In the first year, total sales were \$17,000, so let $a = 17$. The equation is of the form

$g(t) = 17(2)^t$.

b. $g(6) = 17(2)^6 = 1088$

In 2011, the corporation's total sales will be \$1,088,000.

36. a. For every increase in t of 5730 years, the value of $f(t)$ is multiplied by $\dfrac{1}{2}$. $f(t)$ is exponential with base $\dfrac{1}{2}$ and exponent $\dfrac{t}{5730}$. Since at time $t = 0$, 100% of the carbon-14 remains, $a = 100$. The equation is

$f(t) = 100\left(\dfrac{1}{2}\right)^{t/5730}$.

b. $f(100) = 100\left(\dfrac{1}{2}\right)^{100/5730} \approx 98.80$

After 100 years, 98.8% of the carbon-14 remains in the tank.

37.

We know that $a = 121$.

Use $t = 15$ and $f(15) = 996$ to solve for b.

$996 = 121b^{15}$

$b^{15} = 8.23$

$b = 1.15$

Solve for t = 21 (2011).

$f(21) = 121(1.15)^{21} = 2277.4$

The ad revenue for Latino newspapers will be \$2277.4 million, or \$2.277 billion, in 2011.

38. a.

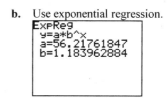

Since the data seem to lie in an upward curve, use an exponential model.

b. Use exponential regression.

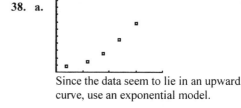

The equation is $f(t) = 56.22(1.184)^t$.

c. The coefficient a is 56.22. This means that there were approximately 56 stores in 1990.

d. The base b is 1.184. This means that the number of Kohl's stores is increasing by 18.4% per year.

e. $f(12) = 56.22(1.184)^{12} = 426.69$
   In 2002, there were approximately 427 Kohl's stores.

39. a.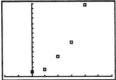

   Use an exponential regression.
   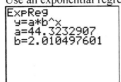

   The equation is $f(t) = 44.32(2.01)^t$.

   b. $f(15) = 44.32(2.01)^{15} = 1,565,096$
      The number of lawsuits filed in 2008 will be approximately 1.57 million.

   c. If 10% of the cases go to court, $10\% \cdot 1.57$ million $= 0.157$ million. Of these, half are defeated, so $0.157 \cdot \dfrac{1}{2} = 0.0785$ million or 78,500. If the tobacco companies pay \$10 million per lost case, the total pay out will be 78,500(\$10 million) $= \$785$ billion.

   d. No, the tobacco industry will pay much more with this strategy.

Chapter 4 Test

1. $32^{2/5} = \left(32^{1/5}\right)^2 = 2^2 = 4$

2. $-8^{-4/3} = \dfrac{1}{-8^{4/3}} = \dfrac{1}{-\left(8^{1/3}\right)^4} = \dfrac{1}{-(2)^4} = -\dfrac{1}{16}$

3. $\left(2b^3c^8\right)^3 = 2^3 b^{3\cdot3} c^{8\cdot3} = 8b^9 c^{24}$

4. $\left(\dfrac{4b^{-3}c}{25b^5 c^{-9}}\right)^0 = 1$

5. $\dfrac{b^{1/2}}{b^{1/3}} = b^{\frac{1}{2}-\frac{1}{3}} = b^{\frac{3}{6}-\frac{2}{6}} = b^{1/6}$

6. $\dfrac{25b^{-9}c^{-8}}{35b^{-10}c^{-3}} = \dfrac{5b^{-9-(-10)}c^{-8-(-3)}}{7}$

   $= \dfrac{5bc^{-5}}{7}$

   $= \dfrac{5b}{7c^5}$

7. $\left(\dfrac{6b\left(b^3 c^{-2}\right)}{3b^2 c^5}\right)^2 = \left(\dfrac{2bb^3 c^{-2}}{b^2 c^5}\right)^2$

   $= \left(2b^{1+3-2}c^{-2-5}\right)^2$

   $= \left(2b^2 c^{-7}\right)^2$

   $= 2^2 b^{2\cdot2} c^{-7\cdot2}$

   $= \dfrac{4b^4}{c^{14}}$

8. $\dfrac{\left(25b^8 c^{-6}\right)^{3/2}}{\left(7b^{-2}\right)\left(2c^3\right)^{-1}} = \dfrac{25^{3/2}2b^{8(3/2)}b^2 c^{-6(3/2)}c^3}{7}$

   $= \dfrac{\left(25^{1/2}\right)^3 2b^{12}b^2 c^{-9}c^3}{7}$

   $= \dfrac{5^3 \cdot 2b^{12+2}c^{-9+3}}{7}$

   $= \dfrac{125\cdot 2b^{14}c^{-7}}{7}$

   $= \dfrac{250b^{14}}{7c^7}$

9. $8^{x/3}2^{x+3} = \left(2^3\right)^{x/3}2^{x+3}$

   $= 2^x 2^{x+3}$

   $= 2^{2x+3}$

   $= 2^{2x}2^3$

   $= 8\left(2^2\right)^x$

   $= 8(4)^x$

10. $f(-2) = 4^{-2} = \dfrac{1}{4^2} = \dfrac{1}{16}$

11. $f\left(-\dfrac{3}{2}\right) = 4^{-3/2} = \dfrac{1}{4^{3/2}} = \dfrac{1}{\left(4^{1/2}\right)^3} = \dfrac{1}{2^3} = \dfrac{1}{8}$

12. $f(x) = -5(2)^x$

x	$f(x)$
-1	-2.5
0	-5
1	-10
2	-20

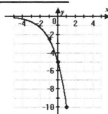

The domain is all real numbers. The range is all negative real numbers.

13. $f(x) = 18\left(\dfrac{1}{3}\right)^x$

x	$g(x)$
-1	54
0	18
1	6
2	2
3	$2/3$

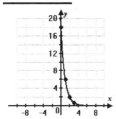

The domain is all real numbers. The range is all positive real numbers.

14. Answers may vary. One example is as follows.

$f(x) = 2\left(\dfrac{2}{3}\right)^x$ $h(x) = 3(2)^x$

$g(x) = 4\left(\dfrac{9}{8}\right)^x$ $k(x) = 3\left(\dfrac{1}{2}\right)^x$

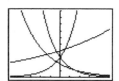

15. For every increase of 1 in t, the value of $f(t)$ is multiplied by $\dfrac{1}{2}$. $f(t)$ is exponential with base $\dfrac{1}{2}$ and y-intercept 160. $f(t) = 160\left(\dfrac{1}{2}\right)^t$.

16. $3b^6 + 5 = 84$
$3b^6 = 79$
$b^6 = 26.33$
$b = \pm(26.33)^{1/6}$
$b = \pm 1.72$

17. (0, 70) and (6, 20)
The y-intercept is (0, 70), so the equation is of the form $y = 70b^x$. Substitute 6 for x and 20 for y to find b.
$20 = 70b^6$
$\dfrac{20}{70} = b^6$
$b = \left(\dfrac{20}{70}\right)^{1/6}$
$b \approx 0.81$
The equation is $y = 70(0.81)^x$.

18. (4, 9) and (7, 50)
We can form a system of equations since both points satisfy $y = a(b)^x$.
$50 = ab^7$
$9 = ab^4$
Combining the two equations yields the following.
$\dfrac{50}{9} = \dfrac{ab^7}{ab^4}$
$\dfrac{50}{9} = b^3$
$b = \left(\dfrac{50}{9}\right)^{1/3}$
$b \approx 1.77$
Use b and one of the points to solve for a. Substitute 4 for x and 9 for y.

$9 = a(1.771)^4$

$a = \dfrac{9}{(1.771)^4}$

$a \approx 0.915$

The equation of the curve is $y = 0.915(1.771)^x$.

19. $f(0) = 6$

20. When $f(x) = 3$, $x = 1$.

21. From the graph, we see that the points, (0, 6) and (1, 3), lie on the curve. The *y*-intercept is (0, 6), so the equation is of the form $y = 6b^x$. Substitute 1 for *x* and 3 for *y* to find *b*.

$3 = 6b^1$

$b = \dfrac{1}{2}$

The equation is $y = 6\left(\dfrac{1}{2}\right)^x$.

22. a. Complete a table for $f(t)$.

t (weeks)	$f(t)$ (leaves)
0	400
1	1200
2	3600
3	10,800
4	32,400

For every increase of 1 in *t*, the value of $f(t)$ is multiplied by 3. $f(t)$ is exponential with base 3 and *y*-intercept 400. The equation is $f(t) = 400(3)^t$.

b. $f(6) = 400(3)^6 = 291,600$
There will be 291,600 leaves on the tree 6 weeks after March 1.

c. $f(52) = 400(3)^{52} \approx 2.58 \times 10^{27}$
The model predicts there will be about 2.58 x 10^{27} leaves on the tree 1 year after March 1. This is unrealistic, model breakdown has occurred.

23. a. Use an exponential regression.

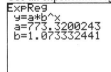

The equation is $f(t) = 773.32(1.073)^t$.

b. The base *b* is 1.073, so the percent growth per year is 7.3%.

c. $a = 773.32$ is the *y*-intercept. This means that there were approximately 773 multiple births in 1970.

d. $f(40) = 773.32(1.073)^{40} \approx 12,952.34$
The model predicts there will be about 12,952 multiple births in 2010.

Chapter 5
Logarithmic Functions

1. $f^{-1}(7) = 4$

3. $f(4) = 6$

5. $f^{-1}(4) = 5$, since $f(5) = 4$.

7.

x	$f^{-1}(x)$
2	6
4	5
6	4
8	3
10	2

9. $g(2) = 6$

11. $g^{-1}(2) = 1$, since $f(1) = 2$.

13.

x	$g^{-1}(x)$
2	1
6	2
18	3
54	4
162	5
486	6

15.

x	$f^{-1}(x)$
4	6
10	5
16	4
22	3
28	2
34	1

17. Answers may vary. Begin by creating a table of values for $f(x)$, then build a table for $f^{-1}(x)$ from that information.

x	$f(x)$
0	3
1	6
2	12
3	24
4	48

x	$f^{-1}(x)$
3	0
6	1
12	2
24	3
48	4

19. $f(3) = 3(2)^3$
$\qquad = 3(8)$
$\qquad = 24$

21. $f^{-1}(3) = 0$, since $f(0) = 3$.

23.

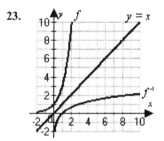

25.

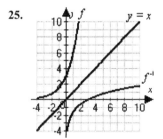

27.

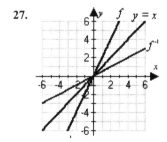

132

29.

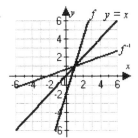

31.

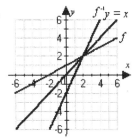

33.

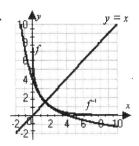

35.

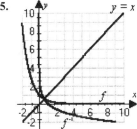

37. Since g sends 2 to 1, $g(2) = 1$.

39. Since g sends 6 to 2, g^{-1} sends 2 back to 6. So, $g^{-1}(2) = 6$.

41. Since g sends 0 to 0, g^{-1} sends 0 back to 0. So, $g^{-1}(0) = 0$.

43. Since f sends 2 to 1, $f(2) = 1$.

45. Since f sends 3 to 4, f^{-1} sends 4 back to 3. So, $f^{-1}(4) = 3$.

47.

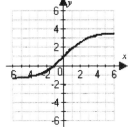

49. a. $f(t) = 0.77t - 42.90$

Replace $f(t)$ with p.

$p = 0.77t - 42.90$

Solve for t.

$p = 0.77t - 42.90$

$p + 42.90 = 0.77t$

$\dfrac{p + 42.90}{0.77} = t$

An approximate equation is
$t = 1.30p + 55.71$.

Replace t with $f^{-1}(p)$.

$f^{-1}(p) = 1.30p + 55.71$

b. $f(100) = 0.77(100) - 42.90$

$\quad\quad = 34.10$

According to the model, in 2000, 34.1% of births were outside of marriage.

c. $f^{-1}(100) = 1.30(100) + 55.71$

$\quad\quad\quad = 185.71$

According to the inverse model, all births will be outside marriage in 2085. This is likely a model breakdown.

d. The slope of $f^{-1}(p)$ is 1.30. This means that the rate of change of p with respect to t is 1.30. According to the model f^{-1}, 1.30 years pass for each 1% increase in outside of marriage births.

51. a.

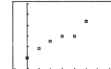

The plotted data lies mostly in a straight line. Therefore, a linear model better fits the data.

b. Using the linear regression feature, $f(t) = 6.03t + 51.10$.

c. $f(t) = 6.03t + 51.10$
Replace $f(t)$ with n.
$n = 6.03t + 51.10$
Solve for t.
$n - 51.10 = 6.03t$
$\dfrac{n - 51.10}{6.03} = t$
$0.17n - 8.47 = t$
An approximate equation is
$0.17n - 8.47 = t$.
Replace t with $f^{-1}(n)$.
$f^{-1}(n) = 0.17n - 8.47$

d. $f(t) = 6.03t + 51.10$
$115 = 6.03t + 51.10$
$\dfrac{63.9}{6.03} = \dfrac{6.03t}{6.03}$
$10.60 = t$

$2000 + 10.6 \approx 2011$.

e. $f^{-1}(n) = 0.17n - 8.47$
$f^{-1}(115) = 0.17(115) - 8.47$
$= 11.08$
$2000 + 11.08 \approx 2011$.

f. The results are the same.

53. a

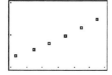

The plotted data lies mostly in a straight line. Therefore, a linear model better fits the data.

b. Using the linear regression feature,
$f(a) = 2.17a + 581.49$.

c. $f(a) = 2.17a + 581.49$
Replace $f(a)$ with c.
$c = 2.17a + 581.49$

Solve for t.
$c - 581.49 = 2.17t$
$\dfrac{c - 581.49}{2.17} = t$
$0.46c - 267.97 = t$
An approximate equation is
$0.46c - 267.97 = t$.
Replace t with $f^{-1}(a)$.
$f^{-1}(c) = 0.46c - 267.97$

d. $f^{-1}(677) = 0.46(677) - 267.97$
$= 43.45$

According to the model, the age of adults whose average credit score is 677 points is about 43 years.

e. $f^{-1}(830) = 0.46(830) - 267.97$
$= 113.83$

According to the model, the age of adults whose average credit score is 830 points is about 114 years.

f. The slope of f^{-1} is 0.46 and it represents a credit score increase by 1 point for each age increase of 0.46 years.

55. $f(x) = x + 8$
Replace $f(x)$ with y.
$y = x + 8$
Solve for x.
$y - 8 = x$
Replace x with $f^{-1}(y)$.
$f^{-1}(y) = y - 8$
Write equation in terms of x.
$f^{-1}(x) = x - 8$

57. $f(x) = -4x$
Replace $f(x)$ with y.
$y = -4x$
Solve for x.
$\dfrac{y}{-4} = x$

Replace x with $f^{-1}(y)$.

$$f^{-1}(y) = -\frac{y}{4}$$

Write equation in terms of x.

$$f^{-1}(x) = -\frac{x}{4}$$

$$= -\frac{1}{4}x$$

59. $f(x) = \dfrac{x}{7}$

Replace $f(x)$ with y.

$$y = \frac{x}{7}$$

Solve for x.

$$7y = x$$

Replace x with $f^{-1}(y)$.

$$f^{-1}(y) = 7y$$

Write equation in terms of x.

$$f^{-1}(x) = 7x$$

61. $f(x) = -6x - 2$

Replace $f(x)$ with y.

$$y = -6x - 2$$

Solve for x.

$$y + 2 = -6x$$

$$-6x = y + 2$$

$$x = \frac{y+2}{-6}$$

$$x = -\frac{1}{6}y - \frac{2}{6}$$

Replace x with $f^{-1}(y)$.

$$f^{-1}(y) = -\frac{1}{6}y - \frac{1}{3}$$

Write equation in terms of x.

$$f^{-1}(x) = -\frac{1}{6}x - \frac{1}{3}$$

63. $f(x) = 0.4x - 7.9$

Replace $f(x)$ with y.

$$y = 0.4x - 7.9$$

Solve for x.

$$f^{-1}(x) = 2.5x + 19.75$$

$$y + 7.9 = 0.4x$$

$$\frac{y+7.9}{0.4} = x$$

$$x = \frac{y}{0.4} + \frac{7.9}{0.4}$$

Replace x with $f^{-1}(y)$.

$$f^{-1}(y) = 2.5y + 19.75$$

Write equation in terms of x.

$$f^{-1}(x) = 2.5x + 19.75$$

65. $f(x) = \dfrac{7}{3}x + 1$

Replace $f(x)$ with y.

$$y = \frac{7}{3}x + 1$$

Solve for x.

$$y - 1 = \frac{7}{3}x$$

$$\frac{3}{7}(y-1) = x$$

$$x = \frac{3y-3}{7}$$

Replace x with $f^{-1}(y)$.

$$f^{-1}(y) = \frac{3}{7}y - \frac{3}{7}$$

Write equation in terms of x.

$$f^{-1}(x) = \frac{3}{7}x - \frac{3}{7}$$

67. $f(x) = -\dfrac{5}{6}x - 3$

Replace $f(x)$ with y.

$$y = -\frac{5}{6}x - 3$$

Solve for x.

$$y + 3 = -\frac{5}{6}x$$

$$-\frac{6}{5}(y+3) = x$$

$$x = \frac{-6y-18}{5}$$

Replace x with $f^{-1}(y)$.

$$f^{-1}(y) = -\frac{6}{5}y - \frac{18}{5}$$

Write equation in terms of x.

$$f^{-1}(x) = -\frac{6}{5}x - \frac{18}{5}$$

69. $f(x) = \dfrac{6x - 2}{5}$

Replace $f(x)$ with y.

$$y = \frac{6x - 2}{5}$$

Solve for x.

$$5y = 6x - 2$$

$$5y + 2 = 6x$$

$$\frac{5y + 2}{6} = x$$

$$x = \frac{5y}{6} + \frac{2}{6}$$

Replace x with $f^{-1}(y)$.

$$f^{-1}(y) = \frac{5}{6}y + \frac{1}{3}$$

Write equation in terms of x.

$$f^{-1}(x) = \frac{5}{6}x + \frac{1}{3}$$

71. $f(x) = 7 - 8(x + 1)$

Replace $f(x)$ with y.

$$y = 7 - 8(x + 1)$$

Solve for x.

$$y = 7 - 8x - 8$$

$$y = -8x - 1$$

$$y + 1 = -8x$$

$$\frac{y + 1}{-8} = x$$

$$x = -\frac{1}{8}y - \frac{1}{8}$$

Replace x with $f^{-1}(y)$.

$$f^{-1}(y) = -\frac{1}{8}y - \frac{1}{8}$$

Write equation in terms of x.

$$f^{-1}(x) = -\frac{1}{8}x - \frac{1}{8}$$

73. $f(x) = x$

Replace $f(x)$ with y.

$$y = x$$

Solve for x.

$$x = y$$

Replace x with $f^{-1}(y)$.

$$f^{-1}(y) = y$$

Write equation in terms of x.

$$f^{-1}(x) = x$$

75. $f(x) = x^3$

Replace $f(x)$ with y.

$$y = x^3$$

Solve for x.

$$\sqrt[3]{y} = x$$

Replace x with $f^{-1}(y)$.

$$f^{-1}(y) = \sqrt[3]{y} = y^{\frac{1}{3}}$$

Write equation in terms of x.

$$f^{-1}(x) = \sqrt[3]{x} \ \text{ or } f^{-1}(x) = x^{\frac{1}{3}}$$

77. a. $f(x) = 5x - 9$

Replace $f(x)$ with y.

$$y = 5x - 9$$

Solve for x.

$$\frac{y + 9}{5} = \frac{5x}{5}$$

$$\frac{1}{5}y + \frac{9}{5} = x$$

Replace x with $f^{-1}(y)$.

$$f^{-1}(y) = \frac{1}{5}y + \frac{9}{5}$$

Write equation in terms of x.

$$f^{-1}(x) = \frac{1}{5}x + \frac{9}{5}$$

b. $f(x) = 5x - 9$

$$f(4) = 5(4) - 9$$

$$= 11$$

c.
$$f^{-1}(x) - \frac{1}{5}x + \frac{9}{5}$$

$$f^{-1}(4) = \frac{1}{5}(4) + \frac{9}{5}$$

$$= \frac{13}{5}$$

79. a. $f(x) = 3x - 5$

Replace $f(x)$ with y.

$y = 3x - 5$

Solve for x.

$$\frac{y+5}{3} = \frac{3x}{3}$$

$$\frac{1}{3}y + \frac{5}{3} = x$$

Replace x with $f^{-1}(y)$.

$$f^{-1}(y) = \frac{1}{3}y + \frac{5}{3}$$

Write equation in terms of x.

$$f^{-1}(x) = \frac{1}{3}x + \frac{5}{3}$$

b. Answers may vary.

x	$f^{-1}(x)$
-2	$\frac{1}{3}(-2) + \frac{5}{3} = 1$
0	$\frac{1}{3}(0) + \frac{5}{3} = \frac{5}{3}$
1	$\frac{1}{3}(1) + \frac{5}{3} = 2$
4	$\frac{1}{3}(4) + \frac{5}{3} = 3$
7	$\frac{1}{3}(7) + \frac{5}{3} = 4$

c.

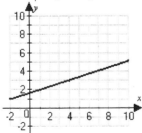

d. For each input-output pair, the output is $\frac{5}{3}$

less than $\frac{1}{3}$ times the input.

81. Answers may vary. One example follows. It makes sense that $g(x) = x - 5$ is the inverse function of $f(x) = x + 5$ because addition and subtraction are inverse operations of each other (or, 5 and -5 are additive inverses).

83. $f(x) = 3$ is not one-to-one. For example, $f(1) = 3$ and $f(2) = 3$. So, the inverse of f would send 3 to both 1 and 2, making the inverse of f not a function. Since f^{-1} is not a function, f was not invertible.

85. a. $f(x) = mx + b$

Replace $f(x)$ with y.

$y = mx + b$

Solve for x.

$y - b = mx$

$$\frac{y-b}{m} = x$$

$$x = \frac{y-b}{m}$$

$$x = \frac{1}{m}y - \frac{b}{m}$$

Replace x with $f^{-1}(y)$.

$$f^{-1}(y) = \frac{1}{m}y - \frac{b}{m}$$

Write equation in terms of x.

$$f^{-1}(x) = \frac{1}{m}x - \frac{b}{m}$$

b. The function $f(x)$ given in part a is a linear function with nonzero slope (since $m \neq 0$). The inverse function is also a linear function as its slope is nonzero ($\frac{1}{m}$ is nonzero since $m \neq 0$).

87. a

The point of intersection is (4, 5).

b. $f(x) = 2x - 3$

Replace $f(x)$ with y.

$y = 2x - 3$

Solve for x.

$$\frac{y+3}{2} = \frac{2x}{2}$$

$$\frac{1}{2}y + \frac{3}{2} = x$$

Replace x with $f^{-1}(y)$.

$$f^{-1}(y) = \frac{1}{2}y + \frac{3}{2}$$

Write equation in terms of x.

$$f^{-1}(x) = \frac{1}{2}x + \frac{3}{2}$$

c. $g(x) = \frac{1}{2}x + 3$

Replace $g(x)$ with y.

$y = \frac{1}{2}x + 3$

Solve for x.

$$2(y-3) = 2\left(\frac{1}{2}x\right)$$

$$2y - 6 = x$$

Replace x with $g^{-1}(y)$.

$g^{-1}(y) = 2y - 6$

Write equation in terms of x.

$g^{-1}(x) = 2x - 6$

d.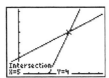

The point of intersection is (5, 4).

e. The x- and y-coordinates are exchanged. An inverse function exchanges the input and output values.

89. Multiply the first equation by 5 and the second equation by 4. Then add the equations.

$12x - 20y = 40$

$\underline{35x + 20y = 195}$

$47x = 235$

$x = 5$

Solve for y.

$3x - 5y = 10$

$3(5) - 5y = 10$

$15 - 5y = 10$

$$\frac{-5y}{-5} = \frac{-5}{-5}$$

$y = 1$

The solution is (5, 1). The two equations form a linear system in two variables.

91.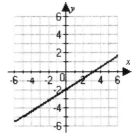

This is a linear equation in two variables.

Homework 5.2

1. $\log_9(81) = 2$, since $9^2 = 81$.

3. $\log_3(27) = 3$ since $3^3 = 27$.

5. $\log_4(256) = 4$ since $4^4 = 256$.

7. $\log_6(216) = 3$ since $6^3 = 216$.

9. $\log(100) = 2$ since $10^2 = 100$.

11. $\log_4\left(\frac{1}{4}\right) = -1$ since $4^{-1} = \frac{1}{4}$.

13. $\log_2\left(\frac{1}{8}\right) = -3$ since $2^{-3} = \frac{1}{8}$.

15. $\log\left(\frac{1}{10,000}\right) = -4$ since $10^{-4} = \frac{1}{10,000}$.

17. $\log_5(1) = 0$ since $5^0 = 1$.

19. $\log_9(9) = 1$ since $9^1 = 9$.

138

21. $\log_9(3) = \dfrac{1}{2}$ since $9^{\frac{1}{2}} = 3$.

23. $\log_8(2) = \dfrac{1}{3}$ since $8^{\frac{1}{3}} = 2$.

25. $\log_7\left(\sqrt{7}\right) = \dfrac{1}{2}$ since $7^{\frac{1}{2}} = \sqrt{7}$.

27. $\log_5\left(\sqrt[4]{5}\right) = \dfrac{1}{4}$ since $5^{\frac{1}{4}} = \sqrt[4]{5}$.

29. $\log_2(\log_2(16)) = \log_2(4)$ since $2^4 = 16$
$\qquad = 2$ since $2^2 = 4$.

31. $\log_{10}(\log_{10}(10)) = \log_{10}(1)$ since $10^1 = 10$
$\qquad = 0$ since $10^0 = 1$.

33. $\log_b(b) = 1$ since $b^1 = b$.

35. $\log_b\left(b^4\right) = 4$ since $b^4 = b^4$.

37. $\log_b\left(\dfrac{1}{b^5}\right) = -5$ since $b^{-5} = \dfrac{1}{b^5}$.

39. $\log_b\left(\sqrt{b}\right) = \dfrac{1}{2}$ since $b^{\frac{1}{2}} = \sqrt{b}$.

41. $\log_b(\log_b(b)) = \log_b(1)$ since $b^1 = b$.
$\qquad = 0$ since $b^0 = 1$.

43. $f(x) = 3^x$
$\quad f^{-1}(x) = \log_3(x)$

45. $h(x) = 10^x$
$\quad h^{-1}(x) = \log(x)$

47. $f(x) = \log_5(x)$
$\quad f^{-1}(x) = 5^x$

49. $h(x) = \log(x)$
$\quad h^{-1}(x) = 10^x$

51. $f(2) = 2^2$
$\qquad = 4$

53. $f^{-1}(2) = \log_2(2)$
$\qquad = 1$, since $2^1 = 2$.

55. $g(3) = \log_3(3)$
$\qquad = 1$

57. $g^{-1}(3) = 3^3$
$\qquad = 27$

59. $f(1) = 3$

61. $f^{-1}(1) = \log_3(1)$
$\qquad = 0$

63.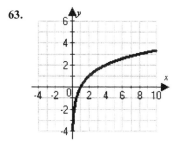

65.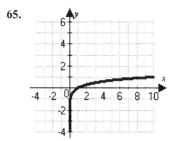

67.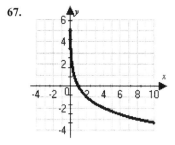

69. a

71. d

73. a.

x	$f(x) = \log_5(x)$
$\dfrac{1}{5}$	$\log_5\left(\dfrac{1}{5}\right) = -1$
1	$\log_5(1) = 0$
5	$\log_5(5) = 1$
25	$\log_5(25) = 2$
125	$\log_5(125) = 3$

b.

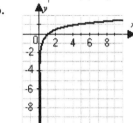

c. For each input-output pair, the output is the logarithm, base 5, of the input.

75. a. $x = 2$, since $5^2 = 25$.

b. $\log_5(25) = 2$, since $5^2 = 25$.

c. 5^x and $\log_5(x)$ are inverses of each other.

77. a.
$$R = \log\left(\frac{1.6 \times 10^9 A_0}{A_0}\right)$$
$$= \log(1.6 \times 10^9)$$
$$= 9.2$$
The Richter number for the Indian Ocean earthquake was 9.2.

b.
$$R = \log\left(\frac{6.3 \times 10^7 A_0}{A_0}\right)$$
$$= \log(6.3 \times 10^7)$$
$$= 7.8$$
The Richter number for the Mexico City earthquake was 7.8.

c.
$$\frac{1.6 \times 10^9}{6.3 \times 10^7} = 25.40$$
The ratio of the Indian Ocean earthquake's amplitude to the Mexico City earthquake's amplitude is 25.40.

79.
$$L = 10\log\left(\frac{1}{I_0}\right)$$

Sound	Intesity of Sound (w/m^2)	Decibel Reading (L)
Faintest sound heard by humans	10^{-12}	0
Whisper	10^{-10}	20
Inside a running car	10^{-8}	40
Conversation	10^{-6}	60
Noisy street corner	10^{-4}	80
Soft rock concert	10^{-2}	100
Threshold of pain	1	120

81. Answers may vary. Make a table of values for $f(x) = 5^x$, and then build a table for $f^{-1}(x)$.

x	$f(x)$
0	1
1	5
2	25
3	125
4	625

so

x	$f^{-1}(x)$
1	0
5	1
25	2
125	3
625	4

Another name for $f^{-1}(x)$ is $\log_5(x)$.

83. a.

x	$f(x) = \log_2(x)$	$g(x) = 2x$	$h(x) = 2^x$
1	0	2	2
2	1	4	4
4	2	8	16
8	3	16	256
16	4	32	65,536

b. The outputs of h are growing the fastest, followed by g.

85. Use the data points (3, 5) and (7, 89) and the exponential regression feature on a graphing calculator.

$$y = 0.58(2.05)^x$$

This is an exponential equation.

87. $4b^{2/3}c^{-5/4}\left(2b^{-1/5}c^{3/4}\right)$

$$8b^{10/15}b^{-3/15}c^{-5/4}c^{3/4}$$

$$8b^{7/15}c^{-2/4}$$

$$\frac{8b^{7/15}}{c^{1/2}}$$

This is an expression in two variables that involves exponents.

Homework 5.3

1. $\log_3(243) = 5$

$$3^5 = 243$$

3. $\log(100) = 2$

$$10^2 = 100$$

5. $\log_b(a) = c$

$$b^c = a$$

7. $\log(m) = n$

$$10^n = m$$

9. $5^3 = 125$

$$\log_5(125) = 3$$

11. $10^3 = 1000$

$$\log(1000) = 3$$

13. $y^w = x$

$$\log_y(x) = w$$

15. $10^p = q$

$$\log(q) = p$$

17. $\log_4(x) = 2$

$$4^2 = x$$

$$x = 16$$

19. $\log(x) = -2$

$$10^{-2} = x$$

$$x = \frac{1}{100}$$

$$= 0.01$$

21. $\log_4(x) = 0$

$$4^0 = x$$

$$x = 1$$

23. $\log_{27}(t) = \frac{4}{3}$

$$27^{\frac{4}{3}} = x$$

$$x = 81$$

25. $2\log_8(2x - 5) = 4$

$$\log_8(2x - 5) = 2$$

$$8^2 = 2x - 5$$

$$\frac{64 + 5}{2} = \frac{2x}{2}$$

$$\frac{69}{2} = x$$

27. $4\log_{81}(x) - 3 = -2$

$$\frac{4\log_{81}(x)}{4} = \frac{1}{4}$$

$$\log_{81}(x) = \frac{1}{4}$$

$$81^{\frac{1}{4}} = x$$

$$3 = x$$

29. $\log_2\left(\log_3(y)\right) = 3$

$$2^3 = \log_3(y)$$

$$8 = \log_3(y)$$

$$3^8 = y$$

$$6561 = y$$

31. $\log_6\left(x^3\right) = 2$

$6^2 = x^3$

$36 = x^3$

$36^{\frac{1}{3}} = x$

$3.3019 \approx x$

33. $\log_b\left(49\right) = 2$

$b^2 = 49$

$b = 49^{\frac{1}{2}}$

$b = 7$

35. $\log_b\left(8\right) = 3$

$b^3 = 8$

$b = 8^{\frac{1}{3}}$

$b = 2$

37. $\log_b\left(16\right) = 5$

$b^5 = 16$

$b = 16^{\frac{1}{5}}$

$b \approx 1.7411$

39. $4^x = 9$

$\log\left(4^x\right) = \log\left(9\right)$

$x\log\left(4\right) = \log\left(9\right)$

$x = \dfrac{\log\left(9\right)}{\log\left(4\right)}$

$x \approx 1.5850$

41. $5\left(4^x\right) = 80$

$4^x = 16$

$\log\left(4^x\right) = \log\left(16\right)$

$x\log\left(4\right) = \log\left(16\right)$

$x = \dfrac{\log\left(16\right)}{\log\left(4\right)}$

$x = 2$

43. $3.83(2.18^x) = 170.91$

$2.18^x = \dfrac{170.91}{3.83}$

$\log\left(2.18^x\right) = \log\left(\dfrac{170.91}{3.83}\right)$

$x\log\left(2.18\right) = \log\left(\dfrac{170.91}{3.83}\right)$

$x = \dfrac{\log\left(\dfrac{170.91}{3.83}\right)}{\log\left(2.18\right)}$

$x \approx 4.8738$

45. $8 + 5\left(2^x\right) = 79$

$5\left(2^x\right) = 71$

$2^x = \dfrac{71}{5}$

$\log\left(2^x\right) = \log\left(\dfrac{71}{5}\right)$

$x\log\left(2\right) = \log\left(\dfrac{71}{5}\right)$

$x = \dfrac{\log\left(\dfrac{71}{5}\right)}{\log\left(2\right)}$

$x \approx 3.8278$

47. $2^{4x+5} = 17$

$\log\left(2^{4x+5}\right) = \log\left(17\right)$

$\left(4x + 5\right)\log\left(2\right) = \log\left(17\right)$

$4x + 5 = \dfrac{\log\left(17\right)}{\log\left(2\right)}$

$4x = \dfrac{\log\left(17\right)}{\log\left(2\right)} - 5$

$x = \dfrac{\left(\dfrac{\log\left(17\right)}{\log\left(2\right)} - 5\right)}{4}$

$x \approx -0.2281$

49.
$$6(3)^x - 7 = 85 + 4(3)^x$$
$$6(3)^x - 4(3)^x = 92$$
$$\frac{2(3)^x}{2} = \frac{92}{2}$$
$$(3)^x = 46$$
$$x\log(3) = \log(46)$$
$$x = \frac{\log(46)}{\log(3)}$$
$$x \approx 3.4850$$

51.
$$\log\left(4^{5p-1}\right) = \log(100)$$
$$(5p-1)\log(4) = 2$$
$$5p - 1 = \frac{2}{\log(4)}$$
$$5p = \frac{2}{\log(4)} + 1$$
$$p = \frac{\left(\frac{2}{\log(4)} + 1\right)}{5}$$
$$p \approx 0.8644$$

53. $3^x = -8$
No real-number solution. 3 raised to any power will *always* be positive.

55. $\log_4(x) = 3$
$$4^3 = x$$
$$x = 64$$

57. $3(4)^t + 15 = 406$
$$\frac{3(4)^t}{3} = \frac{391}{3}$$
$$\log(4^t) = \log\left(\frac{391}{3}\right)$$
$$t = \frac{\log\left(\frac{391}{3}\right)}{\log(4)}$$
$$t = 3.5130$$

59. $\log_b(73) = 5$
$$b^5 = 73$$
$$b = 73^{\frac{1}{5}}$$
$$b \approx 2.3586$$

61. $3\log_{27}(y-1) = 2$
$$\log_{27}(y-1) = \frac{2}{3}$$
$$27^{\frac{2}{3}} = y - 1$$
$$9 + 1 = y$$
$$10 = y$$

63.
$$3(2)^{4x-2} = 83$$
$$\log\left(2^{4x-2}\right) = \log\left(\frac{83}{3}\right)$$
$$(4x-2)\log(2) = \log\left(\frac{83}{3}\right)$$
$$4x - 2 = \frac{\log\left(\frac{83}{3}\right)}{\log(2)}$$
$$\frac{4x}{4} = \frac{\frac{\log\left(\frac{83}{3}\right)}{\log(2)} + 2}{4}$$
$$x \approx 1.6975$$

65. $x = 1$ because $y = 2^x$ and $y = 4\left(\frac{1}{2}\right)^x$ intersect at $x = 1$.

67. $x = 0$ and $x \approx 3.7$ because $y = 4\left(\frac{1}{2}\right)^x$ intersects $y = 4 - x$ in two points with the given x-values.

69. $x = 2$ because $y = 4\left(\frac{1}{2}\right)^x$ is 1 when $x = 2$.

71. Graph $y = 3^x$ and $y = 5 - x$. Then use the intersect feature on a graphing calculator. The x-coordinate, 1.2122, is the approximate solution of the equation $3^x = 5 - x$.

73. Graph $y = 7\left(\dfrac{1}{2}\right)^x$ and $y = 2x$. Then use the intersect feature on a graphing calculator. The x-coordinate, 1.3618, is the approximate solution of the equation

$$7\left(\frac{1}{2}\right)^x = 2x.$$

75. Graph $y = \log(x+1)$ and $y = 3 - \dfrac{2}{5}x$. Then use the intersect feature on a graphing calculator. The x-coordinate, 5.4723, is the approximate solution of the equation

$$\log(x+1) = 3 - \frac{2}{5}x.$$

77. 2. Functions representing each side of the equation have the same y-value when $x = 2$.

79. 5. Functions representing each side of the equation have the same y-value when $x = 5$.

81. (3, 1.5). Functions representing each equation in the system have the same x- and y-values at (3, 1.5).

83. Line 3 includes an error.

$\log[3(8^x)] \neq x\log[3(8)]$

The power property for logarithms would only work in this case if *both* the 3 and the 8 were raised to the x power. The first step the student should have made was to divide both sides of the equation by 3.

$3\left(8^x\right) = 7$

$8^x = \dfrac{7}{3}$

Then take the log of both sides and solve for x.

$\log\left(8^x\right) = \log\left(\dfrac{7}{3}\right)$

$x\log(8) = \log\left(\dfrac{7}{3}\right)$

$x = \dfrac{\log\left(\dfrac{7}{3}\right)}{\log(8)}$

$x \approx 0.4075$

85. $ab^x = c$

$ab^x = c$

$b^x = \dfrac{c}{a}$

$\log\left(b^x\right) = \log\left(\dfrac{c}{a}\right)$

$x\log(b) = \log\left(\dfrac{c}{a}\right)$

$x = \dfrac{\log\left(\dfrac{c}{a}\right)}{\log(b)}$

87. $ab^{kx} + d = c$

$ab^{kx} = c - d$

$b^{kx} = \dfrac{c-d}{a}$

$\log\left(b^{kx}\right) = \log\left(\dfrac{c-d}{a}\right)$

$kx\log(b) = \log\left(\dfrac{c-d}{a}\right)$

$kx = \dfrac{\log\left(\dfrac{c-d}{a}\right)}{\log(b)}$

$x = \dfrac{\log\left(\dfrac{c-d}{a}\right)}{k\log(b)}$

89. $f(4) = 4^{(4)} = 256$

91. $4^x = 3$

$\log\left(4^x\right) = \log(3)$

$x\log(4) = \log(3)$

$x = \dfrac{\log(3)}{\log(4)}$

$x \approx 0.7925$

93. $g(8) = \log_2(8)$

$\quad = 3$

95. $\log_2(a) = 5$

$2^5 = a$

$a = 32$

97. a. False. $\dfrac{\log_2(4)}{\log_2(16)} \neq \dfrac{4}{16}$ because we cannot divide out logarithms of different numbers.

$$\dfrac{\log_2(4)}{\log_2(16)} = \dfrac{2}{4}$$

$$= \dfrac{1}{2}$$

$$\neq \dfrac{4}{16}$$

b. False. We cannot divide out logarithms of different numbers.

$$\dfrac{\log_3(1)}{\log_3(27)} = \dfrac{0}{3}$$

$$= 0$$

$$\neq \dfrac{1}{27}$$

c. False. We cannot divide out logarithms of different numbers.

$$\dfrac{\log(1000)}{\log(10000)} = \dfrac{3}{4}$$

$$\neq \dfrac{1000}{10000}$$

d. False. We cannot divide out logarithms of different numbers.

99. a. The part of the line $y = 1$ where $x > 0$.

b. We cannot take the logarithm of a negative number.

c.
$$f(x) = \log(x^3) - 3\log(x) + 1$$
$$= 3\log(x) - 3\log(x) + 1$$
$$= 1$$

101. Answers may vary. One example follows.
For $x > 0$, $b > 0$, and $b \neq 1$,

$$\log_b(x^p) = p\log_b(x)$$

This does not imply $x^p = px$.

$$x^p \overset{?}{=} px$$
$$\log(x^p) \overset{?}{=} \log(px)$$
$$p\log(x) \neq \log(px)$$

103.
$$5(3p - 7) - 9p = -4p + 23$$
$$15p - 35 - 9p = -4p + 23$$
$$10p = 58$$
$$p = \dfrac{58}{10}$$
$$p = \dfrac{29}{5}$$

105.
$$5b^6 - 88 = 56$$
$$\dfrac{5b^6}{5} = \dfrac{144}{5}$$
$$b = \left(\dfrac{144}{5}\right)^{\frac{1}{6}}$$
$$b \approx \pm 1.7508$$

107.
$$\dfrac{3}{8}r = \dfrac{5}{6}r - \dfrac{2}{3}$$
$$24\left(\dfrac{3}{8}r\right) = 24\left(\dfrac{5}{6}r - \dfrac{2}{3}\right)$$
$$9r = 20r - 16$$
$$\dfrac{-11r}{-11} = \dfrac{-16}{-11}$$
$$r = \dfrac{16}{11}$$

109.
$$3(2)^{4x-2} = 83$$

$$\log_2(x) = -5 \qquad \log_2(x) = -5$$
$$2^{-5} = x \qquad\qquad 2^{-5} = x$$
$$\dfrac{1}{32} = x \qquad\qquad 0.03125 \approx x$$

This is a logarithmic equation in one variable.

111.

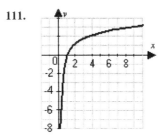

This is a logarithmic function.

Homework 5.4

1. a. $V = f(t)$

We know we can model the situation well by using an exponential model $f(t) = ab^t$. The

V-intercept is (0, 2000), so $a = 2000$ and $f(t) = 2000b^t$. Since the interest rate is 5%, the base must be 1.05, so
$f(t) = 2000(1.05)^t$.

h. The V-intercept is (0, 2000). The original ($t = 0$) value in the account is $2000.

c. $f(t) = 2000(1.05)^t$
$f(5) = 2000(1.05)^5$
$= 2552.56$
In 5 years, the investment will be worth $2,552.56.

d. $2000(1.05)^t = 3000$
$1.05^t = 1.5$
$\log(1.05^t) = \log(1.5)$
$t\log(1.05) = \log(1.5)$
$t = \dfrac{\log(1.5)}{\log(1.05)}$
$t \approx 8.3104$
The balance will be $3000 after 8.31 years.

3. $f(t) = 9300(1.06)^t$
$9300(1.06)^t = 13700$
$1.06^t \approx 1.473$
$\log(1.06^t) = \log(1.473)$
$t\log(1.06) = \log(1.473)$
$t = \dfrac{\log(1.473)}{\log(1.06)}$
≈ 6.65
The balance will be $13,700 after 6.65 years.

5. $f(t) = 6000(1.10)^t$
$6000(1.10)^t = 12000$
$1.10^t = 2$
$\log(1.10^t) = \log(2)$
$t\log(1.10) = \log(2)$
$t = \dfrac{\log(2)}{\log(1.10)}$
≈ 7.27
The balance will double after 7.27 years. The interest is compounded annually so that interest on previous year's interest earnings also grow at 10% per year.

7. $f(t) = 0.18(1.13)^t$

$0.18(1.13)^t = 7$
$1.13^t \approx 38.89$
$\log(1.13^t) = \log(38.89)$
$t\log(1.13) = \log(38.89)$
$t = \dfrac{\log(38.89)}{\log(1.13)}$
$t \approx 29.95$
The annual production of ethanol reaches 7 billion in 1980 + 30 = 2010.

9. a. We know we can model the situation well by using an exponential model $f(t) = ab^t$. Let $p = f(t)$, the total number of people. The p-intercept is (0, 30), and the base is 3.
$f(t) = 30(3)^t$

b. $f(t) = 30(3)^t$
$f(8) = 30(3)^8$
$= 196830$
The total number of Americans who have heard the rumor after 8 days is 196,830.

c. $30(3)^t = 299,000,000$
$(3)^t = \dfrac{299,000,000}{30}$
$\log(3^t) = \log\left(\dfrac{299,000,000}{30}\right)$
$t\log(3) = \log\left(\dfrac{299,000,000}{30}\right)$
$t = \dfrac{\log\left(\dfrac{299,000,000}{30}\right)}{\log(3)}$
$t \approx 14.67$
The model predicts that all Americans will have heard the rumor after about 15 days.

11. a. Use an exponential decay model $T = f(d) = ab^d$. The T-intercept is (0, 8) so $a = 8$. For every increase of 5 decibels d, the exposure time is halved so the base is $\dfrac{1}{2}$ and the exponent is $\dfrac{d}{5}$.

$f(d) = 8\left(\dfrac{1}{2}\right)^{\frac{d}{5}}$

b.
$$f(24) = 8\left(\frac{1}{2}\right)^{\frac{24}{5}}$$
$$= 0.2872$$

The model predicts that at 114 decibels, the bands could play for 0.29 hours (about 17.4 minutes!) without the fans experiencing hearing loss. The average rock concert lasts longer than 18 minutes, so the model predicts that these fans experience hearing loss.

c. $f^{-1}(3)$

$$3 = 8\left(\frac{1}{2}\right)^{\frac{d}{5}}$$

$$\left(\frac{1}{2}\right)^{\frac{d}{5}} = \frac{3}{8}$$

$$\log\left(\frac{1^{\frac{d}{5}}}{2}\right) = \log\left(\frac{3}{8}\right)$$

$$\frac{d}{5}\log\left(\frac{1}{2}\right) = \log\left(\frac{3}{8}\right)$$

$$\frac{d}{5} = \frac{\log\left(\frac{3}{8}\right)}{\log\left(\frac{1}{2}\right)}$$

$$t = \frac{5\log\left(\frac{3}{8}\right)}{\log\left(\frac{1}{2}\right)}$$

$$t \approx 7.08$$

To play for 3 hours, the rock bands should play at 97 decibels.

13. Use the exponential model $y = ab^t$ with 1975 as year 0. Substituting the data point $(0.21, 0)$ yields $a = 0.21$. Solve for b using \$5 million in 2004, when $t = 29$.

$$y = ab^t$$
$$5 = 0.21(b)^{29}$$
$$\frac{5}{0.21} = (b)^{29}$$
$$\left(\frac{5}{0.21}\right)^{\frac{1}{29}} = b$$
$$1.116 \approx b$$

The model is $y = 0.21(1.116)^t$.
Predict when the prize is \$10 million.

$$10 = 0.21(1.116)^t$$
$$\frac{10}{0.21} = \frac{0.21(1.116)^t}{0.21}$$
$$\log\left(\frac{10}{0.21}\right) = \log(1.116)^t$$
$$\frac{\log\left(\frac{10}{0.21}\right)}{\log(1.116)} = \frac{t\log(1.116)}{\log(1.116)}$$
$$35.2 \approx t$$

The prize is \$10 million in $1975 + 35 = 2010$.

15. Use the exponential model $y = ab^t$ with 1990 as year 0. This provides the data point $(471, 0)$ so that $a = 471$. Solve for b using 48 million in 2003, when $t = 13$.

$$y = ab^t$$
$$48 = 471(b)^{13}$$
$$48 = 471(b)^{13}$$
$$\frac{48}{471} = (b)^{13}$$
$$\left(\frac{48}{471}\right)^{\frac{1}{13}} = b$$
$$0.84 \approx b$$

The model is $y = 471(0.84)^t$.
Predict when the harvest is 10 million.

$$10 = 471(0.84)^t$$
$$\frac{10}{471} = \frac{471(0.84)^t}{471}$$
$$\log\left(\frac{10}{471}\right) = \log(0.84)^t$$
$$\frac{\log\left(\frac{10}{471}\right)}{\log(0.84)} = \frac{t\log(0.84)}{\log(0.84)}$$
$$22.09 \approx t$$

The harvest is 10 million in $1990 + 22 = 2012$.

17. a.
$$f(t) = 100.84(1.41)^t$$
$$1 = 100.84(1.41)^t$$
$$\frac{1}{100.84} = \frac{100.84(1.41)^t}{100.84}$$
$$\log\left(\frac{1}{100.84}\right) = \log(1.41)^t$$
$$\frac{\log\left(\dfrac{1}{100.84}\right)}{\log(1.41)} = \frac{t\log(1.41)}{\log(1.41)}$$
$$-13.43 \approx t$$
The first Starbucks store opened in
1990 − 13 = 1977.

b. No, it appears unlikely that Starbucks growth from 1 store to 272 is exponential over its first 18 years.

c. $b = 1.41$
The number of Starbucks stores increase by 41% each year.

d. $(500 \text{ stores}) \cdot (193 \text{ countries}) = 96,500$
$$f(t) = 100.84(1.41)^t$$
$$96500 = 100.84(1.41)^t$$
$$\frac{96500}{100.84} = \frac{100.84(1.41)^t}{100.84}$$
$$\log\left(\frac{96500}{100.84}\right) = \log(1.41)^t$$
$$\frac{\log\left(\dfrac{96500}{100.84}\right)}{\log(1.41)} = \frac{t\log(1.41)}{\log(1.41)}$$
$$19.98 \approx t$$
The average number of Starbucks stores per country will be 500 in 1990 + 20 = 2010.

e.
$$f(t) = 100.84(1.41)^t$$
$$8600000000 = 100.84(1.41)^t$$
$$\frac{8600000000}{100.84} = \frac{100.84(1.41)^t}{100.84}$$
$$\log\left(\frac{8600000000}{100.84}\right) = \log(1.41)^t$$
$$\frac{\log\left(\dfrac{8600000000}{100.84}\right)}{\log(1.41)} = \frac{t\log(1.41)}{\log(1.41)}$$
$$53.15 \approx t$$
There will be 1 store for every person in the world in 1990 + 53 = 2043. The model has broken down.

19. a.

The data point "end" so that an exponential function will better model the data.

b. Use the points (2, 138) and (10, 4) to find an equation of the form $y = ab^t$.
$$138 = ab^2$$
$$4 = ab^{10}$$
Divide and solve for b.
$$\frac{138}{4} = \frac{ab^2}{ab^{10}}$$
$$\frac{138}{4} = b^{-8}$$
$$\left(\frac{138}{4}\right)^{-\frac{1}{8}} = \left(b^{-8}\right)^{-\frac{1}{8}}$$
$$0.64 \approx b$$
Solve for a.
$$138 = a(0.64)^2$$
$$\frac{138}{(0.64)^2} = a$$
$$336.91 \approx a$$
The model is $f(t) = 336.91(0.64)^t$. (Your equation may be slightly different if you chose different points.) Use the graphing calculator to check your results.

c.
$$f(t) = 336.91(0.64)^t$$
$$f(16) = 336.91(0.64)^{16}$$
$$= 0.27$$
No, there are 0.27 thousand or 270 cases (according to this model). (Your equation may be slightly different if you chose different points.) Use the graphing calculator to check your results.

d.
$$f(t) = 336.91(0.64)^t$$
$$0.001 = 336.91(0.64)^t$$
$$\frac{0.001}{336.91} = (0.64)^t$$
$$\log\left(\frac{0.001}{336.91}\right) = \log(0.64)^t$$
$$\frac{\log\left(\frac{0.001}{336.91}\right)}{\log(0.64)} = \frac{t\log(0.64)}{\log(0.64)}$$
$$28.5 \approx t$$

There will be 1 case of polio in
1990 + 29 = 2019 (according to this model).
(Your equation may be slightly different if
you chose different points.) Use the
graphing calculator to check your results.

e. In 1990, $t = 0$.
$$f(t) = 336.91(0.64)^0$$
$$= 336.91(1)$$
$$\approx 337$$

There were about 337 thousand cases of
polio in 1990. Next find when there were
half as many cases, or 168.5.
$$f(t) = 336.91(0.64)^t$$
$$168.5 = 336.91(0.64)^t$$
$$\frac{168.5}{336.91} = (0.64)^t$$
$$\log\left(\frac{168.5}{336.91}\right) = \log(0.64)^t$$
$$\frac{\log\left(\frac{168.5}{336.91}\right)}{\log(0.64)} = \frac{t\log(0.64)}{\log(0.64)}$$
$$1.55 \approx t$$

This model predicts there will be half as
many cases of polio in 1.55 years.

21. a.
$$f(t) = 1.2(1.0162)^t$$
$$9.3 = 1.2(1.0162)^t$$
$$1.0162^t = \frac{9.3}{1.2}$$
$$\log(1.0162^t) = \log\left(\frac{9.3}{1.2}\right)$$
$$t\log(1.0162) = \log\left(\frac{9.3}{1.2}\right)$$
$$t = \frac{\log\left(\frac{9.3}{1.2}\right)}{\log(1.0162)}$$
$$t \approx 127.4219$$

The model predicts the world populations
will reach 9.3 billion in
1900 + 127 = 2027.

b.
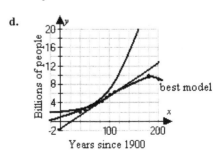

A linear function would best fit these data
points. Using the linear regression feature on
a graphing calculator, $g(t) = 0.079t - 1.85$.

c.
$$g(t) = 0.079t - 1.85$$
$$9.3 = 0.079t - 1.85$$
$$\frac{9.3 + 1.85}{0.079} = \frac{0.079t}{0.079}$$
$$141 = t$$

The year the population reaches 9.3 billion is
1900 + 141 = 2041, which is after the model
in part a. of 2027.

d.

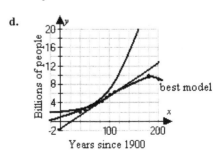

23. a. Use the points (67, 1.1) and (88, 12.9) to find
an equation of the form $y = ab^t$.
$$1.1 = ab^{67}$$
$$12.9 = ab^{88}$$
Divide and solve for b.

$$\frac{1.1}{12.9} = \frac{ab^{67}}{ab^{88}}$$

$$\frac{1.1}{12.9} = b^{-21}$$

$$\left(\frac{1.1}{12.9}\right)^{-\frac{1}{21}} = \left(b^{-21}\right)^{-\frac{1}{21}}$$

$$1.12 \approx b$$

Solve for a.

$$1.1 = a\left(1.12\right)^{67}$$

$$\frac{1.1}{\left(1.12\right)^{67}} = a$$

$$0.00055 \approx a$$

The model is $f(t) = 0.00055\left(1.12\right)^{t}$. (Your equation may be slightly different if you chose different points.) Use the graphing calculator to check your results.

b. The base b is 1.12 and it represents the percentage of seniors with severe memory impairment increases by 12% for each additional year of age. (Your equation may be slightly different if you chose different points.) Use the graphing calculator to check your results.

c.
$$f(t) = 0.00055\left(1.12\right)^{t}$$
$$f(70) = 0.00055\left(1.12\right)^{70}$$
$$= 1.53$$
Based on this model, about 1.53% of 70-year-old seniors have severe memory impairment. (Your equation may be slightly different if you chose different points.) Use the graphing calculator to check your results.

d.
$$f(t) = 0.00055\left(1.12\right)^{t}$$
$$10 = 0.00055\left(1.12\right)^{t}$$
$$\frac{10}{0.00055} = \left(1.12\right)^{t}$$
$$\log\left(\frac{10}{0.00055}\right) = \log\left(1.12\right)^{t}$$
$$\frac{\log\left(\frac{10}{0.00055}\right)}{\log\left(1.12\right)} = \frac{t\log\left(1.12\right)}{\log\left(1.12\right)}$$
$$86.54 \approx t$$
This model predicts 10% of seniors will have severe memory impairment at age 87. (Your equation may be slightly different if you chose different points.) Use the

graphing calculator to check your results.

e. No, memory speed and memory impairment are different phenomena that may correlate better with different mathematical relationships.

25. a. Use exponential regression.
$$E(s) = 0.36(1.0036)^{s}$$
$$R(s) = 0.037(1.0049)^{s}$$

b. $E(1425) = 0.36(1.0036)^{1425} \approx 60.3\%$
$$R(1425) = 0.037(1.0049)^{1425} \approx 39.2\%$$

c. Half = 50%
Use $E(s)$ for early decision applicants.
$$E(s) = 50$$
$$0.36(1.0036)^{s} = 50$$
$$1.0036^{s} = \frac{50}{0.36}$$
$$\log\left(1.0036^{s}\right) = \log\left(\frac{50}{0.36}\right)$$
$$s\log\left(1.0036\right) = \log\left(\frac{50}{0.36}\right)$$
$$s = \frac{\log\left(\frac{50}{0.36}\right)}{\log\left(1.0036\right)}$$
$$s \approx 1373$$
Use $R(s)$ for regular decision applicants.
$$R(s) = 50$$
$$0.037(1.0049)^{s} = 50$$
$$1.0049^{s} = \frac{50}{0.037}$$
$$\log\left(1.0049^{s}\right) = \log\left(\frac{50}{0.037}\right)$$
$$s\log\left(1.0049\right) = \log\left(\frac{50}{0.037}\right)$$
$$s = \frac{\log\left(\frac{50}{0.037}\right)}{\log\left(1.0049\right)}$$
$$s \approx 1475$$

d. $1475 - 1373 = 102$ points

e.

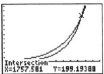

(1757.58, 199.19). Students who score 1758 points on their SAT have the same chance (199%) of being selected from the early decision and regular decision systems. Model breakdown has occurred.

A solution to the Challenge problem follows.

$$0.36(1.0036)^s = 0.037(1.0049)^s$$

$$\frac{(1.0036)^s}{(1.0049)^s} = \frac{0.037}{0.36}$$

$$\left(\frac{1.0036}{1.0049}\right)^s = \frac{0.037}{0.36}$$

$$\log\left(\frac{1.0036}{1.0049}\right)^s = \log\left(\frac{0.037}{0.36}\right)$$

$$\frac{s\log\left(\frac{1.0036}{1.0049}\right)}{\log\left(\frac{1.0036}{1.0049}\right)} = \frac{\log\left(\frac{0.037}{0.36}\right)}{\log\left(\frac{1.0036}{1.0049}\right)}$$

$$s \approx 1757.58$$

27. a. Use the exponential model $f(t) = ab^t$.

At $t = 0$, 100% of the gallium citrate-67 remains. Substitute $(0, 100)$.

$$100 = ab^0$$
$$100 = a$$

To solve for b, substitute $(3.25, 50)$.

$$50 = 100(b)^{3.25}$$

$$\frac{50}{100} = (b)^{3.25}$$

$$\left(\frac{1}{2}\right)^{\frac{1}{3.25}} = b$$

The equation is $f(t) = 100\left(\frac{1}{2}\right)^{\frac{t}{3.25}}$

b.

$$f(t) = 100\left(\frac{1}{2}\right)^{\frac{2}{3.25}}$$
$$= 65.28$$

After 2 days, 65.28% of the gallium citrate-67 remains.

c.

$$f(t) = 100\left(\frac{1}{2}\right)^{\frac{t}{3.25}}$$

$$0.39 = 100\left(\frac{1}{2}\right)^{\frac{t}{3.25}}$$

$$\log\left(\frac{0.39}{100}\right) = \log\left(\frac{1}{2}\right)^{\frac{t}{3.25}}$$

$$\frac{\log\left(\frac{0.39}{100}\right)}{\log\left(\frac{1}{2}\right)} = \frac{\frac{t}{3.25}\log\left(\frac{1}{2}\right)}{\log\left(\frac{1}{2}\right)}$$

$$\frac{\log\left(\frac{0.39}{100}\right)}{\log\left(\frac{1}{2}\right)} = \frac{t}{3.25}$$

$$3.25\left(\frac{\log\left(\frac{0.39}{100}\right)}{\log\left(\frac{1}{2}\right)}\right) = t$$

$$26.0 \approx t$$

After 26 days, 0.39% of the gallium citrate-67 remains.

29.

$$f(t) = 100\left(\frac{1}{2}\right)^{\frac{t}{5730}}$$

$$24.46 = 100\left(\frac{1}{2}\right)^{\frac{t}{5730}}$$

$$\log\left(\frac{24.46}{100}\right) = \log\left(\frac{1}{2}\right)^{\frac{t}{5730}}$$

$$\frac{\log\left(\frac{24.46}{100}\right)}{\log\left(\frac{1}{2}\right)} = \frac{\frac{t}{5730}\log\left(\frac{1}{2}\right)}{\log\left(\frac{1}{2}\right)}$$

$$\frac{\log\left(\frac{24.46}{100}\right)}{\log\left(\frac{1}{2}\right)} = \frac{t}{5730}$$

$$5730\left(\frac{\log\left(\frac{24.46}{100}\right)}{\log\left(\frac{1}{2}\right)}\right) = t$$

$$11640.5 \approx t$$

The ice sheet advanced about 11,641 years ago.

31. a. Since 50% of the wood's carbon-14 remains,

one half-life has passed. The half-life of carbon-14 is 5730 years. The age of the wood is 5730 years.

b. Since 25% of the wood's carbon-14 remains, two half-lives have passed (half of 100% is 50% and then half of 50% is 25%). The age of the wood is $2 \cdot 5730$ or 11,460 years.

c. After three half-lives have passed 12.5% of the wood's carbon-14 remains. This corresponds to $3 \cdot 5730$ or 17,190 years passing. The wood has only 10% of its carbon-14 remaining, so guess a little longer than 17,190 years.

$$f(t) = 100 \left(\frac{1}{2}\right)^{\frac{t}{5730}}$$

$$10 = 100 \left(\frac{1}{2}\right)^{\frac{t}{5730}}$$

$$\left(\frac{1}{2}\right)^{\frac{t}{5730}} = 0.1$$

$$\log\left(\frac{1}{2}\right)^{\frac{t}{5730}} = \log(0.1)$$

$$\frac{t}{5730}\log\left(\frac{1}{2}\right) = -1$$

$$t = \frac{-5730}{\log\left(\frac{1}{2}\right)}$$

$$t \approx 19035$$

The age of the wood is 19,035 years.

33. Use an exponential decay model $f(t) = ab^t$. Let $P = f(t)$ be the percentage of remaining of the element at t years. The P-intercept is (0, 100). Every 100 years the amount of the element is halved so the base is $\frac{1}{2}$ and the exponent is $\frac{t}{100}$.

$$f(t) = 100 \left(\frac{1}{2}\right)^{\frac{t}{100}}$$

Find $f^{-1}(0.01)$.

$$0.01 = 100 \left(\frac{1}{2}\right)^{\frac{t}{100}}$$

$$\left(\frac{1}{2}\right)^{\frac{t}{100}} = 0.0001$$

$$\log\left(\frac{1}{2}\right)^{\frac{t}{100}} = \log(0.0001)$$

$$\frac{t}{100}\log\left(\frac{1}{2}\right) = -4$$

$$\frac{t}{100} = \frac{-4}{\log\left(\frac{1}{2}\right)}$$

$$t = \frac{-400}{\log\left(\frac{1}{2}\right)}$$

$$t \approx 1328.77$$

The tank must remain intact for 1329 years.

35. a. First find the slope.
$$m = \frac{6.62 - 5.34}{4 - 0} = \frac{1.28}{4} = 0.32$$
Given the point (0, 5.34), the y-intercept $b = 5.34$.
The linear model is $L(t) = 0.32t + 5.34$.

Use the exponential model $y = ab^t$. Given the point (0, 5.34), $a = 5.34$.
Solve for b using (4, 6.62).
$$6.62 = 5.34(b)^4$$
$$\frac{6.62}{5.34} = (b)^4$$
$$\left(\frac{6.62}{5.34}\right)^{\frac{1}{4}} = b$$
$$1.055 \approx b$$
The exponential model is
$E(t) = 5.34(1.055)^t$.

b. Yes, the graphs of E and L are similar between 0 and 4. The relationship for these years appears linear because both graphs are essentially straight.

c. 0.32. The slope shows that the combined dump capacity increases by 0.32 billion tons per year.

d. 1.055. The base shows that the combined dump capacity increase by 5.5% per year

37. $\dfrac{-25b^{3/8}}{40b^{2/5}} = \dfrac{-5b^{15/40}}{8b^{16/40}} = -\dfrac{5}{8b^{1/40}}$

This is an expression in one variable that involves exponents.

39. $4(6)^x - 31 = 180$

$\dfrac{4(6)^x}{4} = \dfrac{211}{4}$

$\log(6)^x = \log\left(\dfrac{211}{4}\right)$

$\dfrac{x\log(6)}{\log(6)} = \dfrac{\log\left(\dfrac{211}{4}\right)}{\log(6)}$

$x \approx 2.2132$

This is an exponential equation in one variable.

Homework 5.5

1. $\log_b(x) + \log_b(3x)$

$= \log_b[(x)(3x)]$

$= \log_b(3x^2)$

3. $\log_b(8x) - \log_b(2)$

$= \log_b\left(\dfrac{8x}{2}\right)$

$= \log_b(4x)$

5. $4\log_b(t) + \log_b(5t)$

$= \log_b(t)^4 + \log_b(5t)$

$= \log_b[(t^4)(5t)]$

$= \log_b(5t^5)$

7. $\log_b(3x^2) - 5\log_b(x)$

$= \log_b(3x^2) - \log_b(x)^5$

$= \log_b\left(\dfrac{3x^2}{x^5}\right)$

$= \log_b\left(\dfrac{3}{x^3}\right)$

9. $2\log_b(3x) + 3\log_b(x^3)$

$= \log_b(3x)^2 + \log_b(x^3)^3$

$= \log_b[(9x^2)(x^9)]$

$= \log_b(9x^{11})$

11. $3\log_b(2m) + 5\log_b(m^2) - \log_b(3m)$

$= \log_b(2m)^3 + \log_b(m^2)^5 - \log_b(3m)$

$= \log_b\left[\dfrac{(8m^3)(m^{10})}{3m}\right]$

$= \log_b\left(\dfrac{8m^{12}}{3}\right)$

13. $\log_5(6x) + \log_5(x) = 2$

$\log_5[(6x)(x)] = 2$

$5^2 = 6x^2$

$\dfrac{25}{6} = x^2$

$\left(\dfrac{25}{6}\right)^{\frac{1}{2}} = x$

$2.0412 \approx x$

15. $\log_2(9x) - \log_2(3) = 5$

$\log_2\left(\dfrac{9x}{3}\right) = 5$

$2^5 = \dfrac{9x}{3}$

$32 = 3x$

$\dfrac{32}{3} = x$

$10.6667 \approx x$

17. $\log_7\left(w^2\right) + 2\log_7\left(3w\right) = 2$

$\log_7\left(w^2\right) + \log_7\left(3w\right)^2 = 2$

$\log_7\left[\left(w^2\right)\left(9w^2\right)\right] = 2$

$7^2 = 9w^4$

$\dfrac{49}{9} = w^4$

$\left(\dfrac{49}{9}\right)^{\frac{1}{4}} = w$

$1.5275 \approx w$

19. $2\log\left(x^5\right) - \log\left(x^7\right) = 1$

$\log\left(x^5\right)^2 - \log\left(x^7\right) = 1$

$\log\left(\dfrac{x^{10}}{x^7}\right) = 1$

$10^1 = x^3$

$\left(10\right)^{\frac{1}{3}} = x$

$2.1544 \approx x$

21. $3\log\left(x^2\right) + 4\log\left(2x\right) = 2$

$\log\left(x^2\right)^3 + \log\left(2x\right)^4 = 2$

$\log\left[\left(x^6\right)\left(16x^4\right)\right] = 2$

$10^2 = 16x^{10}$

$\left(\dfrac{100}{16}\right)^{\frac{1}{10}} = x$

$1.2011 \approx x$

23. $3\log_5\left(p^4\right) - 5\log_5\left(2p\right) = 3$

$\log_5\left(p^4\right)^3 - \log_5\left(2p\right)^5 = 3$

$\log_5\left(\dfrac{p^{12}}{32p^5}\right) = 3$

$5^3 = \dfrac{p^7}{32}$

$\left(4000\right)^{\frac{1}{7}} = p$

$3.2702 \approx p$

25. $\log_3\left(7\right) = \dfrac{\log(7)}{\log(3)}$

≈ 1.7712

27. $\log_9\left(3.58\right) = \dfrac{\log(3.58)}{\log(9)} \approx 0.5804$

29. $\log_8\left(\dfrac{1}{70}\right) = \dfrac{\log\left(\dfrac{1}{70}\right)}{\log(8)} \approx -2.0431$

31. Graph $y = \log\left(x+5\right) + \log\left(x+2\right)$ and $y = 3 - x$. Then use "intersect."

The *x*-coordinate, 1.6204, is the approximate solution of the equation $\log\left(x+5\right) + \log\left(x+2\right) = 3 - x$.

33. Given $\log_5\left(x+3\right) + \log_2\left(x+4\right) = -2x+9$, use the change of base formula to graph

$y = \dfrac{\log\left(x+3\right)}{\log 5} + \dfrac{\log\left(x+4\right)}{\log 2}$ and $y = -2x+9$.

The *x*-coordinate, 2.6031, is the approximate solution of the equation $\log_5\left(x+3\right) - \log_2\left(x+4\right) = -2x+9$.

35. Given $\log_5\left(x+3\right) - \log_2\left(x+4\right) = -2x+9$, use the change of base formula to graph

$y = \dfrac{\log\left(x+4\right)}{\log 2} + \dfrac{\log\left(x+5\right)}{\log 3}$ and $y = 2^x + 1$.

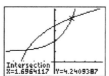

The *x*-coordinates, -2.6876 and 1.6964, are the approximate solutions of the equation

$\log_2(x+4) + \log_3(x+5) = 2^x + 1$.

37. $\dfrac{\log_2(x)}{\log_2(7)} = \log_7(x)$

39. $\dfrac{\log_b(r)}{\log_b(s)} = \log_s(r)$

41. All three students did the problem correctly.

43. $g(17) = \log_{12}(17)$

$= \dfrac{\log(17)}{\log(12)}$

≈ 1.1402

45. $g(8) = \log_{12}(8)$

$= \dfrac{\log(8)}{\log(12)}$

≈ 0.8368

47. $\log_b(b^2) = 2$

$\log_b\left(\dfrac{b^6}{b^4}\right) = \log_b(b^2) = 2$

$\log_b(b^6) = 6$

$\log_b(b^6) - \log_b(b^4) = \log_b\left(\dfrac{b^6}{b^4}\right)$

$= \log_b(b^2)$

$= 2$

$\dfrac{\log_b(b^6)}{\log_b(b^4)} = \dfrac{6}{4} = 1.5$

The expressions $\log_b(b^2)$, $\log_b\left(\dfrac{b^6}{b^4}\right)$, 2, and

$\log_b(b^6) - \log_b(b^4)$ are all equal.

49.
$\log_b(x) - \log_b(x) = \log_b\left(\dfrac{x}{x}\right)$

$= \log_b(1)$

$= 0$

51. a. $\log_2(x^3) + \log_2(x^5)$

$= \log_2[(x^3)(x^5)]$

$= \log_2(x^8)$

b. $\log_2(x^3) + \log_2(x^5) = 7$

$\log_2[(x^3)(x^5)] = 7$

$\log_2(x^8) = 7$

$x^8 = 2^7$

$x = (2^7)^{\frac{1}{8}}$

$x \approx 1.8340$

c. Answers may vary. Simplifying an expression involves combining separate logarithms into one logarithm. Solving the equation involved simplifying and the using the definition of logarithm to modify the statement into an exponential equation to solve.

d. Answers may vary. Simplifying an expression is the first step towards being able to solve an equation.

53. $\log_2(x^4) + \log_2(x^3)$

$\log_2[(x^4)(x^3)]$

$\log_2(x^7)$

55. $\log_2(x^4) + \log_2(x^3) = 4$

$\log_2[(x^4)(x^3)] = 4$

$\log_2(x^7) = 4$

$2^4 = x^7$

$(2^4)^{\frac{1}{7}} = x$

$1.4860 \approx x$

57. $2\log_9(x^3) - 3\log_9(2x) = 2$

$\log_9(x^3)^2 - \log_9(2x)^3 = 2$

$\log_9\left(\dfrac{x^6}{8x^3}\right) = 2$

$$9^2 = \frac{x^3}{8}$$

$$9^2 = \frac{x^3}{8}$$

$$\left(9^2 \cdot 8\right)^{\frac{1}{3}} = x$$

$$8.6535 \approx x$$

59. $2\log_9\left(x^3\right) - 3\log_9\left(2x\right)$

$$\log_9\left(x^3\right)^2 - \log_9\left(2x\right)^3$$

$$\log_9\left(\frac{x^6}{8x^3}\right)$$

$$\log_9\left(\frac{x^3}{8}\right)$$

61. $\left(16b^{16}c^{-7}\right)^{\frac{1}{4}}\left(27b^{27}c^5\right)^{\frac{1}{3}}$

$$\left(16^{\frac{1}{4}}b^{\frac{16}{4}}c^{-\frac{7}{4}}\right)\left(27^{\frac{1}{3}}b^{\frac{27}{3}}c^{\frac{5}{3}}\right)$$

$$\left(2b^4c^{-\frac{7}{4}}\right)\left(3b^9c^{\frac{5}{3}}\right)$$

$$6b^{13}c^{-\frac{21}{12}+\frac{20}{12}}$$

$$6b^{13}c^{-\frac{1}{12}}$$

$$\frac{6b^{13}}{c^{\frac{1}{12}}}$$

63. $3\log_b\left(2x^5\right) + 2\log_b\left(3x^4\right)$

$$\log_b\left(2x^5\right)^3 + \log_b\left(3x^4\right)^2$$

$$\log_b\left[\left(8x^{15}\right)\left(9x^8\right)\right]$$

$$\log_b\left(72x^{23}\right)$$

65. Substitute $3x - 7$ for y in the second equation.
$$y = -2x + 3$$
$$3x - 7 = -2x + 3$$
$$5x = 10$$
$$x = 2$$
Solve for y when $x = 2$.
$$y = 3x - 7$$
$$y = 3(2) - 7$$
$$y = -1$$
The solution is $(2, -1)$.

67. Substitute $\log_2(x) + 2$ for y in the second equation.
$$y = \log_2\left(4x^2\right) - 3$$
$$\log_2(x) + 2 = \log_2\left(4x^2\right) - 3$$
$$\log_2(x) - \log_2\left(4x^2\right) = -5$$
$$\log_2\left(\frac{x}{4x^2}\right) = -5$$
$$2^{-5} = \frac{1}{4x}$$
$$\frac{1}{32} = \frac{1}{4x}$$
$$4x = 32$$
$$x = 8$$
Solve for y when $x = 8$.
$$y = \log_2(x) + 2$$
$$= \log_2(8) + 2$$
$$= \frac{\log(8)}{\log(2)} + 2$$
$$= 3 + 2 = 5$$
The solution is $(8, 5)$.

69. Substitute $\frac{2}{3}x - 2$ for y in the first equation.
$$2x - 3\left(\frac{2}{3}x - 2\right) = 6$$
$$2x - 2x + 6 = 6$$
$$6 = 6$$
$$\text{True}$$
The solution is all points on the line $y = \frac{2}{3}x - 2$.
$$2x - 3y = 6$$
$$y = \frac{2}{3}x - 2$$ is a dependent linear system of
equations in two variables .

71.

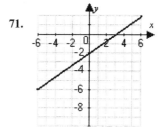

This is a linear equation in two variables.

Homework 5.6

1. $\ln(54.8) \approx 4.0037$

3. $\ln\left(\dfrac{1}{2}\right) \approx -0.6931$

5. $\ln(e^4) = 4$

7. $\ln(e) = \ln(e^1) = 1$

9. $\ln\left(\dfrac{1}{e}\right) = \ln(e^{-1}) = -1$

11. $\dfrac{1}{2}\ln(e^6) = \dfrac{1}{2}(6) = 3$

13. $\ln(x) = 2$
    $e^2 = x$
    $7.3891 \approx x$

15. $\ln(p+5) = 3$
    $e^3 = p + 5$
    $e^3 - 5 = p$
    $p \approx 15.0855$

17. $7e^x = 44$
    $e^x = \dfrac{44}{7}$
    $x = \ln\left(\dfrac{44}{7}\right)$
    $x \approx 1.8383$

19. $5\ln(3x) + 2 = 7$
    $\dfrac{5\ln(3x)}{5} = \dfrac{5}{5}$
    $\ln(3x) = 1$
    $3x = e^1$
    $x = \dfrac{e}{3}$
    $x \approx 0.9061$

21. $4e^{3m-1} = 68$
    $e^{3m-1} = 17$
    $3m - 1 = \ln(17)$
    $3m = \ln(17) + 1$
    $m = \dfrac{\ln(17)+1}{3}$
    $m \approx 1.2777$

23. $e^{3x-5} \cdot e^{2x} = 135$
    $e^{5x-5} = 135$
    $5x - 5 = \ln(135)$
    $\dfrac{5x}{5} = \dfrac{\ln(135)+5}{5}$
    $x \approx 1.9811$

25. $3.1^x = 49.8$
    $\ln(3.1^x) = \ln(49.8)$
    $x\ln(3.1) = \ln(49.8)$
    $x = \dfrac{\ln(49.8)}{\ln(3.1)}$
    $x \approx 3.4541$

27. $3(6^x) - 1 = 97$
    $3(6^x) = 98$
    $6^x = \dfrac{98}{3}$
    $\ln(6^x) = \ln\left(\dfrac{98}{3}\right)$
    $x\ln(6) = \ln\left(\dfrac{98}{3}\right)$
    $x = \dfrac{\ln\left(\dfrac{98}{3}\right)}{\ln(6)}$
    $x \approx 1.9458$

29. $5e^x - 20 = 2e^x + 67$
    $3e^x = 87$
    $e^x = 29$
    $x = \ln(29)$
    $x \approx 3.3673$

31. $\ln(4x) + \ln(3x^4)$

$= \ln\left[(4x)(3x^4)\right]$

$= \ln(12x^5)$

33. $\ln(25x^4) - \ln(5x^3)$

$= \ln\left(\dfrac{25x^4}{5x^3}\right)$

$= \ln(5x)$

35. $2\ln(w^4) + 3\ln(2w)$

$= \ln(w^4)^2 + \ln(2w)^3$

$= \ln\left[(w^8)(8w^3)\right]$

$= \ln(8w^{11})$

37. $3\ln(3x) - 2\ln(x^2)$

$= \ln(3x)^3 - \ln(x^2)^2$

$= \ln(27x^3) - \ln(x^4)$

$= \ln\left(\dfrac{27x^3}{x^4}\right)$

$= \ln\left(\dfrac{27}{x}\right)$

39. $3\ln(2k) + 4\ln(k^2) - \ln(k^7)$

$= \ln(2k)^3 + \ln(k^2)^4 - \ln(k^7)$

$= \ln\left[\dfrac{(8k^3)(k^8)}{(k^7)}\right]$

$= \ln(8k^4)$

41. $\ln(3x) + \ln(x) = 4$

$\ln[(3x)(x)] = 4$

$\ln(3x^2) = 4$

$3x^2 = e^4$

$x^2 = \dfrac{e^4}{3}$

$x = \left(\dfrac{e^4}{3}\right)^{\frac{1}{2}}$

$x \approx 4.2661$

43. $\ln(4x^5) - 2\ln(x^2) = 5$

$\ln(4x^5) - \ln(x^2)^2 = 5$

$\ln(4x^5) - \ln(x^4) = 5$

$\ln\left(\dfrac{4x^5}{x^4}\right) = 5$

$\ln(4x) = 5$

$4x = e^5$

$x = \dfrac{e^5}{4}$

$x \approx 37.1033$

45. $2\ln(3x) + 2\ln(x^3) = 8$

$\ln(3x)^2 + \ln(x^3)^2 = 8$

$\ln(9x^2) + \ln(x^6) = 8$

$\ln\left[(9x^2)(x^6)\right] = 8$

$\ln(9x^8) = 8$

$9x^8 = e^8$

$x^8 = \dfrac{e^8}{9}$

$x = \left(\dfrac{e^8}{9}\right)^{\frac{1}{8}}$

$x \approx 2.0654$

47. $5\ln\left(m^3\right) - 3\ln\left(2m\right) = 7$

$$\ln\left(m^3\right)^5 - \ln\left(2m\right)^3 = 7$$

$$\ln\left(m^{15}\right) - \ln\left(8m^3\right) = 7$$

$$\ln\left(\frac{m^{15}}{8m^3}\right) = 7$$

$$\ln\left(\frac{m^{12}}{8}\right) = 7$$

$$\frac{m^{12}}{8} = e^7$$

$$m^{12} = 8e^7$$

$$m = \left(8e^7\right)^{\frac{1}{12}}$$

$$x \approx 2.1311$$

49. Graph $y = e^x$ and $y = 5 - x$. Then use "intersect."

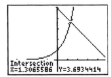

The *x*-coordinate, 1.3066, is the approximate solution of the equation $e^x = 5 - x$.

51. Graph $y = 3\ln(x + 2)$ and $y = -2x + 6$. Then use "intersect."

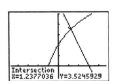

The *x*-coordinate, 1.2377 is the approximate solution of the equation $3\ln(x + 2) = -2x + 6$.

53. Graph $y = 3\ln(x + 3)$ and $y = 0.7x + 2$. Then use "intersect."

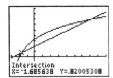 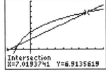

The *x*-coordinates, -1.6856 and 7.0194, are the approximate solutions of the equation $3\ln(x + 3) = 0.7x + 2$.

55. $f(x) = 4\ln(x)$

$$f\left(e^5\right) = 4\ln\left(e^5\right)$$

$$= 4 \cdot 5$$

$$= 20$$

57. $f(x) = 4\ln(x)$

$$-8 = 4\ln\left(x\right)$$

$$\frac{-8}{4} = \frac{4\ln\left(x\right)}{4}$$

$$-2 = \ln(x)$$

$$x = e^{-2}$$

$$x \approx 0.1353$$

59. $\ln(e) = 1$ because $e^1 = e$.

61. $ae^{bx} = c$

$$e^{bx} = \frac{c}{a}$$

$$bx = \ln\left(\frac{c}{a}\right)$$

$$x = \frac{\ln\left(\frac{c}{a}\right)}{b}$$

63. $3\ln(x) = 3\ln(x)$

$$\ln(x^7) - \ln(x^4) = \ln\left(\frac{x^7}{x^4}\right) = \ln(x^3) = 3\ln(x)$$

$$\frac{\ln(x^7)}{\ln(x^4)} = \log_{x^4}(x^7)$$

$$2\ln(x)\ln(x) = 2[\ln(x)]^2$$

$$\ln(x^3) = 3\ln(x)$$

$$\ln(3x) = \ln(3x)$$

$3\ln(x)$, $\ln(x^7) - \ln(x^4)$, and $\ln(x^3)$ are all the equal.

65. a.

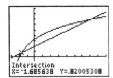

The function appears to be a reasonable

model.

b. $f(t) = 0.15e^{0.33t}$

$= 0.15e^{0.33(10)}$

$= 4.07$

The annual sales in 2010 are predicted to be $4.07 billion.

c. $f(t) = 0.15e^{0.33t}$

$6 = 0.15e^{0.33t}$

$\dfrac{6}{0.15} = e^{0.33t}$

$\ln\left(\dfrac{6}{0.15}\right) = 0.33t$

$\dfrac{\ln\left(\dfrac{6}{0.15}\right)}{0.33} = t$

$11.18 \approx t$

The annual sales is predicted to reach $6 billion in 2011.

67. a. The time when the person bought it is $t = 0$.

$70 + 137e^{-0.66(0)} = 70 + 137e^{0}$

$= 70 + 137$

$= 207$

The temperature was 207°F when the coffee was purchased

b. $180 = 70 + 137e^{-0.06t}$

$110 = 137e^{-0.06t}$

$e^{-0.06t} = \dfrac{110}{137}$

$\ln\left(e^{-0.06t}\right) = \ln\left(\dfrac{110}{137}\right)$

$-0.06t\ln(e) = \ln\left(\dfrac{110}{137}\right)$

$-0.06t = \ln\left(\dfrac{110}{137}\right)$

$t = \dfrac{\ln\left(\dfrac{110}{137}\right)}{-0.06}$

$t \approx 3.6583$

He will be able to drink the coffee in 3.66 minutes.

c.

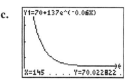

Looking at the graph of y we can see that as t gets larger, y approaches 70. So the temperature of the store is 70°F.

69. a. The poles are at $x = 10$ or $x = -10$

$h(10) = 10(e^{0.03(10)} + e^{-0.03(10)})$

$= 10(1.34986 + 0.740818)$

$= 10(2.090677)$

$= 20.90677$

The poles are 20.91 feet high.

b. $h(6) = 10(e^{0.03(6)} + e^{-0.03(6)})$

$h(6) = 10(1.197217 + 0.835702)$

$= 10(2.0324876)$

$= 20.32488$

The cable is 20.32 feet high when it is 6 feet away from the center (or 4 feet to the left of the rightmost pole).

c. The shortest height happens in the center, where $x = 0$.

$h(0) = 10(e^{0.03(0)} + e^{-0.03(0)})$

$= 10(1 + 1)$

$= 10(2)$

$= 20$

The least height of the cable is 20 feet.

71. a. i.

$3^x = 58$

$\ln(3^x) = \ln(58)$

$\dfrac{x\ln(3)}{\ln(3)} = \dfrac{\ln(58)}{\ln(3)}$

$x \approx 3.6960$

ii.

$3^x = 58$

$\log(3^x) = \log(58)$

$\dfrac{x\log(3)}{\log(3)} = \dfrac{\log(58)}{\log(3)}$

$x \approx 3.6960$

iii. Both results are the same.

b. i. Answers may vary. Sample of the form $b^x = c$.

$$5^x = 25$$
$$\ln\left(5^x\right) = \ln\left(25\right)$$
$$\frac{x\ln(5)}{\ln(5)} = \frac{\ln(25)}{\ln(5)}$$
$$x = 2$$

ii.
$$5^x = 25$$
$$\log\left(5^x\right) = \log\left(25\right)$$
$$\frac{x\log(5)}{\log(5)} = \frac{\log(25)}{\log(5)}$$
$$x = 2$$

iii. Both results are the same.

c. We can take either the common logarithm or the natural logarithm to solve an exponential equation.

73. $\ln\left(x^8\right) - \ln\left(x^3\right)$

$$\ln\left(\frac{x^8}{x^3}\right)$$
$$\ln\left(x^5\right)$$

75. $\ln\left(x^8\right) - \ln\left(x^3\right) = 4$

$$\ln\left(\frac{x^8}{x^3}\right) = 4$$
$$\ln\left(x^5\right) = 4$$
$$x^5 = e^4$$
$$x = \left(e^4\right)^{\frac{1}{5}}$$
$$x \approx 2.2255$$

77. $3e^x - 5 = 7$

$$\frac{3e^x}{3} = \frac{12}{3}$$
$$e^x = 4$$
$$x = \ln\left(4\right)$$
$$x \approx 1.3863$$

79. $7 - 3(2t - 4) = 5t + 6$

$$7 - 6t + 12 = 5t + 6$$
$$\frac{-11t}{-11} = \frac{-13}{-11}$$
$$t = \frac{13}{11}$$

81. $\dfrac{b^7}{b^3} = 16$

$$b^4 = 16$$
$$b = \left(16\right)^{\frac{1}{4}}$$
$$b = \pm 2$$

83. Answers may vary.
One example is $5x^2 - 2x + 1$.

85. Answers may vary.
One example is $\log(2x - 1) = 5$.

$$\log(2x - 1) = 5$$
$$10^5 = 2x - 1$$
$$\frac{10^5 + 1}{2} = x$$

87. Answers may vary.
One example is $y = 5x + 2$.

Chapter 5 Review Exercises

1. $f(2) = 4$

2. $f^{-1}(2) = 1$

3.

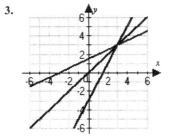

4.

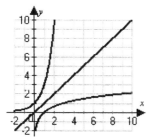

5. a. Using the linear regression feature on a graphing calculator, $f(t) = -16.3t + 507$.

b. Replace $f(t)$ with n.
$n = -16.3t + 507$
Solve for t.
$n - 507 = -16.3t$
$\dfrac{n - 507}{-16.3} = t$
$0.061n + 31.1 \approx t$
An approximate equation is $t = 0.061n + 31.1$.
Replace t with $f^{-1}(n)$.
$f^{-1}(n) = 0.061n + 31.1$

c. $f(11) = -16.3(11) + 507$
$= -179.3 + 507$
$= 327.7$
In 2011, there will be 328 thousand full-time-equivalent employees for all passenger airlines

d. $f^{-1}(300) = -0.061(300) + 31.1$
$= 12.8$
In 2013, there will be 300 thousand full-time-equivalent employees for al passenger airlines.

6. $f(x) = 3x$

Replace $f(x)$ with y.
$y = 3x$
Solve for x.
$x = \dfrac{1}{3}y$
Replace x with $f^{-1}(y)$.
$f^{-1}(y) = \dfrac{1}{3}y$
Write in terms of x.
$f^{-1}(x) = \dfrac{1}{3}x$

7. $g(x) = \dfrac{4x - 7}{8}$
Replace $g(x)$ with y.
$y = \dfrac{4x - 7}{8}$
Solve for x.
$4x - 7 = 8y$
$4x = 8y + 7$
$x = \dfrac{8y + 7}{4}$
Replace x with $g^{-1}(y)$.
$g^{-1}(y) = 2y + \dfrac{7}{4}$
Write in terms of x.
$g^{-1}(x) = 2x + \dfrac{7}{4}$

8. $\log_5(25) = 2$, since $5^2 = 25$.

9. $\log(100,000) = 5$, since $10^5 = 100,000$.

10. $\log_3\left(\dfrac{1}{9}\right) = -2$, since $3^{-2} = \dfrac{1}{9}$

11. $\ln\left(\dfrac{1}{e^3}\right) = \ln(e^{-3})$
$= -3$

12. $\log_4\left(\sqrt[3]{4}\right) = \dfrac{1}{3}$, since $4^{\frac{1}{3}} = \sqrt[3]{4}$.

13. $\log_3(7) = \dfrac{\log(7)}{\log(3)}$

≈ 1.7712

14. $\ln(5) \approx 1.6094$

15. $\log_b(b^7) = 7$, since $b^7 = b^7$.

16. $h(x) = 3^x$

$h^{-1}(x) = \log_3(x)$

17. $h(x) = \log(x)$

$h^{-1}(x) = 10^x$

18.

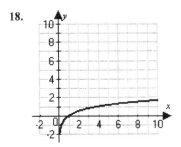

19. $\log_d(k) = t$

20. $y^r = w$

21. $6(2)^x = 30$

$2^x = 5$

$\log(2^x) = \log(5)$

$x\log(2) = \log(5)$

$x = \dfrac{\log(5)}{\log(2)}$

$x \approx 2.3219$

22. $\log_3(x) = -4$

$x = 3^{-4}$

$x = \dfrac{1}{81}$

23. $4.3(9.8)^x - 3.3 = 8.2$

$4.3(9.8)^x = 11.5$

$9.8^x = \dfrac{11.5}{4.3}$

$\log(9.8^x) = \log\left(\dfrac{11.5}{4.3}\right)$

$x\log(9.8) = \log\left(\dfrac{11.5}{4.3}\right)$

$x = \dfrac{\log\left(\dfrac{11.5}{4.3}\right)}{\log(9.8)}$

$x \approx 0.4310$

24. $\log_b(83) = 6$

$b^6 = 83$

$b = 83^{\frac{1}{6}}$

$b \approx 2.0886$

25. $5\log_{32}(m) - 3 = -1$

$\log_{32}(m)^5 = 2$

$m^5 = 32^2$

$m = \left(32^2\right)^{\frac{1}{5}}$

$m = 4$

26. $5(4)^{3r-7} = 40$

$4^{3r-7} = 8$

$\log(4^{3r-7}) = \log(8)$

$(3r - 7)\log(4) = \log(8)$

$3r - 7 = \dfrac{\log(8)}{\log(4)}$

$3r = \dfrac{\log(8)}{\log(4)} + 7$

$r = \dfrac{\dfrac{\log(8)}{\log(4)} + 7}{3}$

$r \approx 2.8333$

27.
$$2^{4t} \cdot 2^{3t-5} = 94$$
$$2^{7t-5} = 94$$
$$\log\left(2^{7t-5}\right) = \log(94)$$
$$(7t-5)\log(2) = \log(94)$$
$$7t - 5 = \frac{\log(94)}{\log(2)}$$
$$7t = \frac{\log(94)}{\log(2)} + 5$$
$$t = \frac{\dfrac{\log(94)}{\log(2)} + 5}{7}$$
$$\approx 1.6507$$

28.
$x = 4$ because $y = \log_2(x)$ and $y = -\dfrac{3}{4}x + 5$
intersect at $x = 4$.

29. $x = 0$ because $y = 2^x - 3$ is -2 when $x = 0$.

30. The solution to the system $y = \log_2(x)$ and
$y = -\dfrac{3}{4}x + 5$ is the point of intersection on the
graph, $(4,2)$.

31.
$$f(x) = 3^x$$
$$f(4) = 3^4$$
$$= 81$$

32. $f(x) = 3^x$, so $f^{-1}(x) = \log_3(x)$
$$f^{-1}(25) = \log_3(25)$$
$$= \frac{\log(25)}{\log(3)}$$
$$\approx 2.9299$$

33.
$$f(x) = 3^x$$
$$6 = 3^x$$
$$\log(6) = \log\left(3^x\right)$$
$$\log(6) = x\log(3)$$
$$\frac{\log(6)}{\log(3)} = x$$
$$1.6309 \approx x$$

34. $f(x) = 3^x$, so $f^{-1}(x) = \log_3(x)$

Substitute using $f^{-1}(x) = 6$.
$$6 = \log_3(x)$$
$$3^6 = x$$
$$729 = x$$

35. a. Use an exponential model $f(t) = ab^t$. Let
$V = f(t)$, where V is the value of the
account. The V-intercept is $(0, 8000)$, so $a = 8000$. Since the interest rate is 5%, the base
is $b = 1.05$. $f(t) = 8000(1.05)^t$.

b. $f(9) = 8000(1.05)^9 \approx 12410.63$
The balance in the account after 9 years is
$12, 410.63.

c. The balance will have doubled when it is
$16,000. Find $f^{-1}(16000)$
$$16000 = 8000(1.05)^t$$
$$1.05^t = 2$$
$$\log(1.05^t) = \log(2)$$
$$t\log(1.05) = \log(2)$$
$$t = \frac{\log(2)}{\log(1.05)}$$
$$t \approx 14.2067$$
The balance will be doubled in 14.2 years.

36. a. Use an exponential model $f(t) = ab^t$. Let
$n = f(t)$ be the number of leaves. The
n-intercept is $(0, 30)$, so $a = 30$. The number
of leaves quadruples every week so the base,
$b = 2$. $f(t) = 30(4)^t$.

b. $f(8) = 30(4)^5 = 30720$
There are 30,720 leaves on the tree 5 weeks
after April 1.

c.
$$f^{-1}(10000)$$
$$100000 = 30(4)^t$$
$$4^t = \frac{100000}{30}$$
$$\log(4^t) = \log\left(\frac{10000}{3}\right)$$

$$t\log(4) = \log\left(\frac{10000}{3}\right)$$

$$t = \frac{\log\left(\dfrac{10000}{3}\right)}{\log(4)}$$

$$t \approx 5.85$$

There are 100,000 leaves on the tree 6 weeks after April 1.

37. a.

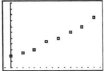

The plotted data "bends" slightly so an exponential function would appear to provide a better model.

b. Use the exponential model $y = ab^t$. Given the point (92, 13) and (100, 20), solve for a.

$$13 = ab^{92}$$
$$20 = ab^{100}$$
$$\frac{13}{20} = \frac{ab^{92}}{ab^{100}}$$
$$\frac{13}{20} = b^{-8}$$
$$\left(\frac{13}{20}\right)^{-\frac{1}{8}} = b$$
$$1.0553 \approx b$$

Solve for a.

$$20 = a(1.0553)^{100}$$
$$\frac{12}{(1.0553)^{100}} = a$$
$$0.092 \approx a$$

The model is $f(t) = 0.092(1.0553)^t$.

(Your equation may be slightly different if you chose different points.)

c.
$$f(t) = 0.092(1.0553)^t$$
$$f(100) = 0.092(1.0553)^{100}$$
$$\approx 20.01$$

In 2000, about 20% of Americans were obese.

d. $f^{-1}(100)$

$$f(t) = 0.092(1.0553)^t$$
$$100 = 0.092(1.0553)^t$$
$$\left(\frac{100}{0.092}\right) = (1.0553)^t$$
$$\log\left(\frac{100}{0.092}\right) = t\log(1.0553)$$
$$\frac{\log\left(\dfrac{100}{0.092}\right)}{\log(1.0553)} = t$$
$$129.89 \approx t$$

In 2030, 100% of Americans will be obese. Model breakdown has likely occurred.

e. $f(t) = 100$ when $t \approx 130$ because $f(t) = 100$ and $f^{-1}(100)$ both represent the data value of 130. So, in 2030, 100% of Americans will be obese. Model breakdown has likely occurred.

38. a. Exponential regression on a graphing calculator yields the equation
$$f(n) = 9.33(1.31)^n.$$

b. 1.31. As each cassette is added to the bag the length increases by 31%

c. 9.33. The initial length of the rubber band is 9.33 inches.

d. $f(8) = 9.33(1.31)^8 \approx 80.92$

The rubber band is stretched to 80.92 inches with 8 cassettes.

There are two scenarios which might cause model breakdown. The rubber band reaches a point where it can stretch no farther, or the rubber band breaks.

e.
$$f^{-1}(139)$$
$$139 = 9.33(1.31)^n$$
$$1.31^n = \frac{139}{9.33}$$
$$\log(1.31^n) = \log\left(\frac{139}{9.33}\right)$$

$$n\log(1.31) = \log\left(\frac{139}{9.33}\right)$$

$$n = \frac{\log\left(\frac{139}{9.33}\right)}{\log(1.31)}$$

$$n \approx 10.00$$

It would take 10 cassettes to stretch the rubber band to 139 inches. If model breakdown occurs with 8 cassettes, then it definitely occurs with 10. Either the rubber band has stopped stretching with the addition of the last two cassettes, or the rubber band is broken.

39.

$$f(t) = 100\left(\frac{1}{2}\right)^{\frac{t}{5.3}}$$

$$15 = 100\left(\frac{1}{2}\right)^{\frac{t}{5.3}}$$

$$\left(\frac{15}{100}\right) = \left(\frac{1}{2}\right)^{\frac{t}{5.3}}$$

$$\log\left(\frac{15}{100}\right) = \left(\frac{t}{5.3}\right)\log\left(\frac{1}{2}\right)$$

$$(5.3)\frac{\log\left(\frac{15}{100}\right)}{\log\left(\frac{1}{2}\right)} = \frac{t}{5.3}(5.3)$$

$$14.51 \approx t$$

About 15% of the cobalt-60 remains after 14.5 years.

40. $\log_b(p) + \log_b(6p) - \log_b(2p)$

$$\log_b[p(6p)] - \log_b(2p)$$

$$\log_b(6p^2) - \log_b(2p)$$

$$\log_b\left(\frac{6p^2}{2p}\right)$$

$$\log_b(3p)$$

41. $3\log_b(2x) + 2\log_b(3x)$

$$\log_b(2x)^3 + \log_b(3x)^2$$

$$\log_b[(2x)^3(3x)^2]$$

$$\log_b[72x^5]$$

42. $4\log_b\left(x^2\right) - 2\log_b\left(x^5\right)$

$$\log_b\left(x^2\right)^4 - \log_b\left(x^5\right)^2$$

$$\log_b\left(\frac{x^8}{x^{10}}\right)$$

$$\log_b\left(\frac{1}{x^2}\right)$$

43. $\dfrac{\log_b(w)}{\log_b(y)} = \log_y(w)$

44. $\log_b(b^5) - \log_b(b^2) = 3$

$$3 = 3$$

$$\frac{\log_b(b^5)}{\log_b(b^2)} = \frac{5}{2}$$

$$\log_b(b^3) = 3$$

$$\log_b(b^5) = 5$$

$$\log_b\left(\frac{b^5}{b^2}\right) = \log_b\left(b^3\right)$$

$$= 3$$

45. $2\log_9\left(3w\right) + 3\log_9\left(w^2\right) = 5$

$$\log_9\left(3w\right)^2 + \log_9\left(w^2\right)^3 = 5$$

$$\log_9\left[\left(9w^2\right)\left(w^6\right)\right] = 5$$

$$\log_9\left(9w^8\right) = 5$$

$$9w^8 = 9^5$$

$$w^8 = \frac{9^5}{9}$$

$$w = \left(9^4\right)^{\frac{1}{8}}$$

$$= 3$$

46. $5\log_6(2x) - 3\log_6(4x) = 2$

$\log_6(2x)^5 - \log_6(4x)^3 = 2$

$\log_6\left(\dfrac{32x^5}{64x^3}\right) = 2$

$\log_6\left(\dfrac{x^2}{2}\right) = 2$

$\dfrac{x^2}{2} = 6^2$

$x^2 = 2 \cdot 36$

$x = (72)^{\frac{1}{2}}$

≈ 8.4853

47. $3\ln(4x) + 2\ln(2x)$

$\ln(4x)^3 + \ln(2x)^2$

$\ln\left[(64x^3)(4x^2)\right]$

$\ln(256x^5)$

48. $\ln(2m^7) - 4\ln(m^3) + 3\ln(m^2)$

$\ln(2m^7) - \ln(m^3)^4 + \ln(m^2)^3$

$\ln\left[\dfrac{(2m^7)(m^6)}{(m^{12})}\right]$

$\ln(2m)$

49. $4e^x = 75$

$e^x = \dfrac{75}{4}$

$x = \ln\left(\dfrac{75}{4}\right)$

≈ 2.9312

50. $-3\ln(p) + 7 = 1$

$-3\ln(p) = -6$

$\ln(p) = 2$

$e^2 = p$

$7.3891 \approx p$

51. $3\ln(t^5) - 5\ln(2t) = 7$

$\ln(t^5)^3 - \ln(2t)^5 = 7$

$\ln\left(\dfrac{t^{15}}{32t^5}\right) = 7$

$\dfrac{t^{10}}{32} = e^7$

$t^{10} = 32e^7$

$t = \left(32e^7\right)^{\frac{1}{10}}$

≈ 2.8479

Chapter 5 Test

1.

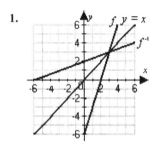

2.

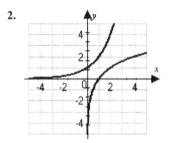

3. a. Using the linear regression feature on a graphing calculator, $f(t) = 2.07t + 28.49$.

b. Replace $f(t)$ with p.
$p = 2.07t + 28.49$
Solve for t.
$$p = 2.07t + 28.49$$
$$p - 28.49 = 2.07t$$
$$\dfrac{p - 28.49}{2.07} = \dfrac{2.07t}{2.07}$$
$$0.48p - 13.76 \approx t$$
An approximate equation is
$t = 0.48p - 13.76$.

Replace t with $f^{-1}(n)$.

$$f^{-1}(n) = 0.48n - 13.76$$

    c. $f^{-1}(n) = 0.48n - 13.76$
$$= 0.48(70) - 13.76$$
$$\approx 19.84$$
An adult one-day ticket will be \$70 in
1990 + 20 = 2010.

    d. 0.48. The slope shows that the ticket price
increases by \$1 every 0.48 years.

4. $g(x) = 2x - 9$
Replace $g(x)$ with y.
$$y = 2x - 9$$
Solve for x:
$$2x = y + 9$$
$$x = \frac{y + 9}{2}$$
Replace x with $g^{-1}(y)$.
$$g^{-1}(y) = \frac{1}{2}y + \frac{9}{2}$$
Write in terms of x.
$$g^{-1}(x) = \frac{1}{2}x + \frac{9}{2}$$

5. $\log_2(16) = 4$, since $2^4 = 16$.

6. $\log_4\left(\dfrac{1}{64}\right) = -3$, since $4^{-3} = \dfrac{1}{64}$.

7. $\log_7(10) = \dfrac{\log(10)}{\log(7)}$
$$\approx 1.1833$$

8. $\log(0.1) = -1$, since $10^{-1} = 0.1$.

9. $\log_b(\sqrt{b}) = \dfrac{1}{2}$, since $b^{\frac{1}{2}} = \sqrt{b}$.

10. $\ln\left(\dfrac{1}{e^2}\right) = -2$, since $e^{-2} = \dfrac{1}{e^2}$.

11. $h(x) = 4^x$
$$h^{-1}(x) = \log_4(x)$$

12. $f(x) = \log_5(x)$

$$f^{-1}(x) = 5^x$$

13. $\log_s(w) = t$

14. $c^d = a$

15. $\log_b(50) - 4$
$$b^4 = 50$$
$$b = (50)^{\frac{1}{4}}$$
$$\approx 2.6591$$

16. $6(2)^x - 9 = 23$
$$6(2)^x = 32$$
$$2^x = \frac{32}{6}$$
$$\log(2^x) = \log\left(\frac{32}{6}\right)$$
$$x\log(2) = \log\left(\frac{32}{6}\right)$$
$$x = \frac{\log\left(\frac{32}{6}\right)}{\log(2)}$$
$$\approx 2.4150$$

17. $\log_4(7p + 5) = -\dfrac{3}{2}$
$$7p + 5 = 4^{-\frac{3}{2}}$$
$$7p = 4^{-\frac{3}{2}} - 5$$
$$p = \frac{4^{-\frac{3}{2}} - 5}{7}$$
$$= -0.6964$$

18.

Graph $y = 4^x - 8$ and $y = -\dfrac{1}{2}x + 3$. Then use
"intersect."

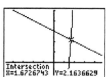

The *x*-coordinate, 1.67, is the approximate
solution of the equation

$4^x - 8 = -\dfrac{1}{2}x + 3$.

19. a. Use the exponential model $y = ab^t$ with 1950 as year 0. This provides the data point $(0, 600)$, so that $a = 600$.
Solve for b using $(30, 5585)$.

$$y = ab^t$$
$$5585 = 600(b)^{30}$$
$$\frac{5585}{600} = (b)^{30}$$
$$\left(\frac{5585}{600}\right)^{\frac{1}{30}} = b$$
$$1.077 \approx b$$

The model is $f(t) = 600(1.077)^t$. (Your equation may be slightly different if you chose different points.)

b. $(0, 600)$. The tuition in 1950 was \$600. (Your answer may be slightly different if you chose different points.)

c. The tuition rate is growing at a rate of about 7.7% per year. (Your answer may be slightly different if you chose different points.)

d. $f(t) = 600(1.077)^{61}$
≈ 55374.41
According to this model, the tuition in 2011 is predicted to be \$55,374. (Your answer may be slightly different if you chose different points.)

e.
$$f(t) = 600(1.077)^t$$
$$60000 = 600(1.077)^t$$
$$\frac{60000}{600} = \frac{600(1.077)^t}{600}$$
$$\log(100) = \log(1.077)^t$$
$$\frac{\log(100)}{\log(1.077)} = \frac{t\log(1.077)}{\log(1.077)}$$
$$62.08 \approx t$$

According to this model, the tuition is predicted to be \$60,000 in 1950 + 62 = 2012. (Your answer may be slightly different if you chose different points.)

20.
$$f(t) = 100\left(\frac{1}{2}\right)^{\frac{t}{5730}}$$
$$78.04 = 100\left(\frac{1}{2}\right)^{\frac{t}{5730}}$$
$$\left(\frac{78.04}{100}\right) = \left(\frac{1}{2}\right)^{\frac{t}{5730}}$$
$$\log\left(\frac{78.04}{100}\right) = \left(\frac{t}{5730}\right)\log\left(\frac{1}{2}\right)$$
$$(5730)\frac{\log\left(\frac{78.04}{100}\right)}{\log\left(\frac{1}{2}\right)} = \frac{t}{5730}(5760)$$
$$2049.70 \approx t$$

The mummy is about 2050 years old.

21. $\log_b(x^3) + \log_b(5x)$
$\log_b[x^3(5x)]$
$\log_b(5x^4)$

22. $3\log_b(4p^2) - 2\log_b(8w^5) + \log_b(2p^4)$
$\log_b(4p^2)^3 - \log_b(8w^5)^2 + \log_b(2p^4)$
$\log_b\left[\dfrac{(64p^6)(2p^4)}{64w^{10}}\right]$
$\log_b\left(\dfrac{2p^{10}}{w^{10}}\right)$

23. $\log_3(x) + \log_3(2x) = 5$
$\log_3[x(2x)] = 5$
$\log_3(2x^2) = 5$
$2x^2 = 3^5$
$x^2 = \dfrac{243}{2}$
$x = \left(\dfrac{243}{2}\right)^{\frac{1}{2}}$
≈ 11.0227

24. $2\log_4(x^4) - 3\log_4(3x) = 3$

$$\log_4(x^4)^2 - \log_4(3x)^3 = 3$$
$$\log_4(x^8) - \log_4(27x^3) = 3$$
$$\log_4\left(\frac{x^8}{27x^3}\right) = 3$$
$$\log_4\left(\frac{x^5}{27}\right) = 3$$
$$\frac{x^5}{27} = 4^3$$
$$x^5 = 27 \cdot 4^3$$
$$x = \left(27 \cdot 4^3\right)^{\frac{1}{5}}$$
$$\approx 4.4413$$

25. $2\ln(5w) + 3\ln\left(w^6\right)$
$$\ln(5w)^2 + \ln\left(w^6\right)^3$$
$$\ln\left[\left(25w^2\right)\left(w^{18}\right)\right]$$
$$\ln\left(25w^{20}\right)$$

26. $2e^{3x-1} = 54$
$$e^{3x-1} = 27$$
$$\ln(e^{3x-1}) = \ln(27)$$
$$(3x-1)\ln e = \ln(27)$$
$$3x - 1 = \ln(27)$$
$$3x = \ln(27) + 1$$
$$x = \frac{\ln(27)+1}{3}$$
$$\approx 1.4319$$

27. $7\ln(x-2) - 1 = 4$
$$7\ln(x-2) = 5$$
$$\ln(x-2) = \frac{5}{7}$$
$$x - 2 = e^{\frac{5}{7}}$$
$$x = e^{\frac{5}{7}} + 2$$
$$\approx 4.0427$$

Cumulative Review of Chapters 1-5

1. $2(4)^{5x-1} = 17$

$$(4)^{5x-1} = \frac{17}{2}$$
$$\log(4^{5x-1}) = \log\left(\frac{17}{2}\right)$$
$$(5x-1)\log(4) = \log\left(\frac{17}{2}\right)$$
$$5x - 1 = \frac{\log\left(\frac{17}{2}\right)}{\log(4)}$$
$$5x = \frac{\log\left(\frac{17}{2}\right)}{\log(4)} + 1$$
$$x = \frac{\dfrac{\log\left(\frac{17}{2}\right)}{\log(4)} + 1}{5}$$
$$\approx 0.5087$$

2. $\log_3(x-5) = 4$
$$x - 5 = 3^4$$
$$x = 81 + 5$$
$$x = 86$$

3. $3b^7 - 18 = 7$
$$3b^7 = 25$$
$$b^7 = \frac{25}{3}$$
$$b = \left(\frac{25}{3}\right)^{\frac{1}{7}}$$
$$\approx 1.3538$$

$$8 + 2e^x = 15$$
$$2e^x = 7$$
$$e^x = \frac{7}{2}$$
$$\ln(e^x) = \ln\left(\frac{7}{2}\right)$$
$$x = \ln\left(\frac{7}{2}\right)$$
$$\approx 1.2528$$

5. $4\log_5(3x^2) + 3\log_5(6x^4) = 3$

$$\log_5(3x^2)^4 + \log_5(6x^4)^3 = 3$$
$$\log_5(81x^8) + \log_5(216x^{12}) = 3$$
$$\log_5[(81x^8)(216x^{12})] = 3$$
$$\log_5(17496x^{20}) = 3$$
$$17496x^{20} = 5^3$$
$$x^{20} = \frac{125}{17496}$$
$$x = \pm\left(\frac{125}{17496}\right)^{\frac{1}{20}}$$
$$\approx \pm 0.7811$$

6. $7 - 3(4w - 2) = 2(3w + 5) - 4(2w + 1)$
$$7 - 12w + 6 = 6w + 10 - 8w - 4$$
$$13 - 12w = -2w + 6$$
$$7 = 10w$$
$$\frac{7}{10} = w$$

7.
$x = 1$ because $y = 3^x$ and $y = 9\left(\frac{1}{3}\right)^x$ intersect

at $x = 1$.

8.
$x = 2$ because $y = 9\left(\frac{1}{3}\right)^x$ and $y = x - 1$

intersect at $x = 2$.

9. Substitute $x = 2y - 5$ into $4x - 5y = -14$.
$$4(2y - 5) - 5y = -14$$
$$8y - 20 - 5y = -14$$
$$3y = 6$$
$$y = 2$$
Find x.
$$x = 2(2) - 5$$
$$= -1$$
The solution is $(-1, 2)$.

10. Simplify $3(2 - 4x) = -10 - 2y$.
$$3(2 - 4x) = -10 - 2y$$
$$6 - 12x = -10 - 2y$$
$$-12x + 2y = -16$$
Multiply equation 2 by 6 and add.
$$-12x + 2y = -16$$
$$\underline{12x - 18y = -48}$$

$$-16y = -64$$
$$y = 4$$
Find x.
$$2x - 3(4) = -8$$
$$2x = 4$$
$$x = 2$$
The solution is $(2, 4)$.

11. $8x - 3 \ge -3(4x - 5)$
$$8x - 3 \ge -12x + 15$$
$$20x \ge 18$$
$$x \ge \frac{18}{20}$$
$$x \ge \frac{9}{10}$$
$$\left[\frac{9}{10}, \infty\right)$$

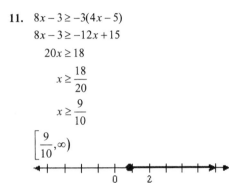

12. $(4b^{-3}c^2)^3(5b^{-7}c^{-1})^2$
$$(64b^{-9}c^6)(25b^{-14}c^{-2})$$
$$(64 \cdot 25)(b^{-9} \cdot b^{-14})(c^6 \cdot c^{-2})$$
$$1600b^{-23}c^4$$
$$\frac{1600c^4}{b^{23}}$$

13.
$$\frac{8b^{\frac{1}{3}}c^{-\frac{1}{2}}}{6b^{-\frac{1}{2}}c^{\frac{3}{4}}}$$
$$= \frac{4b^{\frac{1}{3}-\left(-\frac{1}{2}\right)}c^{-\frac{1}{2}-\frac{3}{4}}}{3}$$
$$= \frac{4b^{\frac{2}{6}+\frac{3}{6}}c^{-\frac{2}{4}-\frac{3}{4}}}{3}$$
$$= \frac{4b^{\frac{5}{6}}c^{-\frac{5}{4}}}{3}$$
$$= \frac{4b^{\frac{5}{6}}}{3c^{\frac{5}{4}}}$$

14. $4\log_b\left(x^7\right) - 2\log_b\left(7x\right)$

$$= \log_b\left(x^7\right)^4 - \log_b\left(7x\right)^2$$
$$= \log_b\left(x^{28}\right) - \log_b\left(49x^2\right)$$
$$= \log_b\left(\frac{x^{28}}{49x^2}\right)$$
$$= \log_b\left(\frac{x^{26}}{49}\right)$$

15. $3\ln\left(p^6\right) + 4\ln\left(p^2\right)$
$$= \ln\left(p^6\right)^3 + \ln\left(p^2\right)^4$$
$$= \ln\left(p^{18}\right) + \ln\left(p^8\right)$$
$$= \ln\left[\left(p^{18}\right)\left(p^8\right)\right]$$
$$= \ln\left(p^{26}\right)$$

16. $f(x) = 5(3)^x$

17. $g(x) = 3x + 25$

18. -7

19. 40

20. $f^{-1}(5) = 0$, since $f(0) = 5$.

21.

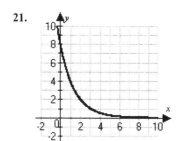

22.

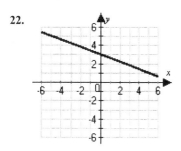

23.

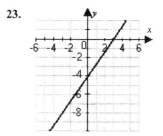

24.

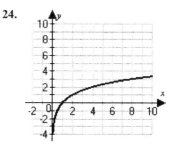

25. First find the slope.
$$m = \frac{-3 - 7}{5 + 4}$$
$$= -\frac{10}{9}$$

So $y = -\frac{10}{9}x + b$. Substitute a point, say $(-4, 7)$ to solve for b.
$$7 = -\frac{10}{9}(-4) + b$$
$$7 = \frac{40}{9} + b$$
$$7 - \frac{40}{9} = b$$
$$\frac{63}{9} - \frac{40}{9} = b$$
$$b = \frac{23}{9}$$

So the equation is $y = -\frac{10}{9}x + \frac{23}{9}$.

26. Both points satisfy the equation $y = ab^x$. This produces a system of equations.
$$13 = ab^7$$
$$85 = ab^3$$
Combine the equations.

$$\frac{13}{85} = \frac{ab^7}{ab^3}$$

$$\frac{13}{85} = b^4$$

$$b = \left(\frac{13}{85}\right)^{\frac{1}{4}}$$

Substitute this value of the base into the equation

$y = a\left(\left(\frac{13}{85}\right)^{\frac{1}{4}}\right)^x$. Substitute (3, 85) to find *a*.

$$85 = a\left(\left(\frac{13}{85}\right)^{\frac{1}{4}}\right)^3$$

$a \approx 347.56$

So the equation is $y = 347.56(0.63)^x$.

27.
$$f(-4) = 2(3)^{-4} = \frac{2}{81}$$

28.
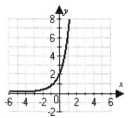

29.
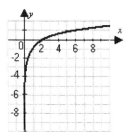

30. $f^{-1}(35)$

$$2(3)^x = 35$$

$$3^x = \frac{35}{2}$$

$$\log(3^x) = \log\left(\frac{35}{2}\right)$$

$$x\log(3) = \log\left(\frac{35}{2}\right)$$

$$x = \frac{\log\left(\frac{35}{2}\right)}{\log(3)}$$

$$\approx 2.6053$$

31.
$\log_3\left(\frac{1}{81}\right) = -4$, since $3^{-4} = \frac{1}{81}$.

32.
$\log_b\left(\sqrt[7]{b}\right) = \frac{1}{7}$, since $b^{\frac{1}{7}} = \sqrt[7]{b}$.

33.
$$\log_8(73) = \frac{\log(73)}{\log(8)}$$

$$\approx 2.0633$$

34. $f(-1) = 1$

35. The *y*-intercept is (0, 2). So the equation is
$y = 2b^x$. Substitute (-1, 1) to find *b*.

$$1 = 2b^{-1}$$

$$b^{-1} = \frac{1}{2}$$

$$b = \left(\frac{1}{2}\right)^{-1}$$

$$b = 2$$

So the equation is $f(x) = 2(2)^x$ or $f(x) = (2)^{x+1}$.

36.
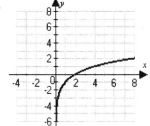

37. $f^{-1}(2)$

$$2 = 2(2)^x$$
$$2^x = 1$$
$$\log(2^x) = \log(1)$$
$$x\log(2) = 0$$
$$x = \frac{0}{\log(2)}$$
$$= 0$$

38.
$$f(x) = \frac{2}{7}x - 3$$

Replace $f(x)$ with y.

$$y = \frac{2}{7}x - 3$$

Solve for x.

$$y + 3 = \frac{2}{7}x$$

$$\frac{7}{2}(y + 3) = x$$

$$x = \frac{7}{2}y + \frac{21}{2}$$

Replace x with $f^{-1}(y)$.

$$f^{-1}(y) = \frac{7}{2}y + \frac{21}{2}$$

Replace y with x.

$$f^{-1}(x) = \frac{7}{2}x + \frac{21}{2}$$

39. $g^{-1}(x) = \log_8(x)$

40. Answers may vary. Example below.

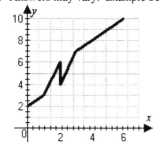

x	y
0	2
1	3
2	4
2	5
2	6
3	7

The relation is not a function because the input x = 2 has three different outputs y = 4, 5, and 6.

41. a. The y-intercept for both functions is (0, 2).

b. For f, as the value of x increases by 2, the value of $f(x)$ increases by 3.

For g, as the value of x increases by 2, the value of $g(x)$ is multiplied by 3.

c. g. Raising 3 to a large power (as happens in g for large x values) will yield a larger number than multiplying that number by 3 power (as happens in f).

d.

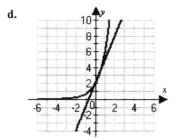

42. a. First find the slope.

$$m = \frac{8 - 3}{7 - 4} = \frac{5}{3}$$

So $y = \frac{5}{3}x + b$. Substitute (4. 3) to solve for b.

$$3 = \frac{5}{3}(4) + b$$

$$3 = \frac{20}{3} + b$$

$$3 - \frac{20}{3} = b$$

$$\frac{9}{3} - \frac{20}{3} = b$$

$$b = -\frac{11}{3}$$

174

So the equation is $y - \dfrac{5}{3}x - \dfrac{11}{3}$.

b. Both points satisfy the equation $y = ab^x$, which produces a system of equations.

$8 = ab^7$

$3 = ab^4$

Combine the equations.

$\dfrac{8}{3} = \dfrac{ab^7}{ab^4}$

$\dfrac{8}{3} = b^3$

$b = \left(\dfrac{8}{3}\right)^{\frac{1}{3}}$

$b \approx 1.3867$

Substitute this value of the base into the equation $y = a(1.3867)^x$. Substitute (4, 3) to find a.

$3 = a(1.3867)^4$

$a = \dfrac{3}{(1.3867)^4}$

$a \approx 0.81$

So the equation is $y = 0.81(1.39)^x$.

c.

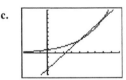

43. a. $f(2) = 3(2)$

$= 6$

$g(2) = 3^2$

$= 9$

b. Find f^{-1} .

$f(x) = 3x$

Replace $f(x)$ with y.

$y = 3x$

Solve for x :

$x = \dfrac{1}{3}y$

Replace x with $f^{-1}(y)$.

$f^{-1}(y) = \dfrac{1}{3}y$

Replace y with x.

$f^{-1}(x) = \dfrac{1}{3}x$

$g^{-1}(x) = \log_3(x)$

c. $f^{-1}(81) = \dfrac{1}{3}(81) = 27$

$g^{-1}(81) = \log_3(81) = 4$, since $3^4 = 81$

44. a. $U(x) = 0.69x + 19.95$

$B(x) = 0.45x + 29.95$

b. The slope of U is 0.69, so U-Haul charges \$0.69 per mile. The slope of B is 0.45, so Budget charges \$0.45 per mile.

c. $0.69x + 19.95 = 0.45x + 29.95$

$0.24x = 10$

$x = \dfrac{10}{0.24}$

≈ 41.67 miles

d. $U(x) < B(x)$

$0.69x + 19.95 < 0.45x + 29.95$

$0.24x < 10$

$x < 41.67$

U-Haul costs less than Budget for mileage less than 41.67 miles.

45. Write the system.

$x + y = 15000$

$43x + 60y = 721500$

Use substitution.

$43(15000 - y) + 60y = 721500$

$645000 - 43y + 60y = 721500$

$17y = 76500$

$y = 4500$

Find x.

$$x + 4500 = 15000$$
$$x = 10500$$
10,500 tickets at \$43 and 4500 tickets at \$60

46. a. $f(t) = 2.51(1.1)^t$, where $t = 0$ in 2003

b. The *n*-intercept is the value with $t = 0$, which is 2.51 million books in print in 2003.

c. 1.1. The number of books has increased by 10% per year.

d.
$$f(t) = 2.51(1.1)^t$$
$$5 = 2.51(1.1)^t$$
$$\frac{5}{2.51} = \frac{2.51(1.1)^t}{2.51}$$
$$\log\left(\frac{5}{2.51}\right) = \log(1.1)^t$$
$$\frac{\log\left(\frac{5}{2.51}\right)}{\log(1.1)} = \frac{t\log(1.1)}{\log(1.1)}$$
$$7.23 \approx t$$
There will be 5 million books in print in 2003 + 7 = 2010.

47. a. Create a scattergram to determine the type of regression to use.

Using exponential regression, the points fit the curve $s = f(t) = 20.69(0.78)^t$.

b. (0, 20.69) There were 20.69 cases of syphilis per 100,000 people in 1990.

c. Rate of decay = $0.1 - 0.78$
$$= 0.22$$
The number of cases decreases by 22% each year.

d. $f(t) = 1$

$$20.69(0.78)^t = 1$$
$$0.78^t = \frac{1}{20.69}$$
$$\log(0.78^t) = \log\left(\frac{1}{20.69}\right)$$
$$t\log(0.78) = \log\left(\frac{1}{20.69}\right)$$
$$t = \frac{\log\left(\frac{1}{20.69}\right)}{\log(0.78)}$$
$$t \approx 12.19$$
There will be 1 case per 100,000 people in 1990 + 12 = 2002.

e. $f^{-1}(0.1)$
$$20.69(0.78)^t = 0.1$$
$$0.78^t = \frac{0.1}{20.69}$$
$$\log(0.78^t) = \log\left(\frac{0.1}{20.69}\right)$$
$$t\log(0.78) = \log\left(\frac{0.1}{20.69}\right)$$
$$t = \frac{\log\left(\frac{0.1}{20.69}\right)}{\log(0.78)}$$
$$t \approx 21.46$$
There will be 1 case per million people in 1990 + 21 = 2011.

f. 2004 is $t = 14$
$$f(14) = 20.69(0.78)^{14} \approx 0.64$$
There are 0.64 cases per 100,000 people. No, the 2004 rate of 2.7 is greater than the 2000 rate of 2.1.

48. a.

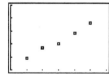

The plotted data appears to lie in a line. A linear function would best model the data.

b. Using the linear regression feature on a graphing calculator, $f(t) = 1.3t + 102.5$.

c. The slope is 1.3. The slope means the

average maximum speed increases by 1.3 miles per hour each year.

d. $f(t) = 1.3t + 102.5$

$0 = 1.3t + 102.5$

$$\frac{-102.5}{1.3} = \frac{1.3t}{1.3}$$

$-78.85 \approx t$

The *t*-intercept, $(-78.85, 0)$, tells when the average maximum speed was 0, which is $1980 - 79 = 1901$.

e. $f(30) = 1.3(30) + 102.5 = 141.5$

In $1980 + 30 = 2010$, the average maximum speed will be 142 miles per hour.

f.   Replace $f(t)$ with *s*.

$s = 1.3t + 102.5$

Solve for *t*.

$s = 1.3t + 102.5$

$s - 102.5 = 1.3t$

$$\frac{s - 102.5}{1.3} = \frac{1.3t}{1.3}$$

$.77s - 78.85 = 141.5$

An approximate equation is

$f^{-1}(s) = 0.77s - 78.85$.

g. $f^{-1}(145) = 0.77(145) - 78.85 = 32.8$

In $1980 + 33 = 2013$, the average maximum speed will be 145 miles per hour.

Chapter 6
Polynomial Functions

Homework 6.1

1. $5x^2 - 6x + 2$ is a quadratic (2nd-degree) polynomial of one variable.

3. $-2x^3 - 4x^2 + 5x - 1$ is a cubic (3rd-degree) polynomial of one variable.

5. $6p^4q^3 + 3p^2q^4 - 2q^5$ is a 5th-degree polynomial of two variables.

7. $6x^2 - 3x - 2x^2 + 4x = 6x^2 - 2x^2 - 3x + 4x$
$$= (6-2)x^2 + (-3+4)x$$
$$= 4x^2 + x$$

9. $-5x^3 - 4x + 2x^2 - 7x^3 + 5 - x$
$$= -5x^3 - 7x^3 + 2x^2 - 4x - x + 5$$
$$= (-5-7)x^3 + 2x^2 + (-4-1)x + 5$$
$$= -12x^3 + 2x^2 - 5x + 5$$

11. $4a^4b^2 - 7ab^3 - 9a^4b^2 + 2ab^3$
$$= 4a^4b^2 - 9a^4b^2 - 7ab^3 + 2ab^3$$
$$= (4-9)a^4b^2 + (-7+2)ab^3$$
$$= -5a^4b^2 - 5ab^3$$

13. $2x^4 - 4x^3y + 2x^2y^2 + x^3y - 2x^2y^2 + xy^3$
$$= 2x^4 - 4x^3y + x^3y + 2x^2y^2 - 2x^2y^2 + xy^3$$
$$= 2x^4 + (-4+1)x^3y + (2-2)x^2y^2 + xy^3$$
$$= 2x^4 - 3x^3y + xy^3$$

15. $\left(3x^2 - 5x - 2\right) + \left(6x^2 + 2x - 7\right)$
$$= 3x^2 + 6x^2 - 5x + 2x - 2 - 7$$
$$= 9x^2 - 3x - 9$$

17. $\left(-2x^3 + 4x - 3\right) + \left(5x^3 - 6x^2 + 2\right)$
$$= -2x^3 + 5x^3 - 6x^2 + 4x - 3 + 2$$
$$= 3x^3 - 6x^2 + 4x - 1$$

19. $\left(8a^2 - 7ab + 2b^2\right) + \left(3a^2 + 4ab - 7b^2\right)$
$$= 8a^2 + 3a^2 - 7ab + 4ab + 2b^2 - 7b^2$$
$$= 11a^2 - 3ab - 5b^2$$

21. $\left(2m^4p + m^3p^2 - 7m^2p^3\right) + \left(m^3p^2 + 7m^2p^3 - 8mp^3\right)$
$$= 2m^4p + m^3p^2 + m^3p^2 - 7m^2p^3 + 7m^2p^3 - 8mp^3$$
$$= 2m^4p + 2m^3p^2 - 8mp^3$$

23. $\left(2x^2 + 4x - 7\right) - \left(9x^2 - 5x + 4\right)$
$$= 2x^2 - 9x^2 + 4x + 5x - 7 - 4$$
$$= -7x^2 + 9x - 11$$

25. $\left(6x^3 - 3x^2 + 4\right) - \left(-7x^3 + x - 1\right)$
$$= 6x^3 + 7x^3 - 3x^2 - x + 4 + 1$$
$$= 13x^3 - 3x^2 - x + 5$$

27. $\left(8m^2 + 3mp - 5p^2\right) - \left(-2m^2 - 7mp - 4p^2\right)$
$$= 8m^2 + 2m^2 + 3mp + 7mp - 5p^2 + 4p^2$$
$$= 10m^2 + 10mp - p^2$$

29. $\left(a^3b - 5a^2b^2 + ab^3\right) - \left(5a^2b^2 - 7ab^3 + b^3\right)$
$$= a^3b - 5a^2b^2 - 5a^2b^2 + ab^3 + 7ab^3 + b^3$$
$$= a^3b - 10a^2b^2 + 8ab^3 + b^3$$

31. $f(3) = -2(3)^2 - 5(3) + 3$
$$= -30$$

33. $g(-4) = 3(-4)^2 - 8(-4) - 1$
$$= 79$$

35. $f(0) = -2(0)^2 - 5(0) + 3$
$$= 3$$

37. $h(3) = 2(3)^3 - 4(3)$
$$= 42$$

39. $h(-2) = 2(-2)^3 - 4(-2)$
$$= -8$$

41. $f(-1) = 3$

43. $f(1) = -1$

45. $a = -1$ or $a = 3$

47. $a = 1$

49. $f(0) = 19$

51. $f(4) = 3$

53. $x = 0$ or $x = 6$

55. $x = 3$

57. a. $x = 1$ or $x = 5$

    b. $f(x)$ does not have an inverse function because $f(2) = f(4) = 3$. There would be two values of $f^{-1}(x)$ for one value of x, and such a relation is not a function.

59.

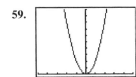

61.

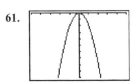

63.

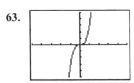

65.

67.
$$f + g = \left(4x^2 - 2x + 8\right) + \left(7x^2 + 5x - 1\right)$$
$$= 4x^2 + 7x^2 - 2x + 5x + 8 - 1$$
$$= 11x^2 + 3x + 7$$
$$(f + g)(3) = 11(3)^2 + 3(3) + 7$$
$$= 115$$

69.
$$f - h = \left(4x^2 - 2x + 8\right) - \left(-3x^2 - 4x - 9\right)$$
$$= 4x^2 + 3x^2 - 2x + 4x + 8 + 9$$
$$= 7x^2 + 2x + 17$$
$$(f - h)(4) = 7(4)^2 + 2(4) + 17$$
$$= 137$$

71.
$$f + g = \left(2x^3 - 4x + 1\right) + \left(-3x^2 + 5x - 3\right)$$
$$= 2x^3 - 3x^2 - 4x + 5x + 1 - 3$$
$$= 2x^3 - 3x^2 + x - 2$$
$$(f + g)(2) = 2(2)^3 - 3(2)^2 + 2 - 2$$
$$= 4$$

73.
$$f - h = \left(2x^3 - 4x + 1\right) - \left(x^3 - 3x^2 + 2x\right)$$
$$= 2x^3 - x^3 + 3x^2 - 4x - 2x + 1$$
$$= x^3 + 3x^2 - 6x + 1$$
$$(f - h)(-1) = (-1)^3 + 3(-1)^2 - 6(-1) + 1$$
$$= 9$$

75. a.
$$M(t) + S(t) = \left(-0.28t + 35.64\right) + \left(0.86t + 8.3\right)$$
$$= -0.28t + 0.86t + 35.64 + 8.3$$
$$= 0.58t + 43.94$$

    b. For the expression $M(t) + S(t)$, we have $M(t)$ = gallons of milk per person + $S(t)$ = gallons of soft drinks per person. The units of the expression are gallons of milk and soft drinks per person.

    c.
$$\left(M + S\right)\left(60\right) = 0.58\left(60\right) + 43.94$$
$$= 78.74$$
In 2010, the annual consumption of milk and soft drinks will be 78.7 gallons per person.

    d.
$$M - S = \left(-0.28t + 35.64\right) - \left(0.86t + 8.3\right)$$
$$= -0.28t - 0.86t + 35.64 - 8.3$$
$$= -1.14t + 27.34$$

e. $(M-S)(60) = -1.14(60) + 27.34$

$\qquad = -41.06$

This means that in 2010, consumption of soft drinks will exceed consumption of milk by 41.06 gallons per person.

77. a. $B+S$

$= (2.3t^2 - 12.1t + 98) + (1.57t^2 - 10.9t + 28)$

$= 2.3t^2 + 1.57t^2 - 12.1t - 10.9t + 98 + 28$

$= 3.87t^2 - 23t + 126$

b. For the expression $B(t) + S(t)$, we have $B(t) =$ base pay in thousands of dollars $+ S(t) =$ signing bonus in thousands of dollars. The expression is the total compensation in thousands of dollars.

c. $(B+S)(11) = 3.87(11)^2 - 23(11) + 126$

$\qquad = 341.27$

In 2011, the total average compensation will be about $341,000.

d. $B-S$

$= (2.3t^2 - 12.1t + 98) - (1.57t^2 - 10.9t + 28)$

$= 2.3t^2 - 1.57t^2 - 12.1t + 10.9t + 98 - 28$

$= 0.73t^2 - 1.2t + 70$

e. $(B-S)(11) = 0.73(11)^2 - 1.2(11) + 70$

$\qquad = 145.13$

In 2011, average base pay will exceed average signing bonuses by about $145, 13.

79. The student did not apply the negative sign to $4x$ and 3.

$(6x^2 + 8x + 5) - (2x^2 + 4x + 3)$

$= 6x^2 + 8x + 5 - 2x^2 - 4x - 3$

$= 4x^2 + 4x + 2$

81. a. $f - g = (3x+7) - (5x+2)$

$\qquad = 3x - 5x + 7 - 2$

$\qquad = -2x + 5$

$g - f = (5x+2) - (3x+7)$

$\qquad = 5x - 3x + 2 - 7$

$\qquad = 2x - 5$

b. $(f-g)(2) = -2(2) + 5 = 1$

$(g-f)(2) = 2(2) - 5 = -1$

$(f-g)(2) = -(g-f)(2)$

c. $(f-g)(4) = -2(4) + 5 = -3$

$(g-f)(4) = 2(4) - 5 = 3$

$(f-g)(4) = -(g-f)(4)$

d. $(f-g)(7) = -2(7) + 5 = -9$

$(g-f)(7) = 2(7) - 5 = 9$

$(f-g)(7) = -(g-f)(7)$

e. In each case, $(f-g)(x) = -(g-f)(x)$. This makes sense because $f - g = (-1)(g-f)$.

83. Answers will vary.

For example, to add two polynomials, combine like terms. To subtract polynomials, first distribute -1 to the second polynomial and then combine like terms.

85. b

87. c

89. a

91.

$\left(\dfrac{25b^5c^{-7}}{4b^{-3}c}\right)^{1/2} = \dfrac{25^{\frac{1}{2}}b^{5\cdot\frac{1}{2}}c^{-7\cdot\frac{1}{2}}}{4^{\frac{1}{2}}b^{-3\cdot\frac{1}{2}}c^{\frac{1}{2}}}$

$= \dfrac{5b^{5/2}c^{-7/2}}{2b^{-3/2}c^{1/2}}$

$= \dfrac{5b^{\frac{5}{2}-\left(-\frac{3}{2}\right)}c^{-\frac{7}{2}-\frac{1}{2}}}{2}$

$= \dfrac{5b^4c^{-4}}{2}$

$= \dfrac{5b^4}{2c^4}$

$\left(\dfrac{25b^5c^{-7}}{4b^{-3}c}\right)^{1/2}$ is a polynomial expression of degree 0 in two variables.

93. $f(x) = -2(2)^x$

$$\left(\frac{25b^5c^{-7}}{4b^{-3}c}\right)^{1/2}$$

$f(x) = -2(2)^x$ is an exponential equation in one variable.

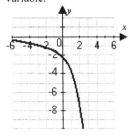

Homework 6.2

1. $3x^2\left(6x^4\right) = 18x^6$

3. $2a^3b^5\left(-4a^2b^3\right) = -8a^5b^8$

5. $-6x\left(5x-2\right) = -30x^2 + 12x$

7. $5ab^2\left(4a^2 - 7ab + 3b^2\right)$
$= 20a^3b^2 - 35a^2b^3 + 15ab^4$

9. $(x+3)(x+6)$
$= x^2 + 3x + 6x + 18$
$= x^2 + 9x + 18$

11. $(3m-2)(5m+4)$
$= 15m^2 + 12m - 10m - 8$
$= 15m^2 + 2m - 8$

13. $(8x-3)(4x-1)$
$= 32x^2 - 8x - 12x + 3$
$= 32x^2 - 20x + 3$

15. $(1.7x - 2.4)(2.3x + 1.2)$
$= 3.91x^2 + 2.04x - 5.52x - 2.88$
$= 3.91x^2 - 3.48x - 2.88$

17. $(2a + 5b)(3a - 7b)$
$= 6a^2 - 14ab + 15ab - 35b^2$
$= 6a^2 + ab - 35b^2$

19. $(4x - 9y)(5x - 2y)$
$= 20x^2 - 8xy - 35xy + 18y^2$
$= 20x^2 - 43xy + 18y^2$

21. $\left(2a^2 - 5b^2\right)\left(7a^2 + 3b^2\right)$
$= 14a^4 + 6a^2b^2 - 35a^2b^2 - 15b^4$
$= 14a^4 - 29a^2b^2 - 15b^4$

23. $3x^2(2x-5)(4x+1)$
$= 3x^2\left(8x^2 + 2x - 20x - 5\right)$
$= 3x^2\left(8x^2 - 18x - 5\right)$
$= 24x^4 - 54x^3 - 15x^2$

25. $5x\left(x^2 + 3\right)(x-4)$
$= 5x\left(x^3 - 4x^2 + 3x - 12\right)$
$= 5x^4 - 20x^3 + 15x^2 - 60x$

27. $(3x + 2)\left(4x^2 + 5x - 3\right)$
$= 12x^3 + 15x^2 - 9x + 8x^2 + 10x - 6$
$= 12x^3 + 23x^2 + x - 6$

29. $(a+b)\left(a^2 - ab + b^2\right)$
$= a^3 - a^2b + ab^2 + a^2b - ab^2 + b^3$
$= a^3 + b^3$

31. $(4x - 3y)\left(2x^2 - xy + 5y^2\right)$
$= 8x^3 - 4x^2y + 20xy^2 - 6x^2y + 3xy^2 - 15y^3$
$= 8x^3 - 10x^2y + 23xy^2 - 15y^3$

33. $\left(x^2 + 2x - 3\right)\left(x^2 - x + 2\right)$
$= x^4 - x^3 + 2x^2 + 2x^3 - 2x^2 + 4x - 3x^2 + 3x - 6$
$= x^4 + x^3 - 3x^2 + 7x - 6$

35. $\left(2x^2 + xy - 3y^2\right)\left(x^2 - 2xy + y^2\right)$
$= 2x^4 - 4x^3y + 2x^2y^2 + x^3y - 2x^2y^2 + xy^3$
$ -3x^2y^2 + 6xy^3 - 3y^4$
$= 2x^4 - 3x^3y - 3x^2y^2 + 7xy^3 - 3y^4$

37. $(x+5)^2 = (x+5)(x+5)$

$\quad = x^2 + 5x + 5x + 25$

$\quad = x^2 + 10x + 25$

39. $(x-8)^2 = (x-8)(x-8)$

$\quad = x^2 - 8x - 8x + 64$

$\quad = x^2 - 16x + 64$

41. $(3x+5)^2 = (3x+5)(3x+5)$

$\quad = 9x^2 + 15x + 15x + 25$

$\quad = 9x^2 + 30x + 25$

43. $(2.6x - 3.2)^2 = (2.6x - 3.2)(2.6x - 3.2)$

$\quad = 6.76x^2 - 8.32x - 8.32x + 10.24$

$\quad = 6.76x^2 - 16.64x + 10.24$

45. $(4a+3b)^2 = (4a+3b)(4a+3b)$

$\quad = 16a^2 + 12ab + 12ab + 9b^2$

$\quad = 16a^2 + 24ab + 9b^2$

47. $(2x^2 - 6y^2)^2 = (2x^2 - 6y^2)(2x^2 - 6y^2)$

$\quad = 4x^4 - 12x^2y^2 - 12x^2y^2 + 36y^4$

$\quad = 4x^4 - 24x^2y^2 + 36y^4$

49. $-2x(2x+5)^2 = -2x(2x+5)(2x+5)$

$\quad = -2x(4x^2 + 10x + 10x + 25)$

$\quad = -2x(4x^2 + 20x + 25)$

$\quad -8x^3 - 40x^2 - 50x$

51. $(x-4)(x+4) = x^2 + 4x - 4x - 16$

$\quad = x^2 - 16$

53. $(3x+6)(3x-6) = 9x^2 - 18x + 18x - 36$

$\quad = 9x^2 - 36$

55. $(2r - 8t)(2r + 8t) = 4r^2 + 16rt - 16rt - 64t^2$

$\quad = 4r^2 - 64t^2$

57. $(3rt - 9w)(3rt + 9w)$

$\quad = 9r^2t^2 - 27rtw + 27rtw - 81w^2$

$\quad = 9r^2t^2 - 81w^2$

59. $(8a^2 + 3b^2)(8a^2 - 3b^2)$

$\quad = 64a^4 - 24a^2b^2 + 24a^2b^2 - 9b^4$

$\quad = 64a^4 - 9b^4$

61. $(x-2)(x+2)(x^2 + 4)$

$\quad = (x^2 + 2x - 2x - 4)(x^2 + 4)$

$\quad = (x^2 - 4)(x^2 + 4)$

$\quad = x^4 + 4x^2 - 4x^2 - 16$

$\quad = x^4 - 16$

63. $(3a + 2b)(3a - 2b)(9a^2 + 4b^2)$

$\quad = (9a^2 - 6ab + 6ab - 4b^2)(9a^2 + 4b^2)$

$\quad = (9a^2 - 4b^2)(9a^2 + 4b^2)$

$\quad = 81a^4 + 36a^2b^2 - 36a^2b^2 - 16b^4$

$\quad = 81a^4 - 16b^4$

65. $f(5b) = (5b)^2 - 3(5b) = 25b^2 - 15b$

67. $f(c+4) = (c+4)^2 - 3(c+4)$

$\quad = c^2 + 8c + 16 - 3c - 12$

$\quad = c^2 + 5c + 4$

69. $f(b-3) = (b-3)^2 - 3(b-3)$

$\quad = b^2 - 6b + 9 - 3b + 9$

$\quad = b^2 - 9b + 18$

71. $f(a+2) - f(a)$

$\quad = \left((a+2)^2 - 3(a+2)\right) - \left((a)^2 - 3(a)\right)$

$\quad = a^2 + 4a + 4 - 3a - 6 - a^2 + 3a$

$\quad = 4a - 2$

73. $f(a+h) - f(a)$

$\quad = \left((a+h)^2 - 3(a+h)\right) - \left((a)^2 - 3(a)\right)$

$\quad = a^2 + 2ah + h^2 - 3a - 3h - a^2 + 3a$

$\quad = 2ah + h^2 - 3h$

75.
$$f(x) = (x+6)^2$$
$$= (x+6)(x+6)$$
$$= x^2 + 6x + 6x + 36$$
$$= x^2 + 12x + 36$$

77.
$$f(x) = 2(x+3)^2 + 1$$
$$= 2(x+3)(x+3) + 1$$
$$= 2(x^2 + 3x + 3x + 9) + 1$$
$$= 2(x^2 + 6x + 9) + 1$$
$$= 2x^2 + 12x + 18 + 1$$
$$= 2x^2 + 12x + 19$$

79.
$$f(x) = -3(x-5)^2 - 1$$
$$= -3(x-5)(x-5) - 1$$
$$= -3(x^2 - 5x - 5x + 25) - 1$$
$$= -3(x^2 - 10x + 25) - 1$$
$$= -3x^2 + 30x - 75 - 1$$
$$= -3x^2 + 30x - 76$$

81.
$$f \cdot g = (2x-3)(3x+2)$$
$$= 6x^2 + 4x - 9x - 6$$
$$= 6x^2 - 5x - 6$$
$$(f \cdot g)(3) = 6(3)^2 - 5(3) - 6 = 33$$

83.
$$f \cdot h = (2x-3)(2x^2 - 4x + 3)$$
$$= 4x^3 - 8x^2 + 6x - 6x^2 + 12x - 9$$
$$= 4x^3 - 14x^2 + 18x - 9$$
$$(f \cdot h)(3) = 4(2)^3 - 14(2)^2 + 18(2) - 9 = 3$$

85.
$$f \cdot f = (2x-3)(2x-3)$$
$$= 4x^2 - 6x - 6x + 9$$
$$= 4x^2 - 12x + 9$$
$$(f \cdot f)(4) = 4(4)^2 - 12(4) + 9 = 25$$

87.
$$f \cdot g = (4x+1)(5x+3)$$
$$= 20x^2 + 12x + 5x + 3$$
$$= 20x^2 + 17x + 3$$
$$(f \cdot g)(-1) = 20(-1)^2 + 17(-1) + 3 = 6$$

89.
$$f \cdot h = (4x+1)(3x^2 - x - 2)$$
$$= 12x^3 - 4x^2 - 8x + 3x^2 - x - 2$$
$$= 12x^3 - x^2 - 9x - 2$$
$$(f \cdot h)(-2) = 12(-2)^3 - (-2)^2 - 9(-2) - 2$$
$$= -84$$

91.
$$h \cdot h = (3x^2 - x - 2)(3x^2 - x - 2)$$
$$= 9x^4 - 3x^3 - 6x^2 - 3x^3 + x^2 + 2x - 6x^2 + 2x + 4$$
$$= 9x^4 - 6x^3 - 11x^2 + 4x + 4$$
$$(h \cdot h)(1) = 9(1)^4 - 6(1)^3 - 11(1)^2 + 4(1) + 4 = 0$$

93. a. $V(t) = 55t + 557$

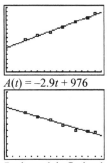

$A(t) = -2.9t + 976$

Both models fit the data well.

b.
$$V \cdot A = (55t + 557)(-2.9t + 976)$$
$$= -159.5t^2 + 52064.7t + 543632$$

c. For the expression $V(t) \cdot A(t)$, we have $V(t) =$ average value of farmland in dollars per acre $\times A(t) =$ amount of farmland in millions of acres. The units of the expression are total value of farmland in millions of dollars.

d. $(V \cdot A)(20)$
$$= -159.5(20)^2 + 52064.7(20) + 543632$$
$$= 1521126$$
The total value of farmland in 2010 will be $1.52 trillion.

e.

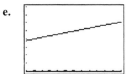

The function is increasing. This means that the total value of farmland is increasing. The average value of farmland is increasing from 1998 to 2010 at a faster rate than the rate of decrease in the total amount of farmland.

95. a. $B(t) = -0.24t^2 + 7.2t - 3.3$

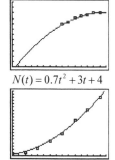

$N(t) = 0.7t^2 + 3t + 4$

Both models fit the data well.

b. $B \cdot N$

$= \left(-0.24t^2 + 7.2t - 3.3\right)\left(0.7t^2 + 3t + 4\right)$

$= -0.168t^4 + 4.32t^3 + 18.33t^2 + 18.9t - 13.2$

c. For the expression $B(t) \cdot N(t)$, we have $B(t) =$ average bill in dollars per month $\times N(t) =$ number of subscribers in millions of people. The units of the expression are millions of dollars per month.

d. $(B \cdot N)(21)$

$= -0.168(21)^4 + 4.32(21)^3 + 18.33(21)^2 +$

$18.9(21) - 13.2$

$= 15801.942$

In 2011, total cell phone bills will be \$15.8 billion.

e.

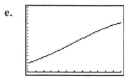

The function is increasing. This means that the total value of cell phone bills will be increasing from 1998 to 2010.

97. The student did not complete the square.

$(x + 8)^2 = (x + 8)(x + 8)$

$= x^2 + 8x + 8x + 64$

$= x^2 + 16x + 64$

99. a. $(x + 2)^2$

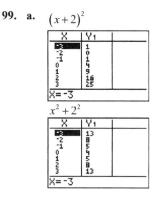

$x^2 + 2^2$

b. $(x + 2)^2 = (x + 2)(x + 2)$

$= x^2 + 2x + 2x + 4$

$= x^2 + 4x + 4$

c. $(x + 2)^2$

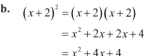

$x^2 + 4x + 4$

101. The student performed subtraction instead of multiplication.

$7x(-2x) = -14x^2$

103. $(2x - 5)(3x + 4) = 6x^2 + 8x - 15x - 20$

$= 6x^2 - 7x - 20$

$3x(2x - 2) - x - 20 = 6x^2 - 6x - x - 20$

$= 6x^2 - 7x - 20$

$(3x + 4)(2x - 5) = 6x^2 - 15x + 8x - 20$

$= 6x^2 - 7x - 20$

$(3x - 4)(2x + 5) = 6x^2 + 15x - 8x - 20$

$= 6x^2 + 7x - 20$

105. $(A - B)^2 = (A - B)(A - B)$

$= A^2 - AB - AB + B^2$

$= A^2 - 2AB + B^2$

107. $7x^{1/3} - 5x^{1/3} = (7-5)x^{1/3} = 2x^{1/3}$

109. $\left(7x^{1/3}\right)\left(-5x^{1/3}\right) = -35x^{2/3}$

111. $f(x) = (2x-5)(3x-1)$
$= 6x^2 - 2x - 15x + 5$
$= 6x^2 - 17x + 5$
This is a quadratic function.

113. $f(x) = x^2 - (x+1)^2$
$= x^2 - (x+1)(x+1)$
$= x^2 - (x^2 + 2x + 1)$
$= -2x - 1$
This is a linear function.

115. $\log_b(x+5) + \log_b(x-3)$
$= \log_b(x+5)(x-3)$
$= \log_b(x^2 + 2x - 15)$

117. $2\log_b(w-3) + \log_b(w+3)$
$= \log_b(w-3)^2(w+3)$
$= \log_b(w-3)(w-3)(w+3)$
$= \log_b(w^2 - 6w + 9)(w+3)$
$= \log_b(w^3 - 3w^2 - 9w + 27)$

119. $4x(3x+5)(2x-3)$
$= 4x(6x^2 - 9x + 10x - 15)$
$= 4x(6x^2 + x - 15)$
$= 24x^3 + 4x^2 - 60x$
$4x(3x+5)(2x-3)$ is a cubic polynomial in one variable.

121. $f(x) = -3(x-4)^2 + 5$
$= -3(x-4)(x-4) + 5$
$= -3(x^2 - 4x - 4x + 16) + 5$
$= -3(x^2 - 8x + 16) + 5$
$= -3x^2 + 24x - 48 + 5$
$= -3x^2 + 24x - 43$
$f(x) = -3(x-4)^2 + 5$ is a quadratic polynomial in one variable.

Homework 6.3

1. $x^2 + 11x + 28 = (x+4)(x+7)$

3. $x^2 - 8x + 12 = (x-6)(x-2)$

5. $r^2 - 4r - 32 = (r-8)(r+4)$

7. $x^2 + 5x - 14 = (x+7)(x-2)$

9. This expression is prime since there are no two integers with a product of -12 and a sum of -7.

11. $x^2 + 10x + 25 = (x+5)(x+5)$

13. $t^2 - 18t + 81 = (t-9)(t-9)$

15. $4x - 5 + x^2 = x^2 + 4x - 5$
$= (x+5)(x-1)$

17. $a^2 + 12ab + 20b^2 = (a+10b)(a+2b)$

19. $w^2 - 5wy + 4y^2 = (w-4y)(w-y)$

21. $p^2 + 3pq - 28q^2 = (p+7q)(p-4q)$

23. This expression is prime since there are no two integers with product -16 and sum 4.

25. $p^2 - 6pq - 16q^2 = (p-8q)(p+2q)$

27. $3x + 21 = 3(x+7)$

29. $16x^2 - 12x = 4x(4x-3)$

31. $9y^5 + 18y^3 = 9y^3(y^2+2)$

33. $3ab - 12a^2b = 3ab(1-4a)$

35. $18a^4b^2 + 12a^2b^3 = 6a^2b^2(3a^2 + 2b)$

37. $-14x^5y + 63x^2y^2 = 7x^2y(-2x^3 + 9y)$

39. $2x^2 + 12x + 18 = 2(x^2 + 6x + 9)$
$= 2(x+3)(x+3)$

41. $3x^2 - 3x + 18 = 3(x^2 - x + 6)$

43. $15k - 50 + 5k^2 = 5(k^2 + 3k - 10)$
$\qquad = 5(k+5)(k-2)$

45. $-4x^2 + 24x - 36 = -4(x^2 - 6x + 9)$
$\qquad = -4(x-3)(x-3)$

47. $-x^2 + 11x - 10 = -1(x^2 - 11x + 10)$
$\qquad = -1(x-10)(x-1)$

49. This expression is prime.

51. $4x^3 - 24x^2 + 32x = 4x(x^2 - 6x + 8)$
$\qquad = 4x(x-4)(x-2)$

53. $a^4 - 21a^3 + 20a^2 = a^2(a^2 - 21a + 20)$
$\qquad = a^2(a-20)(a-1)$

55. $5x^2y + 45xy^2 + 40y^3 = 5y(x^2 + 9xy + 8y^2)$
$\qquad = 5y(x+8y)(x+y)$

57. $4x^4y - 12x^3y^2 - 40x^2y^3 = 4x^2y(x^2 - 3xy - 10y^2)$
$\qquad = 4x^2y(x-5y)(x+2y)$

59. $-2x^3y^2 + 16x^2y^3 - 32xy^4 = -2xy^2(x^2 - 8xy + 16y^2)$
$\qquad = -2xy^2(x-4y)(x-4y)$

61. The student did not complete the factoring.
$2x^2 + 16x + 30 = 2(x^2 + 8x + 15)$
$\qquad = 2(x+5)(x+3)$

63. The student did not complete the factoring.
$12x^3 + 18x^2 = 6x^2(2x+3)$

65. $(x-3)(x+6) = x^2 + 6x - 3x - 18$
$\qquad = x^2 + 3x - 18$
$(x+6)(x-3) = x^2 - 3x + 6x - 18$
$\qquad = x^2 + 3x - 18$

67. a. $x^2 - 5x + 4 = (x-4)(x-1)$

b.

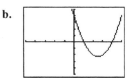

The x-intercepts are $x = 1$ and $x = 4$.

c. The factors in part (a) are equal to the x-intercept of f. This makes sense when $f(x) = 0$

69. Answers may vary.
$x^2 + 5x + 4 = (x+4)(x+1)$
$x^2 + 8x + 16 = (x+4)(x+4)$
$x^2 + 2x - 8 = (x+4)(x-2)$

71. To factor $x^2 + kx + 28$, find all the values of p and q such that $pq = 28$ and $p + q = k$.

Product = 28	Sum = k
$1(28) = 28$	$1 + 28 = 29$
$2(14) = 28$	$2 + 14 = 16$
$4(7) = 28$	$4 + 7 = 11$
$-1(-28) = 28$	$-1 - 28 = -29$
$-2(-14) = 28$	$-2 - 14 = -16$
$-4(-7) = 28$	$-4 - 7 = -11$

73. Answers may vary.

75. $(x+5)(x-3) = x^2 - 3x + 5x - 15$
$\qquad = x^2 + 2x - 15$

77. $k^2 - 7k - 30 = (k-10)(k+3)$

79. $(7x-5)(7x+5) = 49x^2 - 35x + 35x - 25$
$\qquad = 49x^2 - 25$

81. $81r^2 - 49 = (9r+7)(9r-7)$

83. $x^2 + 3x - 28 = (x+7)(x-4)$
$x^2 + 3x - 28$ is a quadratic expression in one variable.

85. $(3w-4)(2w^2 + 3w - 5) = 6w^3 + w^2 - 27w + 20$
$6w^3 + w^2 - 27w + 20$ is a cubic expression in one variable.

Homework 6.4

1. $x^3 + 3x^2 + 4x + 12 = (x^2 + 4)(x+3)$

3. $5x^3 - 20x^2 + 3x - 12 = (5x^2 + 3)(x - 4)$

5. $6m^3 - 15m^2 + 2m - 5 = (3m^2 + 1)(2m - 5)$

7. $10x^3 + 25x^2 - 2x - 5 = (5x^2 - 1)(2x + 5)$

9. $ax - 3ay - 2bx + 6by = (x - 3y)(a - 2b)$

11. $5a^2x + 2a^2y - 5bx - 2by = (a^2 - b)(5x + 2y)$

13. $3x^2 + 11x + 10 = (3x + 5)(x + 2)$

15. $2x^2 - x - 15 = (2x + 5)(x - 3)$

17. $5p^2 - 21p + 4 = (5p - 1)(p - 4)$

19. $4x^2 + 16x + 15 = (2x + 5)(2x + 3)$

21. This expression is prime.

23. $1 + 9w^2 - 6w = (1 - 3w)(1 - 3w)$

25. $15x^2 + x - 6 = (5x - 3)(3x + 2)$

27. $6x^2 - 17x + 12 = (3x - 4)(2x - 3)$

29. $16y^2 - 29y - 6 = (16y + 3)(y - 2)$

31. $10a^2 + 21ab + 9b^2 = (5a + 3b)(2a + 3b)$

33. $20x^2 + 17xy - 3y^2 = (20x - 3y)(x + y)$

35. This expression is prime.

37. $4r^2 - 20ry + 25y^2 = (2r - 5y)(2r - 5y)$

39. $6x^2 + 26x - 20 = (3x - 2)(2x + 10)$

41. $-12x^2 + 3x + 9 = (4x + 3)(-3x + 3)$

43. $12x - 32x^2 + 16x^3 = 4x(3 - 8x + 4x^2)$
$$= 4x(2x - 3)(2x - 1)$$

45. $30x^4 + 4x^3 - 2x^2 = 2x^2(15x^2 + 2x - 1)$
$$= 2x^2(5x - 1)(3x + 1)$$

47. $36t^3 + 48t^2w + 16tw^2 = 8t(4t^2 + 6tw + 2w^2)$
$$= 8t(2t + w)(2t + 2w)$$

49. $20a^3b^2 + 30a^2b^3 - 140ab^4$
$$= 10ab^2(2a^2 + 3ab - 14b^2)$$
$$= 10ab^2(2a + 7b)(a - 2b)$$

51. $x^2 - 6x - 40 = (x + 4)(x - 10)$

53. $3w^3 - 6w^2 + 5w - 10 = (3w^2 + 5)(w - 2)$

55. $3x^4 - 21x^3y - 54x^2y^2$
$$= 3x^2(x^2 - 7xy - 18y^2)$$
$$= 3x^2(x + 2y)(x - 9y)$$

57. This expression is prime.

59. $6x^2 - 19x + 10 = (3x - 2)(2x - 5)$

61. $x^2 + xy - 30y^2 = (x + 6y)(x - 5y)$

63. $-6r^3 + 24r^2 - 24r$
$$= -6r(r^2 - 4r + 4)$$
$$= -6(r - 2)(r - 2)$$

65. $-10 + 12x^2 + 2x$
$$= 2(6x^2 + x - 5)$$
$$= 2(6x - 5)(x + 1)$$

67. $a^2x - 3a^2y - 2bx + 6by = (a^2 - 2b)(x - 3y)$

69. This expression is prime.

71. $10p^3t^2 + 22p^2t^3 - 24pt^4$
$$= 2pt^2(5p^2 + 11pt - 12t^2)$$
$$= 2pt^2(5p - 4t)(p + 3t)$$

73. The student did not complete the factoring.
$$x^3 + 5x^2 - 3x - 15 = x^2(x+5) - 3(x+5)$$
$$= (x^2 - 3)(x+5)$$

75. The student did not first factor out the 3.
$$3x^2 - 9x - 30 = 3(x^2 - 3x - 10)$$
$$= 3(x-5)(x+2)$$

77. $2(x-2)(x-6) = 2x^2 - 16x + 24$
$2(x^2 - 8x + 12) = 2x^2 - 16x + 24$
$(x-2)(2x-12) = 2x^2 - 16x + 24$
$2(x-4)^2 - 8 = 2x^2 - 16x + 24$
$(2x-4)(x-6) = 2x^2 - 16x + 24$

79. $12x^3 - 27x = 3x(4x^2 - 9)$
$$= 3x(2x-3)(2x+3)$$

81. $-2(3p+5)(4p-3)$
$= -2(12p^2 - 9p + 20p - 15)$
$= -2(12p^2 + 11p - 15)$
$= -24p^2 - 22p + 30$

83. $2x^3 - 5x^2 - 18x + 45 = (x^2 - 9)(2x - 5)$
$$= (x+3)(x-3)(2x-5)$$

85. $(3k+4)(2k^2 - k + 3)$
$= 6k^3 - 3k^2 + 9k + 8k^2 - 4k + 12$
$= 6k^3 + 5k^2 + 5k + 12$

87. $-2x(3x-5)^2$
$= -2x(3x-5)(3x-5)$
$= -2x(9x^2 - 30x + 25)$
$= -18x^3 + 60x^2 - 50$
$-2x(3x-5)^2$ is a cubic polynomial in one variable.

89. $8x^3 - 40x^2 + 50x$
$= 2x(4x^2 - 20x + 25)$
$= 2x(2x-5)(2x-5)$
$= 2x(2x-5)^2$
$8x^3 - 40x^2 + 50x$ is a cubic polynomial in one variable.

Homework 6.5

1. $x^2 - 25 = (x+5)(x-5)$

3. $a^2 - 36 = (a+6)(a-6)$

5. $4x^2 - 49 = (2x+7)(2x-7)$

7. This expression is prime.

9. $16p^2 - 25t^2 = (4p+5t)(4p-5t)$

11. $75x^2 - 12 = 3(25x^2 - 4)$
$$= 3(5x+2)(5x-2)$$

13. $18a^3b - 32ab^3 = 2ab(9a^2 - 16b^2)$
$$= 2ab(3a+4b)(3a-4b)$$

15. $16x^4 - 81 = (4x^2 + 9)(4x^2 - 9)$
$$= (4x^2 + 9)(2x+3)(2x-3)$$

17. $t^4 - w^4 = (t^2 + w^2)(t^2 - w^2)$
$$= (t^2 + w^2)(t+w)(t-w)$$

19. $x^3 + 27 = (x+3)(x^2 - 3x + 9)$

21. $x^3 - 8 = (x-2)(x^2 + 2x + 4)$

23. $m^3 + 1 = (m+1)(m^2 - m + 1)$

25. $8x^3 + 27 = (2x+3)(4x^2 - 6x + 9)$

27. $125x^3 - 8 = (5x-2)(25x^2 + 10x + 4)$

29. $27p^3 + 8t^3 = (3p + 2t)(9p^2 - 6pt + 4t^2)$

31. $27x^3 - 64y^3 = (3x - 4y)(9x^2 + 12xy + 16y^2)$

33. $5x^3 + 40 = 5(x^3 + 8)$
$= 5(x + 2)(x^2 - 2x + 4)$

35. $2x^4 - 54xy^3 = 2x(x^3 - 27y^3)$
$= 2x(x - 3y)(x^2 + 3xy + 9y^2)$

37. $k^6 - 1 = (k^3 - 1)(k^3 + 1)$
$= (k - 1)(k^2 + k + 1)(k + 1)(k^2 - k + 1)$

39. $64x^6 - y^6$
$= (8x^3 - y^3)(8x^3 + y^3)$
$= (2x - y)(4x^2 + 2xy + y^2)(2x + y)(4x^2 - 2xy + y^2)$

41. $a^2 - 3ab - 28b^2 = (a - 7b)(a + 4b)$

43. $2x^4 - 16xy^3 = 2x(x^3 - 8y^3)$
$= 2x(x - 2y)(x^2 + 2xy + 4y^2)$

45. $-7x - 18 + x^2 = (x - 9)(x + 2)$

47. $4x^3y - 8x^2y^2 - 96xy^3$
$= 4xy(x^2 - 2xy - 24y^2)$
$= 4xy(x - 6y)(x + 4y)$

49. $-k^2 + 12k - 36$
$= -1(k^2 - 12k + 36)$
$= -1(k - 6)(k - 6)$

51. This expression is prime.

53. $x^3 - 2x^2 - 9x + 18$
$= (x^2 - 9)(x - 2)$
$= (x + 3)(x - 3)(x - 2)$

55. $6x^4 - 33x^3 + 45x^2$
$= 3x^2(2x^2 - 11x + 15)$
$= 3x^2(2x - 5)(x - 3)$

57. $32m^2 - 98t^2 = 2(16m^2 - 49t^2)$
$= 2(4m + 7t)(4m - 7t)$

59. This expression is prime.

61. $12x^2y - 26xy^2 - 10y^3$
$= 2y(6x^2 - 13xy - 5y^2)$
$= 2y(3x + y)(2x - 5y)$

63. This expression is prime.

65. $125x^3 + 27 = (5x + 3)(25x^2 - 15x + 9)$

67. $p^2 + 18p + 81 = (p + 9)(p + 9)$

69. $20x^3 - 8x^2 - 5x + 2 = (4x^2 - 1)(5x - 2)$

71. $49x^2 + 14x + 1 = (7x + 1)(7x + 1)$

73. This expression is prime.

75. $2w^3y + 250y^4$
$= 2y(w^3 + 125y^3)$
$= 2y(w + 5y)(w^2 - 5wy + 25y^2)$

77. $-3x^3 + 3x^2 + 90x$
$= -3x(x^2 - x - 30)$
$= -3x(x + 5)(x - 6)$

79. $27x^3 - 75x$
$= 3x(9x^2 - 25)$
$= 3x(3x + 5)(3x - 5)$

81. $81p^4 - 16q^4$
$= (9p^2 + 4q^2)(9p^2 - 4q^2)$
$= (9p^2 + 4q^2)(3p + 2q)(3p - 2q)$

83. The student factored the *AB* portion of
$A^3 - B^3 = (A - B)(A^2 + AB + B^2)$ incorrectly, as
$A = x$ and $B = 2$.
$x^3 - 8 = (x - 2)(x^2 + 2x + 4)$

85. The student incorrectly factors $x^2 + 25$, which is
a prime expression.
$4x^2 + 100 = 4(x^2 + 25)$

87. a. $x^2 - 4 = (x + 2)(x - 2)$

b.

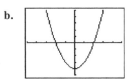

The *x*-intercepts are $x = -2$ and $x = 2$.

c. The factors in (a) match the *x*-intercepts of *f*.
This makes sense because the quadratic
function equals 0 when $x = 2$ or $x = -2$.

89. Answers may vary.
To factor a difference of two squares, find the
product of the sum of the terms and the
difference of the terms. To factor the sum of two
cubes, find the product of the sum of the terms
and the sum of the squares of the terms minus the
difference of the product of the terms. To factor
the difference of two cubes, find the product of
the difference of the terms and the sum of the
squares of the terms plus the product of the
terms.

91. $(3x - 7)(3x + 7) = 9x^2 - 49$

93. $36p^2 - 49 = (6p + 7)(6p - 7)$

95. $(t - 5)(t^2 + 5t + 25) = t^3 - 125$

97. $27p^3 + 1 = (3p + 1)(9p^2 - 3p + 1)$

99. $2(3x - 2y) = 3x + 4$
$6x - 4y = 3x + 4$
$-4y = -3x + 4$
$y = \dfrac{3}{4}x - 1$

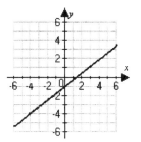

$2(3x - 2y) = 3x + 4$ is a linear equation in two
variables.

101.
$$3x - 5y = 21$$
$$2x + 7y = -17$$
$$x - 12y = 38$$
$$x = 38 + 12y$$
$$3(38 + 12y) - 5y = 21$$
$$114 + 36y - 5y = 21$$
$$31y = -93$$
$$y = -3$$
$$x - 12(-3) = 38$$
$$x = 2$$

The solution is $(2, -3)$.
$3x - 5y = 21$ and $2x + 7y = -17$ are a system of
linear equations in two variables.

Homework 6.6

1. $(x + 4)(w - 7) = 0$
$x = -4$ or $x = 7$

3. $w^2 + w - 12 = 0$
$(w + 4)(w - 3) = 0$
$w = -4$ or $w = 3$

5. $x^2 - 8x + 15 = 0$
$(x - 5)(x - 3) = 0$
$x = 5$ or $x = 3$

7. $14x + 49 + x^2 = 0$
$(x + 7)(x + 7) = 0$
$x = -7$

9. $-24 - 2t + t^2 = 0$
$(t - 6)(t + 4) = 0$

$t = 6$ or $t = -4$

11.
$$25x^2 - 49 = 0$$
$$(5x + 7)(5x - 7) = 0$$
$$x = -\frac{7}{5} \text{ or } x = \frac{7}{5}$$

13.
$$6m^2 - 11m + 3 = 0$$
$$(3m - 1)(2m - 3) = 0$$
$$m = \frac{1}{3} \text{ or } m = \frac{3}{2}$$

15.
$$3x^2 + 3x - 90 = 0$$
$$3(x^2 + x - 30) = 0$$
$$3(x + 6)(x - 5) = 0$$
$$x = -6 \text{ or } x = 5$$

17.
$$8x^3 - 12x^2 - 20x = 0$$
$$4x(2x^2 - 3x - 5) = 0$$
$$4x(2x - 5)(x + 1) = 0$$
$$x = 0, \ x = \frac{5}{2} \text{ or } x = -1$$

19.
$$x^2 = 5x + 14$$
$$x^2 - 5x - 14 = 0$$
$$(x - 7)(x + 2) = 0$$
$$x = 7 \text{ or } x = -2$$

21.
$$4x^2 - 8x = 32$$
$$4x^2 - 8x - 32 = 0$$
$$4(x^2 - 2x - 8) = 0$$
$$4(x - 4)(x + 2) = 0$$
$$x = 4 \text{ or } x = -2$$

23.
$$12t - 36 = t^2$$
$$t^2 - 12t + 36 = 0$$
$$(t - 6)(t - 6) = 0$$
$$t = 6$$

25.
$$16x^2 = 25$$
$$16x^2 - 25 = 0$$
$$(4x + 5)(4x - 5) = 0$$
$$x = -\frac{5}{4} \text{ or } x = \frac{5}{4}$$

27.
$$6x^3 - 24x = 0$$
$$6x(x^2 - 4) = 0$$
$$6x(x - 2)(x + 2) = 0$$
$$x = 0, \ x = 2 \text{ or } x = -2$$

29.
$$3r^2 = 6r$$
$$3r^2 - 6r = 0$$
$$3r(r - 2) = 0$$
$$r = 0 \text{ or } r = 2$$

31.
$$9x = -2x^2 + 5$$
$$2x^2 + 9x - 5 = 0$$
$$(2x - 1)(x + 5) = 0$$
$$x = \frac{1}{2} \text{ or } x = -5$$

33.
$$2x^3 = 6x^2 + 36x$$
$$2x^3 - 6x^2 - 36x = 0$$
$$2x(x^2 - 3x - 18) = 0$$
$$2x(x - 6)(x + 3) = 0$$
$$x = 0, \ x = 6 \text{ or } x = -3$$

35.
$$18y^3 + 3y^2 = 6y$$
$$18y^3 + 3y^2 - 6y = 0$$
$$3y(6y^2 + y - 2) = 0$$
$$3y(3y + 2)(2y - 1) = 0$$
$$y = 0, \ y = -\frac{2}{3} \text{ or } y = \frac{1}{2}$$

37.
$$20x = -4x^2 - 25$$
$$4x^2 + 20x + 25 = 0$$
$$(2x + 5)(2x + 5) = 0$$
$$x = -\frac{5}{2}$$

39.
$$\frac{1}{4}x^2 - \frac{1}{2}x = 6$$
$$\frac{1}{4}x^2 - \frac{1}{2}x - 6 = 0$$
$$\frac{1}{4}\left(x^2 - 2x - 24\right) = 0$$
$$\frac{1}{4}(x-6)(x+4) = 0$$
$$x = 6 \text{ or } x = -4$$

41.
$$\frac{a^2}{2} - \frac{a}{6} = \frac{1}{3}$$
$$\frac{a^2}{2} - \frac{a}{6} - \frac{1}{3} = 0$$
$$\frac{1}{6}\left(3a^2 - a - 2\right) = 0$$
$$\frac{1}{6}(3a+2)(a-1) = 0$$
$$a = -\frac{2}{3} \text{ or } a = 1$$

43.
$$x^2 - \frac{1}{25} = 0$$
$$\left(x - \frac{1}{5}\right)\left(x + \frac{1}{5}\right) = 0$$
$$x = \frac{1}{5} \text{ or } x = -\frac{1}{5}$$

45.
$$(x+2)(x+5) = 40$$
$$x^2 + 7x + 10 - 40 = 0$$
$$x^2 + 7x - 30 = 0$$
$$(x-3)(x+10) = 0$$
$$x = 3 \text{ or } x = -10$$

47.
$$4r^3 - 2r^2 - 36r + 18 = 0$$
$$\left(2r^2 - 18\right)(2r - 1) = 0$$
$$2\left(r^2 - 9\right)(2r - 1) = 0$$
$$2(r+3)(r-3)(2r-1) = 0$$
$$r = -3, \ r = 3 \text{ or } r = \frac{1}{2}$$

49.
$$9x^3 - 12 = 4x - 27x^2$$
$$9x^3 + 27x^2 - 4x - 12 = 0$$
$$\left(9x^2 - 4\right)(x+3) = 0$$
$$(3x+2)(3x-2)(x+3) = 0$$
$$x = -\frac{2}{3}, \ x = \frac{2}{3} \text{ or } x = -3$$

51.
$$2x(x+1) = 5x(x-7)$$
$$5x^2 - 35x - 2x^2 - 2x = 0$$
$$3x^2 - 37x = 0$$
$$x(3x - 37) = 0$$
$$x = 0 \text{ or } x = \frac{37}{3}$$

53.
$$4p(p-1) - 24 = 3p(p-2)$$
$$4p^2 - 4p - 24 - 3p^2 + 6p = 0$$
$$p^2 + 2p - 24 = 0$$
$$(p+6)(p-4) = 0$$
$$p = -6 \text{ or } p = 4$$

55.
$$\left(x^2 + 5x + 6\right)\left(x^2 - 5x - 24\right) = 0$$
$$(x+3)(x+2)(x-8)(x+3) = 0$$
$$x = -3, \ x = -2 \text{ or } x = 8$$

57.
$$f(x) = x^2 - 9x + 20$$
$$= (x-5)(x-4)$$
$$x = 5 \text{ or } x = 4$$

59.
$$f(x) = 36x^2 - 25$$
$$= (6x-5)(6x+5)$$
$$x = \frac{5}{6} \text{ or } x = -\frac{5}{6}$$

61.
$$f(x) = 24x^3 - 14x^2 - 20x$$
$$= 2x\left(12x^2 - 7x - 10\right)$$
$$= 2x(4x-5)(3x+2)$$
$$x = 0, \ x = \frac{5}{4} \text{ or } x = -\frac{2}{3}$$

63. $f(x) = x^3 + 2x^2 - x - 2$

$= (x^2 - 1)(x + 2)$

$= (x - 1)(x + 1)(x + 2)$

$x = 1, x = -1$ or $x = -2$

65. $f(3) = (3)^2 - (3) - 6 = 0$

67. $x^2 - x - 6 = 14$

$x^2 - x - 20 = 0$

$(x - 5)(x + 4) = 0$

$x = 5$ or $x = -4$

69. $x = -5$ or $x = 3$

71. $x = -1$

73. $x = -1$ or $x = 2$

75. $x = -1, x = 1$ or $x = 3$

77.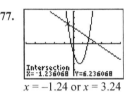

Intersection
X=-1.236068 Y=6.236068

Intersection
X=3.236068 Y=1.763932

$x = -1.24$ or $x = 3.24$

79.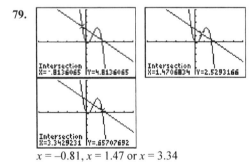

Intersection
X=.8136065 Y=4.8136065

Intersection
X=1.4706034 Y=2.5293166

Intersection
X=3.3429231 Y=.65707692

$x = -0.81, x = 1.47$ or $x = 3.34$

81. $x = -2$ or $x = 4$

83. There is no solution

85. You cannot factor out solutions, as this eliminates possible answers.

$x^2 = x$

$x^2 - x = 0$

$x(x - 1) = 0$

$x = 0$ or $x = 1$

87. The student overlooked one of the factors in the third step.

$x^3 + 4x^2 - 9x - 36 = 0$

$x^2(x + 4) - 9(x + 4) = 0$

$(x^2 - 9)(x + 4) = 0$

$(x + 3)(x - 3)(x + 4) = 0$

$x = -3, x = 3$ or $x = -4$

89. a.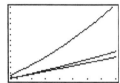

The quadratic model $Q(t)$ describes the situation best.

b.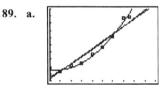

The quadratic model $Q(t)$ predicts the largest participation between 2005 and 2020.

c. For $L(t)$, the n-intercept is 1314. For $E(t)$, the n-intercept is 1324. For $Q(t)$, the n-intercept is 1374. The quadratic model $Q(t)$ describes the situation best.

d. $2t^2 - 4t + 1374 = 1390$

$2t^2 - 4t - 16 = 0$

$2(t^2 - 2t - 8) = 0$

$2(t - 4)(t + 2) = 0$

$t = 4$ or $t = -2$

Since t cannot be negative, $t = 4$ or 1994.

91. a.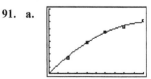

The model fits the data well.

b. $f(7) = -\frac{1}{3}(7)^2 + \frac{22}{3}(7) = 35$

This means that, 7 years after being rated B2, 35% of companies defaulted on their bonds.

c.
$$7 = -\frac{1}{3}t^2 + \frac{22}{3}t$$

$$\frac{1}{3}t^2 - \frac{22}{3}t + 7 = 0$$

$$\frac{1}{3}\left(t^2 - 22t + 21\right) = 0$$

$$\frac{1}{3}(t-21)(t-1) = 0$$

$t = 1$ or $t = 21$

This means that, 1 year and 21 years after begin rated B2, 7% of companies defaulted on their bonds.

d.
$$0 = -\frac{1}{3}t^2 + \frac{22}{3}t$$

$$= -\frac{1}{3}t(t-22)$$

$t = 0$ or $t = 22$

It means that, at the time of the B2 rating and 22 years after receiving a B2 rating, no companies defaulted on their bonds.

93. a.

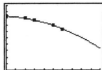

The model fits the data well.

b. The p-intercept is 25, which means that 25% of Americans thought in 1999 that labor unions will become stronger.

c.
$$f(12) = -\frac{1}{8}(12)^2 - \frac{1}{4}(12) + 25 = 4$$

In 2011, 4% of Americans will think that labor unions will become stronger.

d.
$$-\frac{1}{8}t^2 - \frac{1}{4}t + 25 = 15$$

$$-\frac{1}{8}t^2 - \frac{1}{4}t + 10 = 0$$

$$-\frac{1}{8}\left(t^2 + 2t - 80\right) = 0$$

$$-\frac{1}{8}(t+10)(t-8) = 0$$

$t = -10$ or $t = 8$

Since t cannot be negative, $t = 8$ or 2007. So, in 2007, 15% of Americans thought that labor unions will become stronger.

95. a.

The model fits the data well.

b. $f(20) = 0.41(20)^2 - 7.95(20) + 58 = 63$

In 2010, each African person will receive an average of $63 from foreign aid.

c.
$$0.41t^2 - 7.95t + 58 = 58$$

$$0.41t^2 - 7.95t = 0$$

$$t(0.41t - 7.95) = 0$$

$t = 0$ or $t = 19.4$

African people will receive an average of $58 per person in 2009.

97. $A = l \times w = 60$

$l = 2w + 2$

$$(2w+2)w = 60$$

$$2w^2 + 2w - 60 = 0$$

$$2\left(w^2 + w - 30\right) = 0$$

$$2(w+6)(w-5) = 0$$

$w = -6$ or $w = 5$

$l = 2(5) + 2 = 12$

The rug is 12 feet long by 5 feet wide.

99. $l = w + 4$

$2l \times 2w = 48$

$$2(w+4)(2w) - 48 = 0$$

$$2\left(2w^2 + 8w\right) - 48 = 0$$

$$4w^2 + 16w - 48 = 0$$

$$4\left(w^2 + 4w - 12\right) = 0$$

$$4(w+6)(w-2) = 0$$

$w = -6$ or $w = 2$

$l = 2 + 4 = 6$

The original rectangle is 6 meters long and 2 meters wide.

101. $A = 6 \times 10 = 60$

$(6+2x)(10+2x) - 60 = 80$

$4x^2 + 32x - 80 = 0$

$4(x^2 + 8x - 20) = 0$

$4(x+10)(x-2) = 0$

$x = -10$ or $x = 2$

The border is 2 feet wide.

103. $(14+2x)(10+2x) - 140 = 52$

$4x^2 + 48x - 52 = 0$

$4(x^2 + 12x - 13) = 0$

$4(x+13)(x-1) = 0$

$x = -13$ or $x = 1$

The frame has a border width of 1 inch.

105. Answers may vary.

The function $f(x) = x^2 + 4x - 5$ has the x-intercepts $(-5, 0)$ and $(1, 0)$.

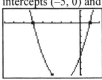

107. Answers may vary.

The cubic function $f(x) = x^3 + 2x^2 - 8x$ has solutions -4, 0, and 2.

109. Answers may vary.

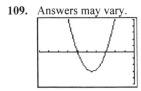

The quadratic function $h(x) = \dfrac{4}{3}x^2 + 12x + 24$ is a possible match for the graph.

111. Answers may vary.

A quadratic equation in one variable can only cross the *x*-axis up to two times, so it can have a maximum of two solutions.

113. $x^2 + 5x + 6 = (x+3)(x+2)$

115. $x^2 + 5x + 6 = 0$

$(x+3)(x+2) = 0$

$x = -3$ or $x = -2$

117. $3p^3 + 8p^2 + 4p = 0$

$p(3p^2 + 8p + 4) = 0$

$p(3p+2)(p+2) = 0$

$p = 0$, $p = -\dfrac{2}{3}$ or $p = -2$

119. $3p^3 + 8p^2 + 4p$

$= p(3p^2 + 8p + 4)$

$= p(3p+2)(p+2)$

121. $3x^2(x-4) = 12x(x-3)$

$3x^3 - 12x^2 = 12x^2 - 36x$

$3x^3 - 24x^2 + 36x = 0$

$3x(x^2 - 8x + 12) = 0$

$3x(x-6)(x-2) = 0$

$x = 0$, $x = 6$ or $x = 2$

123. $3b^8 + 39 = 217$

$3b^8 = 178$

$b^8 = \dfrac{178}{3}$

$b = \pm 1.6660$

125. C $5(2)^t - 24 = 97$

$5(2)^t = 121$

$2^t = 24.2$

$t = 4.5969$

127. $\log(x+3) + \log(x+6) = 1$

$\log[(x+3)(x+6)] = 1$

$x^2 + 9x + 18 = 10$

$x^2 + 9x + 8 = 0$

$(x+8)(x+1) = 0$

$x = -1$ or $x = -8$

129. Answers may vary.

$$x^2 + 8x + 16 = (x+4)(x+4)$$

131. Answers may vary.
$$x^2 + 7x + 6 = 0$$
$$(x+6)(x+1) = 0$$
$$x = -6 \text{ or } x = -1$$

133. Answers may vary.
$$f(x) = 2^x - 4$$

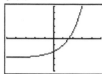

Chapter 6 Review Exercises

1. $\left(-7x^3 + 5x^2 - 9\right) + \left(2x^3 - 8x^2 + 3x\right)$
$$= -5x^3 - 3x^2 + 3x - 9$$

2. $\left(5a^3b - 2a^2b^2 + 9ab^3\right) - \left(8a^3b + 4a^2b^2 - ab^3\right)$
$$= -3a^3b - 6a^2b^2 + 10ab^3$$

3. $f(-2) = 3(-2)^2 - 5(-2) + 2 = 24$

4. $f(2) = 9$

5. $x = 2 \text{ or } x = 4$

6. $(f+g)(x)$
$$= \left(3x^3 - 7x^2 - 4x + 2\right) + \left(-2x^3 + 5x^2 - 3x + 1\right)$$
$$= x^3 - 2x^2 - 7x + 3$$
$$(f+g)(2) = (2)^3 - 2(2)^2 - 7(2) + 3 = -11$$

7.* $(f-g)(x)$
$$= \left(3x^3 - 7x^2 - 4x + 2\right) - \left(-2x^3 + 5x^2 - 3x + 1\right)$$
$$= 5x^3 - 12x^2 - x + 1$$
$$(f-g)(-3) = 5(-3)^3 - 12(-3)^2 - (-3) + 3 = -237$$

8. $(x-7)(x+7) = x^2 - 49$

9. $8a^2b\left(-5a^3b^5\right) = -40a^5b^6$

10. $(4p + 9t)(2p - 5t) = 8p^2 - 2pt - 45t^2$

11. $(4x - 3)\left(5x^2 - 2x + 4\right)$
$$= 20x^3 - 23x^2 + 22x - 12$$

12. $(3x + 7y)^2 = 9x^2 + 42xy + 49y^2$

13. $\left(6p^2 - 9t^3\right)\left(6p^2 + 9t^3\right) = 36p^4 - 81t^6$

14. $-3rt^3\left(2r^2 - 5rt + 3t^2\right) = -6r^3t^3 + 15r^2t^4 - 9rt^5$

15. $-4x(3x - 2)^2 = -36x^3 + 48x^2 - 16x$

16. $\left(3m^2 - mp + 2p^2\right)\left(2m^2 + 3mp - 4p^2\right)$
$$= 6m^4 + 7m^3p - 11m^2p^2 + 10mp^3 - 8p^4$$

17. $f(a - 4) = (a-4)^2 - 2(a-4)$
$$= a^2 - 10a + 24$$

18. $f(a+3) - f(a)$
$$= (a+3)^2 - 2(a+3) - \left(a^2 - 2a\right)$$
$$= 6a + 3$$

19. $f(x) = -2(x-4)^2 + 3$
$$= -2x^2 + 16x - 29$$

20. $f \cdot g = (3x - 7)\left(2x^2 - 4x + 3\right)$
$$= 6x^3 - 26x^2 + 37x - 21$$
$$(f \cdot g)(3) = 6(3)^3 - 26(3)^2 + 37(3) - 21$$
$$= 18$$

21. $x^2 - 25 = (x+5)(x-5)$

22. $x^2 - 12x + 36 = (x-6)(x-6)$

23. $a^2 + 5ab - 36b^2 = (a + 9b)(a - 4b)$

24. $16a^5b^3 - 20a^3b^2 = 4a^3b^2\left(4a^2b - 5\right)$

25. This expression is prime.

26. $3w^2 - 5wy - 8y^2 = (3w - 8y)(w + y)$

27. $81t^4 - 16w^4 = (9t^2 + 4w^2)(3t + 2w)(3t - 2w)$

28. $6x^4 + 20x^3 - 16x^2 = 2x^2(3x - 2)(x + 4)$

29. This expression is prime.

30. $x^2 - 3x - 54 = (x + 6)(x - 9)$

31. $2y^3 - 54 = 2(y - 3)(y^2 + 3y + 9)$

32. $5r^2t + 30rt^2 + 45t^3 = 5t(r + 3t)(r + 3t)$

33. $2ax - 10ay - 3bx + 15by$
$= (2a - 3b)(x - 5y)$

34. $x^2 - 2x - 24 = 0$
$(x - 6)(x + 4) = 0$
$x = 6 \text{ or } x = -4$

35. $64t^2 = 9$
$64t^2 - 9 = 0$
$(8t + 3)(8t - 3) = 0$
$t = -\dfrac{3}{8} \text{ or } t = \dfrac{3}{8}$

36. $3x(x + 10) = 6x^3$
$6x^3 - 3x^2 - 30x = 0$
$3x(2x^2 - x - 10) = 0$
$3x(2x - 5)(x + 2) = 0$
$x = 0, \ x = \dfrac{5}{2} \text{ or } x = -2$

37. $x^3 - 4x = 12 - 3x^2$
$x^3 + 3x^2 - 4x - 12 = 0$
$(x - 2)(x + 2)(x + 3) = 0$
$x = 2, \ x = -2 \text{ or } x = -3$

38. $\dfrac{m^2}{2} - \dfrac{7m}{6} + \dfrac{1}{3} = 0$
$3m^2 - 7m + 2 = 0$
$(3m - 1)(m - 2) = 0$
$m = \dfrac{1}{3} \text{ or } m = 2$

39. $32x^2 = 24x$
$32x^2 - 24x = 0$
$8x(4x - 3) = 0$
$x = 0 \text{ or } x = \dfrac{3}{4}$

40. $4p(5p - 6) = (2p + 3)(2p - 3)$
$20p^2 - 24p = 4p^2 - 9$
$16p^2 - 24p + 9 = 0$
$(4p - 3)(4p - 3) = 0$
$p = \dfrac{3}{4}$

41. $f(x) = 3x^3 + 3x^2 - 18x$
$\qquad = 3x(x^2 - x - 6)$
$\qquad = 3x(x + 3)(x - 2)$
The *x*-intercepts are $(0, 0), (-3, 0), \text{ or } (2, 0)$

42. $x = -5 \text{ and } x = 1$

43. $x = -3 \text{ and } x = 1$

44. **a.** $(E + C)(t)$
$= (12.7t^2 - 35t + 235) + (8t^2 - 24.5t + 125)$
$= 20.7t^2 - 59.5t + 360$

b. For the expression $E(t) + C(t)$, we have $E(t)$ = ExxonMobil's revenue in billions of dollars + $C(t)$ = Chevron's revenue in billions of dollars. The units of the expression are total revenue in billions of dollars.

c. $(E + C)(10) = 20.7(10)^2 - 59.5(10) + 360$
$\qquad\qquad = 1835$
It means that in 2010 the total revenue will be \$1835 billion, or \$1.835 trillion.

d. $(E-C)(t)$
$$= \left(12.7t^2 - 35t + 235\right) - \left(8t^2 - 24.5t + 125\right)$$
$$= 4.7t^2 - 10.5t + 110$$

e. $(E-C)(10) = 4.7(10)^2 - 10.5(10) + 110$
$$= 475$$

It means that ExxonMobil's revenue will exceed Chevron's revenue by $475 billion.

45. a.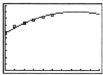

The model fits the data well.

b. $f(11) = -\dfrac{3}{5}(11)^2 + 9(11) + 57 = 83.4$

In 2011, there will be 83 million available nights for extended-stay hotel rooms.

c. $-\dfrac{3}{5}t^2 + 9t + 57 = 87$
$$-\dfrac{3}{5}t^2 + 9t - 30 = 0$$
$$t^2 - 15t + 50 = 0$$
$$(t-5)(t-10) = 0$$
$$t = 5 \text{ or } t = 10$$

In 2005 and 2010 there will be 87 million available nights for extended-stay hotel rooms.

46. $l = w + 8$
$$2l \times 2w = 192$$
$$2(w+8)(2w) = 192$$
$$4w^2 + 32w - 192 = 0$$
$$4(w^2 + 8w - 48) = 0$$
$$4(w+12)(w-4) = 0$$
$$w = -12 \text{ or } w = 4$$
$$l = 4 + 8 = 12$$
The original rectangle is 12 meters long and 4 meters wide.

Chapter 6 Test

1. $\left(4a^3b - 9a^2b^2 - 2ab^3\right) + \left(-5a^3b + 4a^2b^2 + 3ab^3\right)$
$$= -a^3b - 5a^2b^2 + ab^3$$

2. $f - g = \left(4x^2 + 5x - 9\right) - \left(6x^2 - 3x + 7\right)$
$$= -2x^2 + 8x - 16$$
$(f-g)(-2) = -2(-2)^2 + 8(-2) - 16 = -40$

3. $f(-3) = -3$

4. There is no solution.

5. $x = 1$

6. $x = -3$ and $x = 5$

7. $-2xy^2\left(7x^2 - 3xy + 6y^2\right)$
$$= -14x^3y^2 + 6x^2y^3 - 12xy^4$$

8. $(4x - 7y)(3x + 5y) = 12x^2 - xy - 35y^2$

9. $(2w - 5t)\left(3w^2 - wt + 4t^2\right)$
$$= 6w^3 - 17w^2t + 13wt^2 - 20t^3$$

10. $3x(2x+3)^2 = 12x^3 + 36x^2 + 27x$

11. $\left(3x^2 + x - 5\right)\left(2x^2 + 4x - 1\right)$
$$= 6x^4 + 14x^3 - 9x^2 - 21x + 5$$

12. $\left(4x^2 + 9y^2\right)\left(4x^2 - 9y^2\right) = 16x^4 - 81y^4$

13. $f(a-5) = (a-5)^2 - 3(a-5)$
$$= a^2 - 13a + 40$$

14. $f(x) = -3(x+4)^2 - 7$
$$= -3x^2 - 24x - 55$$

15. $f \cdot g = \left(2x^2 - 5x + 4\right)(3x - 2)$
$$= 6x^3 - 19x^2 + 22x - 8$$
$(f \cdot g)(3) = 6(3)^3 - 19(3)^2 + 22(3) - 8 = 49$

16. $x^2 - 10x - 24 = (x - 12)(x + 2)$

17. $18x + 2x^3 - 12x^2 = 2x(x-3)(x-3)$

18. $-16x^2 - 26x + 12 = -2(8x-3)(x+2)$

19. $9m^2 - 64t^2 = (3m+8t)(3m-8t)$

20. $16a^4b - 36a^3b^2 + 18a^2b^3$
$= 2a^2b(4a - 3b)(2a - 3b)$

21. $54m^3 + 128p^3$
$= 2(3m + 4p)(9m^2 - 12mp + 16p^2)$

22. $25x^2 = 16$
$25x^2 - 16 = 0$
$(5x-4)(5x+4) = 0$
$x = \dfrac{4}{5}$ or $x = -\dfrac{4}{5}$

23. $5w^3 - 15w^2 - 50w = 0$
$5w(w^2 - 3w - 10) = 0$
$5w(w-5)(w+2) = 0$
$w = 0,\ w = 5$ or $w = -2$

24. $(2x-7)(x-3) = 10$
$2x^2 - 13x + 11 = 0$
$(2x-11)(x-1) = 0$
$x = \dfrac{11}{2}$ or $x = 1$

25. $2t^3 + 3t^2 = 18t + 27$
$2t^3 + 3t^2 - 18t - 27 = 0$
$(2t+3)(t^2 - 9) = 0$
$(2t+3)(t+3)(t-3) = 0$
$t = -\dfrac{3}{2},\ t = -3$ or $t = 3$

26. $3x(2x-5) + 4x = 2(x-3)$
$6x^2 - 13x + 6 = 0$
$(3x-2)(2x-3) = 0$
$x = \dfrac{2}{3}$ or $x = \dfrac{3}{2}$

27. $f(x) = 10x^2 - 19x + 6$
$= (5x-2)(2x-3)$
$x = \dfrac{2}{5}$ or $x = \dfrac{3}{2}$

28.

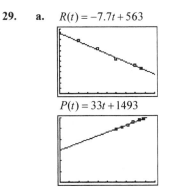

Intersection
X=-2.055701 Y=1.7334206

Intersection
X=2.1890343 Y=-.8134206

$x = -2.06$ and $x = 2.19$

29. **a.** $R(t) = -7.7t + 563$

$P(t) = 33t + 1493$

The models fit the data well.

b. $R \cdot P = (-7.7t + 563)(33t + 1493)$
$= -254.1t^2 + 7082.9t + 840559$

c. For the expression $R(t) \cdot P(t)$, we have $R(t)$ = number of deaths per 100,000 people × $P(t)$ = population in hundred-thousands. The units of the expression are number of total deaths in the US.

d. $(R \cdot P)(51)$
$= -254.1(51)^2 + 7082.9(51) + 840559$
$= 540872.8$
This means that in 2011, there will be about 540,873 deaths.

e. The number of people dying is increasing between the years 2000 and 2010. However, the population is increasing at a faster rate than the number of people dying.

30. **a.**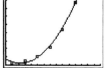

The model fits the data well.

b. $f(20) = 5(20)^2 - 23(20) + 38 = 1578$

In 2010, sales using debit cards will reach $1578 billion, or $1.6 trillion.

c. Sales were about $20 billion in 1992.

31. $(11 + 2x)(15 + 2x) - 120 = 165$

$4x^2 + 52x - 120 = 0$

$4(x + 15)(x - 2) = 0$

$x = -15$ or $x = 2$

The width of the border is 2 inches.

Chapter 7
Quadratic Functions

Homework 7.1

1. Vertex: (0, 0)

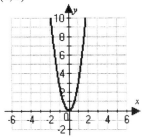

3. Vertex: (0, 0)

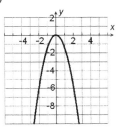

5. Vertex: (0, 5)

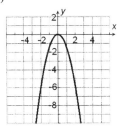

7. Vertex: (1, 0)

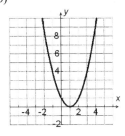

9. Vertex: (–2, 0)

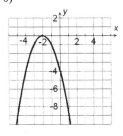

11. Vertex: (–2, – 6)

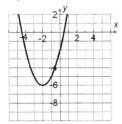

13. Vertex: (1, 3)

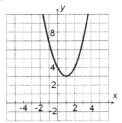

15. Vertex: (–6, –6)

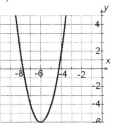

17. Vertex: (6, –2)

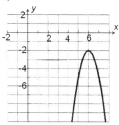

19. Vertex: (2, 3)

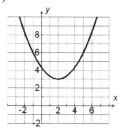

21.

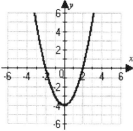

The domain is the set of all real numbers. Since (0, –4) is the minimum point, the range is the set of numbers where $y \geq -4$.

23.

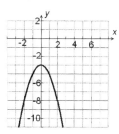

The domain is the set of all real numbers. Since (0, –3) is the maximum point, the range is the set of numbers where $y \leq -3$.

25.

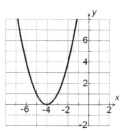

The domain is the set of all real numbers. Since (–4, 0) is the minimum point, the range is the set of numbers where $y \geq 0$.

27.

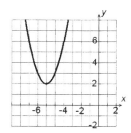

The domain is the set of all real numbers. Since (–6, 2) is the minimum point, the range is the set of numbers where $y \geq 2$.

29.

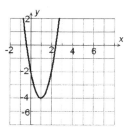

The domain is the set of all real numbers. Since (1, –4) is the minimum point, the range is the set of numbers where $y \geq -4$.

31.

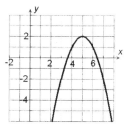

The domain is the set of all real numbers. Since (5, 2) is the maximum point, the range is the set of numbers where $y \leq 2$.

33. a. First make a scattergram of the data.

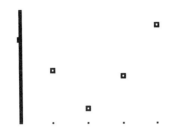

Use the point (2, 228) as the vertex.

$f(t) = a(t-2)^2 + 228$

Now use the point (4, 313) to solve for a.

$313 = a((4)-2)^2 + 228$

$313 = a(2)^2 + 228$

$313 = 4a + 228$

$85 = 4a$

$21.25 = a$

So the equation of f in vertex form is:

$f(t) = 21.25(t-2)^2 + 228$

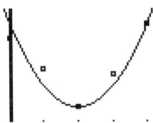

The graph of f is very close to the data points.

b. The vertex of the model is (2, 228). During the year 2002, the model predicts that there were the fewest billionaires, 228 people.

c. To find the n-intercept of the model, let $t = 0$ and solve for n.

$n = 21.25((0)-2)^2 + 228$

$n = 21.25(2)^2 + 228$

$n = 21.25(4) + 228$

$n = 85 + 228$

$n = 313$

The n-intercept is 313. During the year 2000, the model predicts that there were 313 billionaires.

d. To find the number of billionaires in 2010,

let $t-10$ and solve for n.

$n = 21.25(10-2)^2 + 228$

$= 21.25(8)^2 + 228$

$= 21.25(64) + 228$

$= 1360 + 228$

$= 1588$

35. a. First make a scattergram of the data.

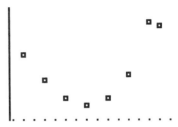

Use the point (8, 311) as the vertex.

$f(t) = a(t-8)^2 + 311$

Now use the point (4, 358) to solve for a.

$358 = a((4)-8)^2 + 311$

$358 = a(-4)^2 + 311$

$358 = 16a + 311$

$47 = 16a$

$2.9375 = a$

So the equation of f in vertex form is:

$f(t) = 2.9375(t-8)^2 + 311$

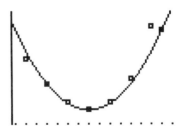

The graph of f is very close to the data points.

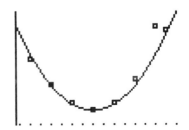

b. The vertex of the model is (8, 311). During 1998, the U.S. Department of Defense spent at least $311 billion.

c. To find the U.S. Department of Defense spending in 2010, let $t = 20$ and solve for f.

$$f(20) = 2.9375((20) - 8)^2 + 311$$
$$= 2.9375(12)^2 + 311$$
$$= 2.9375(144) + 311$$
$$= 423 + 311$$
$$= 734$$

In 2010, the U.S. Department of Defense will spend about $734 billion.

37. a.

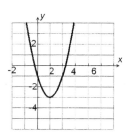

b.

x	y
-2	15
-1	5
0	-1
1	-3
2	-1

c. For each input-output pair, the output variable is 3 less than twice the square of the difference of the input variable and 1.

39. a.

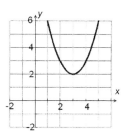

b.
$$3 = (x - 3)^2 + 2$$
$$1 = (x - 3)^2$$
$$\pm 1 = x - 3$$
$$3 \pm 1 = x$$
$$x = 4 \text{ or } x = 2$$

c.
$$2 = (x - 3)^2 + 2$$
$$0 = (x - 3)^2$$
$$0 = x - 3$$
$$3 = x$$

d.
$$1 = (x - 3)^2 + 2$$
$$-1 = (x - 3)^2$$

The next step is to take the square root of both sides. However, this will require taking the square root of -1, which is not a valid step. There is no such value of x such that $f(x) = 1$.

41. Answers my vary: Example:
$$y = a(x + 3)^2 + 4$$
where a is any negative number.

43. a. Because the parabola is face up, and the vertex is in the 3rd quadrant: $a > 0$, $h < 0$, $k < 0$.

b. Because the parabola is face down, and the vertex is in the 2nd quadrant: $a < 0$, $h < 0$, $k > 0$.

c. Because the parabola is face up, and the vertex is on the positive x-axis: $a > 0$, $h > 0$, $k = 0$.

d. Because the parabola is face down, and the vertex is on the negative y-axis: $a < 0$, $h = 0$, $k < 0$.

45. Answers may vary. Example:
$$y = a(x + 5)^2 - 3$$
where $a = -3, -2, -1, -\frac{1}{2}, \frac{1}{2}, 1, 2, 3$

47. The graph shows that the vertex is $(5, -6)$, so
$$f(x) = a(x - 5)^2 - 6.$$
To solve for a, substitute the point $(1, 4)$ into the equation for f.
$$4 = a((1) - 5)^2 - 6$$
$$4 = a(-4)^2 - 6$$
$$4 = 16a - 6$$
$$10 = 16a$$
$$\frac{5}{8} = a$$
So the equation is:

$$f(x) - \frac{5}{8}(x-5)^2 - 6$$

49. The value of a for the function f is the opposite of the value of a for the function g since g has a maximum point and f has a minimum point and we can assume that the graphs of f and g have the same "shape". Since the vertex (h, k) of g is $(-7, 3.71)$ and $a = -2.1$, an equation for g is:

$$g(x) = -2.1(x+7)^2 + 3.71$$

51. It is possible. Example: $y = x^2 + 2$

53. It is possible. Example: $y = x^2 - 2$

55. Both equations have the same vertex (2, 5). From the graph notice this is the only point that lies on both graphs.

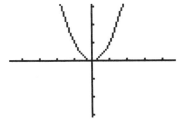

57. **a.**

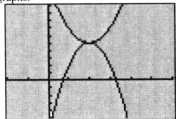

b.

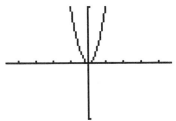

The graph in part (a) is wider than the graph in part (b).

c.

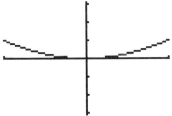

The graph in part (c) is much wider than the graph in parts (a) and (b).

d. Answers may vary.

59. No, the student is not correct. Moving $y = x^2$ to the left by 4 units would result in $y = (x+4)^2$. The equation $y = (x-4)^2$ would move $y = x^2$ to the right by 4 units.

61. Adjust the WINDOW settings. Make your x-min and x-max much larger.

63. **a.**

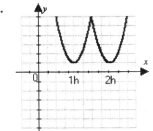

b.

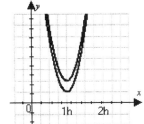

c.

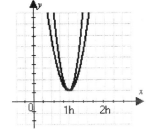

d.

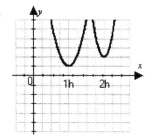

65. Written answers will vary. Example:
Start at the vertex of the parabola (h, k). Next make a table of the function, starting with $x = h - 5$, up through $x = h + 5$. Plot these points on the graph. Connect the points in a parabola.

67. a.

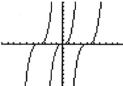

Translate the graph of f 4 units to the right to get the graph of g. Translate the graph of f 4 units to the left to get the graph of h.

b.

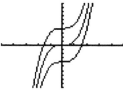

Translate the graph of f 4 units down to get the graph of g. Translate the graph of f 4 units up to get the graph of h.

c. Yes, the translations of x^3 match the translations of x^2. In each case add a constant to f to move the graph up or down; add a constant to x to move the graph left or right. The up and down movement is consistent with the sign, while the right and left movement is opposite its sign.

d.

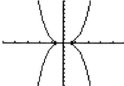

There should be four different graphs, as there are parts i-iv here.

69.

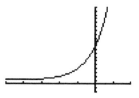

71.

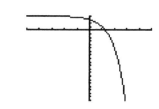

73. $\log_4\left(3x^2\right) + 2\log_4\left(2x^4\right) = 6$

$\log_4\left(3x^2\right) + \log_4\left(2x^4\right)^2 = 6$

$\log_4\left(3x^2\right) + \log_4\left(4x^8\right) = 6$

$\log_4\left(3x^2 \cdot 4x^8\right) = 6$

$\log_4\left(12x^{10}\right) = 6$

$4^6 = 12x^{10}$

$4096 = 12x^{10}$

$341.33 = x^{10}$

$\pm 1.7919 = x$

The equation is logarithmic in one variable.

75. $\log_4\left(3x^2\right) + 2\log_4\left(2x^4\right) = \log_4\left(3x^2\right) + \log_4\left(2x^4\right)^2$

$= \log_4\left(3x^2\right) + \log_4\left(4x^8\right)$

$= \log_4\left(3x^2 \cdot 4x^8\right)$

$= \log_4\left(12x^{10}\right)$

The expression is logarithmic in one variable.

77. $\log_4\left(3x^2\right) - 2\log_4\left(2x^4\right) = \log_4\left(3x^2\right) - \log_4\left(2x^4\right)^2$

$= \log_4\left(3x^2\right) - \log_4\left(4x^8\right)$

$= \log_4\left(\dfrac{3x^2}{4x^8}\right)$

$= \log_4\left(\dfrac{3}{4x^6}\right)$

The expression is logarithmic in one variable.

Homework 7.2

1. Since $\dfrac{0+10}{2} = 5$, the x-coordinate of the vertex must be 5.

3. Since the points have the same y-coordinate, they are symmetric on the parabola.
   Since $\dfrac{0+6}{2} = 3$, the x-coordinate of the vertex must be 3.

5. Since the points have the same y-coordinate, they are symmetric on the parabola.
   Since $\dfrac{0+(-7)}{2} = -3.5$, the x-coordinate of the vertex must be -3.5.

7. Since the points have the same y-coordinate, they are symmetric on the parabola.
   Since $\dfrac{0+7.29}{2} \approx 3.65$, the x-coordinate of the vertex must be 3.65.

9. A symmetric point to the y-intercept has a value of x that is 2 units to the right of $x = 2$ (value of x at the vertex). The value of y is the same as that of the y-intercept, so another point on the parabola is $(4,9)$.

11. First, find the y-intercept by substituting 0 for x in the function:
    $y = 0^2 - 6(0) + 7 = 7$
    The y-intercept is $(0,7)$. Next find the symmetric point to $(0,7)$. Substitute 7 for y in the function and solve for x:
    $7 = x^2 - 6x + 7$
    $0 = x^2 - 6x$
    $0 = x(x-6)$
    $x = 0$ or $x - 6 = 0$
    $x = 0$ or $x = 6$
    Therefore, the symmetric points are $(0,7)$ and $(6,7)$. Since $\dfrac{0+6}{2} = 3$, the x-coordinate of the vertex is 3. To find the y-coordinate of the vertex, substitute 3 for x and solve for y:
    $y = 3^2 - 6(3) + 7 = -2$. So the vertex is $(3,-2)$.

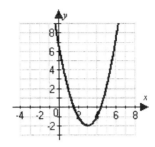

13. First, find the y-intercept by substituting 0 for x in the function:
    $y = 0^2 + 8(0) + 9 = 9$
    The y-intercept is $(0,9)$. Next find the symmetric point to $(0,9)$. Substitute 9 for y in the function and solve for x:
    $9 = x^2 + 8x + 9$
    $0 = x^2 + 8x$
    $0 = x(x+8)$
    $x = 0$ or $x + 8 = 0$
    $x = 0$ or $x = -8$
    Therefore, the symmetric points are $(0,9)$ and $(-8,9)$. Since $\dfrac{0+(-8)}{2} = -4$, the x-coordinate of the vertex is -4. To find the y-coordinate of the vertex, substitute -4 for x and solve for y:
    $y = (-4)^2 + 8(-4) + 9 = -7$. So the vertex is $(-4,-7)$.

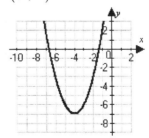

15. First, find the y-intercept by substituting 0 for x in the function:
    $y = -(0)^2 + 8(0) - 10 = -10$
    The y-intercept is $(0,-10)$. Next find the symmetric point to $(0,-10)$. Substitute -10 for y in the function and solve for x:

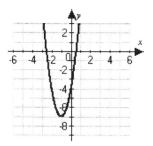

$-10 = -x^2 + 8x - 10$

$0 = -x^2 + 8x$

$0 = -x(x-8)$

$-x = 0$ or $x - 8 = 0$

$x = 0$ or $x = 8$

Therefore, the symmetric points are $(0,-10)$ and

$(8,-10)$. Since $\dfrac{0+8}{2} = 4$, the x-coordinate of the

vertex is 4. To find the y-coordinate of the vertex, substitute 4 for x and solve for y:

$y = -(4)^2 + 8(4) - 10 = 6$. So the vertex is

$(4,6)$.

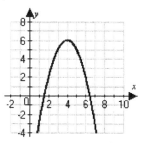

17. First, find the y-intercept by substituting 0 for x in the function:

$y = 3(0)^2 + 6(0) - 4 = -4$

The y-intercept is $(0,-4)$. Next find the

symmetric point to $(0,-4)$. Substitute -4 for y in the function and solve for x:

$-4 = 3x^2 + 6x - 4$

$0 = 3x^2 + 6x$

$0 = 3x(x+2)$

$3x = 0$ or $x + 2 = 0$

$x = 0$ or $x = -2$

Therefore, the symmetric points are $(0,-4)$ and

$(-2,-4)$. Since $\dfrac{0+(-2)}{2} = -1$, the x-coordinate

of the vertex is -1. To find the y-coordinate of the vertex, substitute -1 for x and solve for y:

$y = 3(-1)^2 + 6(-1) - 4 = -7$. So the vertex is

$(-1,-7)$.

19. First, find the y-intercept by substituting 0 for x in the function:

$y = -3(0)^2 + 12(0) - 5 = -5$

The y-intercept is $(0,-5)$. Next find the

symmetric point to $(0,-5)$. Substitute -5 for y in the function and solve for x:

$-5 = -3x^2 + 12x - 5$

$0 = -3x^2 + 12x$

$0 = -3x(x-4)$

$-3x = 0$ or $x - 4 = 0$

$x = 0$ or $x = 4$

Therefore, the symmetric points are $(0,-5)$ and

$(4,-5)$. Since $\dfrac{0+4}{2} = 2$, the x-coordinate of the

vertex is 2. To find the y-coordinate of the vertex, substitute 2 for x and solve for y:

$y = -3(2)^2 + 12(2) - 5 = 7$. So the vertex is

$(2,7)$.

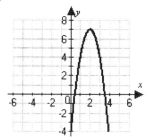

21. First, find the y-intercept by substituting 0 for x in the function:

$y = -4(0)^2 - 9(0) - 5 = -5$

The y-intercept is $(0,-5)$. Next find the

symmetric point to $(0,-5)$. Substitute -5 for y in the function and solve for x:

$-5 = 4x^2 - 9x - 5$

$0 = -4x^2 - 9x$

$0 = -x(4x + 9)$

$-x = 0$ or $4x + 9 = 0$

$x = 0$ or $4x = -9$

$x = 0$ or $x = -\dfrac{9}{4} \approx -2.25$

Therefore, the symmetric points are $(0, -5)$ and

$(-2.25, -5)$. Since $\dfrac{0 + (-2.25)}{2} = -1.13$, the x-

coordinate of the vertex is -1.13. To find the y-coordinate of the vertex, substitute -1.13 for x and solve for y:

$y = -3(-1.13)^2 + 12(-1.13) - 5 = 0.06$. So the

vertex is $(-1.13, 0.06)$.

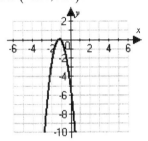

23. First, find the y-intercept by substituting 0 for x in the function:

$$y = 2(0)^2 - 7(0) + 7 = 7$$

The y-intercept is $(0, 7)$. Next find the

symmetric point to $(0, 7)$. Substitute 7 for y in

the function and solve for x:

$7 = 2x^2 - 7x + 7$

$0 = 2x^2 - 7x$

$0 = x(2x - 7)$

$x = 0$ or $2x - 7 = 0$

$x = 0$ or $2x = 7$

$x = 0$ or $x = \dfrac{7}{2} = 3.5$

Therefore, the symmetric points are $(0, 7)$ and

$(3.5, 7)$. Since $\dfrac{0 + 3.5}{2} = 1.75$, the x-coordinate

of the vertex is 1.75. To find the y-coordinate of the vertex, substitute 1.75 for x and solve for y:

$y = 2(1.75)^2 - 7(1.75) + 7 = 0.88$. So the vertex

is $(1.75, 0.88)$.

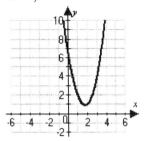

25. First, change the equation to standard form:

$4x^2 - y + 6 = 8x$

$y = 4x^2 - 8x + 6$

Next, find the y-intercept by substituting 0 for x in the function:

$$y = 4(0)^2 - 8(0) + 6 = 6$$

The y-intercept is $(0, 6)$. Next find the

symmetric point to $(0, 6)$. Substitute 6 for y in

the function and solve for x:

$6 = 4x^2 - 8x + 6$

$0 = 4x^2 - 8x$

$0 = 4x(x - 2)$

$4x = 0$ or $x - 2 = 0$

$x = 0$ or $x = 2$

Therefore, the symmetric points are $(0, 6)$ and

$(2, 6)$. Since $\dfrac{0 + 2}{2} = 1$, the x-coordinate of the

vertex is 1. To find the y-coordinate of the vertex, substitute 1 for x and solve for y:

$y = 4(1)^2 - 8(1) + 6 = 2$. So the vertex is $(1, 2)$.

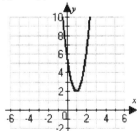

27. First, find the y-intercept by substituting 0 for x in the function:

$y = 2.8(0)^2 - 8.7(0) + 4 = 4$

The *y*-intercept is $(0,4)$. Next find the symmetric point to $(0,4)$. Substitute the 4 for *y* in the function and solve for *x*:

$4 = 2.8x^2 - 8.7x + 4$

$0 = 2.8x^2 - 8.7x$

$0 = x(2.8x - 8.7)$

$x = 0 \text{ or } 2.8x - 8.7 = 0$

$x = 0 \text{ or } 2.8x = 8.7$

$x = 0 \text{ or } x = \dfrac{8.7}{2.8} \approx 3.11$

Therefore, the symmetric points are $(0,4)$ and

$(3.11,4)$. Since $\dfrac{0 + 3.11}{2} \approx 1.56$, the *x*-coordinate of the vertex is 1.56. To find the *y*-coordinate of the vertex, substitute 1.56 for *x* and solve for *y*:

$y = 2.8(1.56)^2 - 8.7(1.56) + 4 \approx -2.76$. So the vertex is $(1.56, -2.76)$.

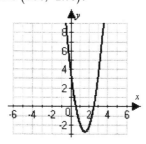

29. First, find the *y*-intercept by substituting 0 for *x* in the function:

$y = 3.9(0)^2 + 6.9(0) - 3.4 = -3.4$

The *y*-intercept is $(0, -3.4)$. Next find the symmetric point to $(0, -3.4)$. Substitute –3.4 for *y* in the function and solve for *x*:

$-3.4 = 3.9x^2 + 6.9x - 3.4$

$0 = 3.9x^2 + 6.9x$

$0 = x(3.9x + 6.9)$

$x = 0 \text{ or } 3.9x + 6.9 = 0$

$x = 0 \text{ or } 3.9x = -6.9$

$x = 0 \text{ or } x = -\dfrac{6.9}{3.9} \approx -1.77$

Therefore, the symmetric points are $(0, -3.4)$

and $(-1.77, -3.4)$. Since $\dfrac{0 + (-1.77)}{2} \approx -0.88$, the *x*-coordinate of the vertex is –0.88. To find the *y*-coordinate of the vertex, substitute –0.88 for *x* and solve for *y*:

$y = 3.9(-0.88)^2 + 6.9(-0.88) - 3.4 \approx -6.45$. So the vertex is $(-0.88, -6.45)$.

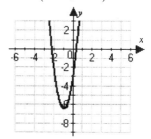

31. First, change the equation to standard form:

$3.6y - 2.63x = 8.3x^2 - 7.1$

$3.6y = 8.3x^2 + 2.63x - 7.1$

$y = \dfrac{8.3x^2 + 2.63x - 7.1}{3.6}$

$y = 2.31x^2 + 7.31x - 1.97$

Next, find the *y*-intercept by substituting 0 for *x* in the function:

$y = 2.31(0)^2 + 7.31(0) - 1.97 = -1.97$

The *y*-intercept is $(0, -1.97)$. Next find the symmetric point to $(0, -1.97)$. Substitute – 1.97 for *y* in the function and solve for *x*:

$-1.97 = 2.31x^2 + 7.31x - 1.97$

$0 = 2.31x^2 + 7.31x$

$0 = x(2.31x + 7.31)$

$x = 0 \text{ or } 2.31x + 7.31 = 0$

$x = 0 \text{ or } 2.31x = -7.31$

$x = 0 \text{ or } x = -\dfrac{7.31}{2.31} \approx -3.16$

Therefore, the symmetric points are $(0, -1.97)$

and $(-3.16, -1.97)$. Since $\dfrac{0 + (-3.16)}{2} = -1.58$, the *x*-coordinate of the vertex is -1.58. To find the *y*-coordinate of the vertex, substitute -1.58 for *x* and solve for *y*:

$y = 2.31(-1.58)^2 + 7.31(-1.58) - 1.97 = -7.75$. So the vertex is $(-1.58, -7.75)$.

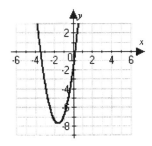

33. Since the x-intercepts are symmetric points and $\dfrac{2+6}{2} = 4$, the x-coordinate of the vertex is 4.

35. Since the x-intercepts are symmetric points and $\dfrac{-9+4}{2} = -\dfrac{5}{2}$, the x-coordinate of the vertex is $-\dfrac{5}{2}$.

37. To find the x-intercepts, let $y = 0$ and solve for x:

$0 = 5x^2 - 10x$

$0 = 5x(x-2)$

$5x = 0$ or $x - 2 = 0$

$x = 0$ or $x = 2$

The x-intercepts are $(0,0)$ and $(2,0)$. The y-intercept is, therefore, $(0,0)$. Since the x-intercepts are symmetric points and $\dfrac{0+2}{2} = 1$, the x-coordinate of the vertex is 1. Substitute 1 for x in the function and solve for y:

$y = 5(1)^2 - 10(1) = -5$. So, the vertex is $(1,-5)$.

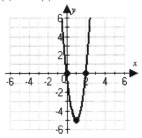

39. To find the x-intercepts, let $y = 0$ and solve for x:

$0 = -2x^2 + 6x$

$0 = 2x(-x+3)$

$2x = 0$ or $-x + 3 = 0$

$x = 0$ or $x = 3$

The x-intercepts are $(0,0)$ and $(3,0)$. The y-intercept is, therefore, $(0,0)$. Since the x-intercepts are symmetric points and $\dfrac{0+3}{2} = 1.5$, the x-coordinate of the vertex is 1.5. Substitute 1.5 for x in the function and solve for y:

$y = -2(1.5)^2 + 6(1.5) = 4.5$. So, the vertex is $(1.5, 4.5)$.

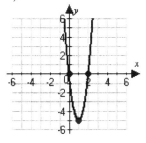

41. To find the x-intercepts, let $y = 0$ and solve for x:

$0 = x^2 - 10x + 24$

$0 = (x-6)(x-4)$

$x - 6 = 0$ or $x - 4 = 0$

$x = 6$ or $x = 4$

The x-intercepts are $(6,0)$ and $(4,0)$. To find the y-intercept, let $x = 0$ and solve for y:

$y = (0)^2 - 10(0) + 24 = 24$. The y-intercept is $(0,24)$. Since the x-intercepts are symmetric points and $\dfrac{6+4}{2} = 5$, the x-coordinate of the vertex is 5. Substitute 5 for x in the function and solve for y: $y = (5)^2 - 10(5) + 24 = -1$. So, the vertex is $(5,-1)$.

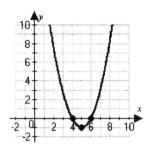

43. To find the *x*-intercepts, let $y = 0$ and solve for *x*:

$$0 = x^2 - 8x + 7$$
$$0 = (x - 7)(x - 1)$$
$$x - 7 = 0 \text{ or } x - 1 = 0$$
$$x = 7 \text{ or } x = 1$$

The *x*-intercepts are $(7, 0)$ and $(1, 0)$. To find the *y*-intercept, let $x = 0$ and solve for *y*:

$y = (0)^2 - 8(0) + 7 = 7$. The *y*-intercept is $(0, 7)$.

Since the *x*-intercepts are symmetric points and $\frac{7 + 1}{2} = 4$, the *x*-coordinate of the vertex is 4.

Substitute 4 for *x* in the function and solve for *y*:

$y = (4)^2 - 8(4) + 7 = -9$. So, the vertex is $(4, -9)$.

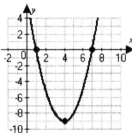

45. To find the *x*-intercepts, let $y = 0$ and solve for *x*:

$$0 = x^2 - 9$$
$$0 = (x - 3)(x + 3)$$
$$x - 3 = 0 \text{ or } x + 3 = 0$$
$$x = 3 \text{ or } x = -3$$

The *x*-intercepts are $(3, 0)$ and $(-3, 0)$. To find the *y*-intercept, let $x = 0$ and solve for *y*:

$y = (0)^2 - 9 = -9$. The *y*-intercept is $(0, -9)$.

Since the *x*-intercepts are symmetric points and

$\frac{3 + (-3)}{2} = 0$, the *x*-coordinate of the vertex is 0.

So the vertex is $(0, -9)$.

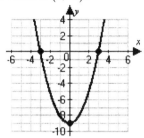

47. a. When the batter hits the ball, $t = 0$.

$$h(0) = -16(0)^2 + 140(0) + 3$$
$$= 0 + 0 + 3$$
$$= 3$$

b. The maximum height corresponds to the vertex of the graph.

$$t = -\frac{140}{2(-16)}$$
$$= \frac{-140}{-32}$$
$$= 4.375$$
$$h(4.375) = -16(4.375)^2 + 140(4.375) + 3$$
$$= -16(19.14) + 612.5 + 3$$
$$= -306.25 + 615.5$$
$$= 309.25$$

So after 4.375 seconds the ball is at its maximum height of 309.25 feet.

c.

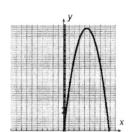

49. a.

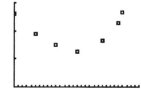

The function is a quadratic function.

b.

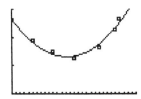

Yes, the function approximates the data very closely.

c. $f(31) = 0.0075(31)^2 - 0.2(31) + 2.65$ In

$\qquad = 3.6575$

2011, the average price of gasoline (in 2006 dollars) will be $3.66 per gallon.

d.   The lowest price corresponds with the vertex of the graph.

$t = -\dfrac{-0.2}{2(0.0075)}$

$ = \dfrac{0.2}{0.015}$

$ = 13.33$

$f(13) = 0.0075(13)^2 - 0.2(13) + 2.65$

$\qquad = 1.3175$

The average price (in 2006 dollars) was at its lowest in 1993 at $1.32 per gallon.

51. a.

The function is a quadratic function.

b.

Yes, the function approximates the data very closely.

c. $f(18) = -0.035(18)^2 + 3.25(18) - 26.34$ The

$\qquad = 20.82$

average annual expenditure of 18-year-old Americans is $20.8 thousand.

d.   The highest average annual expenditure corresponds with the vertex of the graph.

$t = -\dfrac{3.25}{2(-0.035)}$

$ = \dfrac{-3.25}{-0.07}$

$ = 46.4$

$f(46) = -0.035(46)^2 + 3.25(46) - 26.34$

$\qquad = 49.1$

The highest average annual expenditure is fo 46-year-old Americans at $49.1 thousand.

53. a.

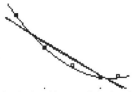

The quadratic function models the data the best.

b.   The linear function predicts the lowest student-to-faculty ratios.

c. $15.9 = 0.011t^2 - 0.48t + 15.9$

$ 0 = 0.011t^2 - 0.48t$

$ 0 = t(0.011t - 0.48)$

$ 0 = 0.011t - 0.48$

$t = 0 \quad$ or $\quad 0.48 = 0.011t$

$ 44 \approx t$

According to the model, during the year 2024, the student-to-faculty ratio will be 15.9.

d.   The lowest student-to-faculty ratio corresponds with the vertex of the graph.

$t = -\dfrac{-0.48}{2(0.011)}$

$ = \dfrac{0.48}{0.022}$

$ = 21.8$

$f(22) = 0.011(22)^2 - 0.48(22) + 15.9$

$\qquad = 10.664$

The student-to-faculty ratio was at its lowest in 2002 at 10.7.

55. Let w be the width of the fenced in area, l be the length of the fenced in area, and A be the fenced in area. The perimeter and area of the fencing and fenced in area is given by:

$80 = 2w + 2l$

$A = wl$

Solving the first equation for l.

$80 = 2w + 2l$

$80 - 2w = 2l$

$40 - w = l$

Substituting this for l in the area equation:

$A = w(40 - w)$

$= 40w - w^2$

Find the maximum point of the parabola by finding the vertex.

$w = -\dfrac{40}{2(-1)}$

$= \dfrac{-40}{-2}$

$= 20$

So the maximum width is 20 feet.

$A = 40(20) - (20)^2$

$= 800 - 400$

$= 400$

The maximum area is 400 feet.

$80 = 2(20) + 2l$

$80 = 40 + 2l$

$40 = 2l$

$20 = l$

The maximum length is 20 feet.

57. Let w be the width of the fenced in area, l be the length of the fenced in area, and A be the fenced in area. The perimeter and area of the fencing and fenced in area is given by:

$400 = 2w + l$

$A = wl$

Solving the first equation for l.

$400 = 2w + l$

$400 - 2w = l$

Substituting this for l in the area equation:

$A = w(400 - 2w)$

$= 400w - 2w^2$

Find the maximum point of the parabola by finding the vertex.

$w = -\dfrac{400}{2(-2)}$

$= \dfrac{-400}{-4}$

$= 100$

So the maximum width is 100 feet.

$A = 400(100) - 2(100)^2$

$= 40,000 - 20,000$

$= 20,000$

The maximum area is 20,000 feet.

$400 = 2(100) + l$

$400 = 200 + l$

$200 = l$

The maximum length is 200 feet.

59. a.

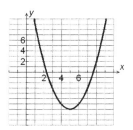

b. Answers may vary. Example:

x	y
3	−3
4	−6
5	−7
6	−6
7	−3

c. For each input-output pair, the output variable is 18 more than the difference between the square of the input and 10 times the input.

61. $f(-5) = -1$

63. When $x = -3, f(x) = 3$.

65. When $x = -2$ or $-4, f(x) = 2$.

67. The maximum value of f is 3.

69. a. $y = (0)^2 + 4(0) - 12$

$y = -12$

Solve for x when $y = -12$.

$$12 = x^2 + 4x - 12$$
$$0 = x^2 + 4x$$
$$0 = x(x+4)$$
$$0 = x \quad \text{or} \quad \begin{matrix} 0 = x+4 \\ -4 = x \end{matrix}$$

Take the average of the *y*-intercept and it's symmetric point:

$$\frac{0+(-4)}{2} = \frac{-4}{2} = -2$$

The *x*-coordinate of the vertex is –2.

b.
$$0 = x^2 + 4x - 12$$
$$0 = (x+6)(x-2)$$
$$\begin{matrix} 0 = x+6 \\ -6 = x \end{matrix} \quad \text{or} \quad \begin{matrix} 0 = x-2 \\ 2 = x \end{matrix}$$

Taking the average of the *x*-intercepts:

$$\frac{(-6)+2}{2} = \frac{-4}{2} = -2$$

The *x*-coordinate of the vertex is –2.

c. Yes, both methods produce the same result.

d. Averaging the *x*-coordinates of the *y*-intercept and its symmetric point.

e. Averaging the *x*-coordinates of the *y*-intercept and its symmetric point.

f. Answers may vary.

71. (3, 2) is the vertex for both *f* and *k*. The vertex of *g* is approximately (2.7, 1.8). The vertex of *h* is approximately (3.3, 1.7).

73. Answers may vary. See the box "Sketching a Quadratic Function in Standard Form" on page 297 of the text or the "Key Points of This Section" preceding this homework.

75.

77.

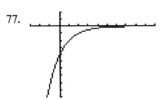

79. a.
$$f(x) = a(x-h)^2 + k$$
$$= a\left(x^2 - 2xh + h^2\right) + k$$
$$= ax^2 - 2axh + ah^2 + k$$

b.
$$x = -\frac{-2ah}{2(a)}$$
$$= \frac{2ah}{2a}$$
$$= h$$

Substituting *h* for *x*.
$$f(h) = a(h-h)^2 + k$$
$$= a(0)^2 + k$$
$$= k$$

The vertex of the parabola is (*h*, *k*).

81.
$$\frac{2b^{-2}c^4\left(3b^{-5}c^{-1}\right)^2}{8b^{-6}c^{-4}} = \frac{2b^{-2}c^4\left(9b^{-10}c^{-2}\right)}{8b^{-6}c^{-4}}$$
$$= \frac{18b^{-12}c^2}{8b^{-6}c^{-4}}$$
$$= \frac{9c^6}{4b^6}$$

This is an expression in two variables involving exponents.

83.

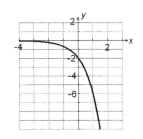

This is an exponential function in one variable.

85.
$$-2(3)^x = -200$$
$$3^x = 100$$
$$\log_3 100 = x$$
$$4.19 = x$$

This is an exponential equation in one variable.

Homework 7.3

1. $\sqrt{169} = \sqrt{13 \cdot 13} = 13$

3. $\sqrt{12} = \sqrt{4 \cdot 3} = \sqrt{4} \cdot \sqrt{3} = 2\sqrt{3}$

5. $\sqrt{\dfrac{4}{9}} = \dfrac{\sqrt{4}}{\sqrt{9}} = \dfrac{2}{3}$

7. $\sqrt{\dfrac{6}{49}} = \dfrac{\sqrt{6}}{\sqrt{49}} = \dfrac{\sqrt{6}}{7}$

9. $\dfrac{5}{\sqrt{2}} = \dfrac{5}{\sqrt{2}} \cdot \dfrac{\sqrt{2}}{\sqrt{2}} = \dfrac{5\sqrt{2}}{\sqrt{4}} = \dfrac{5\sqrt{2}}{2}$

11. $\dfrac{3}{\sqrt{32}} = \dfrac{3}{\sqrt{16 \cdot 2}} = \dfrac{3}{4\sqrt{2}} \cdot \dfrac{\sqrt{2}}{\sqrt{2}} = \dfrac{3\sqrt{2}}{4\sqrt{4}} = \dfrac{3\sqrt{2}}{4 \cdot 2} = \dfrac{3\sqrt{2}}{8}$

13. $\sqrt{\dfrac{3}{2}} = \dfrac{\sqrt{3}}{\sqrt{2}} \cdot \dfrac{\sqrt{2}}{\sqrt{2}} = \dfrac{\sqrt{6}}{\sqrt{4}} = \dfrac{\sqrt{6}}{2}$

15. $\sqrt{\dfrac{11}{20}} = \dfrac{\sqrt{11}}{\sqrt{20}} = \dfrac{\sqrt{11}}{\sqrt{4 \cdot 5}} = \dfrac{\sqrt{11}}{2\sqrt{5}} \cdot \dfrac{\sqrt{5}}{\sqrt{5}} = \dfrac{\sqrt{55}}{2\sqrt{25}} = \dfrac{\sqrt{55}}{10}$

17. $x^2 = 25$
$\sqrt{x^2} = \sqrt{25}$
$x = \pm 5$

19. $x^2 - 3 = 0$
$x^2 = 3$
$x = \pm\sqrt{3}$

21. $t^2 = 32$
$\sqrt{t^2} = \pm\sqrt{32}$
$t = \pm\sqrt{16 \cdot 2}$
$\quad = \pm 4\sqrt{2}$

23. $5x^2 = 3$
$x^2 = \dfrac{3}{5}$
$\sqrt{x^2} = \sqrt{\dfrac{3}{5}}$
$x = \pm\dfrac{\sqrt{3}}{\sqrt{5}}$
$x = \pm\dfrac{\sqrt{3}}{\sqrt{5}} \cdot \dfrac{\sqrt{5}}{\sqrt{5}}$
$x = \pm\dfrac{\sqrt{15}}{5}$

25. $3p^2 - 11 = 3$
$3p^2 = 14$
$p^2 = \dfrac{14}{3}$
$\sqrt{p^2} = \pm\sqrt{\dfrac{14}{3}}$
$p = \pm\dfrac{\sqrt{14}}{\sqrt{3}}$
$p = \pm\dfrac{\sqrt{14}}{\sqrt{3}} \cdot \dfrac{\sqrt{3}}{\sqrt{3}}$
$p = \pm\dfrac{\sqrt{42}}{3}$

27. $(x+4)^2 = 7$
$\sqrt{(x+4)^2} = \pm\sqrt{7}$
$x + 4 = \pm\sqrt{7}$
$x = -4 \pm\sqrt{7}$

29. $(x-5)^2 = 27$
$\sqrt{(x-5)^2} = \pm\sqrt{27}$
$x - 5 = \pm 3\sqrt{3}$
$x = 5 \pm 3\sqrt{3}$

31. $(8y+3)^2 = 36$

$\sqrt{(8y+3)^2} = \pm\sqrt{36}$

$8y+3 = \pm 6$

$8y = -3 \pm 6$

$y = \dfrac{-3 \pm 6}{8}$

$y = \dfrac{-9}{8}$ or $y = \dfrac{3}{8}$

33. $(9x-5)^2 = 0$

$\sqrt{(9x-5)^2} = \sqrt{0}$

$9x - 5 = 0$

$9x = 5$

$x = \dfrac{5}{9}$

35. $\left(x+\dfrac{3}{4}\right)^2 = \dfrac{41}{16}$

$\sqrt{\left(x+\dfrac{3}{4}\right)^2} = \pm\sqrt{\dfrac{41}{16}}$

$x + \dfrac{3}{4} = \pm\dfrac{\sqrt{41}}{\sqrt{16}}$

$x + \dfrac{3}{4} = \pm\dfrac{\sqrt{41}}{4}$

$x = \dfrac{-3 \pm \sqrt{41}}{4}$

37. $\left(w-\dfrac{7}{3}\right)^2 = \dfrac{5}{9}$

$\sqrt{\left(w-\dfrac{7}{3}\right)^2} = \pm\sqrt{\dfrac{5}{9}}$

$w - \dfrac{7}{3} = \pm\dfrac{\sqrt{5}}{\sqrt{9}}$

$w - \dfrac{7}{3} = \pm\dfrac{\sqrt{5}}{3}$

$w = \dfrac{7 \pm \sqrt{5}}{3}$

39. $5(x-6)^2 + 3 = 33$

$5(x-6)^2 = 30$

$(x-6)^2 = 6$

$\sqrt{(x-6)^2} = \pm\sqrt{6}$

$x - 6 = \pm\sqrt{6}$

$x = 6 \pm \sqrt{6}$

41. $-3(x+1)^2 + 2 = -5$

$-3(x+1)^2 = -7$

$(x+1)^2 = \dfrac{7}{3}$

$\sqrt{(x+1)^2} = \pm\sqrt{\dfrac{7}{3}}$

$x + 1 = \pm\dfrac{\sqrt{7}}{\sqrt{3}}$

$x + 1 = \pm\dfrac{\sqrt{7}}{\sqrt{3}} \cdot \dfrac{\sqrt{3}}{\sqrt{3}}$

$x + 1 = \pm\dfrac{\sqrt{21}}{3}$

$x = \dfrac{-1 \pm \sqrt{21}}{3}$

43. Solve for x when $f(x) = 0$

$0 = x^2 - 17$

$x^2 = 17$

$x = \pm\sqrt{17}$

The *x*-intercepts are $\left(\sqrt{17}, 0\right)$ and $\left(-\sqrt{17}, 0\right)$.

45. Solve for x when $f(x) = 0$

$$0 = 2(x-3)^2 - 7$$

$$7 = 2(x-3)^2$$

$$\frac{7}{2} = (x-3)^2$$

$$\pm\sqrt{\frac{7}{2}} = \sqrt{(x-3)^2}$$

$$\pm\frac{\sqrt{7}}{\sqrt{2}} = x-3$$

$$\pm\frac{\sqrt{7}}{\sqrt{2}} \cdot \frac{\sqrt{2}}{\sqrt{2}} = x-3$$

$$\pm\frac{\sqrt{14}}{2} = x-3$$

$$3 \pm \frac{\sqrt{14}}{2} = x$$

$$\frac{6 \pm \sqrt{14}}{2} = x$$

The x-intercepts are $\left(\dfrac{6-\sqrt{14}}{2}, 0\right)$ and $\left(\dfrac{6+\sqrt{14}}{2}, 0\right)$.

47. Solve for x when $f(x) = 0$

$$0 = -4(x-2)^2 - 16$$

$$16 = -4(x-2)^2$$

$$-4 = (x-2)^2$$

The next step would be to take the square root of both sides, resulting in an imaginary number. Since the x-intercept must be a real number, there are no x-intercepts.

49. $\sqrt{-36} = i\sqrt{36} = 6i$

51. $-\sqrt{-45} = -i\sqrt{45} = -i\sqrt{9 \cdot 5} = -3i\sqrt{5}$

53. $\sqrt{-\dfrac{5}{49}} = i\sqrt{\dfrac{5}{49}} = i\dfrac{\sqrt{5}}{\sqrt{49}} = i\dfrac{\sqrt{5}}{7}$

55. $\sqrt{-\dfrac{13}{5}} = i\sqrt{\dfrac{13}{5}} = i\dfrac{\sqrt{13}}{\sqrt{5}} = i\dfrac{\sqrt{13}}{\sqrt{5}} \cdot \dfrac{\sqrt{5}}{\sqrt{5}} = i\dfrac{\sqrt{65}}{5}$

57.

$$x^2 = -49$$

$$\sqrt{x^2} = \pm\sqrt{-49}$$

$$x = \pm i\sqrt{49}$$

$$x = \pm 7i$$

59.

$$x^2 = -18$$

$$\sqrt{x^2} = \pm\sqrt{-18}$$

$$x = \pm i\sqrt{18}$$

$$x = \pm i\sqrt{9 \cdot 2}$$

$$x = \pm 3i\sqrt{2}$$

61. $7x^2 + 26 = 5$

$$7x^2 = -21$$

$$x^2 = -3$$

$$\sqrt{x^2} = \pm\sqrt{-3}$$

$$x = \pm i\sqrt{3}$$

63.

$$(m+4)^2 = -8$$

$$\sqrt{(m+4)^2} = \pm\sqrt{-8}$$

$$m+4 = \pm i\sqrt{8}$$

$$m+4 = \pm 2i\sqrt{2}$$

$$m = -4 \pm 2i\sqrt{2}$$

65.

$$\left(x-\frac{5}{4}\right)^2 = -\frac{3}{16}$$

$$\sqrt{\left(x-\frac{5}{4}\right)^2} = \pm\sqrt{-\frac{3}{16}}$$

$$x-\frac{5}{4} = \pm\frac{\sqrt{-3}}{\sqrt{16}}$$

$$x-\frac{5}{4} = \pm\frac{i\sqrt{3}}{4}$$

$$x = \frac{5 \pm i\sqrt{3}}{4}$$

67. $-2(y+3)^2 +1 = 9$

$\quad\quad -2(y+3)^2 = 8$

$\quad\quad\quad (y+3)^2 = -4$

$\quad\quad \sqrt{(y+3)^2} = \pm\sqrt{-4}$

$\quad\quad\quad\quad y+3 = \pm i\sqrt{4}$

$\quad\quad\quad\quad y+3 = \pm 2i$

$\quad\quad\quad\quad\quad y = -3 \pm 2i$

69. a. First make a scattergram of the data.

Use the point (1, 64) as the vertex.

$f(t) = a(t-1)^2 + 64$

Now use the point (4, 253) to solve for *a*.

$253 = a(4-1)^2 + 64$

$253 = a(3)^2 + 64$

$253 = 9a + 64$

$189 = 9a$

$\;\;21 = a$

So the equation of *f* in vertex form is:

$f(t) = 21(t-1)^2 + 64$

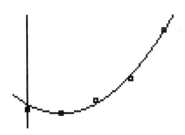

The graph of *f* is very close to the data points.

b. To find when the price of scrap iron and sheet metal will be $1250 per metric ton, substitute 1250 for *f* and solve for *t*.

$1250 = 21(t-1)^2 + 64$

$1186 = 21(t-1)^2$

$56.48 = (t-1)^2$

$7.52 = t-1$

$8.52 = t$

So in the year 2009, the model predicts that scrap iron and sheet metal will cost $1250 per metric ton.

c. To find the price of scrap iron and sheet metal in 2010, let *t* = 10 and solve for *f*.

$f(10) = 21((10)-1)^2 + 64$

$\quad\quad = 21(9)^2 + 64$

$\quad\quad = 21(81) + 64$

$\quad\quad = 1701 + 64$

$\quad\quad = 1765$

In 2010, the price of scrap iron will be $1765 per metric ton.

d. A 125-pound manhole cover weights 0.0567 metric tons. So the price of a manhole cover is $0.0567 \cdot 1765 \approx 100$, or about $100.

71. a. First make a scattergram of the data.

Use the point (1.62, 476.88) as the vertex.

$f(t) = a(t-1.62)^2 + 476.88$

Now use the point (1, 480) to solve for *a*.

$480 = a((1)-1.62)^2 + 476.88$

$480 = a(-0.62)^2 + 476.88$

$480 = 0.3844a + 476.88$

$3.12 = 0.3844a$

$8.12 = a$

So the equation of *f* in vertex form is:

$f(t) = 8.12(t-1.62)^2 + 476.88$

The graph of f is very close to the data points.

b. The vertex of the model is $(1.62, 476.88)$. This means that the minimum spending on domestic travel occurred in 2002, at \$477 billion.

c. To find the spending on domestic travel in 2009, let $t = 9$ and solve for f.
$$f(9) = 8.12((9) - 1.62)^2 + 476.88$$
$$= 8.12(7.38)^2 + 476.88$$
$$= 8.12(54.46) + 476.88$$
$$= 442.22 + 476.88$$
$$= 919.1$$
The model predicts that in 2009, \$919.1 billion dollars will be spent on domestic travel.

d. To find the year domestic travel will reach \$1 trillion, or \$1,000 billion, substitute 1,000 for f and solve for t.
$$1,000 = 8.12(t - 1.62)^2 + 476.88$$
$$523.12 = 8.12(t - 1.62)^2$$
$$64.42 = (t - 1.62)^2$$
$$8.03 = t - 1.62$$
$$9.65 = t$$
In 2010 spending on domestic travel will be \$1 trillion.

73. No, the student did not solve it correctly. They should have factored the left hand side first.
$$x^2 - 10x + 25 = 0$$
$$(x - 5)(x - 5) = 0$$
$$(x - 5)^2 = 0$$
$$x - 5 = 0$$
$$x = 5$$

75. The graphs of the two equations meet when $x = 1.4$ or 4.2.

77. The graph of the equation meets the line $y = 2$ when $x = 2$ or 4.

79. The graphs of the equations meet at the points $(1.1, -3.5)$ and $(4.7, -1.7)$.

81. a. The vertex of the graph is $(3, 5)$.

b. Since $2 > 0$, the graph of f opens upward.

c. **i.** The equation has two solutions.

ii. The equation has one solutions.

iii. The equation has no solutions.

83. a.
$$25x^2 - 49 = 0$$
$$x^2 - \frac{49}{25} = 0$$
$$x^2 - \left(\frac{7}{5}\right)^2 = 0$$
$$\left(x - \frac{7}{5}\right)\left(x + \frac{7}{5}\right) = 0$$
$$x - \frac{7}{5} = 0 \qquad x + \frac{7}{5} = 0$$
$$x = \frac{7}{5} \qquad x = -\frac{7}{5}$$

b.
$$25x^2 - 49 = 0$$
$$25x^2 = 49$$
$$x^2 = \frac{49}{25}$$
$$\sqrt{x^2} = \pm\sqrt{\frac{49}{25}}$$
$$x = \pm\frac{\sqrt{49}}{\sqrt{25}}$$
$$x = \pm\frac{7}{5}$$

c. Both solutions are the same.

d. Answers may vary.

85. a. Yes it can be solved with the square root property.

$$(x+4)^2 = 5$$
$$\sqrt{(x+4)^2} = \pm\sqrt{5}$$
$$x+4 = \pm\sqrt{5}$$
$$x = -4 \pm \sqrt{5}$$

b. No, it cannot be solved by factoring.

c. No, not all equations that can be solved with the square root property can be solved by factoring.

87. $a^2 + b^2 = c^2$
$$a^2 = c^2 - b^2$$
$$a = \pm\sqrt{c^2 - b^2}$$

89. $(mt+b)^2 = p$
$$\sqrt{(mt+b)^2} = \pm\sqrt{p}$$
$$mt + b = \pm\sqrt{p}$$
$$mt = -b \pm \sqrt{p}$$
$$t = \frac{-b \pm \sqrt{p}}{m}$$

91. Answers may vary.

93. $x^6 = 142$
$$\sqrt[6]{x^6} = \pm\sqrt[6]{142}$$
$$x = \pm 2.2841$$

95. $(t-4)^3 = 88$
$$\sqrt[3]{(t-4)^3} = \sqrt[3]{88}$$
$$t - 4 = 4.4480$$
$$t = 8.4480$$

97. $3(x+1)^5 - 4 = 44$
$$3(x+1)^5 = 48$$
$$(x+1)^5 = 16$$
$$\sqrt[5]{(x+1)^5} = \sqrt[5]{16}$$
$$x + 1 = 1.7411$$
$$x = 0.7411$$

99. $2w^3 + 3w^2 - 18w - 27 = w^2(2w+3) - 9(2w+3)$
$$= (w^2 - 9)(2w+3)$$
$$= (w+3)(w-3)(2w+3)$$
This is a cubic polynomial in one variable.

101. From problem 99 we know that:
$$2w^3 + 3w^2 - 18w - 27 = (w-3)(w+3)(2w+3)$$
So:
$$0 = 2w^3 + 3w^2 - 18w - 27$$
$$= (w-3)(w+3)(2w+3)$$

$w - 3 = 0$	$w + 3 = 0$	$2w + 3 = 0$
$w = 3$	$w = -3$	$2w = -3$
		$w = -\dfrac{3}{2}$

This is a cubic equation in one variable.

103. $(5w^2 - 2)(4w + 3) = 20w^3 + 15w^2 - 8w - 6$
This is a cubic polynomial in one variable.

Homework 7.4

1. $\left(\dfrac{12}{2}\right)^2 = 6^2 = 36 = c$

This expression is $x^2 + 12x + 36$ and its factored form is $(x+6)^2$.

3. $\left(\dfrac{-14}{2}\right)^2 = (-7)^2 = 49 = c$

This expression is $x^2 - 14x + 49$ and its factored form is $(x-7)^2$.

5. $\left(\dfrac{7}{2}\right)^2 = \dfrac{7^2}{2^2} = \dfrac{49}{4} = c$

This expression is $x^2 + 7x + \dfrac{49}{4}$ and its factored form is $\left(x + \dfrac{7}{2}\right)^2$.

7. $\left(\dfrac{-3}{2}\right)^2 = \dfrac{(-3)^2}{2^2} = \dfrac{9}{4} = c$

This expression is $x^2 - 3x + \dfrac{9}{4}$ and its factored form is $\left(x - \dfrac{3}{2}\right)^2$.

9. $\left(\dfrac{1}{2}\cdot\dfrac{1}{2}\right)^2 = \left(\dfrac{1}{4}\right)^2 = \dfrac{1^2}{4^2} = \dfrac{1}{16} = c$

This expression is $x^2 + \dfrac{1}{2}x + \dfrac{1}{16}$ and its factored

form is $\left(x + \dfrac{1}{4}\right)^2$.

11. $\left(-\dfrac{4}{5}\cdot\dfrac{1}{2}\right)^2 = \left(\dfrac{-4}{10}\right)^2 = \dfrac{(-4)^2}{(10)^2} = \dfrac{16}{100} = \dfrac{4}{25} = c$

This expression is $x^2 - \dfrac{4}{5}x + \dfrac{4}{25}$ and its factored

form is $\left(x - \dfrac{2}{5}\right)^2$.

13.
Since $\left(\dfrac{6}{2}\right)^2 = 3^2 = 9$, add 9 to both sides of the

equation.

$x^2 + 6x = 1$

$x^2 + 6x + 9 = 1 + 9$

$(x+3)^2 = 10$

$x + 3 = \pm\sqrt{10}$

$x = -3 \pm \sqrt{10}$

15.
Since $\left(\dfrac{2}{2}\right)^2 = 1^2 = 1$, add 1 to both sides of the

equation.

$p^2 - 2p = 19$

$p^2 - 2p + 1 = 19 + 1$

$(p-1)^2 = 20$

$p - 1 = \pm\sqrt{20}$

$p = 1 \pm 2\sqrt{5}$

17.
Since $\left(\dfrac{4}{2}\right)^2 = 2^2 = 4$, add 4 to both sides of the

equation.

$x^2 + 4x - 24 = 0$

$x^2 + 4x = 24$

$x^2 + 4x + 4 = 28$

$(x+2)^2 = 28$

$(x+2)^2 = 28$

$x + 2 = \pm\sqrt{28}$

$x = -2 \pm 2\sqrt{7}$

19.
Since $\left(\dfrac{-7}{2}\right)^2 = \dfrac{(-7)^2}{2^2} = \dfrac{49}{4}$, add $\dfrac{49}{4}$ to both

sides of the equation.

$x^2 - 7x = 3$

$x^2 - 7x + \dfrac{49}{4} = 3 + \dfrac{49}{4}$

$\left(x - \dfrac{7}{2}\right)^2 = \dfrac{12}{4} + \dfrac{49}{4}$

$\left(x - \dfrac{7}{2}\right)^2 = \dfrac{61}{4}$

$x - \dfrac{7}{2} = \pm\sqrt{\dfrac{61}{4}}$

$x - \dfrac{7}{2} = \pm\dfrac{\sqrt{61}}{2}$

$x = \dfrac{7}{2} \pm \dfrac{\sqrt{61}}{2}$

$x = \dfrac{7 \pm \sqrt{61}}{2}$

21.
Since $\left(\dfrac{5}{2}\right)^2 = \dfrac{5^2}{2^2} = \dfrac{25}{4}$, add $\dfrac{25}{4}$ to both sides of

the equation.

$$t^2 + 5t - 4$$

$$t^2 + 5t + \frac{25}{4} = 4 + \frac{25}{4}$$

$$\left(t + \frac{5}{2}\right)^2 = \frac{41}{4}$$

$$t + \frac{5}{2} = \pm\sqrt{\frac{41}{4}}$$

$$t + \frac{5}{2} = \pm\frac{\sqrt{41}}{\sqrt{4}}$$

$$t + \frac{5}{2} = \pm\frac{\sqrt{41}}{2}$$

$$t = \frac{-5 \pm \sqrt{41}}{2}$$

23. Since $\left(\dfrac{-5}{2} \cdot \dfrac{1}{2}\right)^2 = \left(\dfrac{-5}{4}\right)^2 = \dfrac{(-5)^2}{4^2} = \dfrac{25}{16}$, add $\dfrac{25}{16}$

to both sides of the equation.

$$x^2 - \frac{5}{2}x = \frac{1}{2}$$

$$x^2 - \frac{5}{2}x + \frac{25}{16} = \frac{1}{2} + \frac{25}{16}$$

$$\left(x - \frac{5}{4}\right)^2 = \frac{8}{16} + \frac{25}{16}$$

$$\left(x - \frac{5}{4}\right)^2 = \frac{33}{16}$$

$$x - \frac{5}{4} = \pm\sqrt{\frac{33}{16}}$$

$$x - \frac{5}{4} = \pm\frac{\sqrt{33}}{4}$$

$$x = \frac{5}{4} \pm \frac{\sqrt{33}}{4}$$

$$x = \frac{5 \pm \sqrt{33}}{4}$$

25. First write the equation with an x^2 coefficient of 1:

$$2x^2 + 8x = 3$$

$$x^2 + 4x = \frac{3}{2}$$

Since $\left(\dfrac{4}{2}\right)^2 = 2^2 = 4$, add 4 to both sides of the equation.

$$x^2 + 4x = \frac{3}{2}$$

$$x^2 + 4x + 4 = \frac{3}{2} + 4$$

$$(x + 2)^2 = \frac{11}{2}$$

$$x + 2 = \pm\sqrt{\frac{11}{2}}$$

$$x + 2 = \pm\frac{\sqrt{11}}{\sqrt{2}}$$

$$x + 2 = \pm\frac{\sqrt{11}}{\sqrt{2}} \cdot \frac{\sqrt{2}}{\sqrt{2}}$$

$$x + 2 = \pm\frac{\sqrt{22}}{2}$$

$$x = \frac{-4 \pm \sqrt{22}}{2}$$

27. First write the equation with an x^2 coefficient of 1:

$$2r^2 - r - 7 = 0$$

$$r^2 - \frac{1}{2}r - \frac{7}{2} = 0$$

Since $\left(-\dfrac{1}{2} \cdot \dfrac{1}{2}\right)^2 = \left(-\dfrac{1}{4}\right)^2 = \dfrac{1}{16}$, add $\dfrac{1}{16}$ to both

sides of the equation.

$$r^2 - \frac{1}{2}r - \frac{7}{2} = 0$$

$$r^2 - \frac{1}{2}r = \frac{7}{2}$$

$$r^2 - \frac{1}{2}r + \frac{1}{16} = \frac{7}{2} + \frac{1}{16}$$

$$\left(r - \frac{1}{4}\right)^2 = \frac{57}{16}$$

$$r - \frac{1}{4} = \pm\sqrt{\frac{57}{16}}$$

$$r - \frac{1}{4} = \pm\frac{\sqrt{57}}{\sqrt{16}}$$

$$r - \frac{1}{4} = \pm\frac{\sqrt{57}}{4}$$

$$r = \frac{1 \pm \sqrt{57}}{4}$$

29. First write the equation with an x^2 coefficient of 1:

$3x^2 + 4x - 5 = 0$

$x^2 + \dfrac{4}{3}x - \dfrac{5}{3} = 0$

Since $\left(\dfrac{4}{3} \cdot \dfrac{1}{2}\right)^2 = \left(\dfrac{2}{3}\right)^2 = \dfrac{2^2}{3^2} = \dfrac{4}{9}$, add $\dfrac{4}{9}$ to both

sides of the equation.

$x^2 + \dfrac{4}{3}x - \dfrac{5}{3} = 0$

$x^2 + \dfrac{4}{3}x = \dfrac{5}{3}$

$x^2 + \dfrac{4}{3}x + \dfrac{4}{9} = \dfrac{5}{3} + \dfrac{4}{9}$

$\left(x + \dfrac{2}{3}\right)^2 = \dfrac{19}{9}$

$x + \dfrac{2}{3} = \pm\sqrt{\dfrac{19}{9}}$

$x + \dfrac{2}{3} = \pm\dfrac{\sqrt{19}}{\sqrt{9}}$

$x + \dfrac{2}{3} = \pm\dfrac{\sqrt{19}}{3}$

$x = \dfrac{-2 \pm \sqrt{19}}{3}$

31. First write the equation with an x^2 coefficient of 1:

$6x^2 - 8x = -1$

$x^2 - \dfrac{4}{3}x = -\dfrac{1}{6}$

Since $\left(-\dfrac{4}{3} \cdot \dfrac{1}{2}\right)^2 = \left(\dfrac{2}{3}\right)^2 = \dfrac{2^2}{3^2} = \dfrac{4}{9}$, add $\dfrac{4}{9}$ to both sides of the equation.

$x^2 - \dfrac{4}{3}x = -\dfrac{1}{6}$

$x^2 - \dfrac{4}{3}x + \dfrac{4}{9} = -\dfrac{1}{6} + \dfrac{4}{9}$

$\left(x - \dfrac{2}{3}\right)^2 = \dfrac{5}{18}$

$x - \dfrac{2}{3} = \pm\sqrt{\dfrac{5}{18}}$

$x - \dfrac{2}{3} = \pm\dfrac{\sqrt{5}}{\sqrt{18}}$

$x - \dfrac{2}{3} = \pm\dfrac{\sqrt{5}}{3\sqrt{2}}$

$x - \dfrac{2}{3} = \pm\dfrac{\sqrt{5}}{3\sqrt{2}} \cdot \dfrac{\sqrt{2}}{\sqrt{2}}$

$x - \dfrac{2}{3} = \pm\dfrac{\sqrt{10}}{6}$

$x = \dfrac{4 \pm \sqrt{10}}{6}$

33. First write the equation with an x^2 coefficient of 1:

$8w^2 + 4w - 3 = 0$

$w^2 + \dfrac{1}{2}w - \dfrac{3}{8} = 0$

Since $\left(\dfrac{1}{2} \cdot \dfrac{1}{2}\right)^2 = \left(\dfrac{1}{4}\right)^2 = \dfrac{1}{16}$ add $\dfrac{1}{16}$ to both

sides of the equation.

$w^2 + \dfrac{1}{2}w - \dfrac{3}{8} = 0$

$w^2 + \dfrac{1}{2}w = \dfrac{3}{8}$

$w^2 + \dfrac{1}{2}w + \dfrac{1}{16} = \dfrac{3}{8} + \dfrac{1}{16}$

$\left(w + \dfrac{1}{4}\right)^2 = \dfrac{7}{16}$

$w + \dfrac{1}{4} = \pm\sqrt{\dfrac{7}{16}}$

$w + \dfrac{1}{4} = \pm\dfrac{\sqrt{7}}{\sqrt{16}}$

$w + \dfrac{1}{4} = \pm\dfrac{\sqrt{7}}{4}$

$w = \dfrac{-1 \pm \sqrt{7}}{4}$

35. Since $\left(\dfrac{2}{2}\right)^2 = 1^2 = 1$, add 1 to both sides of the equation.

$$x^2 + 2x = -7$$
$$x^2 + 2x + 1 = -7 + 1$$
$$(x+1)^2 = -6$$
$$x + 1 = \pm\sqrt{-6}$$
$$x = -1 \pm i\sqrt{6}$$

37. Since $\left(\dfrac{6}{2}\right)^2 = 3^2 = 9$, add 9 to both sides of the equation.

$$x^2 - 6x + 17 = 0$$
$$x^2 - 6x = -17$$
$$x^2 - 6x + 9 = -17 + 9$$
$$(x-3)^2 = -8$$
$$x - 3 = \pm\sqrt{-8}$$
$$x = 3 \pm 2i\sqrt{2}$$

39. Since $\left(\dfrac{3}{2}\right)^2 = \dfrac{3^2}{2^2} = \dfrac{9}{4}$, add $\dfrac{9}{4}$ to both sides of the equation.

$$k^2 + 3k + 4 = 0$$
$$k^2 + 3k = -4$$
$$k^2 + 3k + \dfrac{9}{4} = -4 + \dfrac{9}{4}$$
$$\left(k + \dfrac{3}{2}\right)^2 = \dfrac{-7}{4}$$
$$k + \dfrac{3}{2} = \pm\sqrt{\dfrac{-7}{4}}$$
$$k + \dfrac{3}{2} = \pm\dfrac{\sqrt{-7}}{\sqrt{4}}$$
$$k + \dfrac{3}{2} = \pm\dfrac{i\sqrt{7}}{2}$$
$$k = \dfrac{-3 \pm i\sqrt{7}}{2}$$

41. Since $\left(\dfrac{2}{3}\cdot\dfrac{1}{2}\right)^2 = \left(\dfrac{1}{3}\right)^2 = \dfrac{1^2}{3^2} = \dfrac{1}{9}$, add $\dfrac{1}{9}$ to both sides of the equation.

$$x^2 + \dfrac{2}{3}x + \dfrac{7}{3} = 0$$
$$x^2 + \dfrac{2}{3}x = -\dfrac{7}{3}$$
$$x^2 + \dfrac{2}{3}x + \dfrac{1}{9} = -\dfrac{7}{3} + \dfrac{1}{9}$$
$$\left(x + \dfrac{1}{3}\right)^2 = -\dfrac{20}{9}$$
$$x + \dfrac{1}{3} = \pm\sqrt{\dfrac{-20}{9}}$$
$$x + \dfrac{1}{3} = \pm\dfrac{\sqrt{-20}}{\sqrt{9}}$$
$$x + \dfrac{1}{3} = \pm\dfrac{2i\sqrt{5}}{3}$$
$$x = \dfrac{-1 \pm 2i\sqrt{5}}{3}$$

43. First write the equation with an x^2 coefficient of one:

$$4r^2 - 3r = -5$$
$$r^2 - \dfrac{3}{4}r = -\dfrac{5}{4}$$

Since $\left(-\dfrac{3}{4}\cdot\dfrac{1}{2}\right)^2 = \left(-\dfrac{3}{8}\right)^2 = \dfrac{(-3)^2}{8^2} = \dfrac{9}{64}$, add $\dfrac{9}{64}$ to both sides of the equation.

$$r^2 - \dfrac{3}{4}r = -\dfrac{5}{4}$$
$$r^2 - \dfrac{3}{4}r + \dfrac{9}{64} = -\dfrac{5}{4} + \dfrac{9}{64}$$
$$\left(r - \dfrac{3}{8}\right)^2 = -\dfrac{71}{64}$$
$$r - \dfrac{3}{8} = \pm\sqrt{-\dfrac{71}{64}}$$
$$r - \dfrac{3}{8} = \pm\dfrac{\sqrt{-71}}{\sqrt{64}}$$
$$r - \dfrac{3}{8} = \pm\dfrac{i\sqrt{71}}{8}$$
$$r = \dfrac{3 \pm i\sqrt{71}}{8}$$

45. First write the equation with an x^2 coefficient of one:

$4p^2 + 6p + 3 = 0$

$p^2 + \dfrac{3}{2}p + \dfrac{3}{4} = 0$

Since $\left(\dfrac{3}{2} \cdot \dfrac{1}{2}\right)^2 = \left(\dfrac{3}{4}\right)^2 = \dfrac{3^2}{4^2} = \dfrac{9}{16}$, add $\dfrac{9}{16}$ to both sides of the equation.

$p^2 + \dfrac{3}{2}p + \dfrac{3}{4} = 0$

$p^2 + \dfrac{3}{2}p = -\dfrac{3}{4}$

$p^2 + \dfrac{3}{2}p + \dfrac{9}{16} = -\dfrac{3}{4} + \dfrac{9}{16}$

$\left(p + \dfrac{3}{4}\right)^2 = -\dfrac{3}{16}$

$p + \dfrac{3}{4} = \pm\sqrt{-\dfrac{3}{16}}$

$p + \dfrac{3}{4} = \pm\dfrac{\sqrt{-3}}{\sqrt{16}}$

$p + \dfrac{3}{4} = \pm\dfrac{i\sqrt{3}}{4}$

$p = \dfrac{-3 \pm i\sqrt{3}}{4}$

47. Solve for x when $f(x) = 0$:

$0 = x^2 - 8x + 3$

$x^2 - 8x = -3$

$x^2 - 8x + 16 = -3 + 16$

$(x - 4)^2 = 13$

$x - 4 = \pm\sqrt{13}$

$x = 4 \pm \sqrt{13}$

49. Solve for x when $f(x) = 0$:

$0 = 2x^2 - 5x - 4$

$0 = x^2 - \dfrac{5}{2}x - 2$

$x^2 - \dfrac{5}{2}x = 2$

$x^2 - \dfrac{5}{2}x + \dfrac{25}{16} = 2 + \dfrac{25}{16}$

$\left(x - \dfrac{5}{4}\right)^2 = \dfrac{57}{16}$

$x - \dfrac{5}{4} = \pm\sqrt{\dfrac{57}{16}}$

$x - \dfrac{5}{4} = \pm\dfrac{\sqrt{57}}{\sqrt{16}}$

$x - \dfrac{5}{4} = \pm\dfrac{\sqrt{57}}{4}$

$x = \dfrac{5 \pm \sqrt{57}}{4}$

51. Solve for x when $f(x) = 0$:

$0 = x^2 + 10x + 25$

$(x + 5)^2 = 0$

$x + 5 = 0$

$x = -5$

53. No, the student did not solve the equation correctly. The student should have first divided both sides by 4 and then completed the square and extracted the roots. The correct solution is:

$$4x^2 + 6x = 1$$

$$x^2 + \frac{3}{2}x = \frac{1}{4}$$

$$x^2 + \frac{3}{2}x + \frac{9}{16} = \frac{1}{4} + \frac{9}{16}$$

$$\left(x + \frac{3}{4}\right)^2 = \frac{4}{16} + \frac{9}{16}$$

$$\left(x + \frac{3}{4}\right)^2 = \frac{13}{16}$$

$$x + \frac{3}{4} = \pm\sqrt{\frac{13}{16}}$$

$$x + \frac{3}{4} = \pm\frac{\sqrt{13}}{\sqrt{16}}$$

$$x + \frac{3}{4} = \pm\frac{\sqrt{13}}{4}$$

$$x = -\frac{3}{4} \pm \frac{\sqrt{13}}{4}$$

$$x = \frac{-3 \pm \sqrt{13}}{4}$$

55. a.

$$3 = x^2 + 6x + 13$$

$$-10 = x^2 + 6x$$

$$-10 + 9 = x^2 + 6x + 9$$

$$-1 = (x + 3)^2$$

The next step is to take the square root of both sides. However, this will produce imaginary numbers. There is no real number such that $f(x) = 3$.

b.

$$4 = x^2 + 6x + 13$$

$$-9 = x^2 + 6x$$

$$-9 + 9 = x^2 + 6x + 9$$

$$0 = (x + 3)^2$$

$$0 = x + 3$$

$$-3 = x$$

When $x = -3$, $f(x) = 4$.

c.

$$6 = x^2 + 6x + 13$$

$$-7 = x^2 + 6x$$

$$-7 + 9 = x^2 + 6x + 9$$

$$2 = (x + 3)^2$$

$$\pm\sqrt{2} = x + 3$$

$$-3 \pm \sqrt{2} = x$$

When $x = -3 \pm \sqrt{2}$ $f(x) = 6$.

57. When $x = 1$ or 3, both sides of the equation are the same.

59. When $x = 2$ or 3, the left side of the equation is equal to -2.

61. The two equations have the points $(0, -0.5)$ and $(5, -8)$ in common.

63. Answers may vary.

65. Answers may vary.

67. $w^2 - 10w + 25 = (w - 5)^2$

69.

$$x^2 + \frac{5}{3}x + \frac{25}{36} = \left(x + \frac{5}{6}\right)^2$$

71.

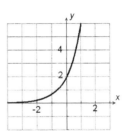

This is an exponential function in one variable.

73.

$$65 = 2(3)^x$$

$$32.5 = 3^x$$

$$\log_3 32.5 = x$$

$$3.17 = x$$

This is an exponential function in one variable.

75. $\log_3(3x+2) = 4$

$$3^4 = 3x+2$$
$$81 = 3x+2$$
$$79 = 3x$$
$$26.33 = x$$

This is a logarithmic equation in one variable.

Homework 7.5

1. $a = 2,\ b = 5,\ c = -2$

$$x = \frac{-5 \pm \sqrt{5^2 - 4(2)(-2)}}{2(2)}$$

$$x = \frac{-5 \pm \sqrt{41}}{4}$$

3. $a = 3,\ b = -6,\ c = 1$

$$x = \frac{-(-6) \pm \sqrt{(-6)^2 - 4(3)(1)}}{2(3)}$$

$$x = \frac{6 \pm \sqrt{24}}{6}$$

$$x = \frac{6 \pm 2\sqrt{6}}{6}$$

$$x = \frac{3 \pm \sqrt{6}}{3}$$

5. $t^2 = 4t + 3$

$$t^2 - 4t - 3 = 0$$
$$a = 1,\ b = -4,\ c = -3$$

$$x = \frac{-(-4) \pm \sqrt{(-4)^2 - 4(1)(-3)}}{2(1)}$$

$$x = \frac{4 \pm \sqrt{28}}{2}$$

$$x = \frac{4 \pm 2\sqrt{7}}{2}$$

$$x = 2 \pm \sqrt{7}$$

7. $-2x^2 + 5x = 3$

$$-2x^2 + 5x - 3 = 0$$
$$a = -2,\ b = 5,\ c = -3$$

$$x = \frac{-(5) \pm \sqrt{(5)^2 - 4(-2)(-3)}}{2(-2)}$$

$$x = \frac{-5 \pm \sqrt{1}}{-4}$$

$$x = \frac{-5 \pm 1}{-4}$$

$$x = 1 \ \text{ or } \ x = \frac{3}{2}$$

9. $a = 3,\ b = 0,\ c = -17$

$$x = \frac{0 \pm \sqrt{(0)^2 - 4(3)(-17)}}{2(3)}$$

$$x = \pm \frac{\sqrt{204}}{6}$$

$$x = \pm \frac{2\sqrt{51}}{6}$$

$$x = \pm \frac{\sqrt{51}}{3}$$

11. $2y^2 = -5y$

$$2y^2 + 5y = 0$$
$$a = 2,\ b = 5,\ c = 0$$

$$x = \frac{-(5) \pm \sqrt{(5)^2 - 4(2)(0)}}{2(2)}$$

$$x = \frac{-5 \pm \sqrt{25}}{4}$$

$$x = \frac{-5 \pm 5}{4}$$

$$x = 0 \ \text{ or } \ x = -\frac{5}{2}$$

13. $\dfrac{2}{3}x^2 - \dfrac{5}{6}x = \dfrac{1}{3}$

$$\frac{2}{3}x^2 - \frac{5}{6}x - \frac{1}{3} = 0$$

$$a = \frac{2}{3},\ b = -\frac{5}{6},\ c = -\frac{1}{3}$$

$$x = \frac{-\left(-\frac{5}{6}\right) \pm \sqrt{\left(-\frac{5}{6}\right)^2 - 4\left(\frac{2}{3}\right)\left(-\frac{1}{3}\right)}}{2\left(\frac{2}{3}\right)}$$

$$x = \frac{\frac{5}{6} \pm \sqrt{\frac{25}{36} + \frac{8}{9}}}{\frac{4}{3}}$$

$$x = \frac{\frac{5}{6} \pm \sqrt{\frac{57}{36}}}{\frac{4}{3}}$$

$$x = \frac{\frac{5}{6} \pm \frac{\sqrt{57}}{\sqrt{36}}}{\frac{4}{3}}$$

$$x = \frac{\frac{5}{6} \pm \frac{\sqrt{57}}{6}}{\frac{4}{3}}$$

$$x = \frac{5 \pm \sqrt{57}}{8}$$

15. $(3x+2)(x-1) = 1$

$3x^2 - x - 2 = 1$

$3x^2 - x - 3 = 0$

$a = 3, \ b = -1, \ c = -3$

$$x = \frac{-(-1) \pm \sqrt{(-1)^2 - 4(3)(-3)}}{2(3)}$$

$$x = \frac{1 \pm \sqrt{37}}{6}$$

17. $2x^2 = 5x + 4$

$2x^2 - 5x - 4 = 0$

$a = 2, \ b = -5, \ c = -4$

$$x = \frac{-(-5) \pm \sqrt{(-5)^2 - 4(2)(-4)}}{2(2)}$$

$$x = \frac{5 \pm \sqrt{57}}{4}$$

$$x = \frac{5 \pm 7.55}{4}$$

$x = 3.14 \ \text{or} \ x = -0.64$

19. $2.85p^2 - 7.12p = 4.49$

$2.85p^2 - 7.12p - 4.49 = 0$

$a = 2.85, b = -7.12, c = -4.49$

$$x = \frac{-(-7.12) \pm \sqrt{(-7.12)^2 - 4(2.85)(-4.49)}}{2(2.85)}$$

$$x = \frac{7.12 \pm \sqrt{101.88}}{5.7}$$

$$x \approx \frac{7.12 + 10.09}{5.7} \ \text{or} \ x \approx \frac{7.12 - 10.09}{5.7}$$

$x \approx 3.02 \ \text{or} \ x \approx -0.52$

21. $-5.4x(x+9.8) + 4.1 = 3.2 - 6.9x$

$a = -5.4, \ b = -46.02, \ c = 0.9$

$$x = \frac{-(-46.02) \pm \sqrt{(-46.02)^2 - 4(-5.4)(0.9)}}{2(-5.4)}$$

$$x = \frac{46.02 \pm \sqrt{2137.2804}}{-10.8}$$

$$x \approx \frac{46.02 + \sqrt{2137.28}}{-10.8} \ \text{or} \ x \approx \frac{46.02 - \sqrt{2137.28}}{-10.8}$$

$x \approx -8.54 \ \text{or} \ x \approx 0.020$

23. $a = 1, \ b = -3, \ c = 8$

$$x = \frac{-(-3) \pm \sqrt{(-3)^2 - 4(1)(8)}}{2(1)}$$

$$x = \frac{3 \pm \sqrt{-23}}{2}$$

$$x = \frac{3 \pm i\sqrt{23}}{2}$$

25. $-w^2 + 2w = 5$

$-w^2 + 2w - 5 = 0$

$a = -1, \ b = 2, \ c = -5$

$$w = \frac{-(2) \pm \sqrt{(2)^2 - 4(-1)(-5)}}{2(-1)}$$

$$w = \frac{-2 \pm \sqrt{-16}}{-2}$$

$$w = \frac{-2 \pm 4i}{-2}$$

$w = 1 \pm 2i$

27.
$$\frac{1}{4}x^2 = 2x - \frac{9}{2}$$

$$\frac{1}{4}x^2 - 2x + \frac{9}{2} = 0$$

$$a = \frac{1}{4},\ b = -2,\ c = \frac{9}{2}$$

$$x = \frac{-(-2) \pm \sqrt{(-2)^2 - 4\left(\frac{1}{4}\right)\left(\frac{9}{2}\right)}}{2\left(\frac{1}{4}\right)}$$

$$x = \frac{2 \pm \sqrt{-\frac{1}{2}}}{\frac{1}{2}}$$

$$x = 4 \pm 2i\sqrt{\frac{1}{2}}$$

$$x = 4 \pm 2i\frac{\sqrt{1}}{\sqrt{2}}$$

$$x = 4 \pm 2i\frac{\sqrt{1}}{\sqrt{2}} \cdot \frac{\sqrt{2}}{2}$$

$$x = 4 \pm 2i\frac{\sqrt{2}}{2}$$

$$x = 4 \pm i\sqrt{2}$$

29.
$$3x(3x - 2) = -2$$
$$9x^2 - 6x = -2$$
$$9x^2 - 6x + 2 = 0$$
$$a = 9, b = -6, c = 2$$

$$x = \frac{-(-6) \pm \sqrt{(-6)^2 - 4(9)(2)}}{2(9)}$$

$$x = \frac{6 \pm \sqrt{-36}}{18}$$

$$x = \frac{6 \pm 6i}{18}$$

$$x = \frac{1 \pm i}{3}$$

31.
$$3k^2 = 4k - 5$$

$$3k^2 - 4k + 5 = 0$$
$$a = 3, b = -4, c = 5$$

$$x = \frac{-(-4) \pm \sqrt{(-4)^2 - 4(3)(5)}}{2(3)}$$

$$x = \frac{4 \pm \sqrt{-44}}{6}$$

$$x = \frac{4 \pm 2i\sqrt{11}}{6}$$

$$x = \frac{2 \pm i\sqrt{11}}{3}$$

33.
$$4x^2 - 80 = 0$$
$$4x^2 = 80$$
$$x^2 = 20$$
$$x = \pm\sqrt{20}$$
$$x = \pm 2\sqrt{5}$$

35.
$$5(w + 3)^2 + 2 = 8$$
$$5(w + 3)^2 = 6$$
$$(w + 3)^2 = \frac{6}{5}$$

$$w + 3 = \pm\sqrt{\frac{6}{5}}$$

$$w + 3 = \pm\frac{\sqrt{6}}{\sqrt{5}}$$

$$w + 3 = \pm\frac{\sqrt{6}}{\sqrt{5}} \cdot \frac{\sqrt{5}}{\sqrt{5}}$$

$$w + 3 = \pm\frac{\sqrt{30}}{5}$$

$$w = \frac{-15 \pm \sqrt{30}}{5}$$

37.
$$m^2 = -12m - 36$$
$$m^2 + 12m + 36 = 0$$
$$(m + 6)^2 = 0$$
$$m + 6 = 0$$
$$m = -6$$

39.
$$-24x^2 + 18x = -60$$
$$-24x^2 + 18x + 60 = 0$$
$$a = -24, b = 18, c = 60$$

$$x = \frac{-(18) \pm \sqrt{(18)^2 - 4(-24)(60)}}{2(-24)}$$

$$x = \frac{-18 \pm \sqrt{6084}}{-48}$$

$$x = \frac{-18 \pm 78}{-48}$$

$$x = -\frac{5}{4} \text{ or } x = 2$$

41. $\frac{1}{3}x^2 - \frac{3}{2}x = \frac{1}{6}$

$$2x^2 - 9x = 1$$

$$2x^2 - 9x - 1 = 0$$

$$a = 2, \; b = -9, \; c = -1$$

$$x = \frac{-(-9) \pm \sqrt{(-9)^2 - 4(2)(-1)}}{2(2)}$$

$$x = \frac{9 \pm \sqrt{89}}{4}$$

43. $(x-5)(x+2) = 3(x-1) + 2$

$$x^2 - 3x - 10 = 3x - 3 + 2$$

$$x^2 - 6x = 9$$

$$x^2 - 6x + 9 = 9 + 9$$

$$(x-3)^2 = 18$$

$$x - 3 = \pm\sqrt{18}$$

$$x - 3 = \pm 3\sqrt{2}$$

$$x = 3 \pm 3\sqrt{2}$$

45. $25r^2 = 49$

$$r^2 = \frac{49}{25}$$

$$r = \pm\sqrt{\frac{49}{25}}$$

$$r = \pm\frac{\sqrt{49}}{\sqrt{25}}$$

$$r = \pm\frac{7}{5}$$

47. $(x-1)^2 + (x+2)^2 = 6$

$$x^2 - 2x + 1 + x^2 + 4x + 4 = 6$$

$$2x^2 + 2x + 5 = 6$$

$$2x^2 + 2x - 1 = 0$$

$$a = 2, \; b = 2, \; c = 1$$

$$x = \frac{-(2) \pm \sqrt{(2)^2 - 4(2)(-1)}}{2(2)}$$

$$x = \frac{-2 \pm \sqrt{12}}{4}$$

$$x = \frac{-2 \pm 2\sqrt{3}}{4}$$

$$x = \frac{-1 \pm \sqrt{3}}{2}$$

49. $4x^2 = -25$

$$x^2 = -\frac{25}{4}$$

$$x = \pm\sqrt{-\frac{25}{4}}$$

$$x = \pm\frac{\sqrt{-25}}{\sqrt{4}}$$

$$x = \pm\frac{5i}{2}$$

51. $-2t^2 + 5t = 6$

$$-2t^2 + 5t - 6 = 0$$

$$a = -2, \; b = 5, \; c = -6$$

$$t = \frac{-(5) \pm \sqrt{(5)^2 - 4(-2)(-6)}}{2(-2)}$$

$$t = \frac{-5 \pm \sqrt{-23}}{-4}$$

$$t = \frac{5 \pm i\sqrt{23}}{4}$$

53. $(x-6)^2 + 5 = -43$

$$(x-6)^2 = -48$$

$$x - 6 = \pm\sqrt{-48}$$

$$x - 6 = \pm 4i\sqrt{3}$$

$$x = 6 \pm 4i\sqrt{3}$$

55. $(y-2)(y-5)=-4$

$y^2-7y+10=-4$

$y^2-7y=-14$

$y^2-7y+\dfrac{49}{4}=-14+\dfrac{49}{4}$

$\left(y-\dfrac{7}{2}\right)^2=\dfrac{-7}{4}$

$y-\dfrac{7}{2}=\pm\sqrt{\dfrac{-7}{4}}$

$y-\dfrac{7}{2}=\pm\dfrac{\sqrt{-7}}{\sqrt{4}}$

$y-\dfrac{7}{2}=\pm\dfrac{i\sqrt{7}}{2}$

$y=\dfrac{7\pm i\sqrt{7}}{2}$

57. Since $(4)^2-4(3)(-5)=76>0$, there are 2 real solutions.

59. Since $(-5)^2-4(2)(7)=-31<0$, there are 2 imaginary solutions.

61. $(-12)^2-4(4)(9)=0$, there is 1 real solution.

63. a. Substitute 3 for $f(x)$:

$3=x^2-4x+8$

$x^2-4x+5=0$

$a=1,b=-4,c=5$

$b^2-4ac=(-4)^2-4(1)(5)=16-20=-4<0$

So, there are no real number solutions, which means there are no points on f at $y=3$.

b. Substitute 4 for $f(x)$:

$4=x^2-4x+8$

$x^2-4x+4=0$

$a=1,b=-4,c=4$

$b^2-4ac=(-4)^2-4(1)(4)=16-16=0$

So, there is one solution to the equation, which means there is one point on f at $y=4$.

c. Substitute 5 for $f(x)$:

$5=x^2-4x+8$

$x^2-4x+3=0$

$a=1,b=-4,c=3$

$b^2-4ac=(-4)^2-4(1)(3)=16-12=4>0$

So, there are two real number solutions, which means there are two points on f at $y=5$.

d.

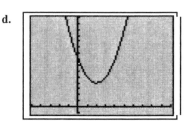

Answers may vary.

65. Solve for x when $f(x)=2$:

$2=x^2-6x+7$

$x^2-6x+5=0$

$(x-5)(x-1)=0$

$x-5=0$ or $x-1=0$

$x=5$ or $x=1$

Therefore, two points at height 2 are $(1,2)$ and $(5,2)$. Since these points are symmetric and the average of the x-coordinates at these points is $\dfrac{1+5}{2}=3$ the x-coordinate of the vertex is 3.

Substitute 3 for x in $f(x)=x^2-6x+7$ to find the y-coordinate of the vertex:

$f(3)=3^2-6(3)+7=-2$. So the vertex is $(3,-2)$.

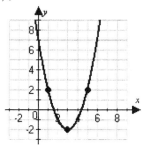

67. a.

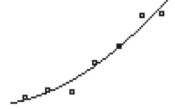

Yes, the model fits the data very well.

b. To find the capacity of the U.S. nuclear power plants in 2006, let $t = 36$ and solve for f.

$$f(36) = 0.027(36)^2 + 0.22(36) + 53.3$$
$$= 0.027(1296) + 7.92 + 53.3$$
$$= 34.99 + 61.42$$
$$= 96.412$$

The model estimates that U.S. nuclear power plants were working at 96% capacity in 2006.

c. To find the year when U.S. power plants will be working at full capacity, substitute 100 for f and solve for t.

$$100 = 0.027t^2 + 0.22t + 53.3$$
$$0 = 0.027t^2 + 0.22t - 46.7$$
$$a = 0.027, b = 0.22, c = -46.7$$
$$x = \frac{-(0.22) \pm \sqrt{(0.22)^2 - 4(0.027)(-46.7)}}{2(0.027)}$$
$$x = \frac{-0.22 \pm \sqrt{5.09}}{0.054}$$
$$x \approx \frac{-0.22 \pm 2.26}{0.054}$$
$$x \approx 37.78 \text{ or } x \approx -45.93$$

Data was not used before 1970, so the year was not 1924. The model predicts that in 2008 U.S. power plants will be working at full capacity.

d. Answers may vary.

69. a.

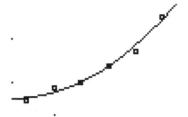

The model fits the data very well.

b. To find the percentage of Americans who felt good about the morals and values of Americans in general in 2006, let $t = 16$ and solve for f.

$$f(16) = 0.59(16)^2 - 10.04(16) + 79.3$$
$$= 0.59(256) - 160.64 + 79.3$$
$$= 151.04 - 81.34$$
$$= 69.7$$

So about 70% of Americans felt good about the morals and values of Americans in general in 2006.

c. To find when all Americans will feel good about the morals and values of Americans, let $f = 100$ and solve for t.

$$100 = 0.59t^2 - 10.04t + 79.3$$
$$0 = 0.59t^2 - 10.04t - 20.7$$
$$t = \frac{-(-10.04) \pm \sqrt{(-10.04)^2 - 4(0.59)(-20.}}{2(0.59)}$$
$$t = \frac{10.04 \pm \sqrt{149.65}}{1.18}$$
$$t \approx 19 \text{ or } t \approx -2$$

The model predicts future values, not past ones. So in 2009 all Americans will feel good about the morals and values of Americans

71. a. $h(3) = -16(3)^2 + 52(3) + 4$
$$= -16(9) + 156 + 4$$
$$= -144 + 160$$
$$= 16$$

After 3 seconds the stone's height is 16 feet.

b.
$$30 = -16t^2 + 52t + 4$$
$$26 = -16t^2 + 52t$$
$$-\frac{13}{8} = t^2 - \frac{13}{4}t$$
$$-\frac{13}{8} + \frac{169}{64} = t^2 - \frac{13}{4}t + \frac{169}{64}$$
$$\frac{65}{64} = \left(t - \frac{13}{8}\right)^2$$
$$\pm\sqrt{\frac{65}{64}} = t - \frac{13}{8}$$
$$\pm\frac{\sqrt{65}}{\sqrt{64}} = t - \frac{13}{8}$$
$$\pm\frac{\sqrt{65}}{8} = t - \frac{13}{8}$$
$$\frac{13 \pm \sqrt{65}}{8} = t$$
$$t \approx 2.63 \ \text{ or } \ t \approx 0.62$$

The stone is at a height of 30 feet at 0.62 second and 2.63 seconds.

c. $0 = -16t^2 + 52t + 4$
$$a = -16, b = 52, c = 4$$
$$t = \frac{-(52) \pm \sqrt{(52)^2 - 4(-16)(4)}}{2(-16)}$$
$$t = \frac{-52 \pm \sqrt{2960}}{-32}$$
$$t \approx 3.33 \ \text{ or } \ t \approx -0.08$$
Since we are looking for the time the stone hit the ground after it was thrown, we should not use –0.08 seconds.
The stone will hit the ground 3.33 seconds after being thrown.

73. The graphs of the two equations meet when $x = -2$ or 1.3.

75. The graph of the equation is equal to 4 when $x = \pm 2.4$.

77. The graphs of the two equations meet at the points $(-3.4, -3.4)$ and $(2.0, -1.2)$.

79. $0 = 2x^2 - x - 7$
$$x = \frac{-(-1) \pm \sqrt{(-1)^2 - 4(2)(-7)}}{2(2)}$$
$$x = \frac{1 \pm \sqrt{57}}{4}$$

81. $0 = 3x^2 + 2x + 5$
$$x = \frac{-(2) \pm \sqrt{(2)^2 - 4(3)(5)}}{2(3)}$$
$$x = \frac{-2 \pm \sqrt{-56}}{6}$$
The only way to take the square root of a negative number is to use imaginary numbers. Therefore, there are no x-intercepts.

83. $0 = x^2 + 2x - 5$
$$x = \frac{-(2) \pm \sqrt{(2)^2 - 4(1)(-5)}}{2(1)}$$
$$x = \frac{-2 \pm \sqrt{24}}{2}$$
$$x = \frac{-2 \pm 2\sqrt{6}}{2}$$
$$x = -1 \pm \sqrt{6}$$

85. No, the student did not solve the equation correctly because they did not change the form into $ax^2 + bx + c = 0$ first. Here is the correct way:

$$2x^2 + 5x = 1$$
$$2x^2 + 5x - 1 = 0$$
So, $a = 2, \ b = 5, \ c = -1$
$$x = \frac{-5 \pm \sqrt{(5)^2 - 4(2)(-1)}}{2(2)}$$
$$x = \frac{-5 \pm \sqrt{33}}{4}$$

87. a.
$$mx + b = 0$$
$$mx + b - b = 0 - b$$
$$mx = -b$$
$$\frac{mx}{m} = -\frac{b}{m}$$
$$x = -\frac{b}{m}$$

b. $7x + 21 = 0$

So, $m = 7$ and $b = -21$. Using the formula from part a:
$$x = -\frac{21}{7} = -3$$

Solving for x in the usual way:
$$7x + 21 = 0$$
$$7x + 21 - 21 = 0 - 21$$
$$7x = -21$$
$$\frac{7x}{7} = -\frac{21}{7}$$
$$x = -3$$

89. Factor:
$$x^2 - x - 20 = 0$$
$$(x - 5)(x + 4) = 0$$
$$x - 5 = 0 \text{ or } x + 4 = 0$$
$$x = 5 \text{ or } x = -4$$
Completing the square:
$$x^2 - x = 20$$
$$x^2 - x + \frac{1}{4} = 20 + \frac{1}{4}$$
$$\left(x - \frac{1}{2}\right)^2 = \frac{81}{4}$$
$$x - \frac{1}{2} = \pm\sqrt{\frac{81}{4}}$$
$$x - \frac{1}{2} = \pm\frac{9}{2}$$
$$x = \frac{1}{2} + \frac{9}{2} \text{ or } x = \frac{1}{2} - \frac{9}{2}$$
$$x = \frac{10}{2} \text{ or } x = -\frac{8}{2}$$
$$x = 5 \text{ or } x = -4$$

Quadratic formula:

$$x^2 - x - 20 = 0$$
$$x = \frac{-(-1) \pm \sqrt{(-1)^2 - 4(1)(-20)}}{2(1)}$$
$$x = \frac{1 \pm \sqrt{81}}{2}$$
$$x = \frac{1 \pm 9}{2}$$
$$x = \frac{1 + 9}{2} \text{ or } x = \frac{1 - 9}{2}$$
$$x = 5 \text{ or } x = -4$$

91. Answers may vary.

93.
$$(x + 2)(x - 5) = x^2 - 5x + 2x - 10$$
$$= x^2 - 3x - 10$$

95.
$$(x + 2)(x - 5) = 3$$
$$x^2 - 5x + 2x - 10 = 3$$
$$x^2 - 3x = 13$$
$$x^2 - 3x + \frac{9}{4} = 13 + \frac{9}{4}$$
$$\left(x - \frac{3}{2}\right)^2 = \frac{61}{4}$$
$$x - \frac{3}{2} = \pm\sqrt{\frac{61}{4}}$$
$$x - \frac{3}{2} = \pm\frac{\sqrt{61}}{\sqrt{4}}$$
$$x - \frac{3}{2} = \pm\frac{\sqrt{61}}{2}$$
$$x = \frac{3 \pm \sqrt{61}}{2}$$

97.
$$-4(x - 2)^2 + 3 = -1$$
$$-4(x - 2)^2 = -4$$
$$(x - 2)^2 = 1$$
$$x - 2 = \pm\sqrt{1}$$
$$x - 2 = \pm 1$$
$$x = 2 \pm 1 = 3, 1$$

99.
$$-4(x - 2)^2 + 3 = -4(x^2 - 4x + 4) + 3$$
$$= -4x^2 + 16x - 16 + 3$$
$$= -4x^2 + 16x - 13$$

101. $4b^5 - 12 = 173$

$\qquad 4b^5 = 185$

$\qquad b^5 = 46.25$

$\qquad b \approx 2.1529$

103. $4x - (7x - 5) = 3x + 1$

$\qquad 4x - 7x + 5 = 3x + 1$

$\qquad -3x + 5 = 3x + 1$

$\qquad 4 = 6x$

$\qquad \dfrac{2}{3} = x \ $ or $\ x \approx 0.67$

105. $7(3)^t + 8 = 271$

$\qquad 7(3)^t = 263$

$\qquad (3)^t = 37.57$

$\qquad \log_3 37.57 = t$

$\qquad 3.3007 = t$

107. $8x^2 - 18x + 9 = (4x - 3)(2x - 3)$

This is a quadratic polynomial in one variable.

109. $f(-2) = 8(-2)^2 - 18(-2) + 9$

$\qquad = 8(4) + 36 + 9$

$\qquad = 32 + 45$

$\qquad = 77$

This is a quadratic function in one variable.

111. $0 = 8x^2 - 18x + 9$

$\qquad 0 = (4x - 3)(2x - 3)$

$\qquad 0 = 4x - 3 \qquad 0 = 2x - 3$

$\qquad 3 = 4x \quad$ or $\quad 3 = 2x$

$\qquad \dfrac{3}{4} = x \qquad\qquad \dfrac{3}{2} = x$

This is a quadratic equation in one variable.

Homework 7.6

1. Add the first and third equations:

$x + y + z = 0$

$\underline{x + 2y - z = -7}$

$2x + 3y \quad\ = -7 \quad (4)$

Add the second and the third equations:

$x - y + z = 6$

$\underline{x + 2y - z = -7}$

$2x + y \quad\ \ = -1 \quad (5)$

Subtract the two new equations:

$2x + 3y = -7$

$\underline{-2x - y = 1}$

$\qquad 2y = -6$

$\qquad y = -3$

Solve for x:

$2x + 3(-3) = -7$

$\qquad 2x - 9 = -7$

$\qquad 2x = 2$

$\qquad x = 1$

Solve for z:

$(1) + (-3) + z = 0$

$\qquad 1 - 3 + z = 0$

$\qquad -2 + z = 0$

$\qquad z = 2$

The solution of the system is the point $(1, -3, 2)$.

3. Multiply the first equation by 2 and add it to the second equation.

$2x + 2y - 2z = -2$

$\underline{2x - 2y + 3z = 8}$

$4x \qquad + z = 6 \quad (4)$

Add equations (1) and (3):

$x + y - z = -1$

$\underline{2x - y + 2z = 9}$

$3x \qquad + z = 8 \quad (5)$

Subtract equations (4) and (5).

$4x + z = 6$

$\underline{-3x - z = -8}$

$\ x \qquad\ = -2$

Solve for z:

$4(-2) + z = 6$

$\qquad -8 + z = 6$

$\qquad z = 14$

Solve for y:

$$(-2)+y-(14)=-1$$
$$-2+y-14=-1$$
$$y-16=-1$$
$$y=15$$

The solution of the system is the point $(-2, 15, 14)$.

5. Add the first and third equations:
$$3x-y+2z=0$$
$$\underline{x+y+6z=0}$$
$$4x+8z=0 \quad (4)$$

Add 3 times to the first equation to the second equation:
$$9x-3y+6z=0$$
$$\underline{2x+3y+8z=8}$$
$$11x+14z=8 \quad (5)$$

Subtract 11 times the fourth equation from 4 times the fifth equation:
$$44x+56z=32$$
$$\underline{-44x-88z=0}$$
$$-32z=32$$
$$z=-1$$

Solve for x:
$$4x+8(-1)=0$$
$$4x-8=0$$
$$4x=8$$
$$x=2$$

Solve for y:
$$(2)+y+6(-1)=0$$
$$2+y-6=0$$
$$y-4=0$$
$$y=4$$

The solution to the system is the point $(2, 4, -1)$.

7. Add the first and second equations:
$$2x+y+z=3$$
$$\underline{2x-y-z=9}$$
$$4x=12$$
$$x=3$$

Add the first and third equations:

$$2x+y+z=3$$
$$\underline{x+y-z=0}$$
$$3x+2y=3$$

Solve for y:
$$3(3)+2y=3$$
$$9+2y=3$$
$$2y=-6$$
$$y=-3$$

Solve for z:
$$(3)+(-3)-z=0$$
$$3-3-z=0$$
$$-z=0$$
$$z=0$$

The solution to the system is the point $(3, -3, 0)$.

9. Add the first equation to 2 times the second equation:
$$2x+2y+z=1$$
$$\underline{-2x+2y+4z=6}$$
$$4y+5z=7 \quad (4)$$

Add the second equation to the third equation:
$$-x+y+2z=3$$
$$\underline{x+2y+4z=0}$$
$$3y+6z=3 \quad (5)$$

Subtract 4 times the fifth equation from 3 times the fourth equation.
$$12y+15z=21$$
$$\underline{-12y-24z=-12}$$
$$-9z=9$$
$$z=-1$$

Solve for y:
$$3y+6(-1)=3$$
$$3y-6=3$$
$$3y=9$$
$$y=3$$

Solve for x:

237

$$-x + (3) + 2(-1) = 3$$
$$-x + 3 - 2 = 3$$
$$-x + 1 = 3$$
$$x = -2$$

The solution to the system is the point $(-2, 3, 1)$.

11. Add the first and second equations:
$$2x - y + 2z = 6$$
$$3x + y - z = 5$$
$$\overline{5x \quad + z = 11} \quad (4)$$

Add 2 times the first equation to the third equation:
$$4x - 2y + 4z = 12$$
$$x + 2y + z = 3$$
$$\overline{5x \quad + 5z = 15} \quad (5)$$

Subtract the fourth equation from the fifth equation:
$$5x + 5z = 15$$
$$-5x - z = -11$$
$$\overline{ 4z = 4}$$
$$z = 1$$

Solve for x:
$$5x + (1) = 11$$
$$5x + 1 = 11$$
$$5x = 10$$
$$x = 2$$

Solve for y:
$$(2) + 2y + (1) = 3$$
$$2 + 2y + 1 = 3$$
$$2y + 3 = 3$$
$$2y = 0$$
$$y = 0$$

The solution to the system is the point $(2, 0, 1)$.

13. Add 2 times the first equation to 3 times the second equation:
$$2x \quad - 6z = 12$$
$$3y + 6z = 6$$
$$\overline{2x + 3y \quad = 18} \quad (4)$$

Add 5 times the second equation to 2 times the

third equation:
$$5y + 10z = 10$$
$$14x - 6y - 10z = 28$$
$$\overline{14x - y \quad = 38} \quad (5)$$

Add the fourth equation to 3 times the fifth equation:
$$2x + 3y = 18$$
$$42x - 3y = 114$$
$$\overline{44x \quad = 132}$$
$$x \quad = 3$$

Solve for y:
$$14(3) - y = 38$$
$$42 - y = 38$$
$$-y = -4$$
$$y = 4$$

Solve for z:
$$(3) - 3z = 6$$
$$-3z = 3$$
$$z = -1$$

The solution to the system is the point $(3, 4, -1)$.

15. Add the first equation to the third equation:
$$2x - y \quad = -8$$
$$y + 3z = 22$$
$$\overline{2x \quad + 3z = 14} \quad (4)$$

Add the fourth equation to 3 times the third equation:
$$2x + 3z = 14$$
$$3x - 3z = -24$$
$$\overline{5x \quad = -10}$$
$$x \quad = -2$$

Solve for z:
$$(-2) - z = -8$$
$$-z = -6$$
$$z = 6$$

Solve for y:

$$2(-2) - y = -8$$
$$-4 - y = -8$$
$$-y = -4$$
$$y = 4$$

The solution to the system is the point $(-2, 4, 6)$.

17. Substitute the given points into $y = ax^2 + bx + c$.

$$(1,6): 6 = a(1)^2 + b(1) + c$$
$$(2,11): 11 = a(2)^2 + b(2) + c$$
$$(3,8): 8 = a(3)^2 + b(3) + c$$

Simplify these equations:

$$a + b + c = 6 \qquad (1)$$
$$4a + 2b + c = 11 \qquad (2)$$
$$9a + 3b + c = 18 \qquad (3)$$

Eliminate c by multiplying both sides of equation (1) by -1:

$$-a - b - c = -6 \qquad (4)$$

Adding the left sides and right sides of equations (2) and (4) gives:

$$3a + b = 5 \qquad (5)$$

Adding the left sides and right sides of equations (3) and (4) gives:

$$8a + 2b = 12 \qquad (6)$$

Simplify:

$$4a + b = 6 \qquad (7)$$

Eliminate b by multiplying equation (5) by -1 and add each side to the corresponding side of equation (7):

$$a = 1$$

Next, substitute 1 for a in equation (5):

$$3(1) + b = 5$$
$$b = 2$$

Then, substitute 1 for a and 2 for b in equation (1):

$$a + b + c = 6$$
$$1 + 2 + c = 6$$
$$c = 3$$

Therefore, $a = 1$, $b = 2$, and $c = 3$. So, the equation is $y = x^2 + 2x + 3$.

19. Substitute the given points into $y = ax^2 + bx + c$.

$$(1,9): 9 = a(1)^2 + b(1) + c$$
$$(2,7): 7 = a(2)^2 + b(2) + c$$
$$(4,-15): -15 = a(4)^2 + b(4) + c$$

Simplify these equations:

$$a + b + c = 9 \qquad (1)$$
$$4a + 2b + c = 7 \qquad (2)$$
$$16a + 4b + c = -15 \qquad (3)$$

Eliminate c by multiplying both sides of equation (1) by -1:

$$-a - b - c = -9 \qquad (4)$$

Adding the left sides and right sides of equations (2) and (4) gives:

$$3a + b = -2 \qquad (5)$$

Adding the left sides and right sides of equations (3) and (4) gives:

$$15a + 3b = -24 \qquad (6)$$

Simplify:

$$5a + b = -8 \qquad (7)$$

Eliminate b by multiplying equation (5) by -1 and add each side to the corresponding side of equation (7):

$$2a = -6$$
$$a = -3$$

Next, substitute -3 for a in equation (5):

$$3(-3) + b = -2$$
$$b = 7$$

Then, substitute -3 for a and 7 for b in equation (1):

$$a + b + c = 9$$
$$-3 + 7 + c = 9$$
$$c = 5$$

Therefore, $a = -3$, $b = 7$, and $c = 5$. So, the equation is $y = -3x^2 + 7x + 5$.

21. Substitute the given points into $y = ax^2 + bx + c$.

$(2,2): 2 = a(2)^2 + b(2) + c$

$(3,11): 11 = a(3)^2 + b(3) + c$

$(4,24): 24 = a(4)^2 + b(4) + c$

Simplify these equations:

$4a + 2b + c = 2$ (1)

$9a + 3b + c = 11$ (2)

$16a + 4b + c = 24$ (3)

Eliminate c by multiplying both sides of equation (1) by -1:

$-4a - 2b - c = -2$ (4)

Adding the left sides and right sides of equations (2) and (4) gives:

$5a + b = 9$ (5)

Adding the left sides and right sides of equations (3) and (4) gives:

$12a + 2b = 22$ (6)

Simplify:

$6a + b = 11$ (7)

Eliminate b by multiplying equation (5) by -1 and add each side to the corresponding side of equation (7):

$a = 2$

Next, substitute 2 for a in equation (5):

$5(2) + b = 9$

$b = -1$

Then, substitute 2 for a and -1 for b in equation (1):

$4a + 2b + c = 2$

$4(2) + 2(-1) + c = 2$

$8 - 2 + c = 2$

$c = -4$

Therefore, $a = 2$, $b = -1$, and $c = -4$. So, the equation is $y = 2x^2 - x - 4$.

23. Substitute the given points into $y = ax^2 + bx + c$.

$(1,-3): -3 = a(1)^2 + b(1) + c$

$(3,9): 9 = a(3)^2 + b(3) + c$

$(5,29): 29 = a(5)^2 + b(5) + c$

Simplify these equations:

$a + b + c = -3$ (1)

$9a + 3b + c = 9$ (2)

$25a + 5b + c = 29$ (3)

Eliminate c by multiplying both sides of equation (1) by -1:

$-a - b - c = 3$ (4)

Adding the left sides and right sides of equations (2) and (4) gives:

$8a + 2b = 12$ (5)

Simplify:

$4a + b = 6$ (6)

Adding the left sides and right sides of equations (3) and (4) gives:

$24a + 4b = 32$ (7)

Simplify:

$6a + b = 8$ (8)

Eliminate b by multiplying equation (6) by -1 and add each side to the corresponding side of equation (8):

$2a = 2$

$a = 1$

Next, substitute 1 for a in equation (6):

$4(1) + b = 6$

$b = 2$

Then, substitute 1 for a and 2 for b in equation (1):

$a + b + c = -3$

$1 + 2 + c = -3$

$c = -6$

Therefore, $a = 1$, $b = 2$, and $c = -6$. So, the equation is $y = x^2 + 2x - 6$.

25. Substitute the given points into $y = ax^2 + bx + c$.

$(3,7): 7 = a(3)^2 + b(3) + c$

$(4,0): 0 = a(4)^2 + b(4) + c$

$(5,-11): -11 = a(5)^2 + b(5) + c$

Simplify these equations:

$9a + 3b + c = 7 \qquad (1)$

$16a + 4b + c = 0 \qquad (2)$

$25a + 5b + c = -11 \qquad (3)$

Eliminate c by multiplying both sides of equation (1) by -1:

$-9a - 3b - c = -7 \qquad (4)$

Adding the left sides and right sides of equations (2) and (4) gives:

$7a + b = -7 \qquad (5)$

Adding the left sides and right sides of equations (3) and (4) gives:

$16a + 2b = -18 \qquad (6)$

Simplify:

$8a + b = -9 \qquad (7)$

Eliminate b by multiplying equation (5) by -1 and add each side to the corresponding side of equation (7):

$a = -2$

Next, substitute -2 for a in equation (5):

$7(-2) + b = -7$

$b = 7$

Then, substitute -2 for a and 7 for b in equation (1):

$9a + 3b + c = 7$

$9(-2) + 3(7) + c = 7$

$-18 + 21 + c = 7$

$c = 4$

Therefore, $a = -2$, $b = 7$, and $c = 4$. So, the equation is $y = -2x^2 + 7x + 4$.

27. Substitute the given points into $y = ax^2 + bx + c$.

$(2, -5): -5 = a(2)^2 + b(2) + c$

$(4, 3): 3 = a(4)^2 + b(4) + c$

$(5, 13): 13 = a(5)^2 + b(5) + c$

Simplify these equations:

$4a + 2b + c = -5 \qquad (1)$

$16a + 4b + c = 3 \qquad (2)$

$25a + 5b + c = 13 \qquad (3)$

Eliminate c by multiplying both sides of equation (1) by -1:

$-4a - 2b - c = 5 \qquad (4)$

Adding the left sides and right sides of equations (2) and (4) gives:

$12a + 2b = 8 \qquad (5)$

Simplify:

$6a + b = 4 \qquad (6)$

Adding the left sides and right sides of equations (3) and (4) gives:

$21a + 3b = 18 \qquad (7)$

Simplify:

$7a + b = 6 \qquad (8)$

Eliminate b by multiplying equation (6) by -1 and add each side to the corresponding side of equation (8):

$a = 2$ \qquad Next, substitute 2 for a in equation (6):

$6(2) + b = 4$

$b = -8$

Then, substitute 2 for a and -8 for b in equation (1):

$4a + 2b + c = -5$

$4(2) + 2(-8) + c = -5$

$8 - 16 = -5$

$c = 3$

Therefore, $a = 2$, $b = -8$, and $c = 3$. So, the equation is $y = 2x^2 - 8x + 3$.

29. Substitute the given points into $y = ax^2 + bx + c$.

$(0, 4): 4 = a(0)^2 + b(0) + c$

$(2, 8): 8 = a(2)^2 + b(2) + c$

$(3, 1): 1 = a(3)^2 + b(3) + c$

Simplify these equations:

$c = 4 \qquad (1)$

$4a + 2b + c = 8 \qquad (2)$

$9a + 3b + c = 1 \qquad (3)$

Since $c = 4$, substitute 4 for c in equations (2) and (3):

$4a + 2b + 4 = 8$

$9a + 3b + 4 = 1$

Simplifying these equations gives:

$4a + 2b = 4 \qquad (4)$

$9a + 3b = -3 \qquad (5)$

To eliminate b, multiply both sides of equation (4) by -3 and both sides of equation (5) by 2:

$-12a - 6b = -12 \qquad (6)$

$18a + 6b = -6 \qquad (7)$

Adding the left and the right sides of equations (6) and (7) gives:

$6a = -18$

$a = -3$

Next, substitute -3 for a in equation (4):

$4(-3) + 2b = 4$

$2b = 16$

$b = 8$

Therefore, $a = -3$, $b = 8$, and $c = 4$. So, the equation is $y = -3x^2 + 8x + 4$.

31. Substitute the given points into $y = ax^2 + bx + c$.

$(0, -1) : -1 = a(0)^2 + b(0) + c$

$(1, 3) : 3 = a(1)^2 + b(1) + c$

$(2, 13) : 13 = a(2)^2 + b(2) + c$

Simplify these equations:

$c = -1 \qquad (1)$

$a + b + c = 3 \qquad (2)$

$4a + 2b + c = 13 \qquad (3)$

Since $c = -1$, substitute -1 for c in equations (2) and (3):

$a + b + (-1) = 3$

$4a + 2b + (-1) = 13$

Simplifying these equations gives:

$a + b = 4 \qquad (4)$

$4a + 2b = 14 \qquad (5)$

To eliminate b, multiply both sides of equation (4) by -2 and add each side to the corresponding side in equation (5):

$2a = 6$

$a = 3$

Next, substitute 3 for a in equation (4):

$3 + b = 4$

$b = 1$

Therefore, $a = 3$, $b = 1$, and $c = -1$. So, the equation is $y = 3x^2 + x - 1$.

33. Substitute the given points into $y = ax^2 + bx + c$.

$(1, 1) : 1 = a(1)^2 + b(1) + c$

$(2, 4) : 4 = a(2)^2 + b(2) + c$

$(3, 9) : 9 = a(3)^2 + b(3) + c$

Simplify these equations:

$a + b + c = 1 \qquad (1)$

$4a + 2b + c = 4 \qquad (2)$

$9a + 3b + c = 9 \qquad (3)$

Eliminate c by multiplying both sides of equation (1) by -1:

$-a - b - c = -1 \qquad (4)$

Adding the left sides and right sides of equations (2) and (4) gives:

$3a + b = 3 \qquad (5)$

Adding the left sides and right sides of equations (3) and (4) gives:

$8a + 2b = 8 \qquad (6)$

Simplify:

$4a + b = 4 \qquad (7)$

Eliminate b by multiplying equation (5) by -1 and add each side to the corresponding side of equation (7):

$a = 1$

Next, substitute 1 for a in equation (5):

$3(1) + b = 3$

$b = 0$

Then, substitute 1 for a and 0 for b in equation (1):

$a + b + c = 1$

$1 + 0 + c = 1$

$c = 0$

Therefore, $a = 1$, $b = 0$, and $c = 0$. So, the equation is $y = x^2$.

35. Substitute the given points into $y = ax^2 + bx + c$.

$(0,4): 4 = a(0)^2 + b(0) + c$

$(1,0): 0 = a(1)^2 + b(1) + c$

$(2,0): 0 = a(2)^2 + b(2) + c$

Simplify these equations:

$c = 4 \qquad\qquad (1)$

$a + b + c = 0 \qquad (2)$

$4a + 2b + c = 0 \qquad (3)$

Since $c = 4$, substitute 4 for c in equations (2) and (3):

$a + b + 4 = 0$

$4a + 2b + 4 = 0$

Simplify these equations:

$a + b = -4 \qquad (4)$

$4a + 2b = -4 \qquad (5)$

Eliminate b by multiplying equation (4) by -2 and add each side to the corresponding side of equation (5):

$2a = 4$

$a = 2$

Next, substitute 2 for a in equation (4):

$2 + b = -4$

$b = -6$

Therefore, $a = 2$, $b = -6$, and $c = 4$. So, the equation is $y = 2x^2 - 6x + 4$.

37. Three possible points are (2, 8), (3, 4), and (6, 4). Substitute the given points into $y = ax^2 + bx + c$.

$(2,8): 8 = a(2)^2 + b(2) + c$

$(3,4): 4 = a(3)^2 + b(3) + c$

$(6,4): 4 = a(6)^2 + b(6) + c$

Simplify these equations:

$4a + 2b + c = 8 \qquad (1)$

$9a + 3b + c = 4 \qquad (2)$

$36a + 6b + c = 4 \qquad (3)$

Eliminate c by multiplying both sides of equation (1) by -1:

$-4a - 2b - c = -8 \qquad (4)$

Adding the left sides and right sides of equations (2) and (4) gives:

$5a + b = -4 \qquad (5)$

Adding the left sides and right sides of equations (3) and (4) gives:

$32a + 4b = -4 \qquad (6)$

Simplify:

$8a + b = -1 \qquad (7)$

Eliminate b by multiplying equation (5) by -1 and add each side to the corresponding side of equation (7):

$3a = 3$

$a = 1$

Next, substitute 1 for a in equation (5):

$5(1) + b = -4$

$b = -9$

Then, substitute 1 for a and -9 for b in equation (1):

$4a + 2b + c = 8$

$4(1) + 2(-9) + c = 8$

$4 - 18 + c = 8$

$c = 22$

Therefore, $a = 1$, $b = -9$, and $c = 22$. So, the equation is $y = x^2 - 9x + 22$.

39. Solve for a in $y = a(x - h)^2 + k$ by substituting 5 for h and 8 for k since (5, 8) is the vertex, and substitute 4 for x and 6 for y since (4, 6) lies on the parabola:

$y = a(x - h)^2 + k$

$6 = a(4 - 5)^2 + 8$

$6 = a + 8$

$a = -2$

Since $a = -2$, $y = -2(x - 5)^2 + 8$ or expanding the solution:

$y = -2(x - 5)(x - 5) - 42$

$\quad = -2(x^2 - 10x + 25) - 42$

$\quad = -2x^2 + 20x - 50 - 42$

$\quad = -2x^2 + 20x - 42$

41. a.

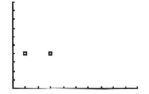

b. Answers may vary. Example:

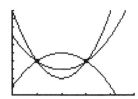

c. Answers may vary. Example:
$$y = (x-2)^2 + 3$$
$$y = -(x-2)^2 + 5$$
$$y = 2(x-2)^2 + 2$$

d. Answers may vary.

43. Answers may vary. Example:
$(0,2)$, $(1,1)$, and $6, 4$.
The equation of the parabola through these points is $y = x^2 - 2x + 2$.

45. Linear:
$$m = \frac{85-13}{7-3} = 18$$
$$y - 13 = 18(x-3)$$
$$y - 13 = 18x - 54$$
$$y = 18x - 41$$
Exponential:
$$13 = Ab^3$$
$$\frac{13}{b^3} = A$$
$$85 = Ab^7$$
$$\frac{85}{b^7} = A$$
$$\frac{13}{b^3} = \frac{85}{b^7}$$
$$13b^7 = 85b^3$$
$$b^4 \approx 6.54$$
$$b \approx 1.60$$

$$A = \frac{13}{(1.60)^3}$$
$$A = \frac{13}{4.096}$$
$$A \approx 3.18$$
$$y = 3.18(1.60)^x$$

47. Linear: $y = 2x + 2$ since the slope is 2 and the y-intercept is $(0, 2)$;
Quadratic: answers may vary. Example:
$y = 2x^2 + 2$;
Exponential: $y = 2(2)^x$.

49. Substitute the given points into
$$f(x) = ax^2 + bx + c.$$
$$(1,1): 1 = a(1)^2 + b(1) + c$$
$$(2,2): 2 = a(2)^2 + b(2) + c$$
$$(3,3): 3 = a(3)^2 + b(3) + c$$

Simplify these equations:
$$a + b + c = 1 \qquad (1)$$
$$4a + 2b + c = 2 \qquad (2)$$
$$9a + 3b + c = 3 \qquad (3)$$

Eliminate c by multiplying both sides of equation (1) by -1:
$$-a - b - c = -1 \qquad (4)$$

Adding the left sides and right sides of equations (2) and (4) gives:
$$3a + b = 1 \qquad (5)$$

Adding the left sides and right sides of equations (3) and (4) gives:
$$8a + 2b = 2 \qquad (6)$$

Simplify:
$$4a + b = 1 \qquad (7)$$
Eliminate b by multiplying equation (5) by -1 and add each side to the corresponding side of equation (7):
$$a = 0$$
Next, substitute 0 for a in equation (5):
$$3(0) + b = 1$$
$$b = 1$$
Then, substitute 0 for a and 1 for b in equation

(1):

$a+b+c=1$

$0+1+c=1$

$c=0$

Therefore, $a = 0$, $b = 1$, and $c = 0$. So, the equation is $f(x) = x$, which is a linear function.

51. Since the parabola has a vertex of $(5, -7)$ it has the form: $f(x) = a(x-5)^2 - 7$. Now substitute the point $(8,11)$ and solve for a:

$11 = a((8)-5)^2 - 7$

$11 = a(3)^2 - 7$

$11 = 9a - 7$

$18 = 9a$

$2 = a$

The equation of the parabola is:

$f(x) = 2(x-5)^2 - 7$ or $f(x) = 2x^2 - 20x + 43$.

53. $2x^2 - 10x + 7 = 0$

$$x = \frac{-(-10) \pm \sqrt{(-10)^2 - 4(2)(7)}}{2(2)}$$

$$x = \frac{10 \pm \sqrt{44}}{4}$$

$$x = \frac{10 \pm 2\sqrt{11}}{4}$$

$$x = \frac{5 \pm \sqrt{11}}{2}$$

This is a quadratic equation in one variable.

55. $f(2) = 2(2)^2 - 10(2) + 7$

$= 2(4) - 20 + 7$

$= 8 - 13$

$= -5$

This is a quadratic function in one variable.

57.

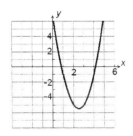

This is a quadratic function in one variable.

Homework 7.7

1. a. A quadratic function would be reasonable.

b. A linear function would be reasonable.

c. An exponential function would be reasonable.

d. None of the mentioned types of functions would be reasonable for this scattergram.

3.

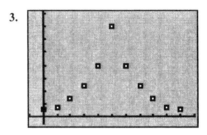

The data does not suggest a quadratic relationship based on the scattergram above. A quadratic function is not a reasonable function.

5. By hand:
Substitute the points $(14, 8.4)$, $(15, 13.6)$, and $(16, 20.1)$ into $f(x) = ax^2 + bx + c$.

$(14, 8.4): 8.4 = a(14)^2 + b(14) + c$

$(15, 13.6): 13.6 = a(15)^2 + b(15) + c$

$(16, 20.1): 20.1 = a(16)^2 + b(16) + c$

Simplify these equations:

$196a + 14b + c = 8.4$ (1)

$225a + 15b + c = 13.6$ (2)

$256a + 16b + c = 20.1$ (3)

Eliminate c by multiplying both sides of equation (1) by -1:

$-196a - 14b - c = -8.4$ (4)

Adding the left sides and right sides of equations (2) and (4) gives:

$29a + b = 5.2$ (5)

Adding the left sides and right sides of equations (3) and (4) gives:

$60a + 2b = 11.7$ (6)

Simplify:

$30a + b = 5.85$ $\quad$ (7)

Eliminate b by multiplying equation (5) by –1 and add each side to the corresponding side of equation (7):

$a = 0.65$

Next, substitute 0 for a in equation (5):

$29(0.65) + b = 5.2$

$\qquad b = -13.65$

Then, substitute 0.65 for a and –13.65 for b in equation (1):

$196(0.65) + 14(-13.65) + c = 8.4$

$\qquad 127.4 - 191.1 + c = 8.4$

$\qquad\qquad c = 72.1$

Therefore, $a = 0.65$, $b = -13.65$, and $c = 72.10$. So, the equation of the parabola is

$f(t) = 0.65t^2 - 13.65t + 72.10$.

By regression:

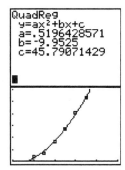

The equation of the parabola is

$f(t) = 0.52x^2 - 9.95x + 45.79$.

Answers may vary.

7. a. Substitute the points (2, 22), (5, 51), and (17, 62) into $f(x) = ax^2 + bx + c$.

$(2, 22): 22 = a(2)^2 + b(2) + c$

$(5, 51): 51 = a(5)^2 + b(5) + c$

$(17, 62): 62 = a(17)^2 + b(17) + c$

Simplify these equations:

$4a + 2b + c = 22$ $\quad$ (1)

$25a + 5b + c = 51$ $\quad$ (2)

$289a + 17b + c = 62$ $\quad$ (3)

Eliminate c by multiplying both sides of

equation (1) by –1:

$-4a - 2b - c = -22$ $\quad$ (4)

Adding the left sides and right sides of equations (2) and (4) gives:

$21a + 3b = 29$ $\quad$ (5)

Adding the left sides and right sides of equations (3) and (4) gives:

$285a + 15b = 40$ $\quad$ (6)

Simplify:

$57a + 3b = 8$ $\quad$ (7)

Eliminate b by multiplying equation (5) by –1 and add each side to the corresponding side of equation (7):

$36a = -21$

$a = -0.58$

Next, substitute –0.58 for a in equation (5):

$21(-0.58) + 3b = 29$

$\qquad b = 13.73$

Then, substitute –0.58 for a and 13.73 for b in equation (1):

$4(-0.58) + 2(13.73) + c = 22$

$\qquad -2.32 + 27.46 + c = 22$

$\qquad\qquad c = -3.14$

Therefore, $a = -0.58$, $b = 13.73$, and $c = -3.14$. So, the equation of the parabola is

$f(t) = -0.58t^2 + 13.73t - 3.14$.

b.

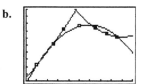

The equation $f(t) = -0.58t^2 + 13.73t - 3.14$ fits the data best because it includes all of the data.

9. a. By regression:

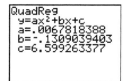

The equation is
$f(t) = 0.0068t^2 - 0.13t + 6.6$.

b.

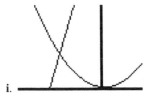

i.

The quadratic function describes the population better for these years, as it includes all of the data.

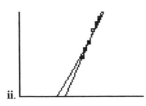

ii.

The linear function describes the population better for these years, as it is designed for this data.

iii. Answers may vary.

iv. It appears to be linear. Answers may vary.

11. a. By regression:
$f(t) = 0.18t^2 + 0.2t + 3.9$
$g(t) = 0.87x + 11.1$

b.

Intersection
X=8.4538142 .Y=18.454818 .

The point of intersection is (8.45, 18.45). This means that in 2008, 18.5 million cases of both brands of beer will be sold.

13. Answers may vary.

15. a. By regression:
Linear: $f(t) = 5.08t + 11.42$

Exponential: $f(t) = 17.26(1.13)^t$

Quadratic: $f(t) = 0.18t^2 + 2.71t + 15.85$

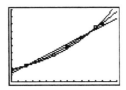

All models fit the data well.

b. The exponential model provides the best estimates before 1980.

17. $\frac{1}{2}x - \frac{2}{3}y = 2$

$\frac{4}{3}x + \frac{5}{2}y = 31$

$3x - 4y = 12$

$8x + 15y = 186$

$3x = 12 + 4y$

$x = 4 + \frac{4}{3}y$

$8\left(4 + \frac{4}{3}y\right) + 15y = 186$

$32 + \frac{32}{3}y + 15y = 186$

$\frac{77}{3}y = 154$

$y = 6$

$x = 4 + \frac{4}{3}(6) = 12$

$(12, 6)$

This is a system of linear equations in two variables.

19. $\frac{1}{2}x - \frac{2}{3}y = 2$

$-\frac{2}{3}y = 2 - \frac{1}{2}x$

$y = \frac{3}{4}x - 3$

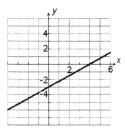

This is a linear equation in two variables.

21.
$$m = \frac{-7+2}{-2+5} = -\frac{5}{3}$$

$$y = -\frac{5}{3}x + b$$

$$-2 = -\frac{5}{3}(-5) + b$$

$$-2 = \frac{25}{3} + b$$

$$b = -\frac{31}{3}$$

$$y = -\frac{5}{3}x - \frac{31}{3}$$

This is a linear equation in two variables.

Homework 7.8

1. a. When $t = 0$, $f(t) = 2.65$, so the p-intercept is (0, 2.65). This means that, in 1980, the price of gasoline was $2.65 per gallon (in 2006 dollars per gallon).

b. $f(23) = 0.0075(23)^2 - 0.2(23) + 2.65$
$$= 2.0175$$
In 2003, the price of gas was $2.02 per gallon (in 2006 dollars per gallon). This involved interpolation.

c. $f(30) = 0.0075(30)^2 - 0.2(30) + 2.65$
$$= 3.4$$
In 201, the price of gas will be $3.40 per gallon (in 2006 dollars per gallon). This involved extrapolation.

d. $5 = 0.0075t^2 - 0.2t + 2.65$
$$0.0075t^2 - 0.2t - 2.35 = 0$$
$$a = 0.0075, b = -0.2, c = -2.35$$
$$t = \frac{0.2 \pm \sqrt{(-0.2)^2 - 4(0.0075)(-2.35)}}{2(0.0075)}$$
$$= 35.5, -17.65$$

The price of gasoline will reach $5 per gallon (in 2006 dollars per gallon) in 2015.

3. a. $-0.64t^2 + 14.47t - 3.40 = 0$
$$a = -0.64, b = 14.47, c = -3.40$$
$$t = \frac{-14.47 \pm \sqrt{(14.47)^2 - 4(-0.64)(-3.40)}}{2(-0.64)}$$
$$= 22.37, 0.24$$

The t-intercepts are (0, 0.24) and (0, 22.37). This means that in 1985 and 2007, no firms performed drug tests.

b. There is likely to be model breakdown when $t < 0.24$ and $t > 22.37$, which involves the years before 1985 and after 2007.

c. The vertex of the graph represents the maximum percentage of firms that performed drug tests.
$$t = -\frac{14.47}{2(-0.64)}$$
$$= 11.3$$
$$f(11) = -0.64(11)^2 + 14.47(11) - 3.40$$
$$= 78.33$$
The maximum percentage is 78%, which occurred in 1996.

d. $-0.64t^2 + 14.47t - 3.40 = 50$
$$-0.64t^2 + 14.47t - 53.40 = 0$$
$$a = -0.64, b = 14.47, c = -53.40$$
$$t = \frac{-14.47 \pm \sqrt{(14.47)^2 - 4(-0.64)(-53.40)}}{2(-0.64)}$$
$$= 17.96, 4.6$$

Half of the firms performed drug tests in 1990 and 2003.

5. a. $f(220) = 0.0068(220)^2 - 0.13(220) + 6.55$

$= 307.07$

In 2010, the U.S. population will be 307 million people.

b. $0.0068t^2 - 0.13t + 6.55 = 315$

$0.0068t^2 - 0.13t - 308.45 = 0$

$a = 0.0068, b = -0.13, c = -308.45$

$t = \dfrac{0.13 \pm \sqrt{(-0.13)^2 - 4(0.0068)(-308.45)}}{2(0.0068)}$

$= 222.75, -203.64$

The U.S. population was 315 million in 1586 (model breakdown has occurred). The U.S. population will be 315 million people in 2013.

c.

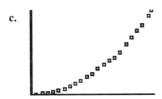

d. There is model breakdown when $t < 9.56$, which involves the years before 1800.

e.

7. a. By regression:

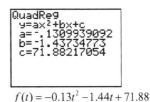

$f(t) = 0.88t^2 + 11.63t - 85.63$

b. $0.88t^2 + 11.63t - 85.63 = 755$

$0.88t^2 + 11.63t - 840.63 = 0$

$a = 0.88, b = 11.63, c = -840.63$

$t = \dfrac{-11.63 \pm \sqrt{(11.63)^2 - 4(0.88)(-840.63)}}{2(0.88)}$

$= 24.997, -38.2$

Barry Bonds will reach 755 home runs in 2005.

c. $f(25) = 0.88(25)^2 + 11.63(25) - 85.63$

$= 755.12$

$f(26) = 0.88(26)^2 + 11.63(26) - 85.63$

$= 811.63$

$f(26) - f(25) = 811.63 - 755.12 = 56.51$

Yes, as he will hit enough home runs in 2006 to reach the record.

d. Answers may vary.

9. $f(t) = 0.18t^2 + 0.2t + 3.9$

$g(t) = 0.87t + 11.1$

$0.18t^2 + 0.2t + 3.9 = 0.87t + 11.1$

$0.18t^2 - 0.67t - 7.2 = 0$

$a = 0.18, b = -0.67, c = -7.2$

$t = \dfrac{0.67 \pm \sqrt{(-0.67)^2 - 4(0.18)(-7.2)}}{2(0.18)}$

$= 8.45, -4.73$

In 2008, the sales of the two brands will be equal.

11. a. By regression:

```
QuadReg
y=ax²+bx+c
a=-.1309939092
b=-1.43734773
c=71.88217054
```

$f(t) = -0.13t^2 - 1.44t + 71.88$

```
LinReg
y=ax+b
a=3.681884058
b=10.63333333
```

$g(t) = 3.68t + 10.63$

b. $f(t) = -0.13t^2 - 1.44t + 71.88$

$g(t) = 3.68t + 10.63$

$-0.13t^2 - 1.44t + 71.88 = 3.68t + 10.63$

$-0.13t^2 - 5.12t + 61.25 = 0$

$a = -0.13, b = 5.12, c = 61.25$

$t = \dfrac{5.12 \pm \sqrt{(-5.12)^2 - 4(-0.13)(61.25)}}{2(-0.13)}$

$= -49, 9.6$

In 2000, the percentage of voters using optical scan or other modern electrical system equaled the percentage of people using punch cards or lever machines. Yes, 2000 is an election year.

c. $h(t) = 100 - (f + g)(t)$ represents the percentage of voters using the three ways to vote.

d. $h(t)$

$= 100 - (f + g)(t)$

$= 100 - \left[\begin{array}{l} (-0.13t^2 - 1.44t + 71.88) \\ + (3.68t + 10.63) \end{array} \right]$

$= 100 - (-0.13t^2 + 2.24t + 82.51)$

$= 0.13t^2 - 2.24t + 17.49$

e. $h(10) = 0.13(10)^2 - 2.24(10) + 17.49$

$= 8.09$

In 2000, 8,1% of registered voters used voting methods other than punch cards, lever machines, optical scan or other modern electronic systems.

13. $p = 250 - 5n$

$R = pn = 250n - 5n^2$

$n = -\dfrac{b}{2a} = -\dfrac{250}{2(-5)} = 25$

A group of 25 people would maximize the bus company's revenue.

15. $p = 28 - 0.2n$

$R = pn = 28n - 0.2n^2$

$n = -\dfrac{b}{2a} = -\dfrac{28}{2(-0.2)} = 70$

A party of 70 people would maximize the restaurant's revenue.

17. $160 = 2l + 2w$

$l = 80 - w$

$A = 8w - w^2$

$w = -\dfrac{b}{2a} = -\dfrac{80}{2(-1)} = 40$

$l = 80 - 40 = 40$

The dimensions are 40 meters long by 40 meters wide. The area is 1600 square meters.

19. Answers may vary.

21. a. Linear: $L(t) = 3.04t - 6.16$

Exponential: $E(t) = 1.58(1.27)^t$

Quadratic: $Q(t) = 0.35t^2 - 1.88t + 3.68$

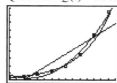

Both the exponential and quadratic models fit the data well. The linear model does not fit the data well.

b. The exponential model fits the data well before 1990.

c. 6.5 billion = 6,500,000,000

1 MW = 1000 people

6,500,000 MW = 6,500,000,000 people

6500 thousand MW is the goal.

$1.58(1.27)^t = 6500$

$1.27^t = 4113.9$

$t = 34.8$

In 2025, wind energy could meet the electricity needs of the entire world.

d. $0.35t^2 - 1.88t + 3.68 = 6500$

$0.35t^2 - 1.88t - 6496.32 = 0$

$a = 0.35, b = -1.88, c = -6496.32$

$t = \dfrac{1.88 \pm \sqrt{(-1.88)^2 - 4(0.35)(-6496.32)}}{2(0.35)}$

$= 138.95, -133.58$

In 2129, wind energy could meet the electricity needs of the world.

e. Answers may vary. The exponential model predicts faster growth than the quadratic.

250

23. Answers may vary.

25. Answers may vary.

27. Answers may vary.

29. Answers may vary.

Chapter 7 Review Exercises

1.

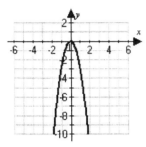

2.

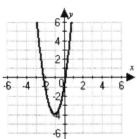

3.

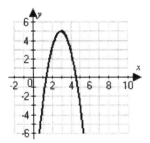

4.

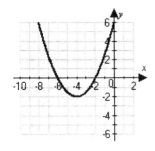

5. Since the parabola has a maximum point, $a < 0$. Since the vertex is in quadrant II, $h < 0$ and $k > 0$.

6.

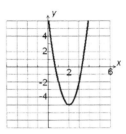

7.

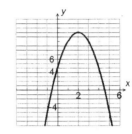

8.

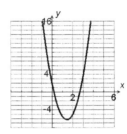

9. $\sqrt{72} = \sqrt{36 \cdot 2} = \sqrt{36}\sqrt{2} = 6\sqrt{2}$

10. $\sqrt{\dfrac{49}{100}} = \dfrac{\sqrt{49}}{\sqrt{100}} = \dfrac{7}{10}$

11. $3x^2 - 2x - 2 = 0$

$$x = \dfrac{2 \pm \sqrt{(-2)^2 - 4(3)(-2)}}{2(3)}$$

$$x = \dfrac{2 \pm \sqrt{28}}{6}$$

$$x = \dfrac{2 \pm 2\sqrt{7}}{6}$$

$$x = \dfrac{2 \pm \sqrt{7}}{3}$$

12. $5x^2 = 7$

$x^2 = \dfrac{7}{5}$

$= \pm\sqrt{\dfrac{7}{5}}$

$= \pm\dfrac{\sqrt{7}}{\sqrt{5}}$

$= \pm\dfrac{\sqrt{7}}{\sqrt{5}} \cdot \dfrac{\sqrt{5}}{\sqrt{5}}$

$= \pm\dfrac{\sqrt{35}}{5}$

13. $5(p-3)^2 + 4 = 7$

$5p^2 - 30p + 42 = 0$

$x = \dfrac{30 \pm \sqrt{(-30)^2 - 4(5)(42)}}{2(5)}$

$x = \dfrac{30 \pm \sqrt{60}}{10}$

$x = \dfrac{30 \pm 2\sqrt{15}}{10}$

$x = \dfrac{15 \pm \sqrt{15}}{5}$

14. $(t+1)(t-7) = 4$

$t^2 - 6t - 11 = 0$

$x = \dfrac{6 \pm \sqrt{(-6)^2 - 4(1)(-11)}}{2(1)}$

$x = \dfrac{6 \pm \sqrt{80}}{2}$

$x = \dfrac{6 \pm 4\sqrt{5}}{2}$

$x = 3 \pm 2\sqrt{5}$

15. $2x^2 = 4 - 5x$

$2x^2 + 5x - 4 = 0$

$x = \dfrac{-5 \pm \sqrt{5^2 - 4(2)(-4)}}{2(5)}$

$x = \dfrac{-5 \pm \sqrt{57}}{10}$

16. $4x - x^2 = 1$

$x^2 - 4x + 1 = 0$

$x = \dfrac{4 \pm \sqrt{(-4)^2 - 4(1)(1)}}{2(1)}$

$x = \dfrac{4 \pm \sqrt{12}}{2}$

$x = \dfrac{4 \pm 2\sqrt{3}}{2}$

$x = 2 \pm \sqrt{3}$

17. $5x^2 - 6x = 2$

$5x^2 - 6x - 2 = 0$

$x = \dfrac{6 \pm \sqrt{(-6)^2 - 4(5)(-2)}}{2(5)}$

$x = \dfrac{6 \pm \sqrt{76}}{10}$

$x = \dfrac{6 \pm 2\sqrt{19}}{10}$

$x = \dfrac{3 \pm \sqrt{19}}{5}$

18. $7x^2 - 20 = 0$

$7x^2 = 20$

$x^2 = \dfrac{20}{7}$

$x = \pm\sqrt{\dfrac{20}{7}}$

$= \pm\dfrac{\sqrt{20}}{\sqrt{7}}$

$= \pm\dfrac{\sqrt{20}}{\sqrt{7}} \cdot \dfrac{\sqrt{7}}{\sqrt{7}}$

$= \pm\dfrac{\sqrt{140}}{7}$

$= \pm\dfrac{2\sqrt{35}}{7}$

19. $(x+2)^2 + (x-3)^2 = 15$

$2x^2 - 2x - 2 = 0$

$x = \dfrac{2 \pm \sqrt{(-2)^2 - 4(2)(-2)}}{2(2)}$

$x = \dfrac{2 \pm \sqrt{20}}{4}$

$x = \dfrac{2 \pm 2\sqrt{5}}{4}$

$x = \dfrac{1 \pm \sqrt{5}}{2}$

20. $5(5x^2 - 8) = 0$

$25x^2 - 40 = 9$

$25x^2 = 49$

$x^2 = \dfrac{49}{25}$

$x = \pm\sqrt{\dfrac{49}{25}}$

$x = \pm\dfrac{7}{5}$

21. $\dfrac{3}{2}x^2 - \dfrac{3}{4}x = \dfrac{1}{2}$

$6x^2 - 3x - 2 = 0$

$x = \dfrac{3 \pm \sqrt{(-3)^2 - 4(6)(-2)}}{2(6)}$

$x = \dfrac{3 \pm \sqrt{57}}{12}$

22. $2.7x^2 - 5.1x = 9.8$

$2.7x^2 - 5.1x - 9.8 = 0$

$x = \dfrac{-(-5.1) \pm \sqrt{(-5.1)^2 - 4(2.7)(-9.8)}}{2(2.7)}$

$x \approx -1.18 \text{ or } x \approx 3.07$

23. $1.7(x^2 - 2.3) = 3.4 - 2.8x$

$1.7x^2 - 3.91 = 3.4 - 2.8x$

$1.7x^2 + 2.8x - 7.31 = 0$

$x = \dfrac{-2.8 \pm \sqrt{2.8^2 - 4(1.7)(-7.31)}}{2(1.7)}$

$x \approx -3.05 \text{ or } x \approx 1.41$

24. $-2(x+4)^2 = 9$

$-2x^2 - 16x - 41 = 0$

$x = \dfrac{16 \pm \sqrt{(-16)^2 - 4(-2)(-41)}}{2(-2)}$

$x = \dfrac{16 \pm \sqrt{-72}}{-4}$

$x = \dfrac{16 \pm 6i\sqrt{2}}{-4}$

$x = \dfrac{-8 \pm 3i\sqrt{2}}{2}$

25. $2x^2 = 4x - 7$

$2x^2 - 4x + 7 = 0$

$x = \dfrac{4 \pm \sqrt{(-4)^2 - 4(2)(7)}}{2(2)}$

$x = \dfrac{4 \pm \sqrt{-40}}{4}$

$x = \dfrac{4 \pm 2i\sqrt{10}}{4}$

$x = \dfrac{2 \pm i\sqrt{10}}{2}$

26. $x^2 + 6x - 4 = 0$

$x^2 + 6x = 4$

$x^2 + 6x + 9 = 4 + 9$

$(x+3)^2 = 13$

$x + 3 = \pm\sqrt{13}$

$x = -3 \pm \sqrt{13}$

27.
$$2t^2 = -3t + 6$$
$$2t^2 + 3t = 6$$
$$t^2 + \frac{3}{2}t = 3$$
$$t^2 + \frac{3}{2}t + \frac{9}{16} = 3 + \frac{9}{16}$$
$$\left(t + \frac{3}{4}\right)^2 = \frac{57}{16}$$
$$t + \frac{3}{4} = \pm\sqrt{\frac{57}{16}}$$
$$t + \frac{3}{4} = \pm\frac{\sqrt{57}}{4}$$
$$t = -\frac{3 \pm \sqrt{57}}{4}$$

28. Solve for x when $h(x) = 0$:
$$3x^2 + 2x - 2 = 0$$
$$x = \frac{-2 \pm \sqrt{2^2 - 4(3)(-2)}}{2(3)}$$
$$x = \frac{-2 \pm \sqrt{28}}{6}$$
$$x = \frac{-2 \pm 2\sqrt{7}}{6}$$
$$x = \frac{-1 \pm \sqrt{7}}{3}$$
The x-intercepts are $\left(\frac{-1 - \sqrt{7}}{3}, 0\right)$ and
$\left(\frac{-1 + \sqrt{7}}{3}, 0\right)$.

29. Solve for x when $k(x) = 0$:
$$-5x^2 + 3x - 1 = 0$$
$$x = \frac{-3 \pm \sqrt{3^2 - 4(-5)(-1)}}{2(-5)}$$
$$x = \frac{-3 \pm \sqrt{-11}}{-10}$$
Since the square root of a negative number is not a real number, there are no real number solutions. Therefore, there are no x-intercepts.

30. Factor:

$$x^2 - 2x - 8 = 0$$
$$(x - 4)(x + 2) = 0$$
$$x - 4 = 0 \text{ or } x + 2 = 0$$
$$x = 4 \text{ or } x = -2$$

Completing the square:
$$x^2 - 2x - 8 = 0$$
$$x^2 - 2x = 8$$
$$x^2 - 2x + 1 = 8 + 1$$
$$(x - 1)^2 = 9$$
$$x - 1 = \pm\sqrt{9}$$
$$x - 1 = \pm 3$$
$$x - 1 = 3 \text{ or } x - 1 = -3$$
$$x = 4 \text{ or } x = -2$$

Quadratic Formula:
$$x^2 - 2x - 8 = 0$$
$$x = \frac{-(-2) \pm \sqrt{(-2)^2 - 4(1)(-8)}}{2(1)}$$
$$x = \frac{2 \pm \sqrt{36}}{2}$$
$$x = \frac{2 \pm 6}{2}$$
$$x = \frac{2 + 6}{2} = \frac{8}{2} \text{ or } x = \frac{2 - 6}{2} = \frac{-4}{2}$$
$$x = 4 \text{ or } x = -2$$

31.
$$3x^2 - 5x + 4 = 0$$
$$(-5)^2 - 4(3)(4) = -23 < 0$$
There are no real solutions. So, there are two imaginary solutions.

32. **a.**
$$3x^2 - 6x + 7 = 3$$
$$3x^2 - 6x + 4 = 0$$
$$x = \frac{-(-6) \pm \sqrt{(-6)^2 - 4(3)(4)}}{2(3)}$$
$$x = \frac{6 \pm \sqrt{-12}}{6}$$
Since the square root of a negative is not a real number, there are no real number solutions. There is no such value for x.

b. $3x^2 - 6x + 7 = 4$

$$3x^2 - 6x + 3 = 0$$

$$x = \frac{-(-6) \pm \sqrt{(-6)^2 - 4(3)(3)}}{2(3)}$$

$$x = \frac{6 \pm \sqrt{0}}{6}$$

$$x = \frac{6}{6} = 1$$

c. $3x^2 - 6x + 7 = 5$

$$3x^2 - 6x + 2 = 0$$

$$x = \frac{-(-6) \pm \sqrt{(-6)^2 - 4(3)(2)}}{2(3)}$$

$$x = \frac{6 \pm \sqrt{12}}{6}$$

$$x = \frac{6 \pm 2\sqrt{3}}{6}$$

$$x = \frac{3 \pm \sqrt{3}}{3}$$

d. Answers may vary.

33. $x = -0.6$ and $x = 1$

34. $x = -3$ or $x = 5$

35. $x = -2.0$ and $x = -5.4$

36. Multiply the first equation by 2, and then subtract the second equation from the first equation.

$$2x + 4y - 6z = -8$$
$$\underline{2x - y + z = 3}$$
$$5y - 7z = -11 \quad (4)$$

Multiply the first equation by 3, and then subtract the third equation from the first equation:

$$3x + 6y - 9z = -12$$
$$\underline{3x + 2y + z = 10}$$
$$4y - 10z = -22 \quad (5)$$

Multiply (4) by 2 so that the right side equals the right side of (5) and then isolate:

$$10y - 14z = -22$$
$$4y - 10z = -22$$
$$4y - 10z = 10y - 14z$$
$$4z = 6y$$
$$y = \frac{2}{3}z$$

Solve for z:

$$5\left(\frac{2}{3}z\right) - 7z = -11$$

$$\frac{10}{3}z - 7z = -11$$

$$\frac{10z - 21z}{3} = -11$$

$$\frac{-11z}{3} = -11$$

$$z = 3$$

Solve for y:

$$y = \frac{2}{3}(3) = 2$$

Solve for x:

$$x + 2(2) - 3(3) = -4$$

$$x = 1$$

The solution to the system is the point (1, 2, 3).

37. Isolate x in the first and second equations, and solve the third equation for x:

$$2x - 3z = -4$$

$$-3z = -4 - 2x$$

$$z = \frac{4 + 2x}{3}$$

$$3x + y = 0$$

$$y = -3x$$

$$x - 4(-3x) + 2\left(\frac{4 + 2x}{3}\right) = 17$$

$$x + 12x + \frac{8 + 4x}{3} = 17$$

$$3x + 36x + 8 + 4x = 51$$

$$43x = 43$$

$$x = 1$$

Solve for y:

$$y = -3(1) = -3$$

Solve for z:

$$z = \frac{4 + 2(1)}{3} = 2$$

The solution to the system is the point (1, −3, 2).

38. Substitute the given points into $y = ax^2 + bx + c$.

$(2,9): 9 = a(2)^2 + b(2) + c$

$(3,18): 18 = a(3)^2 + b(3) + c$

$(5,48): 48 = a(5)^2 + b(5) + c$

Simplify these equations:

$4a + 2b + c = 9$ $\quad(1)$

$9a + 3b + c = 18$ $\quad(2)$

$25a + 5b + c = 48$ $\quad(3)$

Eliminate c by multiplying both sides of equation (1) by -1:

$-4a - 2b - c = -9$ $\quad(4)$

Adding the left sides and right sides of equations (2) and (4) gives:

$5a + b = 9$ $\quad(5)$

Adding the left sides and right sides of equations (3) and (4) gives:

$21a + 3b = 39$ $\quad(6)$

Simplify:

$7a + b = 13$ $\quad(7)$

Eliminate b by multiplying equation (5) by -1 and add each side to the corresponding side of equation (7):

$2a = 4$

$a = 2$

Next, substitute 2 for a in equation (5):

$5(2) + b = 9$

$b = -1$

Then, substitute 2 for a and -1 for b in equation (1):

$4a + 2b + c = 9$

$4(2) + 2(-1) + c = 9$

$8 - 2 + c = 9$

$c = 3$

Therefore, $a = 2$, $b = -1$, and $c = 3$. So, the equation is $y = 2x^2 - x + 3$.

39. Substitute the given points into $y = ax^2 + bx + c$.

$(0,5): 5 = a(0)^2 + b(0) + c$

$(2,3): 3 = a(2)^2 + b(2) + c$

$(4,-15): -15 = a(4)^2 + b(4) + c$

Simplify these equations:

$c = 5$ $\quad(1)$

$4a + 2b + c = 3$ $\quad(2)$

$16a + 4b + c = -15$ $\quad(3)$

Since $c = 5$, substitute 5 for c in equations (2) and (3):

$4a + 2b + (5) = 3$

$16a + 4b + (5) = -15$

Simplifying these equations gives:

$4a + 2b = -2$ $\quad(4)$

$16a + 4b = -20$ $\quad(5)$

To eliminate b, multiply both sides of equation (4) by -2 and add each side to the corresponding side in equation (5):

$8a = -16$

$a = -2$

Next, substitute -2 for a in equation (4):

$4a + 2b = -2$

$4(-2) + 2b = -2$

$2b = 6$

$b = 3$

Therefore, $a = -2$, $b = 3$, and $c = 5$. So, the equation is $y = -2x^2 + 3x + 5$.

40. Linear:

$\text{slope} = m = \dfrac{2-4}{1-0} = -2$

$y - \text{intercept} = (0,4)$

So, $y = -2x + 4$

Exponential:

As the value of x increases by 1, the value of y is multiplied by ½, so the base $b = \dfrac{1}{2}$. The y-intercept is $(0, 4)$. Therefore, the exponential function is $y = 4\left(\dfrac{1}{2}\right)^x$

Quadratic:

Answers may vary. Example: $y = -2x^2 + 4$

41. Substitute the given points into $y = ax^2 + bx + c$.

$(0,7): 7 = a(0)^2 + b(0) + c$

$(2,1): 1 = a(2)^2 + b(2) + c$

$(5,7): 7 = a(5)^2 + b(5) + c$

Simplify these equations:

$c = 7$ (1)

$4a + 2b + c = 1$ (2)

$25a + 5b + c = 7$ (3)

Since $c = 7$, substitute 7 for c in equations (2) and (3):

$4a + 2b + (7) = 1$

$25a + 5b + (7) = 7$

Simplifying these equations gives:

$4a + 2b = -6$ (4)

$25a + 5b = 0$ (5)

Simplify these equations:

$2a + b = -3$ (6)

$5a + b = 0$ (7)

To eliminate b, multiply both sides of equation (6) by –1 and add each side to the corresponding side in equation (7):

$3a = 3$

$a = 1$

Next, substitute 1 for a in equation (5):

$2a + b = -3$

$2(1) + b = -3$

$b = -5$

Therefore, $a = 1$, $b = -5$, and $c = 7$. So, the equation is $y = x^2 - 5x + 7$.

42. **a.** Since the function is in the form $h(t) = at^2 + bt + c$ and $a = -16 < 0$, the vertex is the maximum point. Find the $h(t)$-coordinate of the vertex.

$h(0) = -16(0)^2 + 100(0) + 3 = 3$

So, the h-intercept is (0, 3). Next, find the symmetric point by substituting 3 for $h(t)$ in the function and solve for t:

$3 = -16t^2 + 100t + 3$

$0 = -16t^2 + 100t$

$0 = -4t(4t - 25)$

$-4t = 0$ or $4t - 25 = 0$

$t = 0$ or $4t = 25$

$t = 0$ or $t = \dfrac{25}{4} = 6.25$

The symmetric points are (0, 3) and (6.25, 3). Since the average of the t-coordinates is $\dfrac{0 + 6.25}{2} = 3.125$, the t-coordinate of the vertex is 3.125. Substitute 3.125 for t in the function to find the h-coordinate of the vertex:

$h(3.125) = -16(3.125)^2 + 100(3.125) + 3$

$= 159.25$

So the vertex is (3.125, 159.25), which means that the maximum height of the ball is 159.25 feet and it is reached in 3.125 seconds.

b. Solve for t when $h(t) = 3$. From part a, we see that when $h(t) = 3$, t is either 0 or 6.25. In this case, the fielder had 6.25 seconds to get into position.

c.

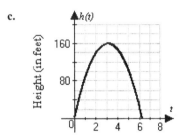

Seconds

43. $l + 2w = 180$

$l = 180 - 2w$

$A = 180w - 2w^2$

$w = -\dfrac{180}{2(-2)} = 45$

$l = 180 - 2(45) = 90$

$A = (90)(45) = 4050$

The rectangle should be 90 feet long and 45 feet wide. The area is 4050 square feet.

44. **a.** By regression:
$$f(t) = -1.14t^2 + 25.26t - 81.2$$

b. $f(15) = -1.14(15)^2 + 25.26(15) - 81.2$
$$= 41.2$$
In 2005, 41% of TV shows were at least 1 hour long.

c. $-1.14t^2 + 25.26t - 81.2 = 50$
$$-1.14t^2 + 25.26t - 131.2 = 0$$
$$t = \frac{-25.26 \pm \sqrt{(25.26)^2 - 4(-1.14)(-131.2)}}{2(-1.14)}$$
$$= 13.8, 8.3$$
In 1998 and 2004, half of all TV shows where at least 1 hour long.

d. $-1.14t^2 + 25.26t - 81.2 = 0$
$$t = \frac{-25.26 \pm \sqrt{(25.26)^2 - 4(-1.14)(-81.2)}}{2(-1.14)}$$
$$= 18.26, 3.90$$
The t-intercepts are (3.90, 0) and (18.26, 0), which means that in 1994 there were no TV shows at least 1 hour long, and in 2008 there will be no TV shows that are at least 1 hour long.

e. Model breakdown is certain in the years before 1994 and after 2008.

45. **a.** $f(t) = -0.084t^2 - 1.29t + 70.56$
$$g(t) = 0.129t^2 - 0.52t + 2.26$$

b. $-0.084t^2 - 1.29t + 70.56$
$$= 0.129t^2 - 0.52t + 2.26$$
$$0.213t^2 + 0.77t - 68.3 = 0$$
$$t = \frac{-0.77 \pm \sqrt{(0.77)^2 - 4(0.213)(-68.3)}}{2(0.213)}$$
$$= 16.2, -19.8$$
In 2006, the percentage of Americans who get their news every day from the nightly news programs will equal the percentage of Americans who get their news every day on the Internet.

Chapter 7 Test

1.

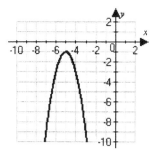

2. Since the vertex lies on the x-axis when $x > 0$, $h > 0$ and $k = 0$. Since the parabola is turned upward (has a minimum point), $a > 0$.

3. Answers may vary. Example: $y = (x-2)^2 - 7$

4.

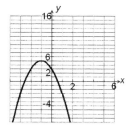

5. **a.** To find the x-intercept, solve for x when
$$f(x) = 0$$
$$0 = x^2 - 2x - 8$$
$$0 = (x-4)(x+2)$$
$$x - 4 = 0 \text{ or } x + 2 = 0$$
$$x = 4 \text{ or } x = -2$$
$$(-2, 0), (4, 0)$$

b. Since the x-intercepts are symmetric points, the average of the x-coordinates for these points is the x-coordinate of the vertex, which is $\frac{4 + (-2)}{2} = 1$. Substitute 1 for x in the function to find the y-coordinate of the vertex:
$$y = (1)^2 - 2(1) - 8 = -9$$
So, the vertex is $(1, -9)$.

c.

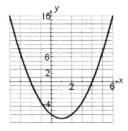

6. $\sqrt{32} = \sqrt{16 \cdot 2} = \sqrt{16}\sqrt{2} = 4\sqrt{2}$

7. $\sqrt{\dfrac{20}{75}} = \dfrac{\sqrt{20}}{\sqrt{75}} = \dfrac{2\sqrt{5}}{5\sqrt{3}} = \dfrac{2\sqrt{5}}{5\sqrt{3}} \cdot \dfrac{\sqrt{3}}{\sqrt{3}} = \dfrac{2\sqrt{15}}{15}$

8.
$$x^2 - 3x - 10 = 0$$
$$(x-5)(x+2) = 0$$
$$x - 5 = 0 \ \text{ or } \ x + 2 = 0$$
$$x = 5 \ \text{ or } \ x = -2$$

9.
$$6x^2 = 100$$
$$x^2 = \dfrac{100}{6}$$
$$x^2 = \dfrac{50}{3}$$
$$x = \pm\sqrt{\dfrac{50}{3}}$$
$$x = \pm\dfrac{\sqrt{50}}{\sqrt{3}}$$
$$x = \pm\dfrac{5\sqrt{2}}{\sqrt{3}} \cdot \dfrac{\sqrt{3}}{\sqrt{3}}$$
$$x = \pm\dfrac{5\sqrt{6}}{3}$$

10.
$$4(r-3)^2 + 1 = 7$$
$$4r^2 - 24r + 30 = 0$$
$$r = \dfrac{24 \pm \sqrt{(-24)^2 - 4(4)(30)}}{2(4)}$$
$$= \dfrac{24 \pm \sqrt{96}}{8}$$
$$= \dfrac{24 \pm 4\sqrt{6}}{8}$$
$$= \dfrac{6 \pm \sqrt{6}}{2}$$

11.
$$\dfrac{5}{6}x^2 - \dfrac{1}{2}x = \dfrac{2}{3}$$
$$5x^2 - 3x - 4 = 0$$
$$x = \dfrac{3 \pm \sqrt{(-3)^2 - 4(5)(-4)}}{2(5)}$$
$$= \dfrac{3 \pm \sqrt{89}}{10}$$

12.
$$(x-3)(x+5) = 6$$
$$x^2 + 5x - 3x - 15 = 6$$
$$x^2 + 2x - 21 = 0$$
$$x^2 + 2x = 21$$
$$x^2 + 2x + 1 = 21 + 1$$
$$(x+1)^2 = 22$$
$$x + 1 = \pm\sqrt{22}$$
$$x = -1 \pm \sqrt{22}$$

13.
$$2x(x+5) = 4x - 3$$
$$2x^2 + 10x = 4x - 3$$
$$2x^2 + 6x + 3 = 0$$
$$x = \dfrac{-6 \pm \sqrt{6^2 - 4(2)(3)}}{2(2)}$$
$$x = \dfrac{-6 \pm \sqrt{12}}{4}$$
$$x = \dfrac{-6 \pm 2\sqrt{3}}{4}$$
$$x = \dfrac{-3 \pm \sqrt{3}}{2}$$

14.
$$3x^2 - 6x = 1$$
$$3x^2 - 6x - 1 = 0$$
$$x = \dfrac{6 \pm \sqrt{(-6)^2 - 4(3)(-1)}}{2(3)}$$
$$= \dfrac{6 \pm \sqrt{48}}{6}$$
$$= \dfrac{6 \pm 4\sqrt{3}}{6}$$
$$= \dfrac{3 \pm 2\sqrt{3}}{3}$$

15.

$$3.7x^2 = 2.4 - 5.9x$$

$$3.7x^2 + 5.9x - 2.4 = 0$$

$$x = \frac{-5.9 \pm \sqrt{(5.9)^2 - 4(3.7)(-2.4)}}{2(3.7)}$$

$$= 0.34, -1.93$$

16.

$$3x^2 - 6x = -5$$

$$3x^2 - 6x + 5 = 0$$

$$x = \frac{-6 \pm \sqrt{(6)^2 - 4(3)(5)}}{2(3)}$$

$$= \frac{-6 \pm \sqrt{-24}}{6}$$

$$= \frac{-6 \pm 2i\sqrt{6}}{6}$$

$$= \frac{-3 \pm i\sqrt{6}}{2}$$

17.

$$-2(p + 4)^2 = 24$$

$$-2p^2 - 16p - 56 = 0$$

$$x = \frac{16 \pm \sqrt{(-16)^2 - 4(-2)(-56)}}{2(-2)}$$

$$= \frac{16 \pm \sqrt{-192}}{-4}$$

$$= \frac{16 \pm 8i\sqrt{3}}{-4}$$

$$= -4 \pm 2i\sqrt{3}$$

18.

$$x^2 - 8x - 2 = 0$$

$$x^2 - 8x = 2$$

$$x^2 - 8x + 16 = 2 + 16$$

$$(x - 4)^2 = 18$$

$$x - 4 = \pm\sqrt{18}$$

$$x - 4 = \pm 3\sqrt{2}$$

$$x = 4 \pm 3\sqrt{2}$$

19.

$$2(x^2 - 4) = -3x$$

$$x^2 - 4 = -\frac{3}{2}x$$

$$x^2 + \frac{3}{2}x = 4$$

$$x^2 + \frac{3}{2}x + \frac{9}{16} = 4 + \frac{9}{16}$$

$$\left(x + \frac{3}{4}\right)^2 = \frac{73}{16}$$

$$x + \frac{3}{4} = \pm\sqrt{\frac{73}{16}}$$

$$x + \frac{3}{4} = \pm\frac{\sqrt{73}}{4}$$

$$x = \frac{-3 \pm \sqrt{73}}{4}$$

20. Solve for x when $f(x) = 0$:

$$3x^2 - 8x + 1 = 0$$

$$x = \frac{-(-8) \pm \sqrt{(-8)^2 - 4(3)(1)}}{2(3)}$$

$$x = \frac{8 \pm \sqrt{52}}{6}$$

$$x = \frac{8 \pm 2\sqrt{13}}{6}$$

$$x = \frac{4 \pm \sqrt{13}}{3}$$

The x-intercepts are $\left(\frac{4 + \sqrt{13}}{3}, 0\right)$ and $\left(\frac{4 - \sqrt{13}}{3}, 0\right)$.

21.

$$-2(x - 3)^2 + 5 = 0$$

$$-2x^2 + 12x - 13 = 0$$

$$x = \frac{-12 \pm \sqrt{(12)^2 - 4(-2)(-13)}}{2(-2)}$$

$$= 4.58, 1.42$$

The x-intercepts are (4.58, 0) and (1.42, 0). The vertex is (3, 5).

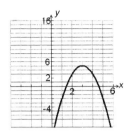

22. $b^2 - 4ac = 0$

$(-4)^2 - 4(a)(4a) = 0$

$16 - 16a^2 = 0$

$16a^2 = 16$

$a^2 = 1$

$a = \pm 1$

23.

Substitute the given points into $y = ax^2 + bx + c$.

$(1,4): 4 = a(1)^2 + b(1) + c$

$(2,9): 9 = a(2)^2 + b(2) + c$

$(3,16): 16 = a(3)^2 + b(3) + c$

Simplify these equations:

$a + b + c = 4$ (1)

$4a + 2b + c = 9$ (2)

$9a + 3b + c = 16$ (3)

Eliminate c by multiplying both sides of equation (1) by –1:

$-a - b - c = -4$ (4)

Adding the left sides and right sides of equations (2) and (4) gives:

$3a + b = 5$ (5)

Adding the left sides and right sides of equations (3) and (4) gives:

$8a + 2b = 12$ (6)

Simplify:

$4a + b = 6$ (7)

Eliminate b by multiplying equation (5) by –1 and add each side to the corresponding side of equation (7):

$a = 1$

Next, substitute 1 for a in equation (5):

$3(1) + b = 5$

$b = 2$

Then, substitute 1 for a and 2 for b in equation (1):

$a + b + c = 4$

$1 + 2 + c = 4$

$c = 1$

Therefore, $a = 1$, $b = 2$, and $c = 1$. So, the equation is $y = x^2 + 2x + 1$.

24.

Using the equation $y = a(x - h)^2 + k$, substitute 5 for h and 3 for k since the vertex is (5, 3). Also, substitute 3 for x and 11 for y since (3, 11) lies on the parabola.

$y = a(x - h)^2 + k$

$11 = a(3 - 5)^2 + 3$

$11 = a(3 - 5)^2 + 3$

$11 = a(-2)^2 + 3$

$11 = 4a + 3$

$8 = 4a$

$a = 2$

So, the equation is $y = 2(x - 5)^2 + 3$.

25. **a.** $x^2 - 6x + 11 = 1$

$x^2 - 6x + 10 = 0$

$x = \dfrac{-(-6) \pm \sqrt{(-6)^2 - 4(1)(10)}}{2(1)}$

$x = \dfrac{6 \pm \sqrt{-4}}{2}$

Since the square root of a negative is not a real number, there are no real number solutions. There is no such value for x.

b. $x^2 - 6x + 11 = 2$

$x^2 - 6x + 9 = 0$

$x = \dfrac{-(-6) \pm \sqrt{(-6)^2 - 4(1)(9)}}{2(1)}$

$x = \dfrac{6 \pm \sqrt{0}}{2}$

$x = \dfrac{6}{2} = 3$

c. $x^2 - 6x + 11 = 3$

$x^2 - 6x + 8 = 0$

$x = \dfrac{-(-6) \pm \sqrt{(-6)^2 - 4(1)(8)}}{2(1)}$

$x = \dfrac{6 \pm \sqrt{4}}{2}$

$x = \dfrac{6 \pm 2}{2}$

$x = \dfrac{8}{2}$ or $x = \dfrac{4}{2}$

$x = 4$ or $x = 2$

26. Multiply the first equation by –2, and then add the first and second equations:

$-2x - 8y - 6z = -4$

$\underline{2x + y + \quad z \;= 10}$

$\quad -7y - 5z = 6$

Add the first and third equations:

$x + 4y + 3z = 2$

$\underline{-x + y + 2z = 8}$

$\quad 5y + 5z = 10$

Isolate y:

$5y + 5z = 10$

$5y = 10 - 5z$

$y = 2 - z$

Solve for z:

$-7(2 - z) - 5z = 6$

$-14 + 7z - 5z = 6$

$2z = 20$

$z = 10$

Solve for y:

$y = 2 - 10 = -8$

Solve for x:

$x + 4(-8) + 3(10) = 2$

$x - 32 + 30 = 2$

$x = 4$

The solution to the system is the point (4, –8, 10).

27. Add the first and second equations:

$2x - 3y \qquad = 4$

$\underline{\quad 3y + 2z \;= 2}$

$2x \qquad + 2z = 6$

Isolate z:

$2x + 2z = 6$

$2x = 6 - 2z$

$x = 3 - z$

Solve for z:

$x - z = -5$

$3 - z - z = -5$

$3 - 2z = -5$

$-2z = -8$

$z = 4$

Solve for y:

$3y + 2(4) = 2$

$3y + 8 = 2$

$3y = -6$

$y = -2$

Solve for x:

$x = 3 - 4 = -1$

The solution to the system is the point (–1, –2, 4).

28. Using a graphing calculator, find that the maximum point of the parabola is approximately (2.50, 103).

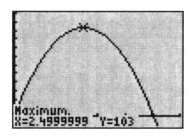

So, the maximum height reached by the ball is 103 feet at 2.5 seconds.

29. **a.** By regression:

$f(t) = -0.028t^2 + 2.54t - 15.92$

b. $f(30) = -0.028(30)^2 + 2.54(30) - 15.92$

$\quad = 35.08$

About 35% of 30-year-old Americans feel that they are taking a great risk of entering personal information into a pop-up ad.

c. $-0.028t^2 + 2.54t - 15.92 = 30$

$-0.028t^2 + 2.54t - 45.92 = 0$

$$t = \frac{-2.54 \pm \sqrt{(2.54)^2 - 4(-0.028)(-45.92)}}{2(-0.028)}$$

$= 24.93, 65.98$

30% of 25-year-old Americans and 30% of 66-year-old Americans feel that they are taking a great risk.

d. $-0.028t^2 + 2.54t - 15.92 = 0$

$$t = \frac{-2.54 \pm \sqrt{(2.54)^2 - 4(-0.028)(-15.92)}}{2(-0.028)}$$

$= 6.77, 83.94$

There are no 7-year-old or 84-year-old Americans who feel that they are taking a great risk. Model breakdown has occurred.

e. $t = -\dfrac{2.54}{2(-0.028)}$

$= 45.36$

$f(45.36)$

$= -0.028(45.36)^2 + 2.54(45.36) - 15.92$

$= 41.68$

The age at which the maximum percentage, 42%, of Americans who feel that they are taking a great risk is 45 years old.

30. $p = 40 - 0.25x$

$Rp = 40x - 0.25x^2$

$x = -\dfrac{40}{2(-0.25)} = 80$

A group of 80 people would maximize the boat owner's revenue.

Cumulative Review of Chapters 1-7

1. $81x^2 - 49 = 0$

$81x^2 = 49$

$x^2 = \dfrac{49}{81}$

$\sqrt{x^2} = \pm\sqrt{\dfrac{49}{81}}$

$x = \pm\dfrac{7}{9}$

2. $\log_4(m+3) = 2$

$4^2 = m + 3$

$16 = m + 3$

$m = 13$

3. $5x^2 - 2x = 4$

$5x^2 - 2x - 4 = 0$

$x = \dfrac{2 \pm \sqrt{(-2)^2 - 4(5)(-4)}}{2(5)}$

$= \dfrac{2 \pm \sqrt{84}}{10}$

$= \dfrac{2 \pm 2\sqrt{21}}{10}$

$= \dfrac{1 \pm \sqrt{21}}{5}$

4. $2(3t^2 - 10) = -7t$

$3t^2 - 10 = -\dfrac{7t}{2}$

$3t^2 + \dfrac{7t}{2} - 10 = 0$

$6t^2 + 7t - 20 = 0$

$t = \dfrac{-7 \pm \sqrt{(7)^2 - 4(6)(-20)}}{2(6)}$

$= \dfrac{-7 \pm \sqrt{529}}{12}$

$= \dfrac{-7 \pm 23}{12}$

$= \dfrac{4}{3}, -\dfrac{5}{2}$

5. $(2p - 5)(3p + 4) = 5p - 2$

$6p^2 - 7p - 20 = 5p - 2$

$6p^2 - 12p - 18 = 0$

$6(p^2 - 2p - 3) = 0$

$6(p - 3)(p + 1) = 0$

$p = 3 \qquad p = -1$

6. $2(5x+2)-1=9(x-3)-(3x-8)$

$10x+4-1=9x-27-3x+8$

$10x+3=6x-19$

$4x=-22$

$x=-\dfrac{11}{2}$

7. $2x(3x-4)+5=4-x^2$

$6x^2-8x+5=4-x^2$

$7x^2-8x+1=0$

$(7x-1)(x-1)=0$

$x=\dfrac{1}{7} \quad x=1$

8. $3\ln(2w)+2\ln(3w)=8$

$\ln(2w)^3+\ln(3w)^2=8$

$\ln(8w^3)(9w^2)=8$

$\ln(72w^5)=8$

$72w^5=e^8$

$72w^5=2980.958$

$w^5=41.40$

$w=2.1057$

9. $5b^6+4=82$

$5b^6=78$

$b^6=\dfrac{78}{5}$

$b=\pm\left(\dfrac{78}{5}\right)^{\frac{1}{6}}\approx\pm1.5807$

10. $3(2)^{4x-5}=95$

$(2)^{4x-5}=\dfrac{95}{3}$

$\log(2)^{4x-5}=\log\left(\dfrac{95}{3}\right)$

$(4x-5)\log(2)=\log\left(\dfrac{95}{3}\right)$

$4x-5=\dfrac{\log\left(\dfrac{95}{3}\right)}{\log(2)}$

$4x=\dfrac{\log\left(\dfrac{95}{3}\right)}{\log(2)}+5$

$x=\dfrac{\dfrac{\log\left(\dfrac{95}{3}\right)}{\log(2)}+5}{4}\approx2.4962$

11. $\log_b(65)=4$

$b^4=65$

$b=65^{\frac{1}{4}}$

$b\approx2.8394$

12. $3e^x-5=49$

$3e^x=54$

$e^x=\dfrac{54}{3}$

$\ln(e^x)=\ln\left(\dfrac{54}{3}\right)$

$x\ln(e)=\ln\left(\dfrac{54}{3}\right)$

$x=\ln\left(\dfrac{54}{3}\right)\approx2.8904$

13. $3\log_2\left(x^4\right) - 2\log_2\left(4x\right) = 5$

$\log_2\left(x^4\right)^3 - \log_2\left(4x\right)^2 = 5$

$\log_2\left(x^{12}\right) - \log_2\left(16x^2\right) = 5$

$\log_2\left(\dfrac{x^{12}}{16x^2}\right) = 5$

$\dfrac{x^{10}}{16} = 2^5$

$\dfrac{x^{10}}{16} = 32$

$x^{10} = 512$

$x = 1.8661$

14. $2x^2 - 6x = -5$

$2x^2 - 6x + 5 = 0$

$x = \dfrac{6 \pm \sqrt{(-6)^2 - 4(2)(5)}}{2(2)}$

$= \dfrac{6 \pm \sqrt{-4}}{4}$

$= \dfrac{6 \pm 2i}{4}$

$= \dfrac{3 \pm i}{2}$

15. $2x^2 + 3x - 6 = 0$

$2x^2 + 3x = 6$

$x^2 + \dfrac{3}{2}x = 3$

$x^2 + \dfrac{3}{2}x + \dfrac{9}{16} = 3 + \dfrac{9}{16}$

$\left(x + \dfrac{3}{4}\right)^2 = \dfrac{48}{16} + \dfrac{9}{16}$

$\left(x + \dfrac{3}{4}\right)^2 = \dfrac{57}{16}$

$x + \dfrac{3}{4} = \pm\sqrt{\dfrac{57}{16}}$

$x + \dfrac{3}{4} = \pm\dfrac{\sqrt{57}}{4}$

$x = -\dfrac{3}{4} \pm \dfrac{\sqrt{57}}{4}$

$x = \dfrac{-3 \pm \sqrt{57}}{4}$

16. Substitute $y = 3x - 1$ in $2x - 3y = -11$.

$2x - 3(3x - 1) = -11$

$2x - 9x + 3 = -11$

$-7x = -14$

$x = 2$

Substitute 2 for x in one of the original equations to solve for y:

$y = 3x - 1$

$= 3(2) - 1$

$= 5$

The solution is (2, 5).

17.

In order to eliminate y, multiply $\dfrac{1}{2}x - y = \dfrac{5}{2}$ by $-\dfrac{3}{5}$. This gives $-\dfrac{3}{10}x + \dfrac{3}{5}y = -\dfrac{15}{10}$. Add the left sides and the right sides of the equations:

$-\dfrac{3}{10}x + \dfrac{3}{5}y = -\dfrac{15}{10}$

$\dfrac{2}{5}x - \dfrac{3}{5}y = \dfrac{6}{5}$

This yields:

$-\dfrac{3}{10}x + \dfrac{2}{5}x = -\dfrac{15}{10} + \dfrac{6}{5}$

$-\dfrac{3}{10}x + \dfrac{4}{10}x = -\dfrac{15}{10} + \dfrac{12}{10}$

$\dfrac{1}{10}x = -\dfrac{3}{10}$

$\dfrac{10}{1} \cdot \dfrac{1}{10}x = -\dfrac{3}{10} \cdot \dfrac{10}{1}$

$x = -3$

Substitute -3 for x in one of the original equations to solve for y:

$\dfrac{1}{2}(-3) - y = \dfrac{5}{2}$

$-\dfrac{3}{2} - y = \dfrac{5}{2}$

$y = -\dfrac{3}{2} - \dfrac{5}{2}$

$y = -\dfrac{8}{2} = -4$

So the solution is (-3, -4).

18. Multiply the first equation by 2 and add the first and second equations:

$$4x - 2y + 6z = 2$$
$$\underline{3x + 2y - z = -6}$$
$$7x \qquad + 5z = -4$$

Multiply the first equation by -3 and add the first and third equations:
$$-6x + 3y - 9z = -3$$
$$\underline{4x - 3y + 2z = -7}$$
$$-2x \qquad - 7z = -10$$

Isolate z:
$$-2x - 7z = -10$$
$$-7z = 2x - 10$$
$$z = \frac{10 - 2x}{7}$$

Solve for x:
$$7x + 5\left(\frac{10 - 2x}{7}\right) = -4$$
$$7x + \frac{50 - 10x}{7} = -4$$
$$49x + 50 - 10x = -28$$
$$39x = -78$$
$$x = -2$$

Solve for z:
$$z = \frac{10 - 2(-2)}{7} = 2$$

Solve for y:
$$4(-2) - 2y + 6(2) = 2$$
$$-8 - 2y + 12 = 2$$
$$-2y = -2$$
$$y = 1$$
The solution to the system is the point $(-2, 1, 2)$.

19. $2(3x - 4) < 5 - 3(6x + 5)$
$$2(3x - 4) < 5 - 3(6x + 5)$$
$$6x - 8 < 5 - 18x - 15$$
$$6x - 8 < -18x - 10$$
$$24x < -2$$
$$x < -\frac{1}{12}$$
$$\left(-\infty, -\frac{1}{12}\right)$$

$$-\frac{1}{12}$$

20. $(2b^4 c^{-5})^3 (3b^{-1} c^{-2})^4$
$$= (2^3 b^{12} c^{-15})(3^4 b^{-4} c^{-8})$$
$$= (8 \cdot 81)(b^{12} b^{-4})(c^{-15} c^{-8})$$
$$= 648 b^8 c^{-23}$$
$$= \frac{648 b^8}{c^{23}}$$

21. $\left(\dfrac{6b^8 c^{-3}}{8b^{-4} c^{-1}}\right)^3$
$$= \left(\frac{3b^{8-(-4)} c^{-3-(-1)}}{4}\right)^3$$
$$= \left(\frac{3b^{12} c^{-2}}{4}\right)^3$$
$$= \left(\frac{3b^{12}}{4c^2}\right)^3$$
$$= \frac{27 b^{36}}{64 c^6}$$

22. $3\log_b (4x) - 4\log_b (x^3)$
$$= \log_b (4x)^3 - \log_b (x^3)^4$$
$$= \log_b (64x^3) - \log_b (x^{12})$$
$$= \log_b \left(\frac{64x^3}{x^{12}}\right)$$
$$= \log_b \left(\frac{64}{x^9}\right)$$

23. $3\ln(x^7) + 2\ln(x^5)$
$$= \ln(x^7)^3 + \ln(x^5)^2$$
$$= \ln(x^{21}) + \ln(x^{10})$$
$$= \ln(x^{21})(x^{10})$$
$$= \ln(x^{31})$$

24. $(3x - 4y)^2 = 9x^2 - 24xy + 16y^2$

266

25. $(5p-7q)(5p+7q)=25p^2-49q^2$

26. $-3x(x^2-5)(x^3+8)$
$=-3x(x^5+8x^2-5x^3-40)$
$=-3x(x^5-5x^3+8x^2-40)$
$=-3x^6+15x^4-24x^3+120x$

27. $(x^2-3x-4)(x^2+4x-5)$
$=x^4+4x^3-5x^2-3x^3-12x^2+15x-4x^2-16x+20$
$=x^4+x^3-21x^2-x+20$

28. $f(x)=-2(x-5)^2+3$
$=-2(x-5)(x-5)+3$
$=-2(x^2-5x-5x+25)+3$
$=-2(x^2-10x+25)+3$
$=-2x^2+20x-50+3$
$=-2x^2+20x-47$

29. $m^4-16n^4=(m^2-4n^2)(m^2+4n^2)$
$=(m+4n)(m-4n)(m^2+4n^2)$

30. $x^3-13x^2+40x=x(x^2-13x+40)$
$=x(x-8)(x-5)$

31. $8p^2+22pq-21q^2=(4p-3q)(2p+7q)$

32. $x^3+4x^2-9x-36=(x^2-9)(x+4)=$
$(x-3)(x+3)(x+4)$

33. Since the y-intercept is $(0, 20)$ and as x increases by 1, $f(x)$ decreases by 3: $f(x)=-3x+20$

34. As x increases by 1, $g(x)$ increases by a factor of 3, so the base $b=3$. Substitute a point from the table into $g(x)=ab^x$ and solve for a.

$12=a(3)^2$
$12=9a$
$a=\dfrac{4}{3}$

So, the equation is:

$g(x)=\dfrac{4}{3}(3)^x$

35. For the function k, as x increases by 1, $k(x)$ increases by 4, so the slope is 4.

36. $g(1)=4$

37. $h(x)=7(2)^{x-4}$
$h(7)=7(2)^{7-4}=7(2)^3=56$
$h^{-1}(7)=7(2)^{y-4}$
$7=7(2)^{y-4}$
$1=2^{y-4}$
$0=(y-4)\ln 2$
$\ln 2^y=\ln 16$
$y=4$

38.

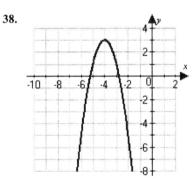

39.

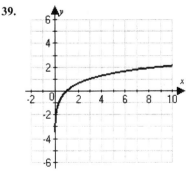

40. First, change the form into $y = mx + b$

$2x - 5y = 20$

$-5y = -2x + 20$

$y = \dfrac{2}{5}x - 4$

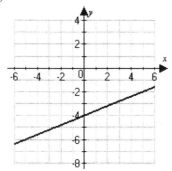

41.

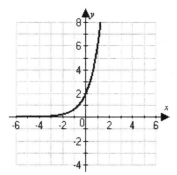

42.

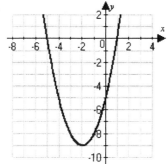

43.

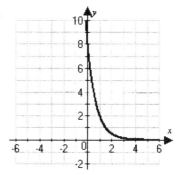

44. The domain goes from -3 to 5. The range goes from 4 to -2. This is a function.

45. First, change the form of the equation given to $y = mx + b$.

$3x - 4y = 5$

$-4y = -3x + 5$

$y = \dfrac{3}{4}x - \dfrac{5}{4}$

The slope of the perpendicular line will be $-\dfrac{4}{3}$.

So the equation of the perpendicular line will be

$y = -\dfrac{4}{3}x + b$. Substitute the given point into this equation to solve for b.

$6 = -\dfrac{4}{3}(-2) + b$

$6 = \dfrac{8}{3} + b$

$b = 6 - \dfrac{8}{3}$

$b = \dfrac{18}{3} - \dfrac{8}{3}$

$b = \dfrac{10}{3}$

So, the equation is $y = -\dfrac{4}{3}x + \dfrac{10}{3}$ or

$y = -1.33x + 3.33$.

46. $27 = ab^2$

$83 = ab^5$

$3.07 = b^3$

$b = 1.45$

$27 = a(1.45)^2$

$a = 12.84$

$y = 12.84(1.45)^x$

47. Substitute the given points into $y = ax^2 + bx + c$.

$(1, -1): -1 = a(1)^2 + b(1) + c$

$(2, 4): 4 = a(2)^2 + b(2) + c$

$(4, 20): 20 = a(4)^2 + b(4) + c$

Simplify these equations:

$a + b + c = -1$ (1)

$4a + 2b + c = 4$ (2)

$16a + 4b + c = 20$ (3)

Eliminate c by multiplying both sides of equation (1) by –1:

$-a - b - c = 1$ (4)

Adding the left sides and right sides of equations (2) and (4) gives:

$3a + b = 5$ (5)

Adding the left sides and right sides of equations (3) and (4) gives:

$15a + 3b = 21$ (6)

Simplify:

$5a + b = 7$ (7)

Eliminate b by multiplying equation (5) by –1 and add each side to the corresponding side of equation (7):

$2a = 2$

$a = 1$

Next, substitute 1 for a in equation (5):

$3(1) + b = 5$

$b = 2$

Then, substitute 1 for a and 2 for b in equation (1):

$a + b + c = -1$

$1 + 2 + c = -1$

$c = -4$

Therefore, $a = 1$, $b = 2$, and $c = -4$. So, the equation is $y = x^2 + 2x - 4$.

48. a. Linear:

slope $= m = \dfrac{6-3}{1-0} = 3$

$y-$intercept $= (0, 3)$

So, $y = 3x + 3$

Exponential:

As the value of x increases by 1, the value of y is multiplied by 2, so the base $b = 2$. The y-intercept is $(0, 3)$. Therefore, the exponential function is $y = 3(2)^x$.

Quadratic:

Answers may vary. Example: $y = 3x^2 + 3$.

b.

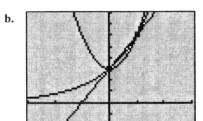

49. $-x^2 + 6x - 5 = 3$

$x^2 - 6x + 8 = 0$

$(x - 4)(x - 2) = 0$

$x - 4 = 0$ or $x - 2 = 0$

$x = 4$ or $x = 2$

50. To find the x-intercepts, let $f(x) = 0$ and solve for x:

$-x^2 + 6x - 5 = 0$

$x^2 - 6x + 5 = 0$

$(x - 5)(x - 1) = 0$

$x - 5 = 0$ or $x - 1 = 0$

$x = 5$ or $x = 1$

The x-intercepts are $(5, 0)$ and $(1, 0)$.

51.

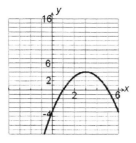

52. $\log_2(16) = 4$ since $2^4 = 16$

53. $\log_5\left(\dfrac{1}{25}\right) = \log_5\left(\dfrac{1}{5^2}\right) = \log_5\left(5^{-2}\right) = -2$

54.

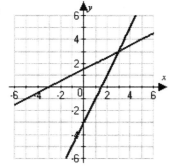

55. $g(x) = 3^x$

$g^{-1}(x) = \log_3(x)$

56. $f(x) = \dfrac{2}{5}x + 1$

Replace $f(x)$ with y:

$y = \dfrac{2}{5}x + 1$

Solve for x:

$y - 1 = \dfrac{2}{5}x$

$\dfrac{5}{2}(y - 1) = x$

$x = \dfrac{5}{2}y - \dfrac{5}{2}$

Replace x with $g^{-1}(y)$:

$g^{-1}(y) = \dfrac{5}{2}y - \dfrac{5}{2}$

Write in terms of x:

$g^{-1}(x) = \dfrac{5}{2}x - \dfrac{5}{2}$

57. Let x = the amount invested at 6%, so $12{,}000 - x$ = the amount invested at 11%.

$0.06x + (12000 - x)(0.11) = 845$

$0.06x + 1320 - 0.11x = 845$

$-0.05x = 475$

$x = 9500$

$12000 - 9500 = 2500$

$9500 is invested at 6% and $2500 is invested at 11%.

58. $ab^0 = 660$

$a = 660$

$ab^8 = 60$

$660b^8 = 60$

$b^8 = 0.091$

$b = 0.74$

$660(0.74)^x = 1$

$0.74^x = 0.015$

$x = 21.56$

In 2017 there will be 1 case of AIDS acquired by birth.

59. a. Linear: $L(t) = 1.35t + 7.23$

Exponential: $E(t) = 7.53(1.14)^t$

Quadratic: $Q(t) = 0.14t^2 + 0.65t + 7.69$

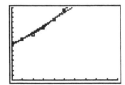

All the models fit the data well.

b.
$$x = -\frac{0.65}{2(0.14)} = -2.32$$

$$Q(-2.32) = 0.14(-2.32)^2 + 0.65(-2.32) + 7.69$$
$$= 6.94$$

The vertex is (–2,32, 6.94), which means that the minimum sales at coffeehouses and doughnut shops, $6.9 billion, occurred in 1998.

c. The exponential model works best for years before 1998.

d. $1.14 - 1 = 0.14$
The rate of growth is 14%.

e. $7.53(1.14)^t = 70$

$1.14^t = 9.296$

$t = 17.02$
Total sales will reach $70 billion in 2017.

f. $0.14t^2 + 0.65t + 7.69 = 70$

$0.14t^2 + 0.65t - 62.31 = 0$

$$t = \frac{-0.65 \pm \sqrt{(0.65)^2 - 4(0.14)(-62.31)}}{2(0.14)}$$

$= 18.9, -23.5$
Total sales will reach $70 billion in 2019.

g. Answers may vary.

60. a.
$$m = \frac{13 - 29}{25 - 5} = -0.8$$

$y = -0.8x + b$

$29 = -0.8(5) + b$

$b = 33$

$f(t) = -0.8t + 33$

b. $f(30) = -0.8(30) + 33 = 9$
In 2010, 9% of union members will work in manufacturing.

c. $-0.8t + 33 = 7$

$-0.8t = -26$

$t = 32.5$
In 2013, 7% of union members will work in manufacturing.

d. $f^{-1}(x) = -0.8y + 33$

$x - 33 = -0.8y$

$y = 41.25 - 1.25x$

$f^{-1}(p) = 41.25 - 1.25p$

e. $f^{-1}(100) = 41.25 - 1.25(100) = -83.75$
In 1896, 100% of union members worked in manufacturing. Model breakdown has likely occurred.

f. $-0.8t + 33 = 0$

$-0.8t = -33$

$t = 41.25$
In 2021, no union members will be working manufacturing. Model breakdown has likely occurred.

g. For $t < -83.75$ and $t > 41.25$, there is model breakdown.

61. a. First, draw a scattergram of the data for h. The linear regression equation, $h(t) = 2.4t + 10.7$, is the best model for this data.

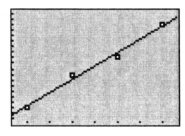

First, draw a scattergram of the data for c. The linear regression equation, $c(t) = t + 53$, is the best model for this data.

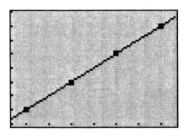

b. The rates of change are the slopes of the respective models.
Rate of change at Hartford: 2.4 percent per year.
Rate of change in Connecticut: 1 percent per year.

c. $h(18) = 2.4(18) + 10.7 = 53.9$. This means that in 2008, the percent of students who will score above the goals in Hartford will be 53.9%.
$c(18) = 18 + 53 = 71$. This means that in 2008, the percent of students who will score above the goals in Connecticut will be 71%.

d. Solve for t when $h(t) = c(t)$

$2.4t + 10.7 = t + 53$

$1.4t = 42.3$

$t \approx 30.21$

So, the percentage of Hartford and Connecticut students who will score above the goals will be equal in 2020.

Chapter 8
Rational Functions

1.
$$f(-1) = \frac{(-1)+1}{(-1)^2 - 9}$$
$$= \frac{0}{1-9}$$
$$= \frac{0}{-8}$$
$$= 0$$

$$f(2) = \frac{(2)+1}{(2)^2 - 9}$$
$$= \frac{3}{4-9}$$
$$= \frac{3}{-5}$$
$$= -\frac{3}{5}$$

$$f(3) = \frac{(3)+1}{(3)^2 - 9}$$
$$= \frac{4}{9-9}$$
$$= \frac{4}{0}$$

$f(3)$ is undefined.

3.
$$f(-1) = \frac{(-1)^3 - 8}{2(-1)^2 + 3(-1) - 1}$$
$$= \frac{-1-8}{2-3-1}$$
$$= \frac{-9}{-2}$$
$$= \frac{9}{2}$$

$$f(0) = \frac{(0)^3 - 8}{2(0)^2 + 3(0) - 1}$$
$$= \frac{0-8}{-1}$$
$$= \frac{-8}{-1}$$
$$= 8$$

$$f(3) = \frac{(3)^3 - 8}{2(3)^2 + 3(3) - 1}$$
$$= \frac{27-8}{2(9)+9-1}$$
$$= \frac{19}{26}$$
$$= \frac{19}{26}$$

5. The only value that will make the function undefined (i.e., the denominator 0) is 0. Therefore, the domain is the set of all real numbers except 0.

7. Since there are no values that will make the function undefined, the domain is the set of all real numbers.

9. $x + 3 = 0$
$x = -3$
Since -3 is the only value that will make the function undefined, the domain is the set of all real numbers except -3.

11. $2x + 1 = 0$
$2x = -1$
$x = -\frac{1}{2}$
The domain is the set of all real numbers except $-\frac{1}{2}$.

13. $x^2 - 3x - 10 = 0$
$(x-5)(x+2) = 0$
$x - 5 = 0 \qquad x + 2 = 0$
$x = 5 \qquad x = -2$

The domain is the set of all real numbers except 5 and -2.

15.
$$4x^2 - 25 = 0$$
$$(2x-5)(2x+5) = 0$$

$$2x - 5 = 0 \qquad 2x + 5 = 0$$
$$2x = 5 \qquad 2x = -5$$
$$x = \frac{5}{2} \qquad x = -\frac{5}{2}$$

The domain is the set of all real numbers except $\frac{5}{2}$ and $-\frac{5}{2}$.

17. $x^2 + 1 = 0$

This equation has no real number solution.
The domain is the set of all real numbers.

19. $2x^2 - 7x - 15 = 0$
$$(x-5)(2x+3) = 0$$

$$x - 5 = 0 \qquad 2x + 3 = 0$$
$$x = 5 \qquad 2x = -3$$
$$x = -\frac{3}{2}$$

The domain is the set of all real numbers except 5 and $-\frac{3}{2}$.

21. $x^2 - 3x + 6 = 0$
$$b^2 - 4ac = (-3)^2 - 4(1)(6)$$
$$= 9 - 24$$
$$= -15$$

Because $b^2 - 4ac < 0$, there are no real number solutions.
The domain is the set of all real numbers.

23. $3x^2 - 2x - 7 = 0$
$$x = \frac{2 \pm \sqrt{4 - 4(3)(-7)}}{6}$$
$$x = \frac{2 \pm \sqrt{4 + 84}}{6}$$

$$x = \frac{2 \pm \sqrt{88}}{6}$$
$$x = \frac{2 \pm \sqrt{4 \cdot 22}}{6}$$
$$x = \frac{2 \pm 2\sqrt{22}}{6}$$
$$x = \frac{1 \pm \sqrt{22}}{3}$$

The domain is the set of all real numbers except $\frac{1 + \sqrt{22}}{3}$ and $\frac{1 - \sqrt{22}}{3}$.

25.
$$4x^3 - 8x^2 - 9x + 18 = 0$$
$$4x^2(x-2) - 9(x-2) = 0$$
$$(x-2)(4x^2 - 9) = 0$$
$$(x-2)(2x-3)(2x+3) = 0$$

$$x - 2 = 0 \qquad 2x - 3 = 0 \qquad 2x + 3 = 0$$
$$x = 2 \qquad 2x = 3 \qquad 2x = -3$$
$$x = \frac{3}{2} \qquad x = -\frac{3}{2}$$

The domain is the set of all real numbers except 2, $\frac{3}{2}$ and $-\frac{3}{2}$.

27.
$$\frac{20x^7}{15x^4} = \frac{\cancel{5} \cdot 4 \cdot \cancel{x} \cdot \cancel{x} \cdot \cancel{x} \cdot \cancel{x} \cdot x \cdot x \cdot x}{\cancel{5} \cdot 3 \cdot \cancel{x} \cdot \cancel{x} \cdot \cancel{x} \cdot \cancel{x}}$$
$$= \frac{4x^3}{3}$$

29.
$$\frac{4x - 28}{5x - 35} = \frac{4\cancel{(x-7)}}{5\cancel{(x-7)}}$$
$$= \frac{4}{5}$$

31.
$$\frac{x^2 + 7x + 10}{x^2 - 7x - 18} = \frac{(x+5)\cancel{(x+2)}}{(x-9)\cancel{(x+2)}}$$
$$= \frac{x+5}{x-9}$$

33.
$$\frac{x^2 - 49}{x^2 - 14x + 49} = \frac{\cancel{(x-7)}(x+7)}{\cancel{(x-7)}(x-7)}$$
$$= \frac{x+7}{x-7}$$

35.
$$\frac{16x^2-25}{8x^2-22x+15}=\frac{(4x-5)(4x+5)}{(4x-5)(2x-3)}$$
$$=\frac{4x+5}{2x-3}$$

37.
$$\frac{x-5}{5-x}=\frac{x-5}{-1(x-5)}$$
$$=\frac{1}{-1}$$
$$=-1$$

39.
$$\frac{4x-12}{18-6x}=\frac{4(x-3)}{-6(x-3)}$$
$$=\frac{4}{-6}$$
$$=-\frac{2}{3}$$

41.
$$\frac{6x-18}{9-x^2}=\frac{6(x-3)}{(3-x)(3+x)}$$
$$=\frac{6(x-3)}{-1(x-3)(x+3)}$$
$$=-\frac{6}{x+3}$$

43.
$$\frac{x^2+2x-35}{-x^2+3x+10}=\frac{x^2+2x-35}{-1(x^2-3x-10)}$$
$$=\frac{(x-5)(x+7)}{-1(x-5)(x+2)}$$
$$=-\frac{x+7}{(x+2)}$$

45.
$$\frac{3x^3+21x^2+36x}{x^2-9}=\frac{3x(x^2+7x+12)}{(x-3)(x+3)}$$
$$=\frac{3x(x+4)(x+3)}{(x-3)(x+3)}$$
$$=\frac{3x(x+4)}{x-3}$$

47.
$$\frac{x^2-2x-8}{4x^3+8x^2-9x-18}=\frac{(x-4)(x+2)}{4x^2(x+2)-9(x+2)}$$
$$=\frac{(x-4)(x+2)}{(4x^2-9)(x+2)}$$
$$=\frac{(x-4)(x+2)}{(2x-3)(2x+3)(x+2)}$$
$$=\frac{x-4}{(2x-3)(2x+3)}$$

49.
$$\frac{x^3+8}{x^2-4}=\frac{x^3+2^3}{(x-2)(x+2)}$$
$$=\frac{(x+2)(x^2-4x+4)}{(x-2)(x+2)}$$
$$=\frac{x^2-4x+4}{x-2}$$

51.
$$\frac{3x^2+7x-6}{27x^3-8}=\frac{(3x-2)(x+3)}{(3x)^3-(2)^3}$$
$$=\frac{(3x-2)(x+3)}{(3x-2)(9x^2+6x+4)}$$
$$=\frac{x+3}{9x^2+6x+4}$$

53.
$$\frac{x^2-6xy+9y^2}{x^2-3xy}=\frac{(x-3y)(x-3y)}{x(x-3y)}$$
$$=\frac{x-3y}{x}$$

55.
$$\frac{6a^2+ab-2b^2}{3a^2-7ab-6b^2}=\frac{(3a+2b)(2a-b)}{(3a+2b)(a-3b)}$$
$$=\frac{2a-b}{a-3b}$$

57.
$$\frac{p^3-q^3}{p^2-q^2}=\frac{(p-q)(p^2+pq+q^2)}{(p-q)(p+q)}$$
$$=\frac{p^2+pq+q^2}{p+q}$$

59. $\left(\dfrac{f}{g}\right)(x) = \dfrac{x^2 + 2x - 8}{x^2 - 8x + 12}$

$= \dfrac{(x+4)\cancel{(x-2)}}{(x-6)\cancel{(x-2)}}$

$= \dfrac{x+4}{x-6}$

$\left(\dfrac{f}{g}\right)(3) = \dfrac{3+4}{3-6}$

$= \dfrac{7}{-3}$

$= -\dfrac{7}{3}$

61. $\left(\dfrac{h}{f}\right)(x) = \dfrac{3x^2 + 17x + 20}{x^2 + 2x - 8}$

$= \dfrac{(3x+5)\cancel{(x+4)}}{\cancel{(x+4)}(x-2)}$

$= \dfrac{3x+5}{x-2}$

$\left(\dfrac{h}{f}\right)(4) = \dfrac{3(4)+5}{4-2}$

$= \dfrac{17}{2}$

63. $\left(\dfrac{f}{h}\right)(x) = \dfrac{3x^3 - x^2}{9x^2 - 1}$

$= \dfrac{x^2\cancel{(3x-1)}}{\cancel{(3x-1)}(3x+1)}$

$= \dfrac{x^2}{3x+1}$

$\left(\dfrac{f}{h}\right)(-2) = \dfrac{(-2)^2}{3(-2)+1}$

$= \dfrac{4}{-6+1}$

$= -\dfrac{4}{5}$

65. $\left(\dfrac{k}{g}\right)(x) = \dfrac{27x^3 + 1}{18x^3 + 12x^2 + 2x}$

$= \dfrac{\cancel{(3x+1)}(9x^2 - 3x + 1)}{\cancel{(3x+1)}(6x^2 + 2x)}$

$= \dfrac{9x^2 - 3x + 1}{2x(3x+1)}$

$\left(\dfrac{k}{g}\right)(-1) = \dfrac{27(-1)^3 + 1}{18(-1)^3 + 12(-1)^2 + 2(-1)}$

$= \dfrac{27(-1)+1}{18(-1)+12(1)-2}$

$= \dfrac{-27+1}{-18+12-2}$

$= \dfrac{-26}{-8}$

$= \dfrac{13}{4}$

67. a. Percentage of people who received food stamps t years after 1990:

$P(t) = \dfrac{F(t)}{U(t)} \times 100$

$= \dfrac{100 \cdot F(t)}{U(t)}$

$= \dfrac{100\left(0.465t^2 - 9.5t + 66\right)}{0.0068t^2 + 2.58t + 251.7}$

$= \dfrac{46.5t^2 - 950t + 6,600}{0.0068t^2 + 2.58t + 251.7}$

b. In the year 2004, $t = 14$:

$P(14) \approx 8.3485$

According to the model, about 8.2379% of Americans received food stamps in the year 2004. The actual percent is:

$\dfrac{23.9}{293.7} \times 100\% = 8.1376\%$

The result of using the model is an overestimate.

c. $P(17) \approx 13.0695\%$, which represents the approximate percent of Americans who are to receive food stamps in the year 2007.

69. a. $A(t) = 0.058t^2 - 0.82t + 3.6$

b.
$$P(t) = \frac{U(t)}{A(t)} \cdot 100$$
$$= \frac{100 \cdot U(t)}{A(t)}$$
$$= \frac{100\left(0.047t^2 - 0.77t + 3.5\right)}{0.058t^2 - 0.82t + 3.6}$$
$$= \frac{4.7t^2 - 77t + 350}{0.058t^2 - 0.82t + 3.6}$$

c. $P(30) \approx 72.8\%$, which represents the approximate percent of cumulative unredeemed frequent flier miles for the year 2010.

d.

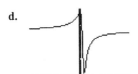

e. The percentage of cumulative unredeemed miles has been increasing since the year 1990. The graph decreases from about 1980 to 1990, then increases after 1990.

71. Answers may vary.

73. Domain: -3, -2, -1, 0, 1, 2, 3; range: 50.4, 25.2, 16.8, 12.6, 10.08, 8.4, 7.2

75. I would tell the student that 2 and 4 are in the domain because they do not make the denominator 0. The only values that must be excluded are 5 and 1 because when we put these into the function, the denominator equals 0.

77.

original	student's
$\dfrac{2(3+4)+3}{(3+4)(3-1)}$	$\dfrac{5}{3-1}$
$\dfrac{2(7)+3}{7(2)}$	$\dfrac{5}{2}$
$\dfrac{14+3}{14}$	
$\dfrac{17}{14}$	

The results are not the same, so the original

expression is not equivalent to the student's expression.

79. Answers may vary.

81. The domain is all real numbers.

83. The domain is all real numbers.

85.
$$x^2 - 4x - 21 = 0$$
$$(x-7)(x+3) = 0$$
$$x - 7 = 0 \qquad x + 3 = 0$$
$$x = 7 \qquad x = -3$$
The domain of f is all real numbers except 7 and -3.
The function $f(x)$ is a *rational function*.

87.
$$3x^3 + 5x^2 = 12x + 20$$
$$3x^3 + 5x^2 - 12x - 20 = 0$$
$$3x^3 - 12x + 5x^2 - 20 = 0$$
$$3x\left(x^2 - 4\right) + 5\left(x^2 - 4\right) = 0$$
$$\left(x^2 - 4\right)\left(3x + 5\right) = 0$$
$$(x-2)(x+2)(3x+5) = 0$$
$$x - 2 = 0 \quad x + 2 = 0 \quad 3x + 5 = 0$$
$$x = 2 \qquad x = -2 \qquad x = -\frac{5}{3}$$
The solutions are 2, -2, and $-\dfrac{5}{3}$.

89.
$$8x^3 - 125$$
$$(2x - 5)(4x^2 + 10x + 25)$$

Homework 8.2

1. $\dfrac{5}{x} \cdot \dfrac{2}{x} = \dfrac{10}{x^2}$

3.
$$\frac{7x^5}{2} \div \frac{5x^3}{6} = \frac{7x^5}{2} \cdot \frac{6}{5x^3}$$
$$= \frac{7 \cdot x^5 \cdot x^2}{2} \cdot \frac{2 \cdot 3}{5 \cdot x^3}$$
$$= \frac{21x^2}{5}$$

5.
$$\frac{5p^3}{4p-8} \cdot \frac{3p-6}{10p^8} = \frac{5p^3}{4(p-2)} \cdot \frac{3(p-2)}{10p^8}$$

$$= \frac{15p^3}{40p^8}$$

$$= \frac{5 \cdot 3 \cdot p^3}{5 \cdot 8 \cdot p^3 \cdot p^5} = \frac{3}{8p^5}$$

7.
$$\frac{6x-18}{5x^5} \div \frac{5x-15}{x^3} = \frac{6x-18}{5x^5} \cdot \frac{x^3}{5x-15}$$

$$= \frac{6(x-3)}{5x^5} \cdot \frac{x^3}{5(x-3)}$$

$$= \frac{6x^3}{25x^5}$$

$$= \frac{6 \cdot x^3}{25 \cdot x^3 \cdot x^2}$$

$$= \frac{6}{25x^2}$$

9.
$$\frac{4a^3}{9b^2} \cdot \frac{3b^5}{8a} = \frac{12a^3b^5}{72ab^2}$$

$$= \frac{12 \cdot a \cdot a^2 \cdot b^3 \cdot b^2}{12 \cdot 6 \cdot a \cdot b^2}$$

$$= \frac{a^2b^3}{6}$$

11.
$$\frac{3y^5}{2x^4} \div \frac{15y^9}{16x^7} = \frac{3y^5}{2x^4} \cdot \frac{16x^7}{15y^9}$$

$$= \frac{48x^7y^5}{30x^4y^9}$$

$$= \frac{6 \cdot 8 \cdot x^4 \cdot x^3 \cdot y^5}{6 \cdot 5 \cdot x^4 \cdot y^5 \cdot y^4}$$

$$= \frac{8x^3}{5y^4}$$

13.
$$\frac{r^2+10r+21}{r-9} \cdot \frac{2r-18}{r^2-9}$$

$$= \frac{(r+7)(r+3)}{(r-9)} \cdot \frac{2(r-9)}{(r-3)(r+3)}$$

$$= \frac{2(r+7)}{r-3}$$

15.
$$\frac{x^2+3x+2}{3x-3} \div \frac{x^2-x-6}{6x-6}$$

$$= \frac{x^2+3x+2}{3x-3} \cdot \frac{6x-6}{x^2-x-6}$$

$$= \frac{(x+2)(x+1)}{3(x-1)} \cdot \frac{6(x-1)}{(x+2)(x-3)}$$

$$= \frac{6(x+1)}{3(x-3)}$$

$$= \frac{2(x+1)}{x-3}$$

17.
$$\frac{2x-12}{x+1} \cdot \frac{4x+4}{18-3x} = \frac{2(x-6)}{(x+1)} \cdot \frac{4(x+1)}{3(6-x)}$$

$$= \frac{8(x-6)}{3(6-x)}$$

$$= \frac{8(x-6)}{-3(x-6)}$$

$$= -\frac{8}{3}$$

19.
$$\frac{2k^2-32}{k^2-2k-24} \div \frac{k+6}{k^2-7k+6}$$

$$= \frac{2k^2-32}{k^2-2k-24} \cdot \frac{k^2-7k+6}{k+6}$$

$$= \frac{2(k^2-16)}{(k-6)(k+4)} \cdot \frac{(k-6)(k-1)}{(k+6)}$$

$$= \frac{2(k-4)(k+4)}{(k-6)(k+4)} \cdot \frac{(k-6)(k-1)}{(k+6)}$$

$$= \frac{2(k-4)(k-1)}{k+6}$$

21. $\dfrac{2a^2+3ab}{3a-6b}\cdot\dfrac{a^2-4b^2}{2ab+3b^2}$

$=\dfrac{a\cancel{(2a+3b)}}{3\cancel{(a-2b)}}\cdot\dfrac{\cancel{(a-2b)}(a+2b)}{b\cancel{(2a+3b)}}$

$=\dfrac{a(a+2b)}{3b}$

23. $\dfrac{4-x}{x^2+10x+25}\div\dfrac{3x^2-9x-12}{25-x^2}$

$=\dfrac{4-x}{x^2+10x+25}\cdot\dfrac{25-x^2}{3x^2-9x-12}$

$=\dfrac{(4-x)}{(x+5)(x+5)}\cdot\dfrac{(5-x)(5+x)}{3(x^2-3x-4)}$

$=\dfrac{-1\cdot\cancel{(4-x)}}{(x+5)\cancel{(x+5)}}\cdot\dfrac{(5-x)\cancel{(5+x)}}{3\cancel{(x-4)}(x+1)}$

$=\dfrac{-(5-x)}{3(x+5)(x+1)}$

$=\dfrac{x-5}{3(x+5)(x+1)}$

25. $\dfrac{t^2-8t+16}{t^2-2t-3}\cdot\dfrac{3-t}{t^2-16}$

$=\dfrac{\cancel{(t-4)}(t-4)}{\cancel{(t-3)}(t+1)}\cdot\dfrac{-1\cdot\cancel{(3-t)}}{\cancel{(t-4)}(t+4)}$

$=\dfrac{-(t-4)}{(t+1)(t+4)}$

$=\dfrac{4-t}{(t+1)(t+4)}$

27. $\dfrac{-x^2+7x-10}{2x^2+5x-12}\div\dfrac{-x^2+4}{8x^2-18}$

$=\dfrac{-x^2+7x-10}{2x^2+5x-12}\cdot\dfrac{8x^2-18}{-x^2+4}$

$=\dfrac{-1(x^2-7x+10)}{(2x-3)(x+4)}\cdot\dfrac{2(4x^2-9)}{-1(x^2-4)}$

$=\dfrac{\cancel{-1}(x-5)\cancel{(x-2)}}{\cancel{(2x-3)}(x+4)}\cdot\dfrac{2\cancel{(2x-3)}(2x+3)}{\cancel{-1}\cancel{(x-2)}(x+2)}$

$=\dfrac{2(x-5)(2x+3)}{(x+4)(x+2)}$

29. $\dfrac{-4x-6}{36-x^2}\cdot\dfrac{4x+24}{6x^2+x-12}$

$=\dfrac{-2(2x+3)}{-1(x^2-36)}\cdot\dfrac{4(x+6)}{(3x-4)(2x+3)}$

$=\dfrac{\cancel{-}2\cancel{(2x+3)}}{\cancel{-}1\cancel{(x+6)}(x-6)}\cdot\dfrac{4\cancel{(x+6)}}{(3x-4)\cancel{(2x+3)}}$

$=\dfrac{8}{(x-6)(3x-4)}$

31. $\dfrac{9x^2-16}{x+2}\div\left(3x^2+5x-12\right)$

$=\dfrac{9x^2-16}{x+2}\cdot\dfrac{1}{3x^2+5x-12}$

$=\dfrac{\cancel{(3x-4)}(3x+4)}{(x+2)}\cdot\dfrac{1}{\cancel{(3x-4)}(x+3)}$

$=\dfrac{3x+4}{(x+2)(x+3)}$

33. $\dfrac{6m^2-17m-14}{m^2+6m+9}\cdot\dfrac{9-m^2}{4m^2-49}$

$=\dfrac{\cancel{(2m-7)}(3m+2)}{(m+3)\cancel{(m+3)}}\cdot\dfrac{(3-m)\cancel{(3+m)}}{\cancel{(2m-7)}(2m+7)}$

$=\dfrac{(3m+2)(3-m)}{(m+3)(2m+7)}$

35. $\dfrac{x^2-4x-32}{x^2+7x+12}\div\dfrac{x^2-2x-48}{x^2+3x-4}$

$=\dfrac{x^2-4x-32}{x^2+7x+12}\cdot\dfrac{x^2+3x-4}{x^2-2x-48}$

$=\dfrac{\cancel{(x-8)}\cancel{(x+4)}}{(x+3)\cancel{(x+4)}}\cdot\dfrac{(x+4)(x-1)}{\cancel{(x-8)}(x+6)}$

$=\dfrac{(x+4)(x-1)}{(x+3)(x+6)}$

37. $\dfrac{p^2+4pt-12t^2}{p^2+pt-12t^2}\cdot\dfrac{p^2+7pt+12t^2}{p^2-7pt+10t^2}$

$=\dfrac{(p+6t)\cancel{(p-2t)}}{\cancel{(p+4t)}(p-3t)}\cdot\dfrac{\cancel{(p+4t)}(p+3t)}{\cancel{(p-2t)}(p-5t)}$

$=\dfrac{(p+6t)(p+3t)}{(p-3t)(p-5t)}$

39. $\dfrac{2x^2 - xy - 3y^2}{3xy - 5y^2} \div \dfrac{4x^2 - 9y^2}{3x^2 - 14xy + 15y^2}$

$= \dfrac{2x^2 - xy - 3y^2}{3xy - 5y^2} \cdot \dfrac{3x^2 - 14xy + 15y^2}{4x^2 - 9y^2}$

$= \dfrac{(2x - 3y)(x + y)}{y(3x - 5y)} \cdot \dfrac{(3x - 5y)(x - 3y)}{(2x - 3y)(2x + 3y)}$

$= \dfrac{(x + y)(x - 3y)}{y(2x + 3y)}$

41. $\dfrac{3x^3 - 15x^2 + 18x}{x^2 + 16x + 64} \cdot \dfrac{x^2 - 64}{4x^4 - 28x^3 + 40x^2}$

$= \dfrac{3x(x^2 - 5x + 6)}{(x + 8)(x + 8)} \cdot \dfrac{(x - 8)(x + 8)}{4x^2(x^2 - 7x + 10)}$

$= \dfrac{3 \cdot x(x - 2)(x - 3)}{(x + 8)(x + 8)} \cdot \dfrac{(x - 8)(x + 8)}{4x \cdot x(x - 2)(x - 5)}$

$= \dfrac{3(x - 3)(x - 8)}{4x(x + 8)(x - 5)}$

43. $\dfrac{w^2 - 2w - 8}{12w^4 + 32w^3 - 12w^2} \div \dfrac{w^2 - 9w + 20}{12w^3 + 54w^2 + 54w}$

$= \dfrac{w^2 - 2w - 8}{12w^4 + 32w^3 - 12w^2} \cdot \dfrac{12w^3 + 54w^2 + 54w}{w^2 - 9w + 20}$

$= \dfrac{(w - 4)(w + 2)}{4w^2(3w^2 + 8w - 3)} \cdot \dfrac{6w(2w^2 + 9w + 9)}{(w - 4)(w - 5)}$

$= \dfrac{(w - 4)(w + 2)}{4w^2(3w - 1)(w + 3)} \cdot \dfrac{6w(2w + 3)(w + 3)}{(w - 4)(w - 5)}$

$= \dfrac{3 \cdot 2w(w + 2)(2w + 3)}{2w \cdot 2w(3w - 1)(w - 5)}$

$= \dfrac{3(w + 2)(2w + 3)}{2w(3w - 1)(w - 5)}$

45. $\dfrac{x^2 + 4x - 5}{x^3 + 6x^2 - 4x - 24} \cdot \dfrac{x^2 + 8x + 12}{x^2 + 10x + 25}$

$= \dfrac{(x + 5)(x - 1)}{x^2(x + 6) - 4(x + 6)} \cdot \dfrac{(x + 2)(x + 6)}{(x + 5)(x + 5)}$

$= \dfrac{(x + 5)(x - 1)}{(x + 6)(x^2 - 4)} \cdot \dfrac{(x + 2)(x + 6)}{(x + 5)(x + 5)}$

$= \dfrac{(x + 5)(x - 1)}{(x + 6)(x - 2)(x + 2)} \cdot \dfrac{(x + 2)(x + 6)}{(x + 5)(x + 5)}$

$= \dfrac{x - 1}{(x - 2)(x + 5)}$

47. $\dfrac{18x^3 + 27x^2 - 8x - 12}{3x^2 - x - 2} \div (6x^2 + 5x - 6)$

$= \dfrac{18x^3 + 27x^2 - 8x - 12}{3x^2 - x - 2} \cdot \dfrac{1}{6x^2 + 5x - 6}$

$= \dfrac{9x^2(2x + 3) - 4(2x + 3)}{(3x + 2)(x - 1)} \cdot \dfrac{1}{(2x + 3)(3x - 2)}$

$= \dfrac{(2x + 3)(9x^2 - 4)}{(3x + 2)(x - 1)} \cdot \dfrac{1}{(2x + 3)(3x - 2)}$

$= \dfrac{(2x + 3)(3x - 2)(3x + 2)}{(3x + 2)(x - 1)} \cdot \dfrac{1}{(2x + 3)(3x - 2)}$

$= \dfrac{1}{x - 1}$

49. $\dfrac{k^3 - 8}{k^3 + 27} \cdot \dfrac{k^2 - 9}{k^2 - 4}$

$= \dfrac{(k - 2)(k^2 + 2k + 4)}{(k + 3)(k^2 - 3k + 9)} \cdot \dfrac{(k - 3)(k + 3)}{(k - 2)(k + 2)}$

$= \dfrac{(k - 3)(k^2 + 2k + 4)}{(k + 2)(k^2 - 3k + 9)}$

51.

$$\frac{8x^3 - 27}{3x^2 - 6x + 12} : \frac{8x^2 + 12x + 18}{6x^3 + 48}$$

$$= \frac{8x^3 - 27}{3x^2 - 6x + 12} \cdot \frac{6x^3 + 48}{8x^2 + 12x + 18}$$

$$= \frac{(2x-3)(4x^2 + 6x + 9)}{3(x^2 - 2x + 4)} \cdot \frac{6(x^3 + 8)}{2(4x^2 + 6x + 9)}$$

$$= \frac{(2x-3)\cancel{(4x^2 + 6x + 9)}}{3\cancel{(x^2 - 2x + 4)}} \cdot \frac{6(x+2)\cancel{(x^2 - 2x + 4)}}{2\cancel{(4x^2 + 6x + 9)}}$$

$$= \frac{\cancel{6}(2x-3)(x+2)}{\cancel{6}}$$

$$= (2x-3)(x+2)$$

53.

$$\frac{a^2 + ab - 2b^2}{a^3 + b^3} \cdot \frac{a^2 + 2ab + b^2}{a^2 - b^2}$$

$$= \frac{(a+2b)\cancel{(a-b)}}{\cancel{(a+b)}(a^2 - ab + b^2)} \cdot \frac{\cancel{(a+b)}\cancel{(a+b)}}{\cancel{(a-b)}\cancel{(a+b)}}$$

$$= \frac{a+2b}{a^2 - ab + b^2}$$

55.

$$(f \cdot g)(x) = \frac{x^2 - 6x - 16}{x^2 + 3x - 40} \cdot \frac{x^2 - 64}{x^2 - 3x - 10}$$

$$= \frac{(x-8)\cancel{(x+2)}}{\cancel{(x+8)}(x-5)} \cdot \frac{(x-8)\cancel{(x+8)}}{(x-5)\cancel{(x+2)}}$$

$$= \frac{(x-8)(x-8)}{(x-5)(x-5)}$$

$$= \frac{(x-8)^2}{(x-5)^2}$$

$$= \left(\frac{x-8}{x-5}\right)^2$$

$$(f \cdot g)(6) = \left(\frac{6-8}{6-5}\right)^2$$

$$= \left(\frac{-2}{1}\right)^2$$

$$= 4$$

57.

$$\left(\frac{g}{f}\right)(x) = \frac{x^2 - 64}{x^2 - 3x - 10} \div \frac{x^2 - 6x \; 16}{x^2 + 3x - 40}$$

$$= \frac{x^2 - 64}{x^2 - 3x - 10} \cdot \frac{x^2 + 3x - 40}{x^2 - 6x - 16}$$

$$= \frac{\cancel{(x-8)}(x+8)}{\cancel{(x-5)}(x+2)} \cdot \frac{(x+8)\cancel{(x-5)}}{\cancel{(x-8)}(x+2)}$$

$$= \frac{(x+8)(x+8)}{(x+2)(x+2)}$$

$$= \left(\frac{x+8}{x+2}\right)^2$$

$$\left(\frac{g}{f}\right)(7) = \left(\frac{7+8}{7+2}\right)^2$$

$$= \left(\frac{15}{9}\right)^2$$

$$= \left(\frac{5}{3}\right)^2$$

$$= \frac{25}{9}$$

59.

$$\left(\frac{f}{g}\right)(x) = \frac{1 - x^2}{x^2 - 3x - 28} \div \frac{x^2 - 8x + 7}{x^2 + 5x + 4}$$

$$= \frac{1 - x^2}{x^2 - 3x - 28} \cdot \frac{x^2 + 5x + 4}{x^2 - 8x + 7}$$

$$= \frac{-1 \cdot \cancel{(1-x)}(1+x)}{(x-7)\cancel{(x+4)}} \cdot \frac{\cancel{(x+4)}(x+1)}{(x-7)\cancel{(x-1)}}$$

$$= \frac{-(1+x)(x+1)}{(x-7)(x-7)}$$

$$= -\left(\frac{x+1}{x-7}\right)^2$$

$$\left(\frac{f}{g}\right)(4) = -\left(\frac{4+1}{4-7}\right)^2$$

$$= -\left(\frac{5}{-3}\right)^2$$

$$= -\frac{25}{9}$$

61.

$$\left(\frac{20x^7}{x^2 - 9} \div \frac{x^2 - 14x + 24}{5x - 15}\right) \cdot \frac{x^2 + x - 6}{8x^{13}}$$

$$= \left(\frac{20x^7}{x^2 - 9} \cdot \frac{5x - 15}{x^2 - 14x + 24} \right) \cdot \frac{x^2 + x - 6}{8x^{13}}$$

$$= \frac{\cancel{4} \cdot 5 \cancel{x^7}}{\cancel{(x+3)}\,\cancel{(x-3)}} \cdot \frac{5\,\cancel{(x-3)}}{(x-12)\cancel{(x-2)}} \cdot \frac{\cancel{(x-2)}\,\cancel{(x+3)}}{\cancel{4} \cdot 2 \cdot \cancel{x^7} \cdot x^6}$$

$$= \frac{25}{2x^6(x - 12)}$$

63.

$$\frac{12x^3}{k^2 - 4} \div \left(\frac{22k^6}{-6k + 12} \cdot \frac{k}{11k + 22} \right)$$

$$= \frac{12k^3}{k^2 - 4} \div \left(\frac{\cancel{11} \cdot 2k^6}{-6(k - 2)} \cdot \frac{k}{\cancel{11}(k + 2)} \right)$$

$$= \frac{12k^3}{k^2 - 4} \div \frac{2k^7}{-6(k - 2)(k + 2)}$$

$$= \frac{12k^3}{k^2 - 4} \cdot \frac{-6(k - 2)(k + 2)}{2k^7}$$

$$= \frac{12\cancel{k^3}}{\cancel{(k-2)}\,\cancel{(k+2)}} \cdot \frac{-\cancel{2} \cdot 3\,\cancel{(k-2)}\,\cancel{(k+2)}}{\cancel{2} \cdot \cancel{k^3} \cdot k^4}$$

$$= \frac{-36}{k^4}$$

65.

$$\left(\left(\frac{x - 4}{x + 5} \right)^2 \cdot \left(\frac{x + 5}{x - 1} \right)^2 \right) \div \left(\frac{x - 4}{x - 1} \right)^2$$

$$= \left(\left(\frac{x - 4}{x + 5} \right)^2 \cdot \left(\frac{x + 5}{x - 1} \right)^2 \right) \cdot \left(\frac{x - 1}{x - 4} \right)^2$$

$$= \frac{\cancel{(x-4)^2}}{\cancel{(x+5)^2}} \cdot \frac{\cancel{(x+5)^2}}{\cancel{(x-1)^2}} \cdot \frac{\cancel{(x-1)^2}}{\cancel{(x-4)^2}}$$

$$= 1$$

67. Substitute $x = 10$ into $\dfrac{x - 2}{x + 8} \div \dfrac{x + 8}{x - 5}$:

$$\frac{10 - 2}{10 + 8} \div \frac{10 + 8}{10 - 5} = \frac{8}{18} \div \frac{18}{5}$$

$$= \frac{8}{18} \cdot \frac{5}{18}$$

$$= \frac{10}{81}$$

Now, substitute $x = 10$ into $\dfrac{x - 2}{x - 5}$:

$$\frac{10 - 2}{10 - 5} = \frac{8}{5}$$

The two values are different, so the students' work is incorrect.

69. a.

$$\frac{1}{x} \div \frac{1}{x} = \frac{1}{x} \cdot \frac{x}{1}$$

$$= \frac{x}{x}$$

$$= 1$$

b.

$$\frac{1}{x} \div \left(\frac{1}{x} \div \frac{1}{x} \right) = \frac{1}{x} \div \left(\frac{1}{x} \cdot \frac{x}{1} \right)$$

$$= \frac{1}{x} \div 1$$

$$= \frac{1}{x}$$

c.

$$\frac{1}{x} \div \left(\frac{1}{x} \div \left(\frac{1}{x} \div \frac{1}{x} \right) \right) = \frac{1}{x} \div \left(\frac{1}{x} \div 1 \right)$$

$$= \frac{1}{x} \div \frac{1}{x}$$

$$= 1$$

d.

$$\frac{1}{x} \div \left(\frac{1}{x} \div \left(\frac{1}{x} \div \left(\frac{1}{x} \div \frac{1}{x} \right) \right) \right)$$

$$= \frac{1}{x} \div \left(\frac{1}{x} \div \left(\frac{1}{x} \div 1 \right) \right)$$

$$= \frac{1}{x} \div \left(\frac{1}{x} \div \frac{1}{x} \right)$$

$$= \frac{1}{x} \div 1$$

$$= \frac{1}{x}$$

e.

$$\underbrace{\frac{1}{x} \div \left(\frac{1}{x} \div \left(\frac{1}{x} \div \cdots \div \left(\frac{1}{x} \div \left(\frac{1}{x} \div \frac{1}{x} \right) \right) \cdots \right) \right)}_{n \text{ division symbols}}$$

The answer will be 1 if n is odd, $\dfrac{1}{x}$, if n is even.

71. a.

$$T(50) = \frac{420}{50} = 8.4 \text{ hours}$$

This represents the driving time, in hours.

b.

$$T(55) = \frac{420}{55} = 7.64 \text{ hours}$$

$$T(60) = \frac{420}{60} = 7.00 \text{ hours}$$

$$T(65) = \frac{420}{65} = 6.46 \text{ hours}$$

$$T(70) = \frac{420}{70} = 6.00 \text{ hours}$$

c. T is decreasing for $s > 0$. This makes sense because the faster a person drives, the less time it will take to arrive at the destination (as shown in part b).

73. $(f \cdot g)(x) = 8^x \cdot 2^x$

$$= \left(2^3\right)^x \cdot 2^x$$

$$= 2^{3x} \cdot 2^x$$

$$= 2^{3x+x}$$

$$= 2^{4x}$$

$$= \left(2^4\right)^x$$

$$= 16^x$$

$$\left(\frac{f}{g}\right)(x) = \frac{8^x}{2^x}$$

$$= \frac{\left(2^3\right)^x}{2^x}$$

$$= \frac{2^{3x}}{2^x}$$

$$= 2^{3x-x}$$

$$= 2^{2x}$$

$$= \left(2^2\right)^x$$

$$= 4^x$$

75. $(f \cdot g)(x) = 12(6)^x \cdot 3(2)^x$

$$= 12 \cdot 3(6)^x (2)^x$$

$$= 36(6 \cdot 2)^x$$

$$= 36(12)^x$$

$$\left(\frac{f}{g}\right)(x) = \frac{12(6)^x}{3(2)^x}$$

$$= 4\left(\frac{6}{2}\right)^x$$

$$= 4(3)^x$$

77. $4\log_b\left(2x^2\right) - 2\log_b\left(3x^3\right) = \log_b\left(2x^2\right)^4 - \log_b\left(3x^3\right)^2$

$$= \log_b\left(16x^8\right) - \log_b\left(9x^6\right)$$

$$= \log_b\left(\frac{16x^8}{9x^6}\right)$$

$$= \log_b\left(\frac{16x^2 \cdot \cancel{x^6}}{9 \cdot \cancel{x^6}}\right)$$

$$= \log_b\left(\frac{16x^2}{9}\right)$$

79. $\log_2(x-3) + \log_2(x-2) = 3$

$$\log_2\left[(x-3)(x-2)\right] = 3$$

$$2^3 = (x-3)(x-2)$$

$$8 = x^2 - 5x + 6$$

$$0 = x^2 - 5x - 2$$

$$x = \frac{-(-5) \pm \sqrt{(-5)^2 - 4(1)(-2)}}{2(1)}$$

$$= \frac{5 \pm \sqrt{25 + 8}}{2}$$

$$= \frac{5 + \sqrt{33}}{2}, \; \cancel{\frac{5 - \sqrt{33}}{2}}$$

The solution is $\dfrac{5 + \sqrt{33}}{2}$.

81.
$$5(4)^x - 23 = 81$$
$$5(4)^x = 104$$
$$(4)^x = \frac{104}{5}$$
$$x = \log_4\left(\frac{104}{5}\right)$$
$$x = \log_4(20.8)$$
$$x = \frac{\log_{10} 20.8}{\log_{10} 4}$$
$$x \approx 2.1893$$

Homework 8.3

1.
$$\frac{5}{x} + \frac{2}{x} = \frac{5+2}{x}$$
$$= \frac{7}{x}$$

3.
$$\frac{x}{x^2-9} + \frac{3}{x^2-9} = \frac{x+3}{x^2-9}$$
$$= \frac{(x+3)}{(x+3)(x-3)}$$
$$= \frac{1}{x-3}$$

5.
$$\frac{6m^2}{m^2-4m+3} - \frac{4m^2+6m}{m^2-4m+3}$$
$$= \frac{6m^2 - (4m^2+6m)}{m^2-4m+3}$$
$$= \frac{6m^2 - 4m^2 - 6m}{m^2-4m+3}$$
$$= \frac{2m^2 - 6m}{m^2-4m+3}$$
$$= \frac{2m(m-3)}{(m-1)(m-3)}$$
$$= \frac{2m}{m-1}$$

7.
$$\frac{3x^2+9x}{x^2+10x+21} - \frac{2x^2+x-15}{x^2+10x+21}$$
$$= \frac{3x^2+9x - (2x^2+x-15)}{x^2+10x+21}$$
$$= \frac{3x^2+9x-2x^2-x+15}{x^2+10x+21}$$
$$= \frac{x^2+8x+15}{x^2+10x+21}$$
$$= \frac{(x+3)(x+5)}{(x+3)(x+7)}$$
$$= \frac{x+5}{x+7}$$

9.
$$\frac{2}{x^6} - \frac{4}{x^2} = \frac{2}{x^6} - \frac{4}{x^2} \cdot \frac{x^4}{x^4}$$
$$= \frac{2}{x^6} - \frac{4x^6}{x^6}$$
$$= \frac{2 - 4x^6}{x^6}$$

11.
$$\frac{3}{10x^6} + \frac{5}{12x^4} = \frac{3}{10x^6} \cdot \frac{6}{6} + \frac{5}{12x^4} \cdot \frac{5x^2}{5x^2}$$
$$= \frac{18}{60x^6} + \frac{25x^2}{60x^6}$$
$$= \frac{18 + 25x^2}{60x^6}$$

13.
$$\frac{7}{4a^2b} - \frac{5}{6ab^3} = \frac{7}{4a^2b} \cdot \frac{3b^2}{3b^2} - \frac{5}{6ab^3} \cdot \frac{2a}{2a}$$
$$= \frac{21b^3}{12a^2b^3} - \frac{10a}{12a^2b^3}$$
$$= \frac{21b^3 - 10a}{12a^2b^3}$$

15.
$$\frac{3}{x+1} + \frac{4}{x-2} = \frac{3}{x+1} \cdot \left(\frac{x-2}{x-2}\right) + \frac{4}{x-2} \cdot \left(\frac{x+1}{x+1}\right)$$
$$= \frac{3x-6}{(x+1)(x-2)} + \frac{4x+4}{(x+1)(x-2)}$$
$$= \frac{7x-2}{(x+1)(x-2)}$$

17. $\dfrac{6}{(x+4)(x-6)} - \dfrac{4}{(x-1)(x+4)}$

$= \dfrac{6}{(x+4)(x-6)} \cdot \left(\dfrac{x-1}{x-1}\right) - \dfrac{4}{(x-1)(x+4)} \cdot \left(\dfrac{x-6}{x-6}\right)$

$= \dfrac{6x-6}{(x+4)(x-6)(x-1)} - \dfrac{4x-24}{(x+4)(x-6)(x-1)}$

$= \dfrac{6x-6-4x+24}{(x+4)(x-6)(x-1)}$

$= \dfrac{2x+18}{(x+4)(x-6)(x-1)}$

$= \dfrac{2(x+9)}{(x+4)(x-6)(x-1)}$

19.

$\dfrac{5}{3t-6} - \dfrac{2}{5t+15} = \dfrac{5}{3(t-2)} - \dfrac{2}{5(t+3)}$

$= \dfrac{5}{3(t-2)} \cdot \dfrac{5(t+3)}{5(t+3)} - \dfrac{2}{5(t+3)} \cdot \dfrac{3(t-2)}{3(t-2)}$

$= \dfrac{25(t+3)}{15(t-2)(t+3)} - \dfrac{6(t-2)}{15(t+3)(t-2)}$

$= \dfrac{25(t+3)-6(t-2)}{15(t-2)(t+3)}$

$= \dfrac{25t+75-6t+12}{15(t-2)(t+3)}$

$= \dfrac{19t+87}{15(t-2)(t+3)}$

21. $\dfrac{3}{x^2-25} + \dfrac{5}{x^2-5x} = \dfrac{3}{(x+5)(x-5)} + \dfrac{5}{x(x-5)}$

$= \dfrac{3}{(x-5)(x+5)} \cdot \dfrac{x}{x} + \dfrac{5}{x(x-5)} \cdot \left(\dfrac{x+5}{x+5}\right)$

$= \dfrac{3x}{x(x-5)(x+5)} + \dfrac{5x+25}{x(x-5)(x+5)}$

$= \dfrac{8x+25}{x(x-5)(x+5)}$

23. $\dfrac{2}{x^2-9} + \dfrac{3}{x^2-7x+12}$

$= \dfrac{2}{(x+3)(x-3)} + \dfrac{3}{(x-4)(x-3)}$

$= \dfrac{2}{(x+3)(x-3)} \cdot \left(\dfrac{x-4}{x-4}\right) + \dfrac{3}{(x-4)(x-3)} \cdot \left(\dfrac{x+3}{x+3}\right)$

$= \dfrac{2x-8}{(x+3)(x-3)(x-4)} + \dfrac{3x+9}{(x+3)(x-3)(x-4)}$

$= \dfrac{5x+1}{(x+3)(x-3)(x-4)}$

25. $2 + \dfrac{k-3}{k+1} = \dfrac{2}{1} \cdot \left(\dfrac{k+1}{k+1}\right) + \dfrac{k-3}{k+1}$

$= \dfrac{2k+2}{k+1} + \dfrac{k-3}{k+1}$

$= \dfrac{3k-1}{k+1}$

27. $2 - \dfrac{2x+4}{x^2+3x+2} = \dfrac{2}{1} - \dfrac{2\,\cancel{(x+2)}}{\cancel{(x+2)}(x+1)}$

$= \dfrac{2}{1} - \dfrac{2}{x+1} = \dfrac{2}{1} \cdot \left(\dfrac{x+1}{x+1}\right) - \dfrac{2}{x+1}$

$= \dfrac{2x+2}{x+1} - \dfrac{2}{x+1} = \dfrac{2x}{x+1}$

29. $\dfrac{8}{x-6} - \dfrac{4}{6-x} = \dfrac{8}{x-6} + \dfrac{4}{x-6}$

$= \dfrac{12}{x-6}$

31. $\dfrac{2x+1}{x^2-4x-21} + \dfrac{3}{14-2x}$

$= \dfrac{2x+1}{(x-7)(x+3)} + \dfrac{3}{-2(x-7)}$

$= \dfrac{2x+1}{(x-7)(x+3)} - \dfrac{3}{2(x-7)}$

$= \dfrac{2x+1}{(x-7)(x+3)} \cdot \dfrac{2}{2} - \dfrac{3}{2(x-7)} \cdot \left(\dfrac{x+3}{x+3}\right)$

$= \dfrac{4x+2}{2(x-7)(x+3)} - \dfrac{3x+9}{2(x-7)(x+3)}$

$= \dfrac{4x+2-3x-9}{2(x-7)(x+3)}$

$= \dfrac{x-7}{2(x-7)(x+3)}$

$= \dfrac{1}{2(x+3)}$

33. $\dfrac{-2c}{7-2c}-\dfrac{c+1}{4c^2-49}$

$=\dfrac{2c}{(2c-7)}-\dfrac{(c+1)}{(2c-7)(2c+7)}$

$=\dfrac{2c}{(2c-7)}\cdot\dfrac{(2c+7)}{(2c+7)}-\dfrac{(c+1)}{(2c-7)(2c+7)}$

$=\dfrac{2c(2c+7)-(c+1)}{(2c-7)(2c+7)}$

$=\dfrac{4c^2+14c-c-1}{(2c-7)(2c+7)}$

$=\dfrac{4c^2+13c-1}{(2c-7)(2c+7)}$

35. $\dfrac{2a}{a^2-b^2}+\dfrac{b}{ab-b^2}$

$=\dfrac{2a}{(a-b)(a+b)}+\dfrac{b}{b(a-b)}$

$=\dfrac{2a}{(a-b)(a+b)}\cdot\dfrac{b}{b}+\dfrac{b}{b(a-b)}\cdot\dfrac{(a+b)}{(a+b)}$

$=\dfrac{2ab+b(a+b)}{b(a-b)(a+b)}$

$=\dfrac{3ab+b^2}{b(a-b)(a+b)}$

$=\dfrac{\cancel{b}(3a+b)}{\cancel{b}(a-b)(a+b)}$

$=\dfrac{3a+b}{(a-b)(a+b)}$

37. $\dfrac{x}{x^2+5x+6}-\dfrac{3}{x^2+7x+12}$

$=\dfrac{x}{(x+2)(x+3)}\cdot\dfrac{(x+4)}{(x+4)}$

$\quad\quad-\dfrac{3}{(x+3)(x+4)}\cdot\dfrac{(x+2)}{(x+2)}$

$=\dfrac{x(x+4)-3(x+2)}{(x+2)(x+3)(x+4)}$

$=\dfrac{x^2+x-6}{(x+2)(x+3)(x+4)}$

$=\dfrac{(x-2)\cancel{(x+3)}}{(x+2)\cancel{(x+3)}(x+4)}$

$=\dfrac{x-2}{(x+2)(x+4)}$

39. $\dfrac{x-1}{x+2}+\dfrac{x+2}{x-1}=\left(\dfrac{x-1}{x+2}\right)\left(\dfrac{x-1}{x-1}\right)+\left(\dfrac{x+2}{x-1}\right)\left(\dfrac{x+2}{x+2}\right)$

$=\dfrac{x^2-2x+1}{(x+2)(x-1)}+\dfrac{x^2+4x+4}{(x+2)(x-1)}$

$=\dfrac{2x^2+2x+5}{(x+2)(x-1)}$

41. $\dfrac{y-5}{y-3}-\dfrac{y+3}{y+5}$

$=\left(\dfrac{y-5}{y-3}\right)\left(\dfrac{y+5}{y+5}\right)-\left(\dfrac{y+3}{y+5}\right)\left(\dfrac{y-3}{y-3}\right)$

$=\dfrac{y^2-25}{(y-3)(y+5)}-\dfrac{y^2-9}{(y-3)(y+5)}$

$=\dfrac{y^2-25-y^2+9}{(y-3)(y+5)}$

$=\dfrac{-16}{(y-3)(y+5)}$

43. $\dfrac{x+4}{x^2-7x+10}-\dfrac{5}{x^2-25}$

$=\dfrac{x+4}{(x-2)(x-5)}-\dfrac{5}{(x-5)(x+5)}$

$=\dfrac{(x+4)}{(x-2)(x-5)}\cdot\dfrac{(x+5)}{(x+5)}-\dfrac{5}{(x-5)(x+5)}\cdot\dfrac{(x-2)}{(x-2)}$

$=\dfrac{(x+4)(x+5)-5(x-2)}{(x-2)(x-5)(x+5)}$

$=\dfrac{x^2+9x+20-5x+10}{(x-2)(x-5)(x+5)}$

$=\dfrac{x^2+4x+30}{(x-2)(x-5)(x+5)}$

45. $\dfrac{x+2}{(x-4)(x+3)^2}+\dfrac{x-1}{(x-4)(x+1)(x+3)}$

$=\left(\dfrac{x+2}{(x-4)(x+3)^2}\right)\left(\dfrac{x+1}{x+1}\right)$

$\quad+\left(\dfrac{x-1}{(x-4)(x+1)(x+3)}\right)\left(\dfrac{x+3}{x+3}\right)$

$=\dfrac{x^2+3x+2}{(x-4)(x+1)(x+3)^2}+\dfrac{x^2+2x-3}{(x-4)(x+1)(x+3)^2}$

$=\dfrac{2x^2+5x-1}{(x-4)(x+1)(x+3)^2}$

47. $\dfrac{c+2}{c^2-4}+\dfrac{3c}{c^2-2c}=\dfrac{c+2}{(c+2)(c-2)}+\dfrac{3c}{c(c-2)}$

$\qquad\qquad\qquad\qquad=\dfrac{1}{c-2}+\dfrac{3}{c-2}$

$\qquad\qquad\qquad\qquad=\dfrac{4}{c-2}$

49. $\dfrac{x-1}{4x^2+20x+25}-\dfrac{x+4}{6x^2+17x+5}$

$=\dfrac{x-1}{(2x+5)(2x+5)}-\dfrac{x+4}{(2x+5)(3x+1)}$

$=\left(\dfrac{x-1}{(2x+5)(2x+5)}\right)\left(\dfrac{3x+1}{3x+1}\right)-$

$\qquad\left(\dfrac{x+4}{(2x+5)(3x+1)}\right)\left(\dfrac{2x+5}{2x+5}\right)$

$=\dfrac{3x^2-2x-1}{(3x+1)(2x+5)^2}-\dfrac{2x^2+13x+20}{(3x+1)(2x+5)^2}$

$=\dfrac{3x^2-2x-1-2x^2-13x-20}{(3x+1)(2x+5)^2}$

$=\dfrac{x^2-15x-21}{(3x+1)(2x+5)^2}$

51. $\dfrac{3x-1}{x^2+4x+4}+\dfrac{2x+1}{3x^2+5x-2}$

$=\dfrac{3x-1}{(x+2)(x+2)}-\dfrac{2x+1}{(3x-1)(x+2)}$

$=\left(\dfrac{3x-1}{(x+2)(x+2)}\right)\left(\dfrac{3x-1}{3x-1}\right)$

$\quad+\left(\dfrac{2x+1}{(3x-1)(x+2)}\right)\left(\dfrac{x+2}{x+2}\right)$

$=\dfrac{9x^2-6x+1}{(3x-1)(x+2)^2}+\dfrac{2x^2+5x+2}{(3x-1)(x+2)^2}$

$=\dfrac{9x^2-6x+1+2x^2-5x+2}{(3x-1)(x+2)^2}$

$=\dfrac{11x^2-x+3}{(3x-1)(x+2)^2}$

53. $\dfrac{3p}{p^2-2pq-24q^2}-\dfrac{2q}{p^2-3pq-18q^2}$

$=\dfrac{3p}{(p-6q)(p+4q)}\cdot\dfrac{(p+3q)}{(p+3q)}$

$\qquad-\dfrac{2q}{(p-6q)(p+3q)}\cdot\dfrac{(p+4q)}{(p+4q)}$

$=\dfrac{3p(p+3q)-2q(p+4q)}{(p-6q)(p+4q)(p+3q)}$

$=\dfrac{3p^2+7pq-8q^2}{(p-6q)(p+4q)(p+3q)}$

55. $\dfrac{x-1}{6x^2-24x}+\dfrac{5}{3x^3-6x^2-24x}$

$=\dfrac{x-1}{6x(x-4)}+\dfrac{5}{3x(x^2-2x-8)}$

$=\dfrac{x-1}{6x(x-4)}+\dfrac{5}{3x(x-4)(x+2)}$

$=\left(\dfrac{x-1}{6x(x-4)}\right)\left(\dfrac{x+2}{x+2}\right)$

$\quad+\left(\dfrac{5}{3x(x-4)(x+2)}\right)\left(\dfrac{2}{2}\right)$

$$= \frac{x^2 + x - 2}{6x(x-4)(x+2)} + \frac{10}{6x(x-4)(x+2)}$$

$$= \frac{x^2 + x + 8}{6x(x-4)(x+2)}$$

57. $\left(\dfrac{2}{x^2 - 4} + \dfrac{3}{x+2} \right) - \dfrac{1}{2x-4}$

$$= \left(\frac{2}{(x+2)(x-2)} + \frac{3}{x+2} \right) - \frac{1}{2(x-2)}$$

$$= \left(\frac{2}{(x+2)(x-2)} + \left(\frac{3}{x+2} \right)\left(\frac{x-2}{x-2} \right) \right) - \frac{1}{2(x-2)}$$

$$= \left(\frac{2}{(x+2)(x-2)} + \frac{3x-6}{(x+2)(x-2)} \right) - \frac{1}{2(x-2)}$$

$$\frac{3x-4}{(x+2)(x-2)} - \frac{1}{2(x-2)}$$

$$= \left(\frac{3x-4}{(x+2)(x-2)} \right)\left(\frac{2}{2} \right) - \left(\frac{1}{2(x-2)} \right)\left(\frac{x+2}{x+2} \right)$$

$$= \frac{6x-8}{2(x+2)(x-2)} - \frac{x+2}{2(x+2)(x-2)}$$

$$= \frac{5x-10}{2(x+2)(x-2)}$$

$$= \frac{5(x-2)}{2(x+2)(x-2)}$$

$$= \frac{5}{2(x+2)}$$

59. $\dfrac{3}{t+1} - \left(\dfrac{2t-3}{t^2 + 6t + 5} + \dfrac{2}{t+5} \right)$

$$= \frac{3}{t+1} - \left(\frac{2t-3}{(t+5)(t+1)} + \frac{2}{t+5} \right)$$

$$= \frac{3}{t+1} - \left(\frac{2t-3}{(t+5)(t+1)} + \left(\frac{2}{t+5} \right)\left(\frac{t+1}{t+1} \right) \right)$$

$$= \frac{3}{t+1} - \left(\frac{2t-3}{(t+5)(t+1)} + \frac{2t+2}{(t+5)(t+1)} \right)$$

$$= \frac{3}{t+1} - \frac{4t-1}{(t+5)(t+1)}$$

$$= \left(\frac{3}{t+1} \right)\left(\frac{t+5}{t+5} \right) - \frac{4t-1}{(t+5)(t+1)}$$

$$= \frac{3t+15}{(t+1)(t+5)} - \frac{4t-1}{(t+1)(t+5)}$$

$$= \frac{3t+15-4t+1}{(t+1)(t+5)}$$

$$= \frac{-t+16}{(t+1)(t+5)}$$

61. $f(x) + g(x) = \dfrac{x+3}{x-4} + \dfrac{x+4}{x-3}$

$$= \left(\frac{x+3}{x-4} \right)\left(\frac{x-3}{x-3} \right) + \left(\frac{x+4}{x-3} \right)\left(\frac{x-4}{x-4} \right)$$

$$= \frac{x^2 - 9}{(x-4)(x+3)} + \frac{x^2 - 16}{(x-4)(x-3)}$$

$$= \frac{2x^2 - 25}{(x-4)(x-3)}$$

63. $g(x) - f(x) = \dfrac{x+4}{x-3} - \dfrac{x+3}{x-4}$

$$= \left(\frac{x+4}{x-3} \right)\left(\frac{x-4}{x-4} \right) - \left(\frac{x+3}{x-4} \right)\left(\frac{x-3}{x-3} \right)$$

$$= \frac{x^2 - 16}{(x-3)(x-4)} - \frac{x^2 - 9}{(x-3)(x-4)}$$

$$= \frac{x^2 - 16 - x^2 + 9}{(x-3)(x-4)}$$

$$= \frac{-7}{(x-3)(x-4)}$$

65. $f(x) - g(x) = \dfrac{x-2}{x^2 - 2x - 8} - \dfrac{x+1}{3x+6}$

$$= \frac{x-2}{(x-4)(x+2)} - \frac{x+1}{3(x+2)}$$

$$-\left(\frac{x-2}{(x-4)(x+2)} \right)\left(\frac{3}{3} \right) - \left(\frac{x+1}{3(x+2)} \right)\left(\frac{x-4}{x-4} \right)$$

$$= \frac{3x-6}{3(x-4)(x+2)} - \frac{x^2 - 3x - 4}{3(x-4)(x+2)}$$

$$= \frac{3x-6-x^2+3x+4}{3(x-4)(x+2)}$$

$$= \frac{-x^2 + 6x - 2}{3(x-4)(x+2)}$$

67. The student did not multiply each expression by "1". The expression $\dfrac{2}{x+1}$ should have been multiplied by $\dfrac{x+2}{x+2}$ not $\dfrac{1}{x+2}$ and the expression $\dfrac{3}{x+2}$ should have been multiplied by $\dfrac{x+1}{x+1}$ not $\dfrac{1}{x+1}$.

69. The student did not subtract the entire numerator in the second expression. The student only subtracted $5x$ and not 1. The correct addition is below:

$$\frac{9x}{x-3} - \frac{5x+1}{x-3} = \frac{9x - 5x - 1}{x-3}$$
$$= \frac{4x-1}{x-3}$$

71. Written response

73.
$$\left(f+g\right)(x) = \left(6x^2 - 4x + 3\right) + \left(2x^2 - 7x - 5\right)$$
$$= 6x^2 - 4x + 3 + 2x^2 - 7x - 5$$
$$= 8x^2 - 11x - 2$$
$$\left(f-g\right)(x) = \left(6x^2 - 4x + 3\right) - \left(2x^2 - 7x - 5\right)$$
$$= 6x^2 - 4x + 3 - 2x^2 + 7x + 5$$
$$= 4x^2 + 3x + 8$$

75.
$$\left(f+g\right)(x) = \left[2\left(5\right)^x\right] + \left[-3\left(5\right)^x\right]$$
$$= 2\left(5\right)^x - 3\left(5\right)^x$$
$$= \left(2-3\right)\cdot\left(5\right)^x$$
$$= -\left(5\right)^x$$
$$\left(f-g\right)(x) = \left[2\left(5\right)^x\right] - \left[-3\left(5\right)^x\right]$$
$$= 2\left(5\right)^x + 3\left(5\right)^x$$
$$= \left(2+3\right)\cdot\left(5\right)^x$$
$$= 5\cdot\left(5\right)^x$$
$$= 5^1 \cdot 5^x$$
$$= 5^{x+1}$$

77.
$$\frac{4x+5}{x+2} + \left(\frac{3x+15}{x^2-4} \cdot \frac{x^2-2x}{x^2+7x+10}\right)$$
$$= \frac{4x+5}{x+2} + \left(\frac{3(x+5)}{(x+2)(x-2)} \cdot \frac{x(x-2)}{(x+5)(x+2)}\right)$$
$$= \frac{4x+5}{x+2} + \frac{3x}{(x+2)^2}$$
$$= \left(\frac{4x+5}{x+2}\right)\left(\frac{x+2}{x+2}\right) + \frac{3x}{(x+2)^2}$$
$$= \frac{4x^2 + 13x + 10}{(x+2)^2} + \frac{3x}{(x+2)^2}$$
$$= \frac{4x^2 + 16x + 10}{(x+2)^2}$$
$$= \frac{2(2x^2 + 8x + 5)}{(x+2)^2}$$

79.
$$\frac{5x+5}{3x+6} \cdot \left(\frac{x^2+4x}{x^2+2x+1} + \frac{4}{x^2+2x+1}\right)$$
$$= \frac{5(x+1)}{3(x+2)} \cdot \left(\frac{x^2+4x+4}{x^2+2x+1}\right)$$
$$= \frac{5(x+1)}{3(x+2)} \cdot \frac{(x+2)(x+2)}{(x+1)(x+1)}$$
$$= \frac{5(x+2)}{3(x+1)}$$

81.

This is an *exponential* function.

83.

$$5b^4 = 66$$

$$5b^4 - 66 = 0$$

$$5\left(b^4 - \frac{66}{5}\right) = 0$$

$$5\left(b^2 - \frac{\sqrt{330}}{5}\right)\cancel{\left(b^2 + \frac{\sqrt{330}}{5}\right)} = 0$$

$$b^2 - \frac{\sqrt{330}}{5} = 0$$

$$b^2 - 3.6332 \approx 0$$

$$b^2 \approx 3.6332$$

$$b \approx \pm\sqrt{3.6332}$$

$$b \approx \pm 1.9061$$

This is a polynomial equation in one variable.

85.

$$95 = a \cdot b^3$$

$$a = \frac{95}{b^3}$$

$$2 = \left(\frac{95}{b^3}\right) \cdot b^7$$

$$2 = 95b^4$$

$$b^4 \approx 0.0211$$

$$b \approx \sqrt[4]{0.0211} \approx 0.38$$

$$a \approx \frac{95}{0.3809^3} \approx 1719.06$$

$$y \approx 1718.87(0.38)^x$$

An exponential function.

Homework 8.4

1.

$$\frac{\dfrac{2}{x}}{\dfrac{3}{x}} = \frac{2}{x} \div \frac{3}{x}$$

$$= \frac{2}{x} \cdot \frac{x}{3}$$

$$= \frac{2}{3}$$

3.

$$\frac{\dfrac{7}{x^2}}{\dfrac{21}{x^5}} = \frac{7}{x^2} \div \frac{21}{x^5}$$

$$= \frac{7}{x^2} \cdot \frac{x^5}{21}$$

$$= \frac{x^3}{3}$$

5.

$$\frac{\dfrac{4a^2}{5b}}{\dfrac{6a}{15b^3}} = \frac{4a^2}{5b} \div \frac{6a}{15b^3}$$

$$= \frac{4a^2}{5b} \cdot \frac{15b^3}{6a}$$

$$= \frac{60a^2b^3}{30ab}$$

$$= 2ab^2$$

7.

$$\frac{\dfrac{3x-3}{2x+10}}{\dfrac{6x^2-6}{4x+20}} = \frac{3x-3}{2x+10} \div \frac{6x^2-6}{4x+20}$$

$$= \frac{3x-3}{2x+10} \cdot \frac{4x+20}{6x^2-6}$$

$$= \frac{3(x-1)}{2(x+5)} \cdot \frac{4(x+5)}{6(x^2-1)}$$

$$= \frac{12(x-1)(x+5)}{12(x+5)(x-1)(x+1)}$$

$$= \frac{1}{x+1}$$

9.

$$\frac{\dfrac{x^2-49}{3x^2-9x}}{\dfrac{x^2-5x-14}{7x-21}} = \frac{x^2-49}{3x^2-9x} \cdot \frac{7x-21}{x^2-5x-14}$$

$$= \frac{(x+7)(x-7)}{3x(x-3)} \cdot \frac{7(x-3)}{(x-7)(x+2)}$$

$$= \frac{7(x+7)}{3x(x+2)}$$

11.
$$\frac{\dfrac{25x^2-4}{9x^2-16}}{\dfrac{25x^2-20x+4}{9x^2-24x+16}} = \frac{25x^2-4}{9x^2-16} \div \frac{25x^2-20x+4}{9x^2-24x+16}$$

$$= \frac{25x^2-4}{9x^2-16} \cdot \frac{9x^2-24x+16}{25x^2-20x+4}$$

$$= \frac{(5x-2)(5x+2)}{(3x-4)(3x+4)} \cdot \frac{(3x-4)(3x-4)}{(5x-2)(5x-2)}$$

$$= \frac{(5x+2)(3x-4)}{(3x+4)(5x-2)}$$

13.
$$\frac{\dfrac{2}{x^3}-\dfrac{3}{x}}{\dfrac{5}{x^3}+\dfrac{4}{x^2}} = \frac{\left(\dfrac{2}{x^3}-\dfrac{3}{x}\right)}{\left(\dfrac{5}{x^3}+\dfrac{4}{x^2}\right)} \cdot \frac{x^3}{x^3}$$

$$= \frac{2-3x^2}{5+4x}$$

15.
$$\frac{4+\dfrac{3}{x}}{\dfrac{2}{x}-3} = \frac{\left(4+\dfrac{3}{x}\right)}{\left(\dfrac{2}{x}-3\right)} \cdot \frac{x}{x}$$

$$= \frac{4x+3}{2-3x}$$

17.
$$\frac{\dfrac{5}{2x^3}-4}{\dfrac{1}{6x^2}-3} = \frac{\left(\dfrac{5}{2x^3}-4\right)}{\left(\dfrac{1}{6x^2}-3\right)} \cdot \frac{6x^3}{6x^3}$$

$$= \frac{3(5-8x^3)}{1-18x^3}$$

19.
$$\frac{\dfrac{a^2}{b}-b}{\dfrac{1}{b}-\dfrac{1}{a}} = \frac{\left(\dfrac{a^2}{b}-b\right)}{\left(\dfrac{1}{b}-\dfrac{1}{a}\right)} \cdot \frac{ab}{ab}$$

$$= \frac{a^3-ab^2}{a-b}$$

$$= \frac{a\left(a^2-b^2\right)}{a-b}$$

$$= \frac{a(a-b)(a+b)}{(a-b)}$$

$$= a(a+b)$$

21.
$$\frac{\dfrac{1}{x}-\dfrac{8}{x^2}+\dfrac{15}{x^3}}{\dfrac{1}{x}-\dfrac{5}{x^2}} = \frac{\left(\dfrac{1}{x}-\dfrac{8}{x^2}+\dfrac{15}{x^3}\right)}{\left(\dfrac{1}{x}-\dfrac{5}{x^2}\right)} \cdot \frac{x^3}{x^3}$$

$$= \frac{x^2-8x+15}{x^2-5x}$$

$$= \frac{(x-5)(x-3)}{x(x-5)}$$

$$= \frac{x-3}{x}$$

23.
$$\frac{\dfrac{x}{x-4}-\dfrac{2x}{x+1}}{\dfrac{x}{x+1}-\dfrac{2x}{x-4}} = \frac{\left(\dfrac{x}{x-4}-\dfrac{2x}{x+1}\right)}{\left(\dfrac{x}{x+1}-\dfrac{2x}{x-4}\right)} \cdot \frac{(x-4)(x+1)}{(x-4)(x+1)}$$

$$= \frac{x(x+1)-2x(x-4)}{x(x-4)-2x(x+1)}$$

$$= \frac{x^2+x-2x^2+8x}{x^2-4x-2x^2-2x}$$

$$= \frac{-x^2+9x}{-x^2-6x}$$

$$= \frac{-x(x-9)}{-x(x+6)}$$

$$= \frac{x-9}{x+6}$$

25.
$$\frac{p+\dfrac{2}{p-4}}{p-\dfrac{3}{p-4}} = \frac{\left(p+\dfrac{2}{p-4}\right)}{\left(p-\dfrac{3}{p-4}\right)} \cdot \frac{(p-4)}{(p-4)}$$

$$= \frac{p(p-4)+2}{p(p-4)-3}$$

$$= \frac{p^2-4p+2}{p^2-4p-3}$$

27.
$$\dfrac{\dfrac{1}{x+3}-\dfrac{1}{x}}{3}=\left(\dfrac{\dfrac{1}{x+3}-\dfrac{1}{x}}{3}\right)\cdot\left(\dfrac{x(x+3)}{x(x+3)}\right)$$

$$=\dfrac{x-(x+3)}{3x(x+3)}$$

$$=\dfrac{-3}{3x(x+3)}$$

$$=\dfrac{-1}{x(x+3)}$$

29.
$$\dfrac{\dfrac{3}{a+b}-\dfrac{3}{a-b}}{2ab}$$

$$=\dfrac{\left(\dfrac{3}{a+b}-\dfrac{3}{a-b}\right)}{2ab}\cdot\dfrac{(a+b)(a-b)}{(a+b)(a-b)}$$

$$=\dfrac{3(a-b)-3(a+b)}{2ab(a+b)(a-b)}$$

$$=\dfrac{3a-3b-3a-3b}{2ab(a+b)(a-b)}$$

$$=\dfrac{-6b}{2ab(a+b)(a-b)}$$

$$=\dfrac{-3}{a(a+b)(a-b)}$$

31.
$$\dfrac{\dfrac{1}{(x+2)^2}-\dfrac{1}{x^2}}{2}=\left(\dfrac{\dfrac{1}{(x+2)^2}-\dfrac{1}{x^2}}{2}\right)\cdot\dfrac{x^2(x+2)^2}{x^2(x+2)^2}$$

$$=\dfrac{x^2-(x+2)^2}{2x^2(x+2)^2}$$

$$=\dfrac{x^2-(x^2+4x+4)}{2x^2(x+2)^2}$$

$$=\dfrac{-4x-4}{2x^2(x+2)^2}$$

$$=\dfrac{-4(x+1)}{2x^2(x+2)^2}$$

33.
$$\dfrac{\dfrac{6}{2x-8}+\dfrac{10}{x^2-4x}}{\dfrac{1}{x^2-x-12}-\dfrac{2}{x^2-16}}$$

$$=\dfrac{\dfrac{6}{2(x-4)}+\dfrac{10}{x(x-4)}}{\dfrac{1}{(x-4)(x+3)}-\dfrac{2}{(x-4)(x+4)}}$$

$$=\dfrac{\dfrac{6}{2(x-4)}\cdot\dfrac{x}{x}+\dfrac{10}{x(x-4)}\cdot\dfrac{2}{2}}{\dfrac{1}{(x-4)(x+3)}\cdot\dfrac{(x+4)}{(x+4)}-\dfrac{2}{(x-4)(x+4)}\cdot\dfrac{(x+3)}{(x+3)}}$$

$$=\dfrac{\dfrac{6x+20}{2x(x-4)}}{\dfrac{x+4}{(x-4)(x+3)(x+4)}-\dfrac{2x+6}{(x-4)(x+3)(x+4)}}$$

$$=\dfrac{\dfrac{6x+20}{2x(x-4)}}{\dfrac{x+4-2x-6}{(x-4)(x+3)(x+4)}}\cdot\dfrac{2x(x-4)(x+3)(x+4)}{2x(x-4)(x+3)(x+4)}$$

$$=\dfrac{(6x+20)(x+3)(x+4)}{(-x-2)\cdot2x}$$

$$=\dfrac{2(3x+10)(x+3)(x+4)}{-2x(x+2)}$$

$$=-\dfrac{(3x+10)(x+3)(x+4)}{x(x+2)}$$

35.
$$\dfrac{\dfrac{x+7}{x^2+7x+10}-\dfrac{6}{x^2+2x}}{\dfrac{x+1}{x^2+7x+10}+\dfrac{6}{x^2+5x}}$$

$$=\dfrac{\dfrac{x+7}{(x+5)(x+2)}-\dfrac{6}{x(x+2)}}{\dfrac{x+1}{(x+5)(x+2)}+\dfrac{6}{x(x+5)}}$$

$$=\dfrac{\dfrac{x+7}{(x+5)(x+2)}\cdot\dfrac{x}{x}-\dfrac{6}{x(x+2)}\cdot\dfrac{(x+5)}{(x+5)}}{\dfrac{x+1}{(x+5)(x+2)}\cdot\dfrac{x}{x}+\dfrac{6}{x(x+5)}\cdot\dfrac{(x+2)}{(x+2)}}$$

$$= \frac{\dfrac{x^2+7x}{x(x+5)(x+2)} - \dfrac{6x+30}{x(x+5)(x+2)}}{\dfrac{x^2+x}{x(x+5)(x+2)} + \dfrac{6x+12}{x(x+5)(x+2)}}$$

$$= \frac{\dfrac{x^2+7x-6x-30}{x(x+5)(x+2)}}{\dfrac{x^2+x+6x+12}{x(x+5)(x+2)}}$$

$$= \frac{\dfrac{x^2+x-30}{x(x+5)(x+2)}}{\dfrac{x^2+7x+12}{x(x+5)(x+2)}}$$

$$= \frac{x^2+x-30}{x(x+5)(x+2)} \cdot \frac{x(x+5)(x+2)}{x^2+7x+12}$$

$$= \frac{x^2+x-30}{x^2+7x+12}$$

$$= \frac{(x+6)(x-5)}{(x+3)(x+4)}$$

37.

$$\left(\frac{f}{g}\right)(x) = \frac{\dfrac{5x+10}{x^2-6x+9}}{\dfrac{4x+8}{x^2-4x+3}}$$

$$= \frac{\dfrac{5(x+2)}{(x-3)(x-3)}}{\dfrac{4(x+2)}{(x-3)(x-1)}}$$

$$= \frac{5(x+2)}{(x-3)(x-3)} \cdot \frac{(x-3)(x-1)}{4(x+2)}$$

$$= \frac{5(x-1)}{4(x-3)}$$

39.

$$\left(\frac{f}{g}\right)(x) = \frac{\left(\dfrac{x}{2}-\dfrac{2}{x}\right)}{\left(\dfrac{3}{2}+\dfrac{3}{x}\right)} \cdot \frac{2x}{2x}$$

$$= \frac{x^2-4}{3x+6}$$

$$= \frac{(x-2)(x+2)}{3(x+2)}$$

$$= \frac{x-2}{3}$$

41.

$$\left(\frac{f}{g}\right)(x) = \frac{\dfrac{2x}{x^2-25}+\dfrac{x+5}{x-5}}{\dfrac{x-5}{x+5}+\dfrac{3x}{x^2-25}}$$

$$= \frac{\left(\dfrac{2x}{(x-5)(x+5)}+\dfrac{x+5}{x-5}\right)}{\left(\dfrac{x-5}{x+5}+\dfrac{3x}{(x-5)(x+5)}\right)} \cdot \frac{(x-5)(x+5)}{(x-5)(x+5)}$$

$$= \frac{2x+(x+5)(x+5)}{(x-5)(x-5)+3x}$$

$$= \frac{2x+x^2+10x+25}{x^2-10x+25+3x}$$

$$= \frac{x^2+12x+25}{x^2-7x+25}$$

43. The student must add the two expressions in the parentheses before taking the reciprocals. The correct simplification is below:

$$\frac{x}{\dfrac{1}{x}+\dfrac{1}{2}} = x \div \left(\frac{1}{x}+\frac{1}{2}\right)$$

$$= x \div \left(\frac{1}{x} \cdot \frac{2}{2}+\frac{1}{2} \cdot \frac{x}{x}\right)$$

$$= x \div \left(\frac{2}{2x}+\frac{x}{2x}\right)$$

$$= x \div \frac{2+x}{2x}$$

$$= x \cdot \frac{2x}{2+x}$$

$$= \frac{2x^2}{x+2}$$

45. Method 1

$$\frac{\dfrac{6}{x^2}-\dfrac{5}{x}}{\dfrac{2}{x^2}+\dfrac{3}{2x}} = \frac{\dfrac{6}{x^2}-\dfrac{5}{x} \cdot \dfrac{x}{x}}{\dfrac{2}{x^2} \cdot \dfrac{2}{2}+\dfrac{3}{2x} \cdot \dfrac{x}{x}} = \frac{\dfrac{6}{x^2}-\dfrac{5x}{x^2}}{\dfrac{4}{2x^2}+\dfrac{3x}{2x^2}}$$

$$= \frac{\dfrac{6-5x}{x^2}}{\dfrac{4+3x}{2x^2}} = \frac{6-5x}{x^2} \div \frac{4+3x}{2x^2} = \frac{6-5x}{x^2} \cdot \frac{2x^2}{4+3x}$$

$$= \frac{2(6-5x)}{4+3x}$$

Method 2

$$\frac{\dfrac{6}{x^2}-\dfrac{5}{x}}{\dfrac{2}{x^2}+\dfrac{3}{2x}}=\frac{\left(\dfrac{6}{x^2}-\dfrac{5}{x}\right)}{\left(\dfrac{2}{x^2}+\dfrac{3}{2x}\right)}\cdot\frac{2x^2}{2x^2}=\frac{12-10x}{4+3x}$$

$$=\frac{2(6-5x)}{4+3x}$$

Written responses may vary.

47. A complex rational expression is a rational expression that has rational expressions in the numerator and in the denominator. Written examples may vary.

49. $\dfrac{8x^{-2}y^5}{6x^{-7}y^8}=\dfrac{4x^{-2-(-7)}}{3y^{8-5}}$

$$=\frac{4x^5}{3y^3}$$

51.

$$\frac{x^{-1}+x^{-2}}{x^{-2}-x^{-1}}=\frac{\dfrac{1}{x}+\dfrac{1}{x^2}}{\dfrac{1}{x^2}-\dfrac{1}{x}}$$

$$=\frac{\left(\dfrac{1}{x}+\dfrac{1}{x^2}\right)\cdot x^2}{\left(\dfrac{1}{x^2}-\dfrac{1}{x}\right)\cdot x^2}$$

$$=\frac{x+1}{1-x}$$

53. $\dfrac{2b^{-2}-4b}{8b^{-1}-6b}\cdot\dfrac{b^2}{b^2}=\dfrac{2-4b^3}{8b-6b^3}$

$$=\frac{2\left(1-2b^3\right)}{2b\left(4-3b^3\right)}$$

$$=\frac{1-2b^3}{b\left(4-3b^3\right)}$$

55. a. $H_e=\dfrac{1}{\dfrac{1}{\dfrac{1}{H_p}+\dfrac{1}{H_b}}}$

$$=\frac{1}{\dfrac{H_b+H_p}{H_bH_p}}$$

$$=\frac{H_bH_p}{H_b+H_p}$$

b. $H_e=\dfrac{H_bH_p}{H_b+H_p}$

$$=\frac{(623)(87.4)}{623+87.4}$$

$$\approx 76.6 \text{ days}$$

57. $\dfrac{x-2}{x^2-2x-24}+\dfrac{x+4}{x^2-8x+12}=$

$$=\frac{x-2}{(x+4)(x-6)}+\frac{x+4}{(x-6)(x-2)}$$

$$=\frac{(x-2)}{(x+4)(x-6)}\cdot\frac{(x-2)}{(x-2)}$$

$$\qquad+\frac{(x+4)}{(x-6)(x-2)}\cdot\frac{(x+4)}{(x+4)}$$

$$=\frac{\left(x^2-4x+4\right)+\left(x^2+8x+16\right)}{(x+4)(x-6)(x-2)}$$

$$=\frac{2x^2+4x+20}{(x+4)(x-6)(x-2)}$$

59. $\dfrac{x-2}{x^2-2x-24}\cdot\dfrac{x+4}{x^2-8x+12}$

$$=\frac{(x-2)}{(x-6)(x+4)}\cdot\frac{(x+4)}{(x-6)(x-2)}$$

$$=\frac{1}{(x-6)^2}$$

61. $x^2-2x-24=0$

$$x-6=0 \qquad x+4=0$$
$$x=6 \qquad\quad x=-4$$

The domain is all real numbers except 6 and –4.

Homework 8.5

1.
$$\frac{7}{x} = \frac{2}{x} + 1$$
$$x \cdot \frac{7}{x} = x\left(\frac{2}{x} + 1\right)$$
$$7 = 2 + x$$
$$5 = x$$

3.
$$12x \cdot \left(\frac{7}{4x} - \frac{5}{6}\right) = \frac{1}{12x} \cdot 12x$$
$$21 - 10x = 1$$
$$-10x = -20$$
$$x = 2$$

5.
$$\frac{x-2}{x-7} = \frac{5}{x-7}$$
$$(x-7) \cdot \frac{x-2}{x-7} = \frac{5}{x-7} \cdot (x-7)$$
$$x - 2 = 5$$
$$x = 7$$
$x = 7$ makes each denominator 0. This equation has no solution.

7.
$$\frac{5}{4p-7} = \frac{2}{2p+3}$$
$$5(2p+3) = 2(4p-7)$$
$$10p + 15 = 8p - 14$$
$$2p = -29$$
$$p = -\frac{29}{2}$$
Check:
$$\frac{5}{4\left(-\frac{29}{2}\right)-7} = \frac{2}{2\left(-\frac{29}{2}\right)+3}$$
$$\frac{5}{-58-7} = \frac{2}{-29+3}$$
$$\frac{5}{-65} = \frac{2}{-26}$$
$$-\frac{1}{13} = -\frac{1}{13}$$
The solution is $-\frac{29}{2}$.

9.
$$\frac{3}{x+1} + \frac{2}{5} = 1$$
$$5(x+1)\left(\frac{3}{x+1} + \frac{2}{5}\right) = 5(x+1) \cdot 1$$
$$15 + 2(x+1) = 5x + 5$$
$$15 + 2x + 2 = 5x + 5$$
$$2x + 17 = 5x + 5$$
$$12 = 3x$$
$$4 = x$$
Check:
$$\frac{3}{(4)+1} + \frac{2}{5} \overset{?}{=} 1$$
$$1 = 1$$
The solution is 4.

11.
$$\frac{1}{x-2} + \frac{1}{x+2} = \frac{4}{x^2-4}$$
$$\frac{1}{x-2} + \frac{1}{x+2} = \frac{4}{(x-2)(x+2)}$$
$$(x-2)(x+2)\left(\frac{1}{x-2} + \frac{1}{x+2}\right) = (x-2)(x+2)\frac{4}{(x-2)(x+2)}$$
$$x + 2 + x - 2 = 4$$
$$2x = 4$$
$$x = 2$$
Check:
$$\frac{1}{(2)-2} + \frac{1}{(2)+2} \overset{?}{=} \frac{4}{(2)^2-4}$$
$$\frac{1}{0} + \frac{1}{4} = \frac{4}{0}$$
Division by zero is undefined. Empty solution set.

13.
$$2 + \frac{4}{k-2} = \frac{8}{k^2-2k}$$
$$2 + \frac{4}{k-2} = \frac{8}{k(k-2)}$$
$$k(k-2)\left(2 + \frac{4}{k-2}\right) = k(k-2)\frac{8}{k(k-2)}$$
$$2k(k-2) + 4k = 8$$
$$2k^2 - 4k + 4k = 8$$
$$2k^2 = 8$$
$$k^2 = 4$$
$$k = \pm 2$$

Check $x = 2$:

$$2 + \frac{4}{(2)-2} \overset{?}{=} \frac{8}{(2)^2 - 2(2)}$$

$$4 = \frac{8}{0}$$

Division by 0 is undefined.
Check $k = -2$:

$$2 + \frac{4}{(-2)-2} \overset{?}{=} \frac{8}{(-2)^2 - 2(-2)}$$

$$1 = 1$$

The solution is $k = -2$.

15. $\dfrac{-48}{x^2 - 2x - 15} - \dfrac{6}{x+3} = \dfrac{7}{x-5}$

$$(x-5)(x+3)$$
$$\cdot \left(\frac{-48}{(x-5)(x+3)} - \frac{6}{x+3} \right)$$
$$= \frac{7}{x-5} \cdot (x-5)(x+3)$$

$$-48 - 6(x-5) = 7(x+3)$$
$$-48 - 6x + 30 = 7x + 21$$
$$-6x - 18 = 7x + 21$$
$$-13x = 39$$
$$x = -3$$

Check:
When $x = -3$, it makes the denominator zero, which is undefined. There is no solution.

17. $\dfrac{x^2 - 23}{2x^2 - 5x - 3} + \dfrac{2}{x-3} = \dfrac{-1}{2x+1}$

$$(2x+1)(x-3) \left(\frac{(x^2 - 23)}{(2x+1)(x-3)} + \frac{2}{x-3} \right) =$$

$$\frac{-1(2x+1)(x-3)}{2x+1}$$

$$x^2 - 23 + 2(2x+1) = -(x-3)$$
$$x^2 - 23 + 4x + 2 = -x + 3$$
$$x^2 + 5x - 24 = 0$$
$$(x+8)(x-3) = 0$$
$$x + 8 = 0 \qquad x - 3 = 0$$
$$x = -8 \qquad x = 3$$

Check:
The solution $x = 3$ is not a solution because it gives a zero in the denominator, which is undefined. The solution is $x = -8$.

19.

$$\frac{w+7}{w^2 - 9} = \frac{-w+2}{w-3}$$

$$(w-3)(w+3)\frac{w+7}{(w-3)(w+3)} = \frac{(w-3)(w+3)(-w+2)}{w-3}$$

$$w + 7 = (w+3)(-w+2)$$
$$w + 7 = -w^2 - 3w + 2w + 6$$
$$w^2 + 2w + 1 = 0$$
$$(w+1)^2 = 0$$
$$w = -1$$

Check:

$$\frac{(-1)+7}{(-1)^2 - 9} \overset{?}{=} \frac{-(-1)+2}{(-1)-3}$$

$$\frac{6}{-8} \overset{?}{=} \frac{3}{-4}$$

$$-\frac{3}{4} = -\frac{3}{4}$$

The solution is $w = -1$.

21. $x^2 \cdot \left(3 + \dfrac{2}{x} \right) = \dfrac{4}{x^2} \cdot x^2$

$$3x^2 + 2x = 4$$
$$3x^2 + 2x - 4 = 0$$

$$x = \frac{-2 \pm \sqrt{2^2 - 4(3)(-4)}}{2(3)}$$

$$x = \frac{-2 \pm \sqrt{4 + 48}}{6}$$

$$= \frac{-2 \pm 2\sqrt{13}}{6}$$

$$= \frac{-1 \pm \sqrt{13}}{3}$$

None of the solutions will make the denominators equal to zero. The solutions are $\dfrac{-1 \pm \sqrt{13}}{3}$.

23. $\dfrac{5}{r^2 - 3r + 2} - \dfrac{1}{r-2} = \dfrac{r+6}{3r-3}$

$$\frac{5}{(r-2)(r-1)} - \frac{1}{r-2} = \frac{r+6}{3(r-1)}$$

$$3(r-2)(r-1)\left(\frac{5}{(r-2)(r-1)}-\frac{1}{r-2}\right)$$

$$=3(r-2)(r-1)\frac{r+6}{3(r-1)}$$

$$15-3(r-1)=(r-2)(r=6)$$

$$15-3r+3=r^2+4r-12$$

$$18-3r=r^2+4r-12$$

$$0=r^2+7r-30$$

$$0=(r+10)(r-3)$$

The solutions are 3 and −10.

25.
$$\frac{2x}{x+1}-\frac{3}{2}=\frac{-2}{x+2}$$

$$2(x+1)(x+2)\left(\frac{2x}{x+1}-\frac{3}{2}\right)=\frac{2(x+1)(x+2)(-2)}{x+2}$$

$$4x(x+2)-3(x+2)(x+1)=-4(x+1)$$

$$4x^2+8x-3\left(x^2+3x+2\right)=-4x-4$$

$$4x^2+8x-3x^2-9x-6=-4x-4$$

$$x^2+3x-2=0$$

$$x=\frac{-(3)\pm\sqrt{(3)^2-4(1)(-2)}}{2(1)}=$$

None of the solutions will make any of the

denominators zero. The solutions are $\dfrac{-3\pm\sqrt{17}}{2}$.

27.
$$\frac{x-4}{x^2-7x+12}-\frac{x+2}{x-3}=0$$

$$\frac{x-4}{x^2-7x+12}=\frac{x+2}{x-3}$$

$$\frac{(x-4)(x-3)(x-4)}{(x-4)(x-3)}=\frac{(x+2)(x-4)(x-3)}{x-3}$$

$$x-4=(x+2)(x-4)$$

$$(x-4)-(x+2)(x-4)=0$$

$$(x-4)\left[1-(x+2)\right]=0$$

$$(x-4)(-x-1)=0$$

$$x=4 \qquad x=-1$$

Check:

$$\frac{4-4}{4^2-7(4)+12}-\frac{4+2}{4-3}\overset{?}{=}0$$

$$\frac{0}{0}-6\neq0$$

Division by zero is not defined, so $x=4$ is not a solution.

$$\frac{(-1)-4}{(-1)^2-7(-1)+12}-\frac{(-1)+2}{(-1)-3}\overset{?}{=}0$$

$$\frac{-5}{1+7+12}-\frac{1}{-4}\overset{?}{=}0$$

$$\frac{-5}{20}+\frac{1}{4}\overset{?}{=}0$$

$$-\frac{1}{4}+\frac{1}{4}\overset{?}{=}0$$

$$0=0$$

The solution is $x=-1$.

29.
$$\frac{t}{t-3}=2-\frac{5}{3-t}$$

$$(t-3)\cdot\frac{t}{t-3}=\left(2+\frac{5}{t-3}\right)\cdot(t-3)$$

$$t=2(t-3)+5$$

$$t=2t-6+5$$

$$-t=1$$

$$t=-1$$

31.
$$\frac{12}{9-x^2}+\frac{3}{x+3}=\frac{-2}{x-3}$$

$$\frac{12}{(3-x)(3+x)}+\frac{3}{3+x}=\frac{2}{3-x}$$

$$(3-x)(3+x)\cdot\left(\frac{12}{(3-x)(3+x)}+\frac{3}{3+x}\right)$$

$$=\frac{2}{3-x}\cdot(3-x)(3+x)$$

$$12+3(3-x)=2(3+x)$$

$$12+9-3x=6+2x$$

$$15=5x$$

$$3=x$$

Check:

$$\frac{12}{9-(3)^2}+\frac{3}{(3)+3}\overset{?}{=}\frac{-2}{(3)-3}$$

$$\frac{12}{0}+\frac{1}{2}=\frac{-2}{0}$$

Division be zero is undefined. There is no solution.

33.

$$\frac{x+2}{x-3} - \frac{x-3}{x+2} = \frac{5x}{x^2-x-6}$$

$$(x-3)(x+2)\left(\frac{x+2}{x-3} - \frac{x-3}{x+2}\right) = \frac{(x-3)(x+2)5x}{(x-3)(x+2)}$$

$$(x+2)^2 - (x-3)^2 = 5x$$

$$x^2 + 4x + 4 - \left(x^2 - 6x + 9\right) = 5x$$

$$10x - 5 = 5x$$

$$5x = 5$$

$$x = 1$$

Check:

$$\frac{1+2}{1-3} - \frac{1-3}{1+2} \overset{?}{=} \frac{5(1)}{(1)^2-(1)-6}$$

$$\frac{3}{-2} - \frac{-2}{3} \overset{?}{=} \frac{5}{-6}$$

$$-\frac{5}{6} = -\frac{5}{6}$$

The solution is $x = 1$.

35.

$$\frac{2y}{y-2} - \frac{2y-5}{y^2-7y+10} = \frac{-4}{y-5}$$

$$(y-2)(y-5) \cdot \left(\frac{2y}{y-2} - \frac{2y-5}{(y-2)(y-5)}\right) = \frac{-4}{y-5} \cdot (y-2)(y-5)$$

$$2y(y-5) - (2y-5) = -4(y-2)$$

$$2y^2 - 10y - 2y + 5 = -4y + 8$$

$$2y^2 - 8y - 3 = 0$$

$$y = \frac{-(-8) \pm \sqrt{(-8)^2 - 4(2)(-3)}}{2(2)}$$

$$= \frac{8 \pm \sqrt{88}}{4}$$

$$= \frac{8 \pm 2\sqrt{22}}{4}$$

$$= \frac{4 \pm \sqrt{22}}{2}$$

None of these solutions give a zero in a denominator of the original equation. The solutions are $\dfrac{4 \pm \sqrt{22}}{2}$.

37.

$$\frac{x-2}{x^2-2x-3} + \frac{x+5}{x^2-1} = \frac{x+3}{x^2-4x+3}$$

$$(x-3)(x-1)(x+1) \cdot \left(\frac{x-2}{(x-3)(x+1)} + \frac{x+5}{(x-1)(x+1)}\right)$$

$$= \frac{(x+3)(x-3)(x-1)(x+1)}{(x-3)(x-1)}$$

$$(x-2)(x-1) + (x+5)(x-3) = (x+3)(x+1)$$

$$x^2 - 3x + 2 + x^2 + 2x - 15 = x^2 + 4x + 3$$

$$x^2 - 5x - 16 = 0$$

$$x = \frac{-(-5) \pm \sqrt{(-5)^2 - 4(1)(-16)}}{2(1)}$$

$$= \frac{5 \pm \sqrt{89}}{2}$$

None of these solutions give a zero in a denominator. The solutions are $\dfrac{5 \pm \sqrt{89}}{2}$.

39.

$$\frac{5}{x} - \frac{2}{x^2} = 4$$

$$x^2 \cdot \left(\frac{5}{x} - \frac{2}{x^2}\right) = 4 \cdot x^2$$

$$5x - 2 = 4x^2$$

$$4x^2 - 5x + 2 = 0$$

$$x = \frac{-(-5) \pm \sqrt{(-5)^2 - 4(4)(2)}}{2(4)}$$

$$= \frac{5 \pm \sqrt{-7}}{8}$$

$$= \frac{5 \pm i\sqrt{7}}{8}$$

The complex solutions are $\dfrac{5 \pm i\sqrt{7}}{8}$.

41.

$$\frac{2}{t-5} - \frac{3t}{t+5} = \frac{35}{t^2 - 25}$$

$$(t-5)(t+5) \cdot \left(\frac{2}{t-5} - \frac{3t}{t+5} \right) = \frac{35(t-5)(t+5)}{(t-5)(t+5)}$$

$$2(t+5) - 3t(t-5) = 35$$

$$2t + 10 - 3t^2 + 15t = 35$$

$$3t^2 - 17t + 25 = 0$$

$$t = \frac{-(-17) \pm \sqrt{(-17)^2 - 4(3)(25)}}{2(3)}$$

$$= \frac{17 \pm \sqrt{-11}}{6}$$

$$= \frac{17 \pm i\sqrt{11}}{6}$$

The solutions are $\dfrac{17 \pm i\sqrt{11}}{6}$.

43.

$$\frac{x-1}{3x-12} + \frac{-x+1}{x-5} = \frac{4x}{x^2 - 9x + 20}$$

$$3(x-4)(x-5) \cdot \left(\frac{x-1}{3(x-4)} + \frac{-x+1}{x-5} \right) = \frac{3(x-4)(x-5)4x}{(x-4)(x-5)}$$

$$(x-5)(x-1) + 3(x-4)(-x+1) = 12x$$

$$x^2 - 6x + 5 + 3(-x^2 + 5x - 4) = 12x$$

$$x^2 - 6x + 5 - 3x^2 + 15x - 12 = 12x$$

$$-2x^2 - 3x - 7 = 0$$

$$x = \frac{-(-3) \pm \sqrt{(-3)^2 - 4(-2)(-7)}}{2(-2)}$$

$$= \frac{3 \pm \sqrt{-47}}{-4} = \frac{3 \pm i\sqrt{47}}{-4} = \frac{-3 \pm i\sqrt{4}}{4}$$

The solutions are $\dfrac{-3 \pm i\sqrt{47}}{4}$.

45.

$$4 = \frac{3}{x-5}$$

$$(x-5)4 = (x-5)\frac{3}{x-5}$$

$$4x - 20 = 3$$

$$4x = 23$$

$$x = \frac{23}{4}$$

Check:

$$4 \overset{?}{=} \frac{3}{\frac{23}{4} - 5}$$

$$4 = 4$$

The value of x is $\dfrac{23}{4}$.

47.

$$-1 = \frac{5}{x-1} + \frac{3}{x+1}$$

$$(x-1)(x+1) \cdot (-1) = (x-1)(x+1)\left(\frac{5}{x-1} + \frac{3}{x+1} \right)$$

$$-1(x^2 - 1) = 5(x+1) + 3(x-1)$$

$$-x^2 + 1 = 5x + 5 + 3x - 3$$

$$-x^2 + 1 = 8x + 2$$

$$0 = x^2 + 8x + 1$$

$$x = \frac{-8 \pm \sqrt{64 - 4(1)(1)}}{2}$$

$$= \frac{-8 \pm \sqrt{60}}{2}$$

$$= \frac{-8 \pm \sqrt{4 \cdot 15}}{2}$$

$$= \frac{-8 \pm 2\sqrt{15}}{2}$$

$$= -4 \pm \sqrt{15}$$

Using a calculator, $-4 \pm \sqrt{15}$ are the solutions.

49.

$$0 = \frac{x-1}{x-5} - \frac{x+2}{x+3}$$

$$(x-5)(x+3) \cdot 0 = (x-5)(x+3)\left(\frac{x-1}{x-5} - \frac{x+2}{x+3} \right)$$

$$0 = (x+3)(x-1) - (x-5)(x+2)$$

$$0 = x^2 + 2x - 3 - (x^2 - 3x - 10)$$

$$0 = x^2 + 2x - 3 - x^2 + 3x + 10$$

$$0 = 5x + 7$$

$$-7 = 5x$$

$$-\frac{7}{5} = x$$

The x-intercept is $\left(-\dfrac{7}{5}, 0 \right)$.

51.

$$F = \frac{mv^2}{r}$$

$$r \cdot F = \frac{mv^2}{r} \cdot r$$

$$\frac{Fr}{F} = \frac{mv^2}{F}$$

$$r = \frac{mv^2}{F}$$

53.

$$F = \frac{-GMm}{r^2}$$

$$r^2 \cdot F = \frac{-GMm}{r^2} \cdot r^2$$

$$\frac{r^2 F}{-Gm} = \frac{-GMm}{-Gm}$$

$$M = -\frac{r^2 F}{Gm}$$

55.

$$P = \frac{A}{1+rt}$$

$$(1+rt) \cdot P = \left(\frac{A}{1+rt}\right) \cdot (1+rt)$$

$$P + \Pr t = A$$

$$\frac{\Pr t}{\Pr} = \frac{A-P}{\Pr}$$

$$t = \frac{A-P}{\Pr}$$

57.

$$74 = \frac{4.7t^2 - 77t + 350}{0.058t^2 - 0.82t + 3.6}$$

$$74\left(0.058t^2 - 0.82t + 3.6\right) = 4.7t^2 - 77t + 350$$

$$4.292t^2 - 60.68t + 266.4 = 4.7t^2 - 77t + 350$$

$$0 = 0.408t^2 - 16.32t + 86.3$$

$$t \approx \frac{-(-16.32) \pm \sqrt{(-16.32)^2 - 4(0.408)(86.3)}}{2(0.408)}$$

$$\approx \frac{16.32 \pm \sqrt{125.5}}{0.816}$$

$$\approx \frac{16.32 \pm 11.2}{0.816} \approx 6 \text{ and } 34$$

74% of the cumulative awarded miles will be redeemed in the year 2014.

59. a.

$$P(t) = \frac{B(t)}{(N+B)(t)} \cdot 100$$

$$= \frac{100 \cdot B(t)}{(N+B)(t)}$$

$$= \frac{100\left(-0.036t^2 + 0.176t + 1.28\right)}{-0.036t^2 + 0.346t + 4.28}$$

$$= \frac{-3.6t^2 + 17.6t + 128}{-0.036t^2 + 0.346t + 4.28}$$

b.

$$P(8) = \frac{-3.6(8)^2 + 17.6(8) + 128}{-0.036(8)^2 + 0.346(8) + 4.28}$$

$$\approx 8.09$$

This means that in the year 2008, about 8.1% of Mattel's sales will be Barbie toys.

c.

$$\frac{-3.6t^2 + 17.6t + 128}{-0.036t^2 + 0.346t + 4.28} = 15$$

$$-3.6t^2 + 17.6t + 128 = 15\left(-0.036t^2 + 0.346t + 4.28\right)$$

$$-3.6t^2 + 17.6t + 128 = -0.54t^2 + 5.19t + 64.2$$

$$-3.06t^2 + 12.41t + 63.8 = 0$$

$$t = \frac{-(12.41) \pm \sqrt{(12.41)^2 - 4(-3.06)(63.8)}}{2(-3.06)} \approx$$

$$\approx \frac{-12.41 \pm \sqrt{934.92}}{-6.12}$$

$$\approx \cancel{-0.12} \text{ and } 7.02$$

This means that in the year 2007, about 7% of Mattel's sales will be Barbie toys.

d. The maximum point on the graph of P over the interval $0 < t < 10$ is approximately $(1.38, 31)$. This point shows that in the year 2001, the percent sales for Barbie toys will reach a maximum of about 31%.

61. The graphs of $y = \frac{5}{x-2}$ and $y = x^2 - 6x + 10$ intersect at approximately $(4.2, 2.3)$. The solution of the equation is $x \approx 4.2$.

63. The graphs of $y = \frac{5}{x-2}$ and $y = 4$ intersect at approximately $(3.3, 4)$. The solution of the equation is $x \approx 3.3$.

65. The graphs of $y = \dfrac{5}{x-2}$ and $y = -x^2 + x - 1$ do not intersect. The system has no solution.

67. $2 = \dfrac{0+a}{0+b}$ and $\dfrac{5}{2} = \dfrac{1+a}{1+b}$

$2 = \dfrac{a}{b}$ $2(1+b)\dfrac{5}{2} = 2(1+b)\dfrac{1+a}{1+b}$

$2b = a$ $5(1+b) = 2(1+a)$

By substituting $2b$ for a in the second equation we get the following:

$5(1+b) = 2(1+2b)$

$5 + 5b = 2 + 4b$

$b = -3$

By substituting -3 in the first equation for b we get:

$2 = \dfrac{a}{-3}$

$-6 = a$

The value for a is -6, and the value for b is -3.

69. A more efficient way would be to start by subtracting $\dfrac{4}{x+2}$ from both sides of the equation. Then, cross multiply:

$\dfrac{4}{x+2} - \dfrac{2}{x} = \dfrac{1}{x+2}$

$\dfrac{\cancel{4}}{\cancel{x+2}} - \dfrac{2}{x} - \dfrac{\cancel{4}}{\cancel{x+2}} = \dfrac{1}{x+2} - \dfrac{4}{x+2}$

$\dfrac{-2}{x} = \dfrac{-3}{x+2}$

$-2(x+2) = -3x$

$-2x - 4 = -3x$

$-4 = -x$

$x = 4$

71. I would tell the student that a solution to a rational equation should be a real number, not a rational expression.

73. $\dfrac{5}{x} + \dfrac{4}{x+1} - \dfrac{3}{x} = \dfrac{5}{x} \cdot \dfrac{(x+1)}{(x+1)} + \dfrac{4}{x+1} \cdot \dfrac{x}{x} - \dfrac{3}{x} \cdot \dfrac{(x+1)}{(x+1)}$

$= \dfrac{5(x+1) + 4x - 3(x+1)}{x(x+1)}$

$= \dfrac{6x+2}{x(x+1)}$

75. $\dfrac{5}{t} + \dfrac{4}{t+1} = \dfrac{3}{t}$

$t(t+1) \cdot \left(\dfrac{5}{t} + \dfrac{4}{t+1} \right) = \dfrac{3}{t} \cdot t(t+1)$

$5(t+1) + 4t = 3(t+1)$

$5t + 5 + 4t = 3t + 3$

$6t = -2$

$t = -\dfrac{1}{3}$

The solution is $-\dfrac{1}{3}$.

77. $\dfrac{x+2}{x^2 - 5x + 6} - \dfrac{x+1}{x^2 - 4} = \dfrac{4}{x^2 - x - 6}$

$(x-2)(x+2)(x-3) \cdot \left(\dfrac{x+2}{(x-2)(x-3)} - \dfrac{x+1}{(x-2)(x+2)} \right)$

$= \dfrac{4(x-2)(x+2)(x-3)}{(x-3)(x+2)} \cdot$

$(x+2)^2 - (x+1)(x-3) = 4(x-2)$

$x^2 + 4x + 4 - \left(x^2 - 2x - 3 \right) = 4x - 8$

$6x + 7 = 4x - 8$

$2x = -15$

$x = -\dfrac{15}{2}$

The solution is $-\dfrac{15}{2}$.

79. $\dfrac{x+2}{x^2-5x+6}-\dfrac{x+1}{x^2-4}+\dfrac{4}{x^2-x-6}$

$\dfrac{x+2}{(x-2)(x-3)}\cdot\dfrac{(x+2)}{(x+2)}-\dfrac{x+1}{(x-2)(x+2)}\cdot\dfrac{(x-3)}{(x-3)}$

$\quad+\dfrac{4}{(x-3)(x+2)}\cdot\dfrac{(x-2)}{(x-2)}$

$=\dfrac{(x+2)^2-(x+1)(x-3)+4(x-2)}{(x-2)(x-3)(x+2)}$

$=\dfrac{x^2+4x+4-\left(x^2-2x-3\right)+4x-8}{(x-2)(x-3)(x+2)}$

$=\dfrac{10x-1}{(x-2)(x-3)(x+2)}$

81.
$$2p^3-p^2=8p-4$$
$$2p^3-p^2-8p+4=0$$
$$2p^3-8p-p^2+4=0$$
$$2p\left(p^2-4\right)-1\cdot\left(p^2-4\right)=0$$
$$\left(p^2-4\right)(2p-1)=0$$
$$(p-2)(p+2)(2p-1)=0$$
$$p=2\quad p=-2\quad p=\dfrac{1}{2}$$

83. $2(4)^x+3=106$

$2(4)^x=103$

$(4)^x=51.5$

$x=\log_4 51.5$

$=\dfrac{\log_{10}(51.5)}{\log_{10}(4)}$

≈ 2.8433

85. $\log_3(5x-4)-\log_3(2x-3)=2$

$\log_3\left(\dfrac{5x-4}{2x-3}\right)=2$

$3^2=\dfrac{5x-4}{2x-3}$

$9\cdot(2x-3)=\dfrac{5x-4}{2x-3}\cdot(2x-3)$

$18x-27=5x-4$

$13x=23$

$x=\dfrac{23}{13}$

87. This graph is a quadratic function with vertex

$(-2,3)$.

89. $-2(x+2)^2+3=-15$

$-2(x+2)^2=-18$

$(x+2)^2=9$

$\sqrt{(x+2)^2}=\sqrt{9}$

$|x+2|=3$

$x+2=3\quad\text{and}\quad x+2=-3$

$x=1\quad\text{and}\quad x=-5$

This is a quadratic equation with solutions 1 and –5.

91. $-2(x+2)^2+3=-2\left(x^2+4x+4\right)+3$

$=-2x^2-8x-8+3$

$=-2x^2-8x-5$

This is a quadratic expression.

Homework 8.6

1. a. $C(n)=1250+350n$

b. $M(n)=\dfrac{1250+350n}{n}$

c. $M(30)=\dfrac{1250+350(30)}{30}$

$\approx\$391.67$

d. $400=\dfrac{1250+350n}{n}$

$400n=1250+350n$

$50n=1250$

$n=25$

The minimum number of students needed to go on the trip is 25.

3. a. $T(n)=500+50n$

b. $M(n)=\dfrac{500+50n}{n}$

c. $M(270)=\dfrac{500+50(270)}{270}$

$\approx\$51.85$

If 270 people attend the reunion, the mean

cost per person is $51.85.

d.
$$60 = \frac{500 + 50n}{n}$$
$$60n = 500 + 50n$$
$$10n = 500$$
$$n = 50$$

e. For the mean cost per person to be $60, 50 people would have to attend the reunion.

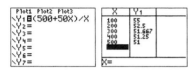

f. As n gets very large, $M(n)$ decreases but never drops below 50. This makes sense in terms of the restaurant fees because each person pays $50 plus an equal share of $500 – the cost for the band. So the more people who attend (i.e., as n gets larger), the closer the mean cost per person gets to $50.

5. a. $C(n) = 90000 + 7000n$

b.
$$B(n) = \frac{90000 + 7000n}{n}$$

c.
$$P(n) = \frac{90000 + 7000n}{n} + 2000$$
$$= \frac{90000 + 7000n}{n} + \frac{2000}{1} \cdot \frac{n}{n}$$
$$= \frac{90000 + 7000n}{n} + \frac{2000n}{n}$$
$$= \frac{90000 + 9000n}{n}$$

d.
$$P(40) = \frac{90000 + 9000(40)}{40}$$
$$= 11250$$
If the manufacturer produces and sells 40 cars, it would have to charge $11250 for each car in order to make a profit of $2000 per car.

e. As the values of n get very large, $P(n)$ gets close to 9000. If a very large number of cars are produced and sold, the price per car can be just a little more than $9000 to insure a profit of $2000 per car.

7. a. $I(t) = 186.25t + 2467.35$

b.
$$M(t) = \frac{I(t)}{H(t)}$$
$$= \frac{186.25t + 2467.35}{0.0016t + 0.09}$$

c. $M(t)$ is measured in dollars per household. This makes sense, since $I(t)$ is measured in dollars and $H(t)$ is measured in households.

d.
$$50,000 = \frac{186.25t + 2467.35}{0.0016t + 0.09}$$
$$50,000(0.0016t + 0.09) = 186.25t + 2467.35$$
$$80t + 4500 = 186.25t + 2467.35$$
$$-106.25t = -2032.65$$
$$t \approx 19$$
The mean household income should reach $50,000 in the year 2009.

e. $M(t)$ is increasing over the interval $5 < t < 20$, which means that the average annual income per household is steadily increasing.

9. a. $B(t) = 288.6t - 1493$

b.
$$E(t) = W(t) + M(t)$$
$$= (0.15t + 5.76) + (0.072t + 5.43)$$
$$= 0.222t + 11.19$$

c.
$$A(t) = \frac{B(t)}{E(t)}$$
$$= \frac{288.6t - 1493}{0.222t + 11.19}$$

d. In the year 2012, $t = 32$, so:
$$A(32) = \frac{288.6(32) - 1493}{0.222(32) + 11.19}$$
$$\approx \$423.21$$
The mean amount of money spent on books per student in the year 2012 will be about $423.21.

e.
$$\frac{288.6t - 1493}{0.222t + 11.19} = 400$$
$$288.6t - 1493 = 400(0.222t + 11.19)$$
$$288.6t - 1493 = 88.8t + 4476$$
$$199.8t = 5969$$
$$t \approx 30$$

The mean amount of money spent on books per student will reach about $400 in the year 2010.

11. a.
$$W(t) = 13.284t + 440.095$$
$$M(t) = 3.419t + 468.14$$

b.
$$W(t) + M(t)$$
$$= (13.284t + 440.095) + (3.419t + 468.14)$$
$$= 16.703t + 908.235$$

The input, *t*, represents the number of years since 1980. The output, $W(t) + M(t)$, represents the total number of people who earned a bachelors degree in that year.

c.
$$P(t) = \frac{M(t)}{W(t) + M(t)}$$
$$= \left(\frac{3.419t + 468.14}{16.703t + 908.235}\right) 100$$
$$= \frac{341.9t + 46814}{16.703t + 908.235}$$

d.
$$40 = \frac{341.9t + 46814}{16.703t + 908.235}$$
$$40(16.703t + 908.235) = 341.9t + 46814$$
$$668.12t + 36329.4 = 341.9t + 46814$$
$$326.22t = 10484.6$$
$$t \approx 32$$

In the year 2012, about 40% of the people who earn bachelor's degrees will be men.

e. The graph of *P* is decreasing over the interval $0 < t < 40$. The number of bachelor's degrees earned by women has been increasing at a faster rate compared to men, which accounts for the decrease in the percentage of bachelor's degrees earned by men.

13. a.
$$M(t) = 18.133t + 386.859$$
$$E(t) - 31.516t + 1382.532$$

b.
$$M(t) + E(t)$$
$$= (18.133t + 386.859) + (-31.516t + 1382.532)$$
$$= -13.39t + 1769.391$$

The input, *t*, represents the number of years since 1980. The output, $M(t) + E(t)$, represents the total number of morning and evening daily newspapers.

c.
$$P(t) = \left(\frac{M(t)}{M(t) + E(t)}\right) 100$$
$$= \frac{1813.3t + 38685.9}{-13.39t + 1769.391}$$

d.
$$P(30) = \frac{1813.3(30) + 38685.9}{-13.383(30) + 1769.391}$$
$$\approx 68$$

In the year 2010, about 68% of all newspapers will be morning dailies.

e.
$$\frac{1813.3t + 38685.9}{-13.383t + 1769.391} = 75$$
$$1813.3t + 38685.9 = 75(-13.383t + 1769.391)$$
$$1813.3t + 38685.9 = -1003.725t + 132704.325$$
$$-94018.425 = -2817.025t$$
$$t \approx 33$$

In the year 2013, about 75% of daily newspapers will be morning dailies.

15. Using $t = \frac{d}{s}$ gives the following:
$$t = \frac{85}{60} \approx 1.4$$

17. a.
$$T(a) = \frac{253}{a + 75} + \frac{410}{a + 65}$$

b.
$$T(3) = \frac{253}{3 + 75} + \frac{410}{3 + 65} \approx 9.3 \text{ hrs.}$$

c. Using a graphing calculator, graph:

$$y_1 = \frac{253}{x+75} + \frac{410}{x+65}$$

$$y_2 = 9$$

The graphs intersect at about $(5.2, 9)$. So, he would have to exceed the speed limit by about 5.2 mph for a 9 hour driving time.

19. a. $T(a) = \frac{83}{a+70} + \frac{37}{a+65}$

b. $T(0) = \frac{83}{0+70} + \frac{37}{0+65} \approx 1.75$

$$T(10) = \frac{83}{10+70} + \frac{37}{10+65} \approx 1.53$$

This means that if the student drives the speed limit, her driving time will be about 1.8 hrs. If she drives 10 mph over the speed limit, her driving time will be about 1.5 hrs.

c. $T(0) - T(10) = 0.22$

This shows the amount of time she will save if she drives 10 mph over the speed limit.

d. Using a graphing calculator, graph:

$$y_1 = \frac{83}{x+70} + \frac{37}{x+65}$$

$$y_2 = 1.6$$

The graphs intersect at about $(6.6, 1.6)$. This means that the driver would have to exceed the speed limit by about 6.6 mph for a 1.6 hour driving time.

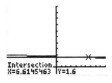

21. a. $\dfrac{164}{a+70} + \dfrac{121}{a+65}$

$$= \left(\frac{164}{a+70}\right)\left(\frac{a+65}{a+65}\right) + \left(\frac{121}{a+65}\right)\left(\frac{a+70}{a+70}\right)$$

$$= \frac{164a+10660}{(a+70)(a+65)} + \frac{121a+8470}{(a+70)(a+65)}$$

$$= \frac{285a+19130}{(a+70)(a+65)}$$

b. $\dfrac{285(10)+19130}{(10+70)(10+65)} \approx 3.66$ hours

23. a. Linear:

$$L(t) = 0.525t - 12.22$$

Exponential:

$$E(t) = 0.433(1.056)^x$$

Quadratic:

$$Q(t) = 0.01t^2 - 0.47t + 6.1$$

The percentage of Americans who have shingles does not increase at a constant rate from year to year. So, the linear model would be the worst fit. The quadratic or exponential models provide a better fit of the data.

b. There is model breakdown for the linear model, because the model takes on negative values for ages less than 23 years. There is model breakdown also for the quadratic model, because it shows a decrease in the percent of Americans who have shingles, up to age 23. The exponential model is the best fit of the data.

c. Graph $y_1 = 0.43(1.06)^x$ and $y_2 = 25$ in a graphing calculator. The graphs intersect at about $(69.73, 25)$. So, about 25% of people of age 74 have shingles.

d. The base of the exponential model is 1.06, which means that the number of Americans who have shingles increases by about 6% for each additional year that a person lives.

e. The model predicts that about 60.87% of Americans age 85 will have shingles. If the new vaccine reduces the number of shingles cases by 51% then about 29.8% of people age 85 will have shingles, with the new vaccine.

25.
$$75x^3 - 50x^2 - 12x + 8$$
$$= 25x^2(3x-2) - 4(3x-2)$$
$$= (3x-2)(25x^2-4)$$
$$= (3x-2)(5x-2)(5x+2)$$

This is a polynomial expression in one variable.

27.
$$75x^3 - 50x^2 = 12x - 8$$
$$75x^3 - 50x^2 - 12x + 8 = 0$$
$$25x^2(3x-2) - 4(3x-2) = 0$$
$$(3x-2)(25x^2-4) = 0$$
$$(3x-2)(5x-2)(5x+2) = 0$$
$$x = \frac{2}{3}, x = \frac{2}{5} \text{ or } x = -\frac{2}{5}$$

29.
$$\left(x^2 + 2x - 3\right)\left(3x^2 - x - 4\right)$$
$$= 3x^2\left(x^2 + 2x - 3\right) - x\left(x^2 + 2x - 3\right) -$$
$$\quad 4\left(x^2 + 2x - 3\right)$$
$$= 3x^4 + 6x^3 - 9x^2 - x^3 - 2x^2 + 3x -$$
$$\quad 4x^2 - 8x + 12$$
$$= 3x^4 + 5x^3 - 15x^2 - 5x + 12$$

This is a polynomial expression in one variable.

Homework 8.7

1. $I = kt$

3. $w = \dfrac{k}{x+4}$

5. w varies inversely as r

7. T varies directly as the square root of w.

9. $c = ku$

To find k, solve the following equation:
$$12 = k(3)$$
$$4 = k$$
$$c = 4u$$

11. $w = \dfrac{k}{\sqrt{t}}$

To find k, solve the following equation:

$$3 = \frac{k}{\sqrt{16}}$$
$$3 = \frac{k}{4}$$
$$12 = k$$
$$w = \frac{12}{\sqrt{t}}$$

13. $y = kx$

To find k, solve the following equation:
$$12 = k(4)$$
$$3 = k$$
$$y = 3x$$

Substitute 9 for x and solve for y to get the required value:
$$y = 3(9) = 27$$

15. $G = \dfrac{k}{r}$

To find k, solve the following equation:
$$G = \frac{k}{r}$$
$$8 = \frac{k}{3}$$
$$24 = k$$
$$G = \frac{24}{r}$$

Substitute 4 for r and solve for G to get the required value:
$$G = \frac{24}{r} = \frac{24}{4} = 6$$

17. $p = kx^2$

To find k, solve the following equation:
$$6 = k(2)^2$$
$$6 = 4k$$
$$\frac{6}{4} = k$$
$$\frac{3}{2} = k$$
$$p = \frac{3}{2}x^2$$

Substitute 24 for p and solve for x to get the required value:

$$p = \frac{3}{2}x^2$$

$$24 = \frac{3}{2}x^2$$

$$48 = 3x^2$$

$$16 = x^2$$

$$x = \pm 4$$

19.
$$I = \frac{k}{r+2}$$

To find k, solve the following equation:

$$I = \frac{k}{r+2}$$

$$9 = \frac{k}{3+2}$$

$$9 = \frac{k}{5}$$

$$45 = k$$

$$I = \frac{45}{r+2}$$

Substitute 7 for I and solve for r to get the required value.

$$I = \frac{45}{r+2}$$

$$7 = \frac{45}{r+2}$$

$$7(r+2) = 45$$

$$7r+14 = 45$$

$$7r = 31$$

$$r = \frac{31}{7}$$

21. As the value of w increases, the value of B will also increase for the given situation.

23. As the value of p increases, the value of w will decrease for the given situation.

25. If the GDP rises, the transaction demand will also rise.

27. A tall person will have less nerve conduction than a short person.

29. Bernice Fitz-Gibbon meant that as the number of cooks increase, the amount of creativity decreases.

31. Let c be the cost of tuition and h be the number of credit hours a student takes.

$$c = kh$$

Let $c = 1395$ and $h = 15$.

$$1395 = k(15)$$

$$93 = k$$

Therefore, $c = 93h$

$$c = 93(12)$$

$$= \$1116$$

33. Let t be the tension in the string and r be the radius of the circle.

$$t = \frac{k}{r}$$

Let $t = 80$ and $r = 60$.

$$80 = \frac{k}{60}$$

$$4800 = k$$

Therefore, $t = \frac{4800}{r}$

$$t = \frac{4800}{50}$$

$$= 96 \text{ newtons}$$

35. Let d be the distance an object falls and t be the time in motion.

$$d = kt^2$$

Let $d = 144.9$ and $t = 3$.

$$144.9 = k \cdot 3^2$$

$$144.9 = 9k$$

$$16.1 = k$$

Therefore, $d = 16.1t^2$

$$d = 16.1(3.4)^2 = 186.116 \text{ feet}$$

37. Let i be the intensity of radiation and d be the distance from the machine.

$$i = \frac{k}{d^2}$$

Let $i = 90$ and $d = 2.5$.

$$90 = \frac{k}{2.5^2}$$

$$90 = \frac{k}{6.25}$$

$$562.5 = k$$

Therefore, $i = \frac{562.5}{d^2}$

$$45 = \frac{562.5}{d^2}$$

$$45d^2 = 562.5$$

$$d^2 = 12.5$$

$$d \approx 3.53 \text{ meters}$$

39. a. $F = kw$

To find k solve the following equation:

$$50 = k(120)$$

$$\frac{5}{12} = k$$

The equation is $F = \frac{5}{12}w.$

b. $F = \frac{5}{12} \cdot 150 = 62.5 \text{ pounds}$

c. Written response

41. a. $T = kd$

Let $T = 3$ and $d = 3313$.

$$3 = k(3313)$$

$$0.000906 = k$$

Therefore, $T = 0.000906d$.

b. $4 = 0.000906d$

$$d \approx 4415 \text{ feet}$$

c. For every additional foot away the lightning strike, it takes another 0.000906 seconds to hear the thunder.

d. Written response.

43. a. $w = f(d) = \frac{k}{d^2}$

$$200 = \frac{k}{4^2}$$

$$200 = \frac{k}{16}$$

$$3200 = k$$

Therefore, $w = f(d) = \frac{3200}{d^2}$.

b. If sea level is about 4 thousand miles from the center of the Earth, then 1 thousand miles above the surface would be a total of 5 thousand miles from the center of the Earth.

$$w = \frac{3200}{5^2} = 128 \text{ pounds}$$

c.
$$1 = \frac{3200}{d^2}$$

$$d^2 = 3200$$

$$d = \sqrt{3200}$$

$$\approx 56.57$$

An astronaut would weight 1 pound at a distance of about 56,5700 miles from the center of Earth.

d. $f(239) = \frac{3200}{239^2}$

$$\approx 0.056 \text{ pounds}$$

e. Written response.

45. a.

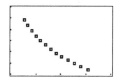

b. The model should be of the form $F(L) = \frac{k}{L}$.

To find k take the average of all products LF from the table.
The sum of the products is 36467.715.
Divide this sum by 13 (the total number of notes in the table) to get the average.

$$\frac{36467.715}{13} \approx 2805.21$$

So $F(L) = \frac{2805.21}{L}$

The graph below shows the equation graphed along with the scattergram of the data. By inspection, it appears the model fits the data extremely well.

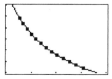

c. F varies inversely as L

d.
$$F(7.58) - \frac{2805.21}{7.58} \approx 370.1 \text{ hertz}$$

$$(eq1)F = \frac{2805.21}{a} \qquad \text{Equati}$$

$$(eq2)F = \frac{2805.21}{\frac{1}{2}a} = 2805.21 \div \frac{1}{2}a$$

$$= 2805.21 \cdot \frac{2}{a} = 2\left(\frac{2805.21}{a}\right)$$

on 2 is 2 times equation 1. So when we halved the effective length the frequency doubled.

e.
$$(eq1)F = \frac{2805.21}{a}$$

$$(eq2)F = \frac{2805.21}{\frac{1}{2}a}$$

$$= 2805.21 \div \frac{1}{2}a$$

$$= 2805.21 \cdot \frac{2}{a}$$

$$= 2\left(\frac{2805.21}{a}\right)$$

Equation 2 is 2 times equation 1. So when we halved the effective length the frequency doubled.

47. a.

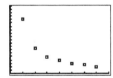

b. The model should be of the form $f(d) = \dfrac{k}{d}$. To find k take the average of all products dh from the table.

$$k = \frac{10 \cdot 16 + 20 \cdot 7.3 + 30 \cdot 4.8 + 40 \cdot 3.8 + 50 \cdot 3 + 60 \cdot 2.5 + 70}{7}$$

$$\approx 148.86$$

So $f(d) = \dfrac{148.86}{d}$

c. The apparent height varies inversely with the distance.

d. This makes sense in this case because the farther you are from the garage (i.e. the bigger d is) the smaller the apparent

height $f(d)$ is.

e.
$$f(100) = \frac{148.86}{100} = 1.4886 \text{ inches}$$

f.
$$f(1) = \frac{148.86}{1} = 148.86 \text{ inches}$$

49. a. $T = k\sqrt{L}$

b. $\dfrac{T}{\sqrt{L}} = k$

c.

L	T	$\dfrac{T}{\sqrt{L}}$
5	0.5	0.22
10	0	0.20
15	0.6	0.23
20	3	0.22
25	0.8	0.23
32.	8	0.22
5	1.0	0.22
45	0	0.23
60	1.1	0.22
85	3	0.21
110	1.2	
	5	
	1.5	
	0	
	1.7	
	5	
	2.0	
	0	
	2.2	
	5	

A reasonable value for k is the average of column 3 which approximately 0.22.

d. $T = 0.22\sqrt{L}$

e. The following is the scattergram and the graph of T.

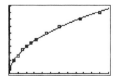

The model fits the data very well

f. $T = 0.22\sqrt{130} \approx 2.51$ seconds

51. $f(L) = 5L$

  $k = 5$

53. $f(n) = \dfrac{2}{n}$

  $k = 2$

55. $f(r) = 2\pi r$

  $k = 2\pi$

57. a. f is an increasing function

   The number of CD's sold increases as more money is spent on advertising.

b. The number of CD's sold does not vary directly as the amount of money spent on advertising. "Varies directly" usually implies a linear relationship. A linear model would not fit this data well.

c. Written response

59. False. As a person gets older, the person doesn't necessarily keep getting taller. At some point we stop growing.

61. True. Coffee will get cooler the longer the time passes since it has been poured.

63. $y = kx$

   Solving this equation for x we get the following:

   $\dfrac{y}{k} = x$

   Yes, it follows that x varies directly as y.

   The variation constant is $\dfrac{1}{k}$.

65. a. If y varies directly as x, x and y are linearly related. This relationship takes the form of $y = kx$, which is a linear relationship.

b. No. Just because w and t are linearly related doesn't mean they are directly related. The relationship may be either

$$w = kt \text{ or } w = \frac{k}{t}.$$

67. $n = kt$

  $310 = k(5)$

  $62 = k$

  $n = 62t$

The slope of the model is 62. This indicates that the typist can type 62 words per minute.

69. Answers may vary. Example:

  $x + y = 2$

  $x - y = 0$

  $y = x$

  $x + x = 2$

  $2x = 2$

  $x = 1$

  $y = 1$

71. Answers may vary. Example:

$$\frac{x-2}{2x+2} - \frac{2x}{2x+2} =$$
$$\frac{x-2-2x}{2x+2} = \frac{-2-x}{2x+2}$$

73. Answers may vary. Example:

  $y = x^2$

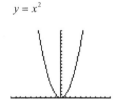

75. Answers may vary. Example:

  $y = e^x$

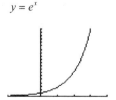

Chapter 8 Review Exercises

1. $f(x) = \dfrac{5x-3}{2x^2-3x+1}$

$f(0) = \dfrac{5(0)-3}{2(0)^2-3(0)+1}$

$f(0) = -3$

$f(2) = \dfrac{5(2)-3}{2(2)^2-3(2)+1}$

$f(2) = \dfrac{7}{3}$

2.
$4x^2 - 49 = 0$

$(2x-7)(2x+7) = 0$

$2x-7 = 0 \quad \text{or} \quad 2x+7 = 0$

$2x = 7 \qquad\qquad 2x = -7$

$x = \dfrac{7}{2} \qquad\qquad x = -\dfrac{7}{2}$

The domain is the set of all real numbers except $\dfrac{7}{2}$ and $-\dfrac{7}{2}$.

3. $12x^2 + 13x - 35 = 0$

$x = \dfrac{-13 \pm \sqrt{169 - 4(12)(-35)}}{24}$

$= \dfrac{-13 \pm \sqrt{169 + 1680}}{24}$

$= \dfrac{-13 \pm \sqrt{1849}}{24}$

$= \dfrac{-13 \pm 43}{24}$

The solutions are $\dfrac{-13+43}{24} = \dfrac{5}{4}$ and

$\dfrac{-13-43}{24} = -\dfrac{7}{3}$. The domain is the set of all real

numbers except $\dfrac{5}{4}$ and $-\dfrac{7}{3}$.

4. The function will be defined for all x except where the denominator is 0.

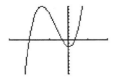

The "intersect" function on the calculator was used to find all instances where the denominator function crosses the x-axis. These values were:

$x = \{-2, \pm\dfrac{1}{3}\}$

5. $\dfrac{3x-12}{x^2-6x+8} = \dfrac{3(x-4)}{(x-2)(x-4)}$

$= \dfrac{3}{x-2}$

6. $\dfrac{16-x^2}{2x^3-16x^2+32x} = \dfrac{(4+x)(4-x)}{2x(x^2-8x+16)}$

$= \dfrac{(4+x)(4-x)}{2x(x-4)(x-4)}$

$= \dfrac{-x-4}{2x(x-4)}$

7. $\dfrac{x+2}{x^3+8} = \dfrac{x+2}{(x+2)(x^2-2x+4)}$

$= \dfrac{1}{(x^2-2x+4)}$

8. $\dfrac{6a^2-17ab+5b^2}{3a^2-4ab+b^2} = \dfrac{(-3a+b)(-2a+5b)}{(-3a+b)(-a+b)}$

$= \dfrac{-2a+5b}{-a+b}$

9. $\dfrac{f(x)}{g(x)} = \dfrac{x^2+3x-28}{x^3-x^2-12x}$

$= \dfrac{(x+7)(x-4)}{x(x^2-x-12)}$

$= \dfrac{(x+7)(x-4)}{x(x-4)(x+3)}$

$= \dfrac{(x+7)}{x(x+3)}$

$f(2) = \dfrac{(-2+7)}{-2(-2+3)}$

$= -\dfrac{5}{2}$

10. $\dfrac{3x+6}{2x-4} \cdot \dfrac{5x-10}{6x+12} = \dfrac{3(x+2)}{2(x-2)} \cdot \dfrac{5(x-2)}{6(x+2)}$

$\qquad\qquad = \dfrac{15}{12}$

$\qquad\qquad = \dfrac{5}{4}$

11. $\dfrac{x^2-49}{9-x^2} \cdot \dfrac{2x^3+8x^2-42x}{5x-35}$

$\quad = \dfrac{(x-7)(x+7)}{-(x^2-9)} \cdot \dfrac{2x(x^2+4x-21)}{5(x-7)}$

$\quad = \dfrac{(x-7)(x+7)}{-(x+3)(x-3)} \cdot \dfrac{2x(x+7)(x-3)}{5(x-7)}$

$\quad = -\dfrac{2x(x+7)^2}{5(x+3)}$

12. $\dfrac{p^3-t^3}{p^2-t^2} \cdot \dfrac{p^2+6pt+5t^2}{p^2t+pt^2+t^3}$

$\quad = \dfrac{(p-t)(p^2+pt+t^2)}{(p-t)(p+t)} \cdot \dfrac{(p+5t)(p+t)}{t(p^2+pt+t^2)}$

$\quad = \dfrac{p+5t}{t}$

13. $\dfrac{x^2-4}{x^2+3x+2} \div \dfrac{4x^2-24x+32}{x^2-5x+4}$

$\quad = \dfrac{x^2-4}{x^2+3x+2} \cdot \dfrac{x^2-5x+4}{4x^2-24x+32}$

$\quad = \dfrac{(x-2)(x+2)}{(x+2)(x+1)} \cdot \dfrac{(x-4)(x-1)}{4(x^2-6x+8)}$

$\quad = \dfrac{(x-2)(x+2)}{(x+2)(x+1)} \cdot \dfrac{(x-4)(x-1)}{4(x-4)(x-2)}$

$\quad = \dfrac{(x-2)}{(x+1)} \cdot \dfrac{(x-1)}{4(x-2)}$

$\quad = \dfrac{x-1}{4(x+1)}$

14. $\dfrac{4-x}{4x} \div \dfrac{16-x^2}{16x^2} = \dfrac{4-x}{4x} \cdot \dfrac{16x^2}{16-x^2}$

$\qquad\qquad = \dfrac{4-x}{4x} \cdot \dfrac{16x^2}{(4-x)(4+x)}$

$\qquad\qquad = \dfrac{4x}{4+x}$

15. $\dfrac{8x^3+4x^2-18x-9}{x^2-6x+9} \div \dfrac{4x^2+8x+3}{x^2-9}$

$\quad = \dfrac{8x^3+4x^2-18x-9}{x^2-6x+9} \cdot \dfrac{x^2-9}{4x^2+8x+3}$

$\quad = \dfrac{4x^2(2x+1)-9(2x+1)}{(x-3)(x-3)} \cdot \dfrac{(x-3)(x+3)}{(2x+1)(2x+3)}$

$\quad = \dfrac{(2x+1)(4x^2-9)}{(x-3)(x-3)} \cdot \dfrac{(x-3)(x+3)}{(2x+1)(2x+3)}$

$\quad = \dfrac{(2x+1)(2x-3)(2x+3)}{(x-3)(x-3)} \cdot \dfrac{(x-3)(x+3)}{(2x+1)(2x+3)}$

$\quad = \dfrac{(2x-3)(x+3)}{x-3}$

16. $\dfrac{x}{x^2-5x+6} + \dfrac{3}{3-x}$

$\quad = \dfrac{x}{(x-3)(x-2)} - \dfrac{3}{x-3}$

$\quad = \dfrac{x}{(x-3)(x-2)} - \dfrac{3}{(x-3)} \cdot \dfrac{(x-2)}{(x-2)}$

$\quad = \dfrac{x-3x+6}{(x-3)(x-2)} = \dfrac{-2x+6}{(x-3)(x-2)} = \dfrac{-2(x-3)}{(x-3)(x-2)}$

$\quad = \dfrac{-2}{x-2}$

17. $\dfrac{x}{2x^3-3x^2-5x} + \dfrac{2}{x^3-x}$

$\quad = \dfrac{x}{x(2x^2-3x-5)} + \dfrac{2}{x(x^2-1)}$

$\quad = \dfrac{x}{x(2x-5)(x+1)} + \dfrac{2}{x(x-1)(x+1)}$

$$-\frac{x}{x(2x-5)(x+1)}\cdot\frac{(x-1)}{(x-1)}$$

$$+\frac{2}{x(x-1)(x+1)}\cdot\frac{(2x-5)}{(2x-5)}$$

$$=\frac{x^2-x}{x(2x-5)(x+1)(x-1)}$$

$$+\frac{4x-10}{x(2x-5)(x+1)(x-1)}$$

$$=\frac{x^2+3x-10}{x(2x-5)(x+1)(x-1)}$$

$$=\frac{(x-2)(x+5)}{x(2x-5)(x+1)(x-1)}$$

18. $\dfrac{x-1}{x^2-4}+\dfrac{x+3}{x^2-4x+4}$

$$=\frac{x-1}{(x-2)(x+2)}+\frac{x+3}{(x-2)(x-2)}$$

$$=\frac{(x-1)(x-2)}{(x-2)(x-2)(x+2)}+\frac{(x+2)(x+3)}{(x-2)(x-2)(x+2)}$$

$$=\frac{(x-1)(x-2)+(x+2)(x+3)}{(x-2)(x-2)(x+2)}$$

$$=\frac{x^2-3x+2+x^2+5x+6}{(x-2)^2(x+2)}$$

$$=\frac{2(x^2+x+4)}{(x-2)^2(x+2)}$$

19. $\dfrac{3}{4x-12}-\dfrac{x}{x^2-2x-3}$

$$=\frac{3}{4(x-3)}-\frac{x}{(x-3)(x+1)}$$

$$=\frac{3}{4(x-3)}\cdot\frac{(x+1)}{(x+1)}-\frac{x}{(x-3)(x+1)}\cdot\frac{(4)}{(4)}$$

$$=\frac{3x+3-4x}{4(x-3)(x+1)}=\frac{-x+3}{4(x-3)(x+1)}$$

$$=\frac{-(x-3)}{4(x-3)(x+1)}=\frac{-1}{4(x+1)}$$

20. $\dfrac{x+1}{25-x^2}-\dfrac{r-4}{2x^2-14x+20}$

$$=-\frac{x+1}{x^2-25}-\frac{x-4}{2x^2-14x+20}$$

$$=-\frac{x+1}{(x-5)(x+5)}-\frac{x-4}{2(x^2-7x+10)}$$

$$=-\frac{x+1}{(x-5)(x+5)}-\frac{x-4}{2(x-5)(x-2)}$$

$$=-\frac{(x+1)}{(x-5)(x+5)}\cdot\frac{2(x-2)}{2(x-2)}-\frac{(x-4)}{2(x-5)(x-2)}\cdot\frac{(x+5)}{(x+5)}$$

$$=-\frac{2(x^2-x-2)}{2(x-5)(x+5)(x-2)}-\frac{x^2+x-20}{2(x-5)(x-2)(x+5)}$$

$$=\frac{-2x^2+2x+4-x^2-x+20}{2(x-5)(x+5)(x-2)}$$

$$=\frac{-3x^2+x+24}{2(x-5)(x+5)(x-2)}$$

21. $\dfrac{2m}{m^2-3mn-10n^2}-\dfrac{4n}{m^2+8mn+12n^2}$

$$=\frac{2m}{(m-5n)(m+2n)}-\frac{4n}{(m+6n)(m+2n)}$$

$$=\frac{2m(m+6n)}{(m-5n)(m+2n)(m+6n)}-\frac{4n(m-5n)}{(m+6n)(m+2n)(m-5n)}$$

$$=\frac{2m^2+12mn-4mn-20n^2}{(m+6n)(m+2n)(m-5n)}$$

$$=\frac{2m^2-8mn-20n^2}{(m+6n)(m+2n)(m-5n)}$$

$$=\frac{(2m+-10n)(m+2n)}{(m+6n)(m+2n)(m-5n)}$$

$$=\frac{2(m-5n)(m+2n)}{(m+6n)(m+2n)(m-5n)}$$

$$=\frac{2}{m+6n}$$

22. $\dfrac{2}{x-5}-\left(\dfrac{x^2+5x+6}{3x^2-75}\div\dfrac{x^2+2x}{3x+15}\right)$

$$=\frac{2}{x-5}-\left(\frac{x^2+5x+6}{3x^2-75}\cdot\frac{3x+15}{x^2+2x}\right)$$

$$=\frac{2}{x-5}-\left(\frac{(x+3)(x+2)}{3(x^2-25)}\cdot\frac{3(x+5)}{x(x+2)}\right)$$

$$=\frac{2}{x-5}-\left(\frac{(x+3)(x+2)}{3(x+5)(x-5)}\cdot\frac{3(x+5)}{x(x+2)}\right)$$

$$= \frac{2}{x-5} - \frac{x+3}{x(x-5)}$$

$$= \frac{2}{x-5} \cdot \left(\frac{x}{x}\right) - \frac{x+3}{x(x-5)}$$

$$-\frac{2x-x+3}{x(x-5)}$$

$$= \frac{x+3}{x(x-5)}$$

23.
$$f(x)g(x) = \frac{x^2-x-2}{x^2+5x+6} \cdot \frac{x+3}{x+2}$$

$$= \frac{(x-2)(x+1)}{(x+2)(x+3)} \cdot \frac{(x+3)}{(x+2)}$$

$$= \frac{(x-2)(x+1)}{(x+2)^2}$$

24.
$$f(x) \div g(x) = \frac{x^2-x-2}{x^2+5x+6} \div \frac{x+3}{x+2}$$

$$= \frac{x^2-x-2}{x^2+5x+6} \cdot \frac{x+2}{x+3}$$

$$= \frac{(x-2)(x+1)}{(x+2)(x+3)} \cdot \frac{x+2}{x+3}$$

$$= \frac{(x-2)(x+1)}{(x+3)^2}$$

25.
$$f(x) + g(x) = \frac{x^2-x-2}{x^2+5x+6} + \frac{x+3}{x+2}$$

$$= \frac{(x-2)(x+1)}{(x+2)(x+3)} + \frac{x+3}{x+2}$$

$$= \frac{(x-2)(x+1)}{(x+2)(x+3)} + \frac{(x+3)}{(x+2)} \cdot \frac{(x+3)}{(x+3)}$$

$$= \frac{x^2-x-2}{(x+2)(x+3)} + \frac{x^2+6x+9}{(x+2)(x+3)}$$

$$= \frac{2x^2+5x+7}{(x+2)(x+3)}$$

26.
$$f(x) - g(x) = \frac{x^2-x-2}{x^2+5x+6} - \frac{x+3}{x+2}$$

$$= \frac{x^2-x-2}{(x+2)(x+3)} - \frac{x+3}{x+2}$$

$$-\frac{x^2-x-2}{(x+2)(x+3)} - \frac{(x+3)}{(x+2)} \cdot \frac{(x+3)}{(x+3)}$$

$$= \frac{x^2-x-2}{(x+2)(x+3)} - \frac{x^2+6x+9}{(x+2)(x+3)}$$

$$= \frac{x^2-x-2-x^2-6x-9}{(x+2)(x+3)} = \frac{-7x-11}{(x+2)(x+3)}$$

27.
$$\frac{\frac{x-2}{x^2-9}}{\frac{x^2-4}{x+3}} = \frac{\frac{x-2}{(x-3)(x+3)}}{\frac{(x-2)(x+2)}{x+3}} = \frac{x-2}{(x-3)(x+3)} \div \frac{(x-2)(x+2)}{x+3}$$

$$= \frac{x-2}{(x-3)(x+3)} \cdot \frac{x+3}{(x-2)(x+2)} = \frac{1}{(x-3)(x+2)}$$

28.
$$\frac{\frac{4}{3x^4} - \frac{2}{6x^2}}{\frac{1}{2x} + \frac{1}{4}} = \left(\frac{\frac{4}{3x^4} - \frac{2}{6x^2}}{\frac{1}{2x} + \frac{1}{4}}\right) \cdot \frac{12x^4}{12x^4} = \frac{16-4x^2}{6x^3+3x^4}$$

$$= \frac{-4(x^2-4)}{3x^3(2+x)} = \frac{-4(x+2)(x-2)}{3x^3(x+2)} = \frac{-4(x-2)}{3x^3}$$

29.
$$\frac{1}{x+5} - \frac{2}{x-2} = \frac{-14}{x^2+3x-10}$$

$$\frac{1}{x+5} - \frac{2}{x-2} = \frac{-14}{(x+5)(x-2)}$$

$$(x+5)(x-2)\left(\frac{1}{x+5} - \frac{2}{x-2}\right)$$

$$= (x+5)(x-2)\frac{-14}{(x+5)(x-2)}$$

$$x-2-2(x+5) = -14$$

$$x-2-2x-10 = -14$$

$$-x-12 = -14$$

$$-x = -2$$

$$x = 2$$

Check. $x = 2$

$$\frac{1}{(2)+5} - \frac{2}{(2)-2} \overset{?}{=} \frac{-14}{(2)^2+3(2)-10}$$

$$\frac{1}{7} - \frac{2}{0} \overset{?}{=} \frac{-14}{0}$$

Division by zero is undefined. Empty solution set.

30.
$$\frac{x}{x+2}+\frac{3}{x+4}-\frac{14}{x^2+6x+8}$$

$$\frac{x}{x+2}+\frac{3}{x+4}=\frac{14}{(x+2)(x+4)}$$

$$(x+2)(x+4)\left(\frac{x}{x+2}+\frac{3}{x+4}\right)$$

$$=(x+2)(x+4)\frac{14}{(x+2)(x+4)}$$

$$x(x+4)+3(x+2)=14$$

$$x^2+4x+3x+6=14$$

$$x^2+7x-8=0$$

$$(x+8)(x-1)=0$$

$$x+8=0 \quad \text{or} \quad x-1=0$$

$$x=-8 \qquad\qquad x=1$$

Check. $x=-8$

$$\frac{(-8)}{(-8)+2}+\frac{3}{(-8)+4}\overset{?}{=}\frac{14}{(-8)^2+6(-8)+8}$$

$$\frac{7}{12}=\frac{7}{12}$$

Check. $x=1$

$$\frac{(1)}{(1)+2}+\frac{3}{(1)+4}\overset{?}{=}\frac{14}{(1)^2+6(1)+8}$$

$$\frac{14}{15}=\frac{14}{15}$$

The solutions are 1 and -8.

31.
$$\frac{5}{x}+3=\frac{4}{x^2}$$

$$x^2\left(\frac{5}{x}+3\right)=x^2\frac{4}{x^2}$$

$$5x+3x^2=4$$

$$3x^2+5x-4=0$$

$$x=\frac{5\pm\sqrt{25-4(3)(-4)}}{6}$$

$$=\frac{5\pm\sqrt{73}}{6}$$

32.
$$\frac{x-3}{2x^2-7x-4}-\frac{5}{2x^2+3x+1}=\frac{x-1}{x^2-3x-4}$$

$$\frac{x-3}{(2x+1)(x-4)}-\frac{5}{(2x+1)(x+1)}=\frac{x-1}{(x-4)(x+1)}$$

$$(2x+1)(x-4)(x+1)\left(\frac{x-3}{(2x+1)(x-4)}-\frac{5}{(2x+1)(x+1)}\right)$$

$$=(2x+1)(x-4)(x+1)\frac{x-1}{(x-4)(x+1)}$$

$$(x+1)(x-3)-5(x-4)=(2x+1)(x-1)$$

$$x^2-2x-3-5x+20=2x^2-x-1$$

$$x^2-7x+17=2x^2-x-1$$

$$-x^2-6x+18=0$$

$$x^2+6x-18=0$$

$$x=\frac{-6\pm\sqrt{36-4(1)(-18)}}{2}$$

$$=\frac{-6\pm\sqrt{36+72}}{2}$$

$$=\frac{-6\pm\sqrt{108}}{2}$$

$$=\frac{-6\pm\sqrt{36\cdot3}}{2}$$

$$=\frac{-6\pm6\sqrt{3}}{2}$$

$$=-3\pm3\sqrt{3}$$

Check $-3\pm3\sqrt{3}$ using a calculator. The solutions are $-3\pm3\sqrt{3}$.

33.
$$\frac{2x}{x+6}-\frac{4}{x-3}=\frac{-37}{x^2+3x-18}$$

$$\frac{2x}{x+6}-\frac{4}{x-3}=\frac{-37}{(x+6)(x-3)}$$

$$\frac{2x(x-3)}{(x+6)(x-3)}-\frac{4(x+6)}{(x+6)(x-3)}=\frac{-37}{(x+6)(x-3)}$$

$$\frac{2x(x-3)-4(x+6)}{(x+6)(x-3)}=\frac{-37}{(x+6)(x-3)}$$

$$2x(x-3)-4(x+6)=-37$$

$$2x^2-6x-4x-24=-37$$

$$2x^2-10x=-13$$

$$2x^2-10x+13=0$$

$$x=\frac{10\pm\sqrt{(-10)^2-4(2)}}{2(2)}$$

$$\frac{10\pm2i}{4}=\frac{5\pm i}{2}$$

$$x=\left\{\frac{5+i}{2},\frac{5-i}{2}\right\}$$

34.

$$0 = \frac{x-7}{x+1} - \frac{x+3}{x-4}$$

$$(x+1)(x-4)\left(0 = \frac{x-7}{x+1} - \frac{x+3}{x-4}\right)$$

$$0 = (x-4)(x-7) - (x+1)(x+3)$$

$$0 = x^2 - 11x + 28 - (x^2 + 4x + 3)$$

$$0 = x^2 - 11x + 28 - x^2 - 4x - 3$$

$$0 = -15x + 25$$

$$15x = 25$$

$$x = \frac{25}{15} = \frac{5}{3}$$

Check.

$$0 \stackrel{?}{=} \frac{\left(\frac{5}{3}\right) - 7}{\left(\frac{5}{3}\right) + 1} - \frac{\left(\frac{5}{3}\right) + 3}{\left(\frac{5}{3}\right) - 4}$$

$$0 = 0$$

The x–intercept is $\left(\frac{5}{3}, 0\right)$.

35.

$$S = \frac{a}{1-r}$$

$$S(1-r) = a$$

$$S - Sr = a$$

$$-Sr = a - S$$

$$r = \frac{a-S}{-S}$$

36. H varies directly as the square of u.

37. w varies inversely as $\log(t)$.

38. $y = k\sqrt{x}$

Solve the following equation to find k.

$$2 = k\sqrt{49}$$

$$2 = 7k$$

$$\frac{2}{7} = k$$

The equation is $y = \frac{2}{7}\sqrt{x}$.

39.

$$B = \frac{k}{r^3}$$

Solve the following equation find k.

$$9 = \frac{k}{2^3}$$

$$9 = \frac{k}{8}$$

$$72 = k$$

The equation is $B = \frac{72}{r^3}$.

40. Let w be the number of inches of water and s be the number of inches of snow.

$$w = ks$$

Solve the following equation to find k.

$$2.24 = k(20)$$

$$0.112 = k$$

Using the equation $w = 0.112s$ we get the following:

$$w = 0.112(37)$$

$$w = 4.144$$

If 37 inches of snow melts, there will be 4.144 inches of water.

41. a. $m = kr^3$

b. $\dfrac{m}{r^3} = k$

c.

r	m	$\dfrac{m}{r^3}$
1.0	17.1	17.1
1.2	29.4	17.01
1.4	46.7	17.02
1.6	69.6	16.99
1.8	99.1	16.99
2.0	135.9	16.99

A reasonable value for k would be the average of column 3 which approximately 17.02.

d. $m = 17.02r^3$

e. The model fits the data very well.

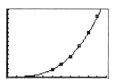

f. $m = 17.02(2.3)^3 \approx 207.08$ grams

42. a. $C(n) = 600 + 40n$

b. $M(n) = \dfrac{600 + 40n}{n}$

c. $M(270) = \dfrac{600 + 40(270)}{(270)} \approx 42.22$

The mean cost per person is $42.22 if 270 people use the room.

d.
$$50 = \dfrac{600 + 40n}{n}$$
$$50 \cdot n = \dfrac{600 + 40n}{n} \cdot n$$
$$50n = 600 + 40n$$
$$10n = 600$$
$$n = 60$$
In order for the mean cost per person to be $50, 60 people must use the room.

43. a. $v(t) = -6.27t^2 + 129.7t - 576.2$

$d(t) = 4.83t^2 - 79.1t + 326.0$

$v + d = -6.27t^2 + 129.7t - 576.2 + 4.83t^2 - 79.1t + 326.0$

$v + d = -1.44t^2 + 50.6t - 250.2$

t is the number of years since 1990. $v + d$ is the total number of videocassettes and dvds sold as a function of this time.

b. $v(t) = -6.27t^2 + 129.7t - 576.2$

$d(t) = 4.83t^2 - 79.1t + 326.0$

$v + d = -6.27t^2 + 129.7t - 576.2 + 4.83t^2 - 79.1t + 326.0$

$v + d = -1.44t^2 + 50.6t - 250.2$

$P(t) = 100\left(\dfrac{d}{v+d}\right) = 100\left(\dfrac{4.83t^2 - 79.1t + 326.0}{-1.44t^2 + 50.6t - 250.2}\right) =$

$P(t) = \dfrac{483t^2 - 7910t + 32600}{-1.44t^2 + 50.6t - 250.2}$

c. $P(10) = \dfrac{482(10)2 \quad 7910(10) + 32600}{-1.44(10)2 - 50.6(10) - 250.2}$

$= 16.1\%$

$P(10) = \dfrac{13.9}{13.9 + 99}(100)$

$= 12.3\%$

d. Using the graphing calculator, find the intersection point between the obtained function and $y = 100$. DVDs will dominate the market in two time locations – 1996 and again in 2004.

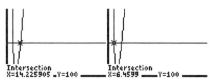

44. a. $T(a) = \dfrac{75}{a + 50} + \dfrac{40}{a + 65}$

b. $T(5) = \dfrac{75}{(5) + 50} + \dfrac{40}{(5) + 65} \approx 1.94$

When the student drives 5 mph above the speed limit, the driving time is 1.94 hours.

c.
$$2 = \dfrac{75}{a + 50} + \dfrac{40}{a + 65}$$
$$(a + 50)(a + 65) \cdot 2$$
$$= (a + 50)(a + 65)\left(\dfrac{75}{a + 50} + \dfrac{40}{a + 65}\right)$$
$$2(a^2 + 115a + 3250) = 75(a + 65) + 40(a + 50)$$
$$2a^2 + 230a + 6500 = 75a + 4875 + 40a + 2000$$
$$2a^2 + 230a + 6500 = 115a + 6875$$
$$2a^2 + 115a - 375 = 0$$
$$a = \dfrac{-115 \pm \sqrt{13225 - 4(2)(-375)}}{4}$$
$$= \dfrac{-115 \pm \sqrt{13225 + 3000}}{4}$$
$$= \dfrac{-115 \pm \sqrt{16225}}{4}$$

The only answer that makes sense in this context is the positive value.

$$\frac{-115+\sqrt{16225}}{4} \approx 3.1 \text{ mph above the}$$
speed limits.

The following graph shows the intersection of $y = 2$ and

$$y = \frac{75}{a+50} + \frac{40}{a+65}.$$

```
Intersection
X=3.094348    Y=2
```

Chapter 8 Test

1. $6x^2 + 11x - 10 = 0$

$$x = \frac{-11 \pm \sqrt{121 - 4(6)(-10)}}{12}$$

$$= \frac{-11 \pm \sqrt{121 + 240}}{12}$$

$$= \frac{-11 \pm \sqrt{361}}{12}$$

$$= \frac{-11 \pm 19}{12}$$

$$x = \frac{-11+19}{12} = \frac{2}{3} \quad \text{or} \quad x = \frac{-11-19}{12} = -\frac{5}{2}$$

The domain is the set of all real numbers except $\frac{2}{3}$ and $-\frac{5}{2}$.

2. $72 - 2x^2 = 0$

$36 - x^2 = 0$

$(6 - x)(6 + x) = 0$

$6 - x = 0 \quad \text{or} \quad 6 + x = 0$

$\phantom{6 - x = 0 \quad \text{or} \quad } 6 = x \qquad\qquad x = -6$

The domain is the set of all real numbers except 6 and −6.

3. Since there is no value that will make the denominator 0, the domain is the set of all real numbers.

4. Answers may vary. Example:

$$f(x) = \frac{4}{(x+3)(x-7)}$$

5. $\dfrac{6-3x}{x^2-5x+6} = \dfrac{-3(x-2)}{(x-2)(x-3)} = -\dfrac{3}{x-3}$

6. $\dfrac{9x^2-1}{18x^3-12x^2+2x} = \dfrac{(3x+1)(3x-1)}{2x(9x^2-6x+1)}$

$$= \dfrac{(3x+1)(3x-1)}{2x(3x-1)(3x-1)} = \dfrac{3x+1}{2x(3x-1)}$$

7. $\dfrac{5x^4}{3x^2+6x+12} \cdot \dfrac{x^3-8}{15x^7}$

$$= \dfrac{5x^4}{3(x^2+2x+4)} \cdot \dfrac{(x-2)(x^2+2x+4)}{3 \cdot 5 \cdot x^4 \cdot x^3}$$

$$= \dfrac{x-2}{9x^3}$$

8. $\dfrac{p^2-4t^2}{p^2+6pt+9t^2} \div \dfrac{p^2-3pt+2t^2}{p^2+3pt}$

$$= \dfrac{p^2-4t^2}{p^2+6pt+9t^2} \cdot \dfrac{p^2+3pt}{p^2-3pt+2t^2}$$

$$= \dfrac{(p-2t)(p+2t)}{(p+3t)(p+3t)} \cdot \dfrac{p(p+3t)}{(p-t)(p-2t)}$$

$$= \dfrac{(p-2t)(p+2t)p}{(p+3t)(p-t)(p-2t)}$$

$$= \dfrac{p(p+2t)}{(p+3t)(p-t)}$$

9. $\dfrac{5x+12}{-2x^2-8x} - \dfrac{2x+1}{x^2+2x-8}$

$$= \dfrac{5x+12}{-2x(x+4)} - \dfrac{2x+1}{(x-2)(x+4)}$$

$$= -\dfrac{(5x+12)}{2x(x+4)}\left(\dfrac{x-2}{x-2}\right) - \dfrac{(2x+1)}{(x-2)(x+4)}\left(\dfrac{2x}{2x}\right)$$

$$= \dfrac{-(5x+12)(x-2)}{2x(x+4)(x-2)} - \dfrac{2x(2x+1)}{2x(x+4)(x-2)}$$

$$= \dfrac{-(5x^2+2x-24)}{2x(x+4)(x-2)} - \dfrac{4x^2+2x}{2x(x+4)(x-2)}$$

$$= \dfrac{-5x^2-2x+24-4x^2-2x}{2x(x+4)(x-2)}$$

$$= \dfrac{-9x^2-4x+24}{2x(x+4)(x-2)}$$

10.
$$\frac{x+2}{x^2-9}+\frac{3}{x^2+11x+24}$$

$$=\frac{x+2}{(x-3)(x+3)}+\frac{3}{(x+3)(x+8)}$$

$$=\frac{(x+2)(x+8)}{(x-3)(x+3)(x+8)}+\frac{3(x-3)}{(x-3)(x+3)(x+8)}$$

$$=\frac{x^2+10x+16+3x-9}{(x-3)(x+3)(x+8)}$$

$$=\frac{x^2+13x+7}{(x-3)(x+3)(x+8)}$$

11.
$$\frac{3}{x^2-2x}\div\left(\frac{x}{5x-10}-\frac{x-1}{x^2-4}\right)$$

$$=\frac{3}{x^2-2x}\div\left(\frac{x}{5(x-2)}-\frac{x-1}{(x+2)(x-2)}\right)$$

$$=\frac{3}{x^2-2x}\div\left(\frac{x}{5(x-2)}\left(\frac{x+2}{x+2}\right)-\frac{(x-1)}{(x+2)(x-2)}\left(\frac{5}{5}\right)\right)$$

$$=\frac{3}{x^2-2x}\div\left(\frac{x^2+2x}{5(x-2)(x+2)}-\frac{5x-5}{5(x-2)(x+2)}\right)$$

$$=\frac{3}{x^2-2x}\div\left(\frac{x^2+2x-5x+5}{5(x-2)(x+2)}\right)$$

$$=\frac{3}{x^2-2x}\div\frac{x^2-3x+5}{5(x-2)(x+2)}$$

$$=\frac{3}{x(x-2)}\cdot\frac{5(x-2)(x+2)}{x^2-3x+5}$$

$$=\frac{15(x+2)}{x(x^2-3x+5)}$$

$$(f-g)(0)=\frac{6}{20}$$

$$=\frac{3}{10}$$

12.
$$f(x)-g(x)=\frac{x+1}{x-5}-\frac{x-2}{x+4}$$

$$=\left(\frac{x+1}{x-5}\right)\left(\frac{x+4}{x+4}\right)-\left(\frac{x-2}{x+4}\right)\left(\frac{x-5}{x-5}\right)$$

$$=\frac{x^2+5x+4}{(x-5)(x+4)}-\frac{x^2-7x+10}{(x-5)(x+4)}$$

13.
$$\frac{5+\frac{2}{x}}{3-\frac{4}{x-1}}=\left(\frac{5+\frac{2}{x}}{3-\frac{4}{x-1}}\right)\left(\frac{x(x-1)}{x(x-1)}\right)$$

$$=\frac{5x(x-1)+2(x-1)}{3x(x-1)-4x}=\frac{5x^2-5x+2x-2}{3x^2-3x-4x}$$

$$=\frac{5x^2-3x-2}{3x^2-7x}=\frac{(5x+2)(x-1)}{x(3x-7)}$$

14.
$$\frac{2}{x-1}-\frac{5}{x+1}=\frac{4x}{x^2-1}$$

$$\frac{2(x+1)-5(x-1)}{(x+1)(x-1)}=\frac{4x}{(x+1)(x-1)}$$

$$2x+2-5x+5=4x$$

$$-3x+7=4x$$

$$7=7x$$

$$1=x$$

$x=1$ is not in the domain so the solution set is the empty set.

15.
$$\frac{5}{x-3}=\frac{x}{x-2}+\frac{x}{x^2-5x+6}$$

$$\frac{5}{x-3}=\frac{x}{x-2}+\frac{x}{(x-3)(x-2)}$$

$$\frac{5(x-2)}{(x-3)(x-2)}=\frac{x(x-3)}{(x-3)(x-2)}+\frac{x}{(x-3)(x-2)}$$

$$\frac{5(x-2)}{(x-3)(x-2)}=\frac{x(x-3)+x}{(x-3)(x-2)}$$

$$5(x-2)=x(x-3)+x$$

$$5x-10=x^2-3x+x$$

$$5x-10=x^2-2x$$

$$x^2-7x+10=0$$

$$(x-5)(x-2)=0$$

$$x=\{5,2\}$$

$x=2$ is not in the domain so the solution is $x=5$.

16.

$$5 = \frac{2}{x-4} + \frac{3}{x+1}$$

$$(x-4)(x+1) \cdot 5 = (x-4)(x+1)\left(\frac{2}{x-4} + \frac{3}{x+1}\right)$$

$$5(x^2 - 3x - 4) = 2(x+1) + 3(x-4)$$

$$5x^2 - 15x - 20 = 2x + 2 + 3x - 12$$

$$5x^2 - 15x - 20 = 5x - 10$$

$$5x^2 - 20x - 10 = 0$$

$$x^2 - 4x - 2 = 0$$

$$x = \frac{4 \pm \sqrt{16 - 4(1)(-2)}}{2}$$

$$= \frac{4 \pm \sqrt{16 + 8}}{2}$$

$$= \frac{4 \pm \sqrt{24}}{2}$$

$$= \frac{4 \pm \sqrt{4 \cdot 6}}{2}$$

$$= \frac{4 \pm 2\sqrt{6}}{2}$$

$$= 2 \pm \sqrt{6}$$

Check $2 \pm \sqrt{6}$ using your calculator. The values of x are $2 \pm \sqrt{6}$.

17.

$$f(-2) = \frac{((-2)-5)((-2)+2)}{((-2)-1)((-2)+3)}$$

$$= \frac{0}{-3}$$

$$= 0$$

18.

$$f(1) = \frac{((1)-5)((1)+2)}{((1)-1)((1)+3)}$$

$$= \frac{-12}{0}$$

undefined

19.

$$0 = \frac{(x-5)(x+2)}{(x-1)(x+3)}$$

$$(x-1)(x+3) \cdot 0$$

$$= (x-1)(x+3)\frac{(x-5)(x+2)}{(x-1)(x+3)}$$

$$0 = (x-5)(x+2)$$

$$0 = x^2 - 3x - 10$$

$$0 = (x-5)(x+2)$$

$$x - 5 = 0 \quad \text{or} \quad x + 2 = 0$$

$$x = 5 \qquad\qquad x = -2$$

Check: $x = 5$

$$0 \overset{?}{=} \frac{((5)-5)((5)+2)}{((5)-1)((5)+3)}$$

$$0 = 0$$

Check. $x = -2$

$$0 \overset{?}{=} \frac{((-2)-5)((-2)+2)}{((-2)-1)((-2)+3)}$$

$$0 = 0$$

The values of x are 5 and -2.

20. $W = kt^2$

To find k solve the following equation:

$$3 = k(7)^2$$

$$3 = 49k$$

$$\frac{3}{49} = k$$

The equation is $W = \frac{3}{49}t^2$.

21.

$$y = \frac{k}{\sqrt{x}}$$

To find k solve the following equation:

$$8 = \frac{k}{\sqrt{25}}$$

$$8 = \frac{k}{5}$$

$$40 = k$$

The equation is $y = \frac{40}{\sqrt{x}}$.

22. a. $C(n) = 200n + 10000$

b.
$$B(n) = \frac{200n + 10000}{n}$$

c.
$$P(n) = \frac{200n + 10000}{n} + 150$$
$$= \frac{200n + 10000}{n} + 150 \cdot \frac{n}{n}$$
$$= \frac{200n + 10000}{n} + \frac{150n}{n}$$
$$= \frac{350n + 10000}{n}$$

d.
$$P(100) = \frac{350(100) + 10000}{100} = 450$$

If the bike manufacturer makes and sells 100 bikes in a month, the price of each bike should be $450 to insure that the manufacturer makes a profit of $150 per bike.

23. a.
$$T(a) = \frac{400}{a + 70} + \frac{920}{a + 75}$$

b.
$$T(5) = \frac{400}{(5) + 70} + \frac{920}{(5) + 75} \approx 16.83$$

When the student drives 5 mph above the speed limit, the trip takes about 16.8 hours.

c.
$$17 = \frac{400}{a + 70} + \frac{920}{a + 75}$$
$$(a + 70)(a + 75) \cdot 17$$
$$= (a + 70)(a + 75)\left(\frac{400}{a + 70} + \frac{920}{a + 75} \right)$$
$$17(a^2 + 145a + 5250)$$
$$= 400(a + 75) + 920(a + 70)$$
$$17a^2 + 2465a + 89250$$
$$= 400a + 30000 + 920a + 64400$$
$$17a^2 + 2465a + 89250 = 1320a + 94400$$
$$17a^2 + 1145a - 5150 = 0$$
$$a = \frac{-1145 \pm \sqrt{1311025 - 4(17)(-5150)}}{34}$$
$$= \frac{-1145 \pm \sqrt{1661225}}{34}$$

The only solution that makes sense in this context is the positive solution.

$$\frac{-1145 + \sqrt{1661225}}{34} \approx 4.23$$

This means the student must drive 4.23 mph above the speed limits for the driving time to be 17 hours.

24. a.
$$F = \frac{k}{L^2}$$

To find k solve the following equation:
$$50 = \frac{k}{8^2}$$
$$50 = \frac{k}{64}$$
$$3200 = k$$

The equation is $g(L) = F = \dfrac{3200}{L^2}$

b.
$$g(L) = F = \frac{3200}{6^2} \approx 88.9 \text{ hertz}$$

c.
$$200 = \frac{3200}{L^2}$$
$$200L^2 = 3200$$
$$L^2 = 16$$
$$L = 4 \text{ cm}$$

d. The graph is decreasing for $L > 0$.

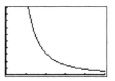

The longer the length of the prongs, the lower the frequency.

Chapter 9
Radical Functions

1. $x^{2/5} = \sqrt[5]{x^2}$

3. $\sqrt[4]{x^3} = x^{3/4}$

5. $\sqrt{w} = w^{1/2}$

7. $(2x+9)^{3/7} = \sqrt[7]{(2x+9)^3}$

9. $\sqrt[7]{(3k+2)^4} = (3k+2)^{4/7}$

11. $\sqrt{50} = \sqrt{25 \cdot 2} = \sqrt{25}\sqrt{2} = 5\sqrt{2}$

13. $\sqrt{x^8} = x^{8/2} = x^4$

15. $\sqrt{36x^6} = \sqrt{36} \cdot \sqrt{x^6} = 6x^3$

17. $\sqrt{5a^2b^{12}} = \sqrt{5} \cdot \sqrt{a^2b^{12}} = ab^6\sqrt{5}$

19. $\sqrt{x^9} = \sqrt{x^8 \cdot x} = \sqrt{x^8} \cdot \sqrt{x} = x^4\sqrt{x}$

21. $\sqrt{24x^5} = \sqrt{4 \cdot 6 \cdot x^4 \cdot x}$
$= \sqrt{4} \cdot \sqrt{6} \cdot \sqrt{x^4} \cdot \sqrt{x}$
$= 2x^2\sqrt{6x}$

23. $\sqrt{80x^3y^8} = \sqrt{16 \cdot 5 \cdot x^2 \cdot x \cdot y^8}$
$= \sqrt{16} \cdot \sqrt{5} \cdot \sqrt{x^2} \cdot \sqrt{x} \cdot \sqrt{y^8}$
$= 4xy^4\sqrt{5x}$

25. $\sqrt{200a^3b^5} = \sqrt{100 \cdot 2 \cdot a^2 \cdot a \cdot b^4 \cdot b}$
$= \sqrt{100} \cdot \sqrt{2} \cdot \sqrt{a^2} \cdot \sqrt{a} \cdot \sqrt{b^4} \cdot \sqrt{b}$
$= 10ab^2\sqrt{2ab}$

27. $\sqrt{(2x+5)^8} = (2x+5)^{8/2} = (2x+5)^4$

29. $\sqrt{(6t+3)^5} = \sqrt{(6t+3)^4(6t+3)}$
$= \sqrt{(6t+3)^4} \cdot \sqrt{6t+3}$
$= (6t+3)^2\sqrt{6t+3}$

31. $\sqrt[3]{27} = 3$

33. $\sqrt[6]{x^6} = x^{6/6} = x^1 = x$

35. $\sqrt[3]{8x^3} = \sqrt[3]{8} \cdot \sqrt[3]{x^3} = 2x$

37. $\sqrt[5]{-32x^{20}} = \sqrt[5]{-32} \cdot \sqrt[5]{x^{20}} = -2x^4$

39. $\sqrt[4]{81a^{12}b^{28}} = \sqrt[4]{81} \cdot \sqrt[4]{a^{12}} \cdot \sqrt[4]{b^{28}} = 3a^3b^7$

41. $\sqrt[6]{x^{17}} = \sqrt[6]{x^{12} \cdot x^5} = \sqrt[6]{x^{12}} \cdot \sqrt[6]{x^5} = x^2\sqrt[6]{x^5}$

43. $\sqrt[3]{-125a^{17}b^{12}} = \sqrt[3]{-125 \cdot a^{15} \cdot a^2 \cdot b^{12}}$
$= \sqrt[3]{-125} \cdot \sqrt[3]{a^{15}} \cdot \sqrt[3]{a^2} \cdot \sqrt[3]{b^{12}}$
$= -5a^5b^4\sqrt[3]{a^2}$

45. $\sqrt[5]{64x^{39}y^7} = \sqrt[5]{32 \cdot 2 \cdot x^{35} \cdot x^4 \cdot y^5 \cdot y^2}$
$= \sqrt[5]{32} \cdot \sqrt[5]{2} \cdot \sqrt[5]{x^{35}} \cdot \sqrt[5]{x^4} \cdot \sqrt[5]{y^5} \cdot \sqrt[5]{y^2}$
$= 2x^7y\sqrt[5]{2x^4y^2}$

47. $\sqrt[5]{(6xy)^5} = (6xy)^{5/5} = (6xy)^1 = 6xy$

49. $\sqrt[4]{(3x+6)^4} = (3x+6)^{4/4} = (3x+6)^1 = 3x+6$

51. $\sqrt[5]{(4p+7)^{20}} = (4p+7)^{20/5} = (4p+7)^4$

53. $\sqrt[6]{(2x+9)^{31}} = \sqrt[6]{(2x+9)^{30}(2x+9)}$
$= \sqrt[6]{(2x+9)^{30}} \cdot \sqrt[6]{2x+9}$
$= (2x+9)^5\sqrt[6]{2x+9}$

55. $\sqrt[8]{x^6} = x^{6/8} = x^{3/4} = \sqrt[4]{x^3}$

57. $\sqrt[6]{x^4} = x^{4/6} = x^{2/3} = \sqrt[3]{x^2}$

59.
$$\sqrt[12]{(2m+7)^{10}} = (2m+7)^{10/12}$$
$$= (2m+7)^{5/6}$$
$$= \sqrt[6]{(2m+7)^5}$$

61.
$$\sqrt[6]{x^{14}} = x^{14/6}$$
$$= x^{7/3}$$
$$= \sqrt[3]{x^7}$$
$$= \sqrt[3]{x^6 \cdot x}$$
$$= \sqrt[3]{x^6} \cdot \sqrt[3]{x}$$
$$= x^2 \sqrt[3]{x}$$

63. $\sqrt[6]{27} = \sqrt[6]{3^3} = 3^{3/6} = 3^{1/2} = \sqrt{3}$

65. $\sqrt[4]{\sqrt[3]{p}} = \sqrt[4]{p^{1/3}} = p^{\frac{1}{3} \cdot \frac{1}{4}} = p^{1/12} = \sqrt[12]{p}$

67.
$$\sqrt[10]{16x^8} = \sqrt[10]{16} \cdot \sqrt[10]{x^8}$$
$$= \sqrt[10]{4^2} \cdot \sqrt[10]{x^8}$$
$$= 4^{2/10} \cdot x^{8/10}$$
$$= 4^{1/5} \cdot x^{4/5}$$
$$= \sqrt[5]{4} \cdot \sqrt[5]{x^4}$$
$$= \sqrt[5]{4x^4}$$

69. $\sqrt[4]{\sqrt{ab}} = \sqrt[4]{ab^{1/2}} = ab^{\frac{1}{2} \cdot \frac{1}{4}} = ab^{1/8} = \sqrt[8]{ab}$

71. $f(-32) = \sqrt[5]{-32} = -2$

73. $g(2) = \sqrt[3]{3(2)+2} = \sqrt[3]{8} = 2$

75. $g(-7) = \sqrt[3]{3(-7)+2} = \sqrt[3]{-19}$

77. $h(49) = 2\sqrt{49} - 5 = 2(7) - 5 = 14 - 5 = 9$

79.

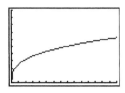

81. a.

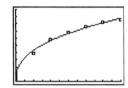

The model fits the data well.

b. $f(24) = 8.5\sqrt[5]{24^2} \approx 30.3$
The average temperature rise is about 30 degrees Fahrenheit.

c. $f(45) = 8.5\sqrt[5]{45^2} \approx 38.97$
$90 + 39 = 129$
The temperature in the car is about 129 degrees Fahrenheit.

d. $107 - 80 = 27$

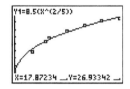

It would take about 18 minutes.

83. a. $f(3890) = \sqrt{9.8(3890)} \approx 195.25$
The speed of tsunami is about 195 meters per second.

b. $f(1000) = \sqrt{9.8(1000)} \approx 98.99$
$f(2000) = \sqrt{9.8(2000)} = 140$
$f(3000) = \sqrt{9.8(3000)} \approx 171.46$
F is an increasing function. This means that the speed of the tsunami increases as the depth of the ocean increases.

c. As a tsunami approaches the shore, the depth of the water decreases, which decreases the speed of the tsunami. At the same time, the height of the tsunami increases.

d. $195 \times 60 \times 60 = 702,000$ meters per hour
$702,000 \div 1609 \approx 436.3$ miles per hour
The tsunami travels at 436 mph.

85. Answers may vary.
$$\sqrt{x^{16}} = \left(x^{16}\right)^{1/2} = x^{16 \cdot \frac{1}{2}} = x^8$$

87.
$$\sqrt[n]{\sqrt[n]{x}} = \sqrt[n]{x^{1/n}}$$
$$= \left(x^{1/n}\right)^{1/n}$$
$$= x^{(1/n) \cdot (1/n)}$$
$$= x^{1/n^2}$$
$$= \sqrt[n^2]{x}$$

89. a. $\left(\sqrt{x}\right)^2 = \left(x^{1/2}\right)^2 = x^{2/2} = x^1 = x$

b. $\left(\sqrt[3]{x}\right)^3 = \left(x^{1/3}\right)^3 = x^{3/3} = x^1 = x$

c. $\left(\sqrt[n]{x}\right)^n = \left(x^{1/n}\right)^n = x^{n/n} = x^1 = x$

91. a.
$$\sqrt{16x^4 y^6} = \sqrt{16} \cdot \sqrt{x^4} \cdot \sqrt{y^6}$$
$$= 4x^2 y^3$$

b.
$$\sqrt{16x^4 y^6} = \left(16x^4 y^6\right)^{1/2}$$
$$= 16^{\frac{1}{2}} x^{4 \cdot \frac{1}{2}} y^{6 \cdot \frac{1}{2}}$$
$$= 4x^2 y^3$$

c. The answers are the same.

93.
$$\frac{2x}{x^2 + x - 6} - \frac{3x-1}{x^2 + 6x + 9} = \frac{-3}{x+3}$$
$$\frac{2x}{(x+3)(x-2)} - \frac{3x-1}{(x+3)(x+3)} = \frac{-3}{x+3}$$
$$2x(x+3) - (3x-1)(x-2) = -3(x+3)(x-2)$$
$$2x^2 + 6x - 3x^2 + 7x - 2 = -3x^2 - 3x + 18$$
$$2x^2 + 6x - 3x^2 + 7x - 2 + 3x^2 + 3x - 18 = 0$$
$$2x^2 + 16x - 20 = 0$$
$$2(x^2 + 8x - 10) = 0$$

$$\frac{-b \pm \sqrt{b^2 - 4ac}}{2a} = \frac{-8 \pm \sqrt{8^2 - 4(1)(-10)}}{2(1)}$$
$$= \frac{-8 \pm \sqrt{104}}{2}$$
$$= -4 \pm \sqrt{26}$$

$\dfrac{2x}{x^2 + x - 6} - \dfrac{3x-1}{x^2 + 6x + 9} = \dfrac{-3}{x+3}$ is a rational equation in one variable.

95.
$$\frac{2x}{x^2 + x - 6} - \frac{3x-1}{x^2 + 6x + 9}$$
$$= \frac{2x}{(x+3)(x-2)} - \frac{3x-1}{(x+3)(x+3)}$$
$$= \frac{2x(x+3) - (3x-1)(x-2)}{(x+3)(x+3)(x-2)}$$
$$= \frac{2x^2 + 6x - 3x^2 + 7x - 2}{(x+3)(x+3)(x-2)}$$
$$= \frac{-x^2 + 13x - 2}{(x+3)(x+3)(x-2)}$$

$\dfrac{2x}{x^2 + x - 6} - \dfrac{3x-1}{x^2 + 6x + 9}$ is a rational expression in one variable.

97.
$$f(x) = \frac{2x}{x^2 + x - 6} = \frac{2x}{(x+3)(x-2)}$$
The domain of $f(x)$ is all real numbers except $x = -3$ and $x = 2$.
$f(x) = \dfrac{2x}{x^2 + x - 6}$ is a rational function.

Homework 9.2

1. $4\sqrt{x} + 5\sqrt{x} = (4+5)\sqrt{x} = 9\sqrt{x}$

3.
$$2\sqrt[3]{5x^2 y} - 6\sqrt[3]{5x^2 y} = (2-6)\sqrt[3]{5x^2 y}$$
$$= -4\sqrt[3]{5x^2 y}$$

5.
$$3\sqrt{5a} + 2\sqrt{3b} - 6\sqrt{3b} + 7\sqrt{5a}$$
$$= \left(3\sqrt{5a} + 7\sqrt{5a}\right) + \left(2\sqrt{3b} - 6\sqrt{3b}\right)$$
$$= (3+7)\sqrt{5a} + (2-6)\sqrt{3b}$$
$$= 10\sqrt{5a} - 4\sqrt{3b}$$

7.
$$2\sqrt{x}+5-7\sqrt[3]{x}-9+5\sqrt[3]{x}$$
$$=2\sqrt{x}+(5-9)+(-7+5)\sqrt[3]{x}$$
$$=2\sqrt{x}-4-2\sqrt[3]{x}$$

9.
$$6\sqrt[3]{x-1}-3\sqrt[3]{x-1}-2\sqrt{x-1}$$
$$=(6-3)\sqrt[3]{x-1}-2\sqrt{x-1}$$
$$=3\sqrt[3]{x-1}-2\sqrt{x-1}$$

11.
$$3.7\sqrt[4]{x}-1.1\sqrt[4]{x}-4.2\sqrt[6]{x}+4.2\sqrt[6]{x}$$
$$=(3.7-1.1)\sqrt[4]{x}+(-4.2+4.2)\sqrt[6]{x}$$
$$=2.6\sqrt[4]{x}$$

13.
$$3\left(7-\sqrt{x}+2\right)-\left(\sqrt{x}+2\right)$$
$$=3\cdot7-3\cdot\sqrt{x}+3\cdot2-\sqrt{x}-2$$
$$=21-3\sqrt{x}+6-\sqrt{x}-2$$
$$=-3\sqrt{x}-\sqrt{x}+21+6-2$$
$$=(-3-1)\sqrt{x}+(21+6-2)$$
$$=-4\sqrt{x}+25$$

15.
$$7\left(\sqrt[3]{x}+1\right)-7\left(\sqrt[3]{x}-1\right)$$
$$=7\cdot\sqrt[3]{x}+7\cdot1-7\cdot\sqrt[3]{x}-7(-1)$$
$$=7\sqrt[3]{x}+7-7\sqrt[3]{x}+7$$
$$=7\sqrt[3]{x}-7\sqrt[3]{x}+7+7$$
$$=14$$

17.
$$\sqrt{12b}+\sqrt{75b}=\sqrt{4\cdot3b}+\sqrt{25\cdot3b}$$
$$=2\sqrt{3b}+5\sqrt{3b}$$
$$=(2+5)\sqrt{3b}$$
$$=7\sqrt{3b}$$

19.
$$\sqrt{18x^5}+2x\sqrt{50x^3}$$
$$=\sqrt{9\cdot2\cdot x^4\cdot x}+2x\sqrt{25\cdot2\cdot x^2\cdot x}$$
$$=\sqrt{9}\sqrt{x^4}\sqrt{2x}+2x\sqrt{25}\sqrt{x^2}\sqrt{2x}$$
$$=3x^2\sqrt{2x}+2x(5x)\sqrt{2x}$$
$$=3x^2\sqrt{2x}+10x^2\sqrt{2x}$$
$$=\left(3x^2+10x^2\right)\sqrt{2x}$$
$$=13x^2\sqrt{2x}$$

21.
$$5\sqrt{4x^3}-x\sqrt{36x}=5\sqrt{4\cdot x^2\cdot x}-x\sqrt{36\cdot x}$$
$$=5\sqrt{4}\sqrt{x^2}\sqrt{x}-x\sqrt{36}\sqrt{x}$$
$$=5(2)x\sqrt{x}-6x\sqrt{x}$$
$$=10x\sqrt{x}-6x\sqrt{x}$$
$$=(10-6)x\sqrt{x}$$
$$=4x\sqrt{x}$$

23.
$$3\sqrt{81x^2}-2\sqrt{100x^2}=3\cdot9x-2\cdot10x$$
$$=27x-20x$$
$$=7x$$

25.
$$a\sqrt{12b^3}+b\sqrt{75ba^2}$$
$$=a\sqrt{4b^2\cdot3b}+b\sqrt{25a^2\cdot3b}$$
$$=a\sqrt{4b^2}\sqrt{3b}+b\sqrt{25a^2}\sqrt{3b}$$
$$=2ab\sqrt{3b}+5ab\sqrt{3b}$$
$$=(2+5)ab\sqrt{3b}$$
$$=7ab\sqrt{3b}$$

27.
$$\sqrt[3]{27x^5}-x\sqrt[3]{8x^2}=\sqrt[3]{27x^3\cdot x^2}-x\sqrt[3]{8\cdot x^2}$$
$$=\sqrt[3]{27x^3}\sqrt[3]{x^2}-x\sqrt[3]{8}\sqrt[3]{x^2}$$
$$=3x\sqrt[3]{x^2}-2x\sqrt[3]{x^2}$$
$$=(3-2)x\sqrt[3]{x^2}$$
$$=x\sqrt[3]{x^2}$$

29.
$$y\sqrt[4]{16x^{11}y^4}-3x\sqrt[4]{x^7y^8}$$
$$=y\sqrt[4]{16\cdot x^8\cdot x^3\cdot y^4}-3x\sqrt[4]{x^4\cdot x^3\cdot y^8}$$
$$=y\sqrt[4]{16x^8y^4}\sqrt[4]{x^3}-3x\sqrt[4]{x^4y^8}\sqrt[4]{x^3}$$
$$=y\left(2x^2y\right)\sqrt[4]{x^3}-3x(xy^2)\sqrt[4]{x^3}$$
$$=2x^2y^2\sqrt[4]{x^3}-3x^2y^2\sqrt[4]{x^3}$$
$$=\left(2x^2y^2-3x^2y^2\right)\sqrt[4]{x^3}$$
$$=-x^2y^2\sqrt[4]{x^3}$$

31.
$$3\sqrt{x}\cdot2\sqrt{x}=3\cdot2\cdot\sqrt{x}\cdot\sqrt{x}$$
$$=6\sqrt{x\cdot x}$$
$$=6\sqrt{x^2}$$
$$=6x$$

33.
$$-2\sqrt{5x} \cdot 4\sqrt{3x} = -2 \cdot 4 \cdot \sqrt{5x} \cdot \sqrt{3x}$$
$$= -8\sqrt{5x \cdot 3x}$$
$$= -8\sqrt{15x^2}$$
$$= -8\sqrt{15}\sqrt{x^2}$$
$$= -8x\sqrt{15}$$

35.
$$2\sqrt{7t}\left(\sqrt{7t} - \sqrt{2t}\right) = 2\sqrt{7t} \cdot \sqrt{7t} - 2\sqrt{7t} \cdot \sqrt{2t}$$
$$= 2\sqrt{7t \cdot 7t} - 2\sqrt{7t \cdot 2t}$$
$$= 2\sqrt{49t^2} - 2\sqrt{14t^2}$$
$$= 2\sqrt{49}\sqrt{t^2} - 2\sqrt{14}\sqrt{t^2}$$
$$= 2 \cdot 7t - 2t\sqrt{14}$$
$$= 14t - 2t\sqrt{14}$$

37.
$$\left(2\sqrt{x} + 6\right)\left(5\sqrt{x} + 4\right)$$
$$= 2\sqrt{x} \cdot 5\sqrt{x} + 6 \cdot 5\sqrt{x} + 2\sqrt{x} \cdot 4 + 6 \cdot 4$$
$$= 10\sqrt{x^2} + 30\sqrt{x} + 8\sqrt{x} + 24$$
$$= 10x + (30 + 8)\sqrt{x} + 24$$
$$= 10x + 38\sqrt{x} + 24$$

39.
$$\left(4\sqrt{x} + \sqrt{3}\right)\left(2\sqrt{x} - \sqrt{5}\right)$$
$$= 4\sqrt{x} \cdot 2\sqrt{x} + \sqrt{3} \cdot 2\sqrt{x} - 4\sqrt{x} \cdot \sqrt{5} - \sqrt{3}\sqrt{5}$$
$$= 8\sqrt{x^2} + 2\sqrt{3x} - 4\sqrt{5x} - \sqrt{15}$$
$$= 8x + 2\sqrt{3x} - 4\sqrt{5x} - \sqrt{15}$$

41.
$$\left(5\sqrt{a} + \sqrt{b}\right)\left(\sqrt{a} - 2\sqrt{b}\right)$$
$$= 5\sqrt{a} \cdot \sqrt{a} + \sqrt{b} \cdot \sqrt{a} - 5\sqrt{a} \cdot 2\sqrt{b} - \sqrt{b} \cdot 2\sqrt{b}$$
$$= 5\sqrt{a^2} + \sqrt{ab} - 10\sqrt{ab} - 2\sqrt{b^2}$$
$$= 5a + (1 - 10)\sqrt{ab} - 2b$$
$$= 5a - 2b - 9\sqrt{ab}$$

43.
$$\left(1 - \sqrt{w}\right)\left(1 + \sqrt{w}\right) = 1^2 - \left(\sqrt{w}\right)^2 = 1 - w$$

45.
$$\left(7x + \sqrt{5}\right)\left(7x - \sqrt{5}\right) = \left(7x\right)^2 - \left(\sqrt{5}\right)^2$$
$$= 49x^2 - 5$$

47.
$$\left(2\sqrt{a} - \sqrt{b}\right)\left(2\sqrt{a} + \sqrt{b}\right) = \left(2\sqrt{a}\right)^2 - \left(\sqrt{b}\right)^2$$
$$= 2^2\left(\sqrt{a}\right)^2 - \left(\sqrt{b}\right)^2$$
$$= 4a - b$$

49.
$$\left(5 + 6\sqrt{x}\right)^2 = 5^2 + 2(5)\left(6\sqrt{x}\right) + \left(6\sqrt{x}\right)^2$$
$$= 25 + 60\sqrt{x} + 6^2\left(\sqrt{x}\right)^2$$
$$= 25 + 60\sqrt{x} + 36x$$
$$= 36x + 60\sqrt{x} + 25$$

51.
$$\left(4\sqrt{x} - \sqrt{5}\right)^2 = \left(4\sqrt{x}\right)^2 - 2\left(4\sqrt{x}\right)\left(\sqrt{5}\right) + \left(\sqrt{5}\right)^2$$
$$= 4^2\left(\sqrt{x}\right)^2 - 8\sqrt{5x} + 5$$
$$= 16x - 8\sqrt{5x} + 5$$

53.
$$\left(\sqrt{a} + 2\sqrt{b}\right)^2 = \left(\sqrt{a}\right)^2 + 2\left(\sqrt{a}\right)\left(2\sqrt{b}\right) + \left(2\sqrt{b}\right)^2$$
$$= a + 4\sqrt{ab} + 2^2\left(\sqrt{b}\right)^2$$
$$= a + 4\sqrt{ab} + 4b$$

55.
$$\left(\sqrt{2x-5} + 3\right)^2$$
$$= \left(\sqrt{2x-5}\right)^2 + 2\left(\sqrt{2x-5}\right)(3) + (3)^2$$
$$= 2x - 5 + 6\sqrt{2x-5} + 9$$
$$= 2x + 6\sqrt{2x-5} + 4$$

57.
$$\sqrt{x}\sqrt[5]{x} = x^{1/2} \cdot x^{1/5} = x^{\frac{1}{2} + \frac{1}{5}}$$
$$= x^{\frac{5}{10} + \frac{2}{10}} = x^{7/10}$$
$$= \sqrt[10]{x^7}$$

59.
$$\sqrt[5]{x^4}\sqrt[5]{x^3} = \sqrt[5]{x^4 \cdot x^3}$$
$$= \sqrt[5]{x^7}$$
$$= \sqrt[5]{x^5 \cdot x^2}$$
$$= \sqrt[5]{x^5}\sqrt[5]{x^2}$$
$$= x\sqrt[5]{x^2}$$

61.
$$-5\sqrt{m}\left(\sqrt[4]{2m}-4\right)=-5\sqrt{m}\cdot\sqrt[4]{2x}-5\sqrt{m}\left(-4\right)$$
$$=-5\sqrt{m}\sqrt[4]{2}\sqrt[4]{m}+20\sqrt{m}$$
$$=-5\sqrt[4]{2}\,m^{1/2}\cdot m^{1/4}+20\sqrt{m}$$
$$=-5\sqrt[4]{2}\,m^{\frac{1}{2}+\frac{1}{4}}+20\sqrt{m}$$
$$=-5\sqrt[4]{2}m^{3/4}+20\sqrt{m}$$
$$=-5\sqrt[4]{2}\sqrt[4]{m^3}+20\sqrt{m}$$
$$=-5\sqrt[4]{2m^3}+20\sqrt{m}$$

63.
$$\left(\sqrt[3]{x}+1\right)^2=\left(\sqrt[3]{x}\right)^2+2\left(\sqrt[3]{x}\right)(1)+(1)^2$$
$$=\sqrt[3]{x^2}+2\sqrt[3]{x}+1$$

65.
$$\left(\sqrt[4]{k}-\sqrt[3]{k}\right)^2=\left(\sqrt[4]{k}\right)^2-2\left(\sqrt[4]{k}\right)\left(\sqrt[3]{k}\right)+\left(\sqrt[3]{k}\right)^2$$
$$=\sqrt[4]{k^2}-2k^{1/4}\cdot k^{1/3}+\sqrt[3]{k^2}$$
$$=k^{2/4}-2k^{\frac{1}{4}+\frac{1}{3}}+\sqrt[3]{k^2}$$
$$=k^{1/2}-2k^{7/12}+\sqrt[3]{k^2}$$
$$=\sqrt{k}-2\sqrt[12]{k^7}+\sqrt[3]{k^2}$$

67.
$$\left(2\sqrt{x}-6\right)\left(3\sqrt[3]{x}+1\right)$$
$$=2\sqrt{x}\cdot 3\sqrt[3]{x}-6\cdot 3\sqrt[3]{x}+2\sqrt{x}\cdot 1-6\cdot 1$$
$$=6x^{1/2}\cdot x^{1/3}-18\sqrt[3]{x}+2\sqrt{x}-6$$
$$=6x^{\frac{1}{2}+\frac{1}{3}}-18\sqrt[3]{x}+2\sqrt{x}-6$$
$$=6x^{5/6}-18\sqrt[3]{x}+2\sqrt{x}-6$$
$$=6\sqrt[6]{x^5}-18\sqrt[3]{x}+2\sqrt{x}-6$$
$$=6\sqrt[6]{x^5}+2\sqrt{x}-18\sqrt[3]{x}-6$$

69.
$$\left(3\sqrt[4]{x}+5\right)\left(3\sqrt[4]{x}-5\right)=\left(3\sqrt[4]{x}\right)^2-(5)^2$$
$$=3^2\left(\sqrt[4]{x}\right)^2-25$$
$$=9\sqrt{x}-25$$

71. a. The flow rate, r, increases much more quickly as the value of d is increased. From the table, when the diameter doubles from 0.5 to 1.0, the flow rate quadruples. In the equation, $r=30d^2\sqrt{P}$, the value of d is squared, so as d increases, the value of r increases by the squared value of d. If you consider the

situation, the flow rate r should increase at a greater rate as you increase the nozzle diameter d because more water is able to leave through the nozzle.

b. i.
$$r=30(0.5)^2\sqrt{100}=75\text{ gallons/minute}$$
$$r=30(1)^2\sqrt{100}=300\text{ gallons/minute}$$
$$r=30(1.5)^2\sqrt{100}=675\text{ gallons/minute}$$
$$r=30(2)^2\sqrt{100}=1200\text{ gallons/minute}$$
$$r=30(2.5)^2\sqrt{100}=1875\text{ gallons/minute}$$

ii. $d=0.5$, error $=75-74=1$
$d=1$, error $=300-297=3$
$d=1.5$, error $=675-668=7$
$d=2$, error $=1200-1188=12$
$d=2.5$, error $=1875-1857=18$
The estimate for $d=2.5$ inches has the largest error at 18 gallons per minute.

iii. $d=0.5$, % error $=\dfrac{1}{74}\times100=1.35\%$

$d=1$, % error $=\dfrac{3}{297}\times100=1.01\%$

$d=1.5$, % error $=\dfrac{7}{668}\times100=1.05\%$

$d=2$, % error $=\dfrac{12}{1188}\times100=1.01\%$

$d=2.5$, % error $=\dfrac{18}{1857}\times100=0.97\%$

The estimate for $d=0.5$ inches has the largest percentage error at 1.35%.

c. $r=30(1.75)^2\sqrt{45}\approx616.3$
The estimated flow rate is 616 gallons per minute.

73. The student squared each term individually instead of using FOIL.
$$\left(x+\sqrt{7}\right)^2=\left(x+\sqrt{7}\right)\left(x+\sqrt{7}\right)$$
$$=(x)^2+2(x)\left(\sqrt{7}\right)+\left(\sqrt{7}\right)^2$$
$$=x^2+2x\sqrt{7}+7$$

75. The student multiplied a number by a radical as if they were both radicals.
$$7\left(2\sqrt{3}\right)=14\sqrt{3}$$

77.
$$\frac{\sqrt{x}}{\sqrt[3]{x}} = \frac{x^{1/2}}{x^{1/3}} = x^{\frac{1}{2}-\frac{1}{3}} = x^{\frac{3}{6}-\frac{2}{6}} = x^{\frac{1}{6}} = \sqrt[6]{x}$$

79. a.
$$\sqrt[3]{x}\sqrt[4]{x} = x^{1/3} \cdot x^{1/4}$$
$$= x^{\frac{1}{3}+\frac{1}{4}}$$
$$= x^{\frac{4}{12}+\frac{3}{12}}$$
$$= x^{7/12}$$
$$= \sqrt[12]{x^7}$$

b.
$$\sqrt[k]{x}\sqrt[n]{x} = x^{1/k} \cdot x^{1/n}$$
$$= x^{\frac{1}{k}+\frac{1}{n}}$$
$$= x^{\frac{n}{n \cdot k}+\frac{k}{n \cdot k}}$$
$$= x^{\frac{n+k}{n \cdot k}}$$
$$= \sqrt[kn]{x^{k+n}}$$

c.
$$\sqrt[3]{x}\sqrt[4]{x} \rightarrow \quad k = 3, n = 4$$
$$\sqrt[3]{x}\sqrt[4]{x} = \sqrt[3 \cdot 4]{x^{3+4}} = \sqrt[12]{x^7}$$
The results are the same.

d.
$$\sqrt[5]{x}\sqrt[7]{x} = \sqrt[5 \cdot 7]{x^{5+7}} = \sqrt[35]{x^{12}}$$

81. Answers will vary. If the indexes are the same, use the Product Property. If the indexes are different, change the radicals to exponents, then use the properties of exponents to solve. Finally, change the exponential expression back into a radical.

83.
$$3\sqrt{x} - 5\sqrt{x} = (3-5)\sqrt{x} = -2\sqrt{x}$$

85.
$$\left(3\sqrt{x}\right)\left(-5\sqrt{x}\right) = -15\sqrt{x^2} = -15x$$

87.
$$\log_b\left(x^2 + 3x - 40\right) - \log_b\left(x^2 - 64\right)$$
$$= \log_b\left(x+8\right)\left(x-5\right) - \log_b\left(x+8\right)\left(x-8\right)$$
$$= \log_b\frac{(x+8)(x-5)}{(x+8)(x-8)}$$
$$= \log_b\frac{x-5}{x-8}$$
$$\log_b\left(x^2 + 3x - 40\right) - \log_b\left(x^2 - 64\right) \text{ is a}$$
logarithmic expression in one variable.

89.
$$\log_2\left(3x-4\right) - \log_2\left(2x-3\right) = 3$$
$$\log_2\left(\frac{3x-4}{2x-3}\right) = 3$$
$$2^3 = \frac{3x-4}{2x-3}$$
$$8 = \frac{3x-4}{2x-3}$$
$$8(2x-3) = 3x-4$$
$$16x - 24 = 3x - 4$$
$$13x = 20$$
$$x = \frac{20}{13}$$
$$\log_2\left(3x-4\right) - \log_2\left(2x-3\right) = 3 \text{ is a}$$
logarithmic equation in one variable.

91.
$$2(3)^{5x-1} = 35$$
$$3^{5x-1} = 17.5$$
$$(5x-1)\ln 3 = \ln 17.5$$
$$5x-1 = \frac{\ln 17.5}{\ln 3}$$
$$5x-1 = 2.6053$$
$$5x = 3.6053$$
$$x \approx 0.7211$$
$$2(3)^{5x-1} = 35 \text{ is an exponential equation in}$$
one variable.

Homework 9.3

1.
$$\frac{8}{\sqrt{x}} = \frac{8}{\sqrt{x}} \cdot \frac{\sqrt{x}}{\sqrt{x}}$$
$$= \frac{8\sqrt{x}}{\left(\sqrt{x}\right)^2}$$
$$= \frac{8\sqrt{x}}{x}$$

3.
$$\frac{3}{\sqrt{5p}} = \frac{3}{\sqrt{5p}} \cdot \frac{\sqrt{5p}}{\sqrt{5p}}$$
$$= \frac{3\sqrt{5p}}{\left(\sqrt{5p}\right)^2}$$
$$= \frac{3\sqrt{5p}}{5p}$$

5.
$$\frac{4}{3\sqrt{2x}} = \frac{4}{3\sqrt{2x}} \cdot \frac{\sqrt{2x}}{\sqrt{2x}}$$
$$= \frac{4\sqrt{2x}}{3\left(\sqrt{2x}\right)^2}$$
$$= \frac{4\sqrt{2x}}{3 \cdot 2x}$$
$$= \frac{2\sqrt{2x}}{3x}$$

7.
$$\frac{10}{\sqrt{8k}} = \frac{10}{\sqrt{8k}} \cdot \frac{\sqrt{8k}}{\sqrt{8k}}$$
$$= \frac{10\sqrt{8k}}{\left(\sqrt{8k}\right)^2}$$
$$= \frac{10\sqrt{4 \cdot 2k}}{8k}$$
$$= \frac{10(2)\sqrt{2k}}{8k}$$
$$= \frac{20\sqrt{2k}}{8k}$$
$$= \frac{5\sqrt{2k}}{2k}$$

9.
$$\sqrt{\frac{4}{x}} = \frac{\sqrt{4}}{\sqrt{x}}$$
$$= \frac{2}{\sqrt{x}} \cdot \frac{\sqrt{x}}{\sqrt{x}}$$
$$= \frac{2\sqrt{x}}{\left(\sqrt{x}\right)^2}$$
$$= \frac{2\sqrt{x}}{x}$$

11.
$$\sqrt{\frac{7}{2}} = \frac{\sqrt{7}}{\sqrt{2}}$$
$$= \frac{\sqrt{7}}{\sqrt{2}} \cdot \frac{\sqrt{2}}{\sqrt{2}}$$
$$= \frac{\sqrt{7 \cdot 2}}{\left(\sqrt{2}\right)^2}$$
$$= \frac{\sqrt{14}}{2}$$

13.
$$\sqrt{\frac{2y}{x}} = \frac{\sqrt{2y}}{\sqrt{x}}$$
$$= \frac{\sqrt{2y}}{\sqrt{x}} \cdot \frac{\sqrt{x}}{\sqrt{x}}$$
$$= \frac{\sqrt{2y \cdot x}}{\left(\sqrt{x}\right)^2}$$
$$= \frac{\sqrt{2xy}}{x}$$

15.
$$\sqrt{\frac{x}{12y}} = \frac{\sqrt{x}}{\sqrt{12y}}$$
$$= \frac{\sqrt{x}}{\sqrt{12y}} \cdot \frac{\sqrt{12y}}{\sqrt{12y}}$$
$$= \frac{\sqrt{x \cdot 12y}}{\left(\sqrt{12y}\right)^2}$$
$$= \frac{\sqrt{x \cdot 4 \cdot 3y}}{12y}$$
$$= \frac{2\sqrt{3xy}}{12y}$$
$$= \frac{\sqrt{3xy}}{6y}$$

17.
$$\frac{3}{\sqrt{x-4}} = \frac{3}{\sqrt{x-4}} \cdot \frac{\sqrt{x-4}}{\sqrt{x-4}}$$
$$= \frac{3\sqrt{x-4}}{\left(\sqrt{x-4}\right)^2}$$
$$= \frac{3\sqrt{x-4}}{x-4}$$

19.
$$\frac{\sqrt{2a^3}}{\sqrt{3b}} = \frac{\sqrt{2a^3}}{\sqrt{3b}} \cdot \frac{\sqrt{3b}}{\sqrt{3b}}$$
$$= \frac{\sqrt{6a^3b}}{\left(\sqrt{3b}\right)^2}$$
$$= \frac{\sqrt{6 \cdot a^2 \cdot a \cdot b}}{3b}$$
$$= \frac{a\sqrt{6ab}}{3b}$$

21.

$$\frac{2}{\sqrt[3]{5}} = \frac{2}{\sqrt[3]{5}} \cdot \frac{\sqrt[3]{25}}{\sqrt[3]{25}}$$

$$= \frac{2\sqrt[3]{25}}{\sqrt[3]{5 \cdot 25}}$$

$$= \frac{2\sqrt[3]{25}}{\sqrt[3]{125}}$$

$$= \frac{2\sqrt[3]{25}}{5}$$

23.

$$\frac{5}{\sqrt[3]{4}} = \frac{5}{\sqrt[3]{4}} \cdot \frac{\sqrt[3]{2}}{\sqrt[3]{2}}$$

$$= \frac{5\sqrt[3]{2}}{\sqrt[3]{4 \cdot 2}}$$

$$= \frac{5\sqrt[3]{2}}{\sqrt[3]{8}}$$

$$= \frac{5\sqrt[3]{2}}{2}$$

25.

$$\frac{4}{5\sqrt[3]{x}} = \frac{4}{5\sqrt[3]{x}} \cdot \frac{\sqrt[3]{x^2}}{\sqrt[3]{x^2}}$$

$$= \frac{4\sqrt[3]{x^2}}{5\sqrt[3]{x \cdot x^2}}$$

$$= \frac{4\sqrt[3]{x^2}}{5\sqrt[3]{x^3}}$$

$$= \frac{4\sqrt[3]{x^2}}{5x}$$

27.

$$\frac{6}{\sqrt[3]{2x^2}} = \frac{6}{\sqrt[3]{2x^2}} \cdot \frac{\sqrt[3]{4x}}{\sqrt[3]{4x}}$$

$$= \frac{6\sqrt[3]{4x}}{\sqrt[3]{2x^2 \cdot 4x}}$$

$$= \frac{6\sqrt[3]{4x}}{\sqrt[3]{8x^3}}$$

$$= \frac{6\sqrt[3]{4x}}{\sqrt[3]{8}\sqrt[3]{x^3}}$$

$$= \frac{6\sqrt[3]{4x}}{2x}$$

$$= \frac{3\sqrt[3]{4x}}{x}$$

29.

$$\frac{7t}{\sqrt[4]{4t^3}} = \frac{7t}{\sqrt[4]{4t^3}} \cdot \frac{\sqrt[4]{4t}}{\sqrt[4]{4t}}$$

$$= \frac{7t\sqrt[4]{4t}}{\sqrt[4]{4t^3 \cdot 4t}}$$

$$= \frac{7t\sqrt[4]{4t}}{\sqrt[4]{16t^4}}$$

$$= \frac{7t\sqrt[4]{4t}}{\sqrt[4]{16}\sqrt[4]{t^4}}$$

$$= \frac{7t\sqrt[4]{4t}}{2t}$$

$$= \frac{7\sqrt[4]{4t}}{2}$$

31.

$$\frac{\sqrt[3]{x}}{\sqrt{x}} = \frac{\sqrt[3]{x}}{\sqrt{x}} \cdot \frac{\sqrt{x}}{\sqrt{x}}$$

$$= \frac{x^{1/3} \cdot x^{1/2}}{\left(\sqrt{x}\right)^2}$$

$$= \frac{x^{\frac{1}{3} + \frac{1}{2}}}{x}$$

$$= \frac{x^{\frac{2}{6} + \frac{3}{6}}}{x}$$

$$= \frac{x^{5/6}}{x}$$

$$= \frac{\sqrt[6]{x^5}}{x}$$

33.

$$\sqrt[5]{\frac{2}{x^3}} = \frac{\sqrt[5]{2}}{\sqrt[5]{x^3}}$$

$$= \frac{\sqrt[5]{2}}{\sqrt[5]{x^3}} \cdot \frac{\sqrt[5]{x^2}}{\sqrt[5]{x^2}}$$

$$= \frac{\sqrt[5]{2 \cdot x^2}}{\sqrt[5]{x^3 \cdot x^2}}$$

$$= \frac{\sqrt[5]{2x^2}}{\sqrt[5]{x^5}}$$

$$= \frac{\sqrt[5]{2x^2}}{x}$$

35.

$$\sqrt[4]{\frac{4}{9x^2}} = \frac{\sqrt[4]{4}}{\sqrt[4]{9x^2}}$$

$$= \frac{\sqrt[4]{4}}{\sqrt[4]{9x^2}} \cdot \frac{\sqrt[4]{9x^2}}{\sqrt[4]{9x^2}}$$

$$= \frac{\sqrt[4]{4 \cdot 9x^2}}{\sqrt[4]{9x^2 \cdot 9x^2}}$$

$$= \frac{\sqrt[4]{36x^2}}{\sqrt[4]{81x^4}}$$

$$= \frac{\sqrt[4]{6^2 x^2}}{3x}$$

$$= \frac{6^{2/4} x^{2/4}}{3x}$$

$$= \frac{6^{1/2} x^{1/2}}{3x}$$

$$= \frac{\sqrt{6x}}{3x}$$

37.

$$\sqrt[5]{\frac{3w}{4x^4 y^2}} = \frac{\sqrt[5]{3w}}{\sqrt[5]{4x^4 y^2}}$$

$$= \frac{\sqrt[5]{3w}}{\sqrt[5]{4x^4 y^2}} \cdot \frac{\sqrt[5]{8xy^3}}{\sqrt[5]{8xy^3}}$$

$$= \frac{\sqrt[5]{3w}\sqrt[5]{8xy^3}}{\sqrt[5]{4x^4 y^2 \cdot 8xy^3}}$$

$$= \frac{\sqrt[5]{3w}\sqrt[5]{8xy^3}}{\sqrt[5]{32x^5 y^5}}$$

$$= \frac{\sqrt[5]{24wxy^3}}{2xy}$$

39.

$$\frac{1}{5+\sqrt{3}} = \frac{1}{5+\sqrt{3}} \cdot \frac{5-\sqrt{3}}{5-\sqrt{3}}$$

$$= \frac{1 \cdot 5 - 1 \cdot \sqrt{3}}{(5)^2 - (\sqrt{3})^2}$$

$$= \frac{5-\sqrt{3}}{25-3}$$

$$= \frac{5-\sqrt{3}}{22}$$

41.

$$\frac{2}{\sqrt{3}+\sqrt{7}} = \frac{2}{\sqrt{3}+\sqrt{7}} \cdot \frac{\sqrt{3}-\sqrt{7}}{\sqrt{3}-\sqrt{7}}$$

$$= \frac{2 \cdot \sqrt{3} - 2 \cdot \sqrt{7}}{(\sqrt{3})^2 - (\sqrt{7})^2}$$

$$= \frac{2\sqrt{3} - 2\sqrt{7}}{3-7}$$

$$= \frac{2\sqrt{3} - 2\sqrt{7}}{-4}$$

$$= \frac{\sqrt{7} - \sqrt{3}}{2}$$

43.

$$\frac{1}{3\sqrt{r}-7} = \frac{1}{3\sqrt{r}-7} \cdot \frac{3\sqrt{r}+7}{3\sqrt{r}+7}$$

$$= \frac{1 \cdot 3\sqrt{r} + 1 \cdot 7}{(3\sqrt{r})^2 - (7)^2}$$

$$= \frac{3\sqrt{r}+7}{9r-49}$$

45.

$$\frac{\sqrt{x}}{\sqrt{x}-1} = \frac{\sqrt{x}}{\sqrt{x}-1} \cdot \frac{\sqrt{x}+1}{\sqrt{x}+1}$$

$$= \frac{\sqrt{x} \cdot \sqrt{x} + \sqrt{x} \cdot 1}{(\sqrt{x})^2 - (1)^2}$$

$$= \frac{x + \sqrt{x}}{x-1}$$

47.

$$\frac{3\sqrt{x}}{4\sqrt{x}-\sqrt{5}} = \frac{3\sqrt{x}}{4\sqrt{x}-\sqrt{5}} \cdot \frac{4\sqrt{x}+\sqrt{5}}{4\sqrt{x}+\sqrt{5}}$$

$$= \frac{3\sqrt{x} \cdot 4\sqrt{x} + 3\sqrt{x} \cdot \sqrt{5}}{(4\sqrt{x})^2 - (\sqrt{5})^2}$$

$$= \frac{12(\sqrt{x})^2 + 3\sqrt{5x}}{4^2(\sqrt{x})^2 - 5}$$

$$= \frac{12x + 3\sqrt{5x}}{16x - 5}$$

49.
$$\frac{\sqrt{x}}{\sqrt{x}-y} = \frac{\sqrt{x}}{\sqrt{x}-y} \cdot \frac{\sqrt{x}+y}{\sqrt{x}+y}$$
$$= \frac{\sqrt{x}\cdot\sqrt{x}+\sqrt{x}\cdot y}{\left(\sqrt{x}\right)^2-(y)^2}$$
$$= \frac{x+y\sqrt{x}}{x-y^2}$$

51.
$$\frac{\sqrt{x}-5}{\sqrt{x}+5} = \frac{\sqrt{x}-5}{\sqrt{x}+5} \cdot \frac{\sqrt{x}-5}{\sqrt{x}-5}$$
$$= \frac{\left(\sqrt{x}\right)^2-2\left(\sqrt{x}\right)(5)+(5)^2}{\left(\sqrt{x}\right)^2-(5)^2}$$
$$= \frac{x-10\sqrt{x}+25}{x-25}$$

53.
$$\frac{2\sqrt{x}+5}{3\sqrt{x}+1} = \frac{2\sqrt{x}+5}{3\sqrt{x}+1} \cdot \frac{3\sqrt{x}-1}{3\sqrt{x}-1}$$
$$= \frac{2\sqrt{x}\cdot3\sqrt{x}-2\sqrt{x}\cdot1+5\cdot3\sqrt{x}-5\cdot1}{\left(3\sqrt{x}\right)^2-(1)^2}$$
$$= \frac{6\left(\sqrt{x}\right)^2-2\sqrt{x}+15\sqrt{x}-5}{3^2\left(\sqrt{x}\right)^2-1}$$
$$= \frac{6x+13\sqrt{x}-5}{9x-1}$$

55.
$$\frac{6\sqrt{x}+\sqrt{5}}{3\sqrt{x}-\sqrt{7}} = \frac{6\sqrt{x}+\sqrt{5}}{3\sqrt{x}-\sqrt{7}} \cdot \frac{3\sqrt{x}+\sqrt{7}}{3\sqrt{x}+\sqrt{7}}$$
$$= \frac{6\sqrt{x}\cdot3\sqrt{x}+6\sqrt{x}\cdot\sqrt{7}+\sqrt{5}\cdot3\sqrt{x}+\sqrt{5}\cdot\sqrt{7}}{\left(3\sqrt{x}\right)^2-\left(\sqrt{7}\right)^2}$$
$$= \frac{18\left(\sqrt{x}\right)^2+6\sqrt{7\cdot x}+3\sqrt{5\cdot x}+\sqrt{5\cdot7}}{3^2\left(\sqrt{x}\right)^2-7}$$
$$= \frac{18x+6\sqrt{7x}+3\sqrt{5x}+\sqrt{35}}{9x-7}$$

57.
$$\frac{\sqrt{x}-\sqrt{y}}{\sqrt{x}+\sqrt{y}} = \frac{\sqrt{x}-\sqrt{y}}{\sqrt{x}+\sqrt{y}} \cdot \frac{\sqrt{x}-\sqrt{y}}{\sqrt{x}-\sqrt{y}}$$
$$= \frac{\left(\sqrt{x}\right)^2-2\left(\sqrt{x}\right)\left(\sqrt{y}\right)+\left(\sqrt{y}\right)^2}{\left(\sqrt{x}\right)^2-\left(\sqrt{y}\right)^2}$$
$$= \frac{x-2\sqrt{xy}+y}{x-y}$$

59.
$$\frac{1}{\sqrt{x+1}-\sqrt{x}} = \frac{1}{\sqrt{x+1}-\sqrt{x}} \cdot \frac{\sqrt{x+1}+\sqrt{x}}{\sqrt{x+1}+\sqrt{x}}$$
$$= \frac{\sqrt{x+1}+\sqrt{x}}{\left(\sqrt{x+1}\right)^2-\left(\sqrt{x}\right)^2}$$
$$= \frac{\sqrt{x+1}+\sqrt{x}}{x+1-x}$$
$$= \sqrt{x+1}+\sqrt{x}$$

61. a.
$$\sqrt{\frac{3h}{2}} = \frac{\sqrt{3h}}{\sqrt{2}} = \frac{\sqrt{3h}}{\sqrt{2}}\cdot\frac{\sqrt{2}}{\sqrt{2}} = \frac{\sqrt{6h}}{\left(\sqrt{2}\right)^2} = \frac{\sqrt{6h}}{2}$$

b.
$$\frac{\sqrt{6(1450)}}{2} = \frac{\sqrt{8700}}{2} \approx 46.64$$
The horizon is about 47 miles from the top of the skyscraper.

c.
$$\frac{\sqrt{6(30,000+1450)}}{2} = \frac{\sqrt{6(31,450)}}{2}$$
$$= \frac{\sqrt{188,700}}{2}$$
$$\approx 217.2$$
The airplane is about 217 miles from the horizon.

63. a. Cut the paper in half so that the dimensions are $\frac{x\sqrt{2}}{2}$ by x.
$$\frac{x}{\frac{x\sqrt{2}}{2}} = \frac{x}{1}\cdot\frac{2}{x\sqrt{2}} = \frac{2x}{x\sqrt{2}} = \frac{2}{\sqrt{2}}$$
$$= \frac{2}{\sqrt{2}}\cdot\frac{\sqrt{2}}{\sqrt{2}} = \frac{2\sqrt{2}}{\left(\sqrt{2}\right)^2} = \frac{2\sqrt{2}}{2} = \frac{\sqrt{2}}{1}$$

b.
$$1 = x \cdot x\sqrt{2}$$
$$1 = x^2\sqrt{2}$$
$$x^2 = \frac{1}{\sqrt{2}}$$
$$x^2 = \frac{\sqrt{2}}{2}$$
$$x = \sqrt{\frac{\sqrt{2}}{2}}$$
$$x = \frac{\sqrt[4]{2}}{\sqrt{2}} \cdot \frac{\sqrt{2}}{\sqrt{2}}$$
$$x = \frac{2^{1/4} \cdot 2^{1/2}}{2}$$
$$x = \frac{\sqrt[4]{2^3}}{2}$$
$$x = \frac{\sqrt[4]{8}}{2}$$
$$x \approx 0.84$$
The page has a width of about 0.84 meters.

65. Student 1 did the work correctly. Student 2's error was to square the entire expression. This changes the value of the expression. To simplify the expression, you need to multiply by something equivalent to 1.

67. Answers may vary. The student did not rationalize the denominator correctly. For the radicand in the denominator to be a perfect cube, $\sqrt[3]{x}$ needs to be multiplied by $\sqrt[3]{x^2}$ to yield
$$\sqrt[3]{x} \cdot \sqrt[3]{x^2} = \sqrt[3]{x^3}.$$
$$\frac{5}{\sqrt[3]{x}} = \frac{5}{\sqrt[3]{x}} \cdot \frac{\sqrt[3]{x^2}}{\sqrt[3]{x^2}}$$
$$= \frac{5\sqrt[3]{x^2}}{\sqrt[3]{x \cdot x^2}}$$
$$= \frac{5\sqrt[3]{x^2}}{\sqrt[3]{x^3}}$$
$$= \frac{5\sqrt[3]{x^2}}{x}$$

69.
$$\frac{\sqrt{x}}{3} = \frac{\sqrt{x}}{3} \cdot \frac{\sqrt{x}}{\sqrt{x}} = \frac{\sqrt{x^2}}{3\sqrt{x}} = \frac{x}{3\sqrt{x}}$$

71.
$$\frac{\sqrt{x+2}-\sqrt{x}}{2} = \frac{\sqrt{x+2}-\sqrt{x}}{2} \cdot \frac{\sqrt{x+2}+\sqrt{x}}{\sqrt{x+2}+\sqrt{x}}$$
$$= \frac{\left(\sqrt{x+2}\right)^2 - \left(\sqrt{x}\right)^2}{2\left(\sqrt{x+2}+\sqrt{x}\right)}$$
$$= \frac{x+2-x}{2\left(\sqrt{x+2}+\sqrt{x}\right)}$$
$$= \frac{2}{2\left(\sqrt{x+2}+\sqrt{x}\right)}$$
$$= \frac{1}{\sqrt{x+2}+\sqrt{x}}$$

73.
$$\frac{\frac{1}{\sqrt{x}}-\frac{3}{x}}{\frac{2}{\sqrt{x}}+\frac{1}{x}} = \frac{\frac{1}{\sqrt{x}} \cdot \frac{\sqrt{x}}{\sqrt{x}} - \frac{3}{x}}{\frac{2}{\sqrt{x}} \cdot \frac{\sqrt{x}}{\sqrt{x}} + \frac{1}{x}}$$
$$= \frac{\frac{\sqrt{x}}{x}-\frac{3}{x}}{\frac{2\sqrt{x}}{x}+\frac{1}{x}}$$
$$= \frac{\frac{\sqrt{x}-3}{x}}{\frac{2\sqrt{x}+1}{x}}$$
$$= \frac{\sqrt{x}-3}{x} \div \frac{2\sqrt{x}+1}{x}$$
$$= \frac{\sqrt{x}-3}{x} \cdot \frac{x}{2\sqrt{x}+1}$$
$$= \frac{\sqrt{x}-3}{2\sqrt{x}+1}$$
$$= \frac{\sqrt{x}-3}{2\sqrt{x}+1} \cdot \frac{2\sqrt{x}-1}{2\sqrt{x}-1}$$
$$= \frac{\sqrt{x} \cdot 2\sqrt{x} - \sqrt{x} \cdot 1 - 3 \cdot 2\sqrt{x} - 3(-1)}{\left(2\sqrt{x}\right)^2 - (1)^2}$$
$$= \frac{2x - \sqrt{x} - 6\sqrt{x} + 3}{4x-1}$$
$$= \frac{2x - 7\sqrt{x} + 3}{4x-1}$$

75.
$$x\sqrt{2} + 3\sqrt{5} = 9\sqrt{5}$$
$$x\sqrt{2} = 9\sqrt{5} - 3\sqrt{5}$$
$$x\sqrt{2} = 6\sqrt{5}$$
$$x = \frac{6\sqrt{5}}{\sqrt{2}}$$
$$x = \frac{6\sqrt{5}}{\sqrt{2}} \cdot \frac{\sqrt{2}}{\sqrt{2}}$$
$$x = \frac{6\sqrt{10}}{2}$$
$$x = 3\sqrt{10}$$

77. Answers may vary.

1. Determine the conjugate of the denominator.

2. Multiply the original fraction by the fraction
$$\frac{\text{conjugate}}{\text{conjugate}}$$

3. Find the product of the fractions and simplify.

79. a. $A^3 + B^3 = (A+B)\left(A^2 - AB + B^2\right)$

b. $(A+B)\left(A^2 - AB + B^2\right)$
$$= A^3 - A^2B + AB^2 + A^2B - AB^2 + B^3$$
$$= A^3 + B^3$$
$(A+B)\left(A^2 - AB + B^2\right)$ is the factored form of $A^3 + B^3$.

c. $(x+2)\left(x^2 - 2x + 4\right)$
$$= x\left(x^2\right) + 2\left(x^2\right) - x(2x) - 2(2x) + x(4) + 2(4)$$
$$= x^3 + 2x^2 - 2x^2 - 4x + 4x + 8$$
$$= x^3 + 8$$
It follows the equation
$(A+B)\left(A^2 - AB + B^2\right) = A^3 + B^3$, where A
$= x$ and $B = 2$.

d. $\left(\sqrt[3]{x} + \sqrt[3]{2}\right)\left(\sqrt[3]{x^2} - \sqrt[3]{2x} + \sqrt[3]{4}\right)$
$$= \left(\sqrt[3]{x}\right)\left(\sqrt[3]{x^2}\right) + \left(\sqrt[3]{2}\right)\left(\sqrt[3]{x^2}\right) - \left(\sqrt[3]{x}\right)\left(\sqrt[3]{2x}\right)$$
$$- \left(\sqrt[3]{2}\right)\left(\sqrt[3]{2x}\right) + \left(\sqrt[3]{x}\right)\left(\sqrt[3]{4}\right) + \left(\sqrt[3]{2}\right)\left(\sqrt[3]{4}\right)$$
$$= \sqrt[3]{x^3} + \sqrt[3]{2x^2} - \sqrt[3]{2x^2} - \sqrt[3]{4x} + \sqrt[3]{4x} + \sqrt[3]{8}$$
$$= x + 2$$
It follows the equation
$(A+B)\left(A^2 - AB + B^2\right) = A^3 + B^3$, where A
$= \sqrt[3]{x}$ and $B = \sqrt[3]{2}$.

e. $\dfrac{1}{\sqrt[3]{x} + \sqrt[3]{2}}$
$$= \frac{1}{\sqrt[3]{x} + \sqrt[3]{2}} \cdot \frac{\sqrt[3]{x^2} - \sqrt[3]{2x} + \sqrt[3]{4}}{\sqrt[3]{x^2} - \sqrt[3]{2x} + \sqrt[3]{4}}$$
$$= \frac{\sqrt[3]{x^2} - \sqrt[3]{2x} + \sqrt[3]{4}}{\sqrt[3]{x^3} + \sqrt[3]{2x^2} - \sqrt[3]{2x^2} - \sqrt[3]{4x} + \sqrt[3]{4x} + \sqrt[3]{8}}$$
$$= \frac{\sqrt[3]{x^2} - \sqrt[3]{2x} + \sqrt[3]{4}}{x + 2}$$

81. $(5x-4)\left(3x^2 - 2x - 1\right)$
$$= 5x \cdot 3x^2 - 4 \cdot 3x^2 - 5x \cdot 2x + 4 \cdot 2x - 5x \cdot 1 + 4 \cdot 1$$
$$= 15x^3 - 12x^2 - 10x^2 + 8x - 5x + 4$$
$$= 15x^3 - 22x^2 + 3x + 4$$
$(5x-4)\left(3x^2 - 2x - 1\right)$ is a cubic polynomial in one variable.

83. $24x^3 - 3000 = 24\left(x^3 - 125\right)$
$$= 24(x-5)\left(x^2 + 5x + 25\right)$$
$24x^3 - 3000$ is a cubic polynomial in one variable.

85.
$$5x^2 - 3 = 4x - 1$$
$$5x^2 - 3 - 4x + 1 = 0$$
$$5x^2 - 4x - 2 = 0$$
$$a = 5, b = -4, c = -2$$
$$x = \frac{4 \pm \sqrt{(-4)^2 - 4(5)(-2)}}{2(5)}$$
$$= \frac{4 \pm \sqrt{56}}{10} = \frac{2 \pm \sqrt{14}}{5}$$

$5x^2 - 3 = 4x - 1$ is a quadratic polynomial in one variable.

Homework 9.4

1.

$y = 2\sqrt{x}$

x	y
0	0
1	2
4	4
9	6
16	8

3.

$y = -\sqrt{x}$

x	y
0	0
1	-1
4	-2
9	-3
16	-4

5.

$y = \sqrt{x} + 3$

x	y
0	3
1	4
4	5
9	6
16	7

7.

$y = 2\sqrt{x} - 5$

x	y
0	-5
1	-3
4	-1
9	1
16	3

9.

$y = -3\sqrt{x} + 4$

x	y
0	4
1	1
4	-2
9	-5
16	-8

11.

$y = \sqrt{x - 2}$

x	y
2	0
3	1
6	2
11	3
18	4

13.

$y = -\sqrt{x + 2}$

x	y
-2	0
-1	-1
2	-2
7	-3
14	-4

15.

$y = \frac{1}{2}\sqrt{x} - 4$

x	y
4	0
5	$\frac{1}{2}$
8	1
13	$\frac{3}{2}$
20	2

17.

$y = \sqrt{x + 3} + 2$

x	y
-3	2
-2	3
1	4
6	5
13	6

19.

$y = -2\sqrt{x + 3} - 4$

x	y
-3	-4
-2	-6
1	-8
6	-10
13	-12

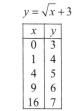

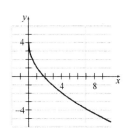

21. $y = 4\sqrt{x-1} - 3$

x	y
1	-3
2	1
5	5
10	9
17	13

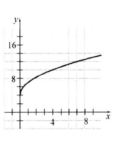

23. $\sqrt{x} + y = 4$

$y = -\sqrt{x} + 4$

x	y
0	4
1	3
4	2
9	1
16	0

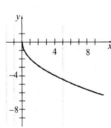

25. $2y - 6\sqrt{x} = 8$

$2y = 6\sqrt{x} + 8$

$y = 3\sqrt{x} + 4$

x	y
0	4
1	7
4	10
9	13
16	16

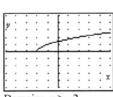

27. $y = -2\sqrt{x}$

x	y
0	0
1	-2
4	-4
9	-6
16	-8

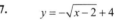

Domain: $x \geq 0$
Range: $y \leq 0$

29. $y = \sqrt{x+2}$

x	y
-2	0
-1	1
2	2
7	3
14	4

Domain: $x \geq -2$
Range: $y \geq 0$

31. $y = \sqrt{x} + 2$

x	y
0	2
1	3
4	4
9	5
16	6

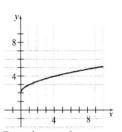

Domain: $x \geq 0$
Range: $y \geq 2$

33. $y = \sqrt{x-5} - 3$

x	y
5	-3
6	-2
9	-1
16	0
21	1

Domain: $x \geq 5$
Range: $y \geq -3$

35. $y = 2\sqrt{x+5} + 1$

x	y
-5	1
-4	3
-1	5
4	7
11	9

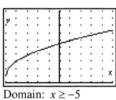

Domain: $x \geq -5$
Range: $y \geq 1$

37. $y = -\sqrt{x-2} + 4$

x	y
2	4
3	3
6	2
11	1
18	0

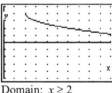

Domain: $x \geq 2$
Range: $y \leq 4$

39. a. $f(x) = 2\sqrt{x-3}$

x	$f(x)$
3	0
4	2
7	4
12	6
19	8

b.

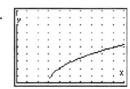

336

c. For each input-output pair, the output variable is equal to 2 times the square root of 3 less than the input variable.

41. a. $a < 0, h = 0,$ and $k > 0$

b. $a > 0, h < 0,$ and $k < 0$

c. $a > 0, h < 0,$ and $k > 0$

d. $a < 0, h > 0,$ and $k = 0$

43. Answers may vary. For the family of curves $y = a\sqrt{x - h} + k$, $k = 2$, and $h = 0$.

Let $a = -4, -3, -2, -1, -\dfrac{1}{2}, \dfrac{1}{2}, 1, 2, 3,$ and 4.

```
WINDOW
Xmin=-10
Xmax=10
Xscl=1
Ymin=-10
Ymax=10
Yscl=1
Xres=1
```

45. If $a < 0$, f has a maximum point at (h, k). If $a > 0$, f has a minimum point at (h, k).

47.
$$f(4) = 7\sqrt{4} - 3$$
$$= 7 \cdot 2 - 3$$
$$= 11$$

49.
$$f(9c) = 7\sqrt{9c} - 3$$
$$= 7 \cdot 3\sqrt{c} - 3$$
$$= 21\sqrt{c} - 3$$

51.
$$f + g = \left(5\sqrt{x} - 9\right) + \left(4\sqrt{x} + 1\right)$$
$$= 5\sqrt{x} - 9 + 4\sqrt{x} + 1$$
$$= 9\sqrt{x} - 8$$

53.
$$f \cdot g = \left(5\sqrt{x} - 9\right)\left(4\sqrt{x} + 1\right)$$
$$= 5\sqrt{x} \cdot 4\sqrt{x} - 9 \cdot 4\sqrt{x} + 5\sqrt{x} \cdot 1 - 9 \cdot 1$$
$$= 20x - 36\sqrt{x} + 5\sqrt{x} - 9$$
$$= 20x - 31\sqrt{x} - 9$$

55.
$$f - g = \left(2\sqrt{x} - 3\sqrt{5}\right) - \left(2\sqrt{x} + 3\sqrt{5}\right)$$
$$= 2\sqrt{x} - 3\sqrt{5} - 2\sqrt{x} - 3\sqrt{5}$$
$$= -6\sqrt{5}$$

57.
$$\frac{f}{g} = \frac{2\sqrt{x} - 3\sqrt{5}}{2\sqrt{x} + 3\sqrt{5}}$$
$$= \frac{2\sqrt{x} - 3\sqrt{5}}{2\sqrt{x} + 3\sqrt{5}} \cdot \frac{2\sqrt{x} - 3\sqrt{5}}{2\sqrt{x} - 3\sqrt{5}}$$
$$= \frac{\left(2\sqrt{x}\right)^2 - 2\left(2\sqrt{x}\right)\left(3\sqrt{5}\right) + \left(3\sqrt{5}\right)^2}{\left(2\sqrt{x}\right)^2 - \left(3\sqrt{5}\right)^2}$$
$$= \frac{4x - 12\sqrt{5x} + 45}{4x - 45}$$

59.
$$f + g = \left(\sqrt{x + 1} - 2\right) + \left(\sqrt{x + 1} + 2\right)$$
$$= \sqrt{x + 1} - 2 + \sqrt{x + 1} + 2$$
$$= 2\sqrt{x + 1}$$

61.
$$f \cdot g = \left(\sqrt{x + 1} - 2\right)\left(\sqrt{x + 1} + 2\right)$$
$$= \left(\sqrt{x + 1}\right)^2 - (2)^2$$
$$= x + 1 - 4$$
$$= x - 3$$

63. a.

The model fits the data well.

b. $f(4) = 21.4\sqrt{4} + 21 = 63.8$

In 2003, about 64% of e-mails were spam. This estimate involves interpolation, as it involves determining a value within existing data values.

c. $f(11) = 21.4\sqrt{11} + 21 \approx 91.98$

In 2010, about 92% of e-mails will be spam. This estimate involves extrapolation, as it involves determining a value beyond existing values.

65. $f(-6) = 0$

67. $f(0) \approx 2.4$

69. $x = -6$

71. $x = 3$

73. $f(x) = 2\sqrt{x+3} + 2; \; g(x) = -2\sqrt{x+3} + 2$

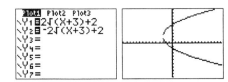

The graph looks like a parabola that opens to the right. The relation is not a function because it would fail the vertical line test.

75. Answers may vary. The graph of *f* can be found by translating the graph of $f(x) = \sqrt{x}$ horizontally by $|h|$ units (left if $h < 0$ and right if $h > 0$), and vertically by $|k|$ units (up if $k > 0$ and down if $k < 0$). Also, if $a > 0$, the graph is increasing and if $a < 0$, the graph is decreasing. The greater the absolute value of *a*, the steeper the slope of the graph.

77.
$$2x - 5y = 20$$
$$-5y = 20 - 2x$$
$$y = \frac{2}{5}x - 4$$

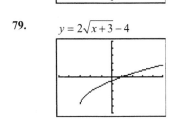

79. $y = 2\sqrt{x+3} - 4$

81.
$$y = 8\left(\frac{1}{2}\right)^x$$

83. $6x^2 - 5x - 6 = (3x + 2)(2x - 3)$

$6x^2 - 5x - 6$ is a quadratic polynomial in one variable.

85.
$$f(x) = 3x^2 - 2x + 4$$
$$6 = 3x^2 - 2x + 4$$
$$0 = 3x^2 - 2x - 2$$
$$\frac{-b \pm \sqrt{b^2 - 4ac}}{2a} = \frac{2 \pm \sqrt{(-2)^2 - 4(3)(-2)}}{2(3)}$$
$$= \frac{2 \pm \sqrt{28}}{6}$$
$$= \frac{1 \pm \sqrt{7}}{3}$$

$f(x) = 3x^2 - 2x + 4$ is a quadratic function.

87.
$$f(x) = ax^2 + bx + c$$
$$14 = 9a + 3b + c$$
$$\underline{4 = a + b + c}$$
$$10 = 8a + 2b$$
$$5 = 4a + b$$
$$b = 5 - 4a$$
$$25 = 16a + 4b + c$$
$$25 = 16a + 4(5 - 4a) + c$$
$$c = 5$$
$$4 = a + 5 - 4a + 5$$
$$a = 2$$
$$b = 5 - 4(2) = -3$$
$$f(x) = 2x^2 - 3x + 5$$

$f(x) = 2x^2 - 3x + 5$ is a quadratic function.

Homework 9.5

1.
$$\sqrt{x} = 5$$
$$\left(\sqrt{x}\right)^2 = 5^2$$
$$x = 25$$
Check: $x = 25$
$$\sqrt{(25)} \overset{?}{=} 5$$
$5 = 5$ true
The solution is 25.

3.
$$\sqrt{x} = -2$$
$$\left(\sqrt{x}\right)^2 = (-2)^2$$
$$x = 4$$
Check $x = 4$
$$\sqrt{(4)} \overset{?}{=} -2$$
$2 \overset{?}{=} -2$ false
There are no real solutions.

5.
$$\sqrt[3]{t} = -2$$
$$\left(\sqrt[3]{t}\right)^3 = (-2)^3$$
$$t = -8$$
Check: $t = -8$
$$\sqrt{(-8)} \overset{?}{=} -2$$
$-2 \overset{?}{=} -2$ true
The solution is -8.

7.
$$3\sqrt{x} - 1 = 5$$
$$3\sqrt{x} = 6$$
$$\sqrt{x} = 2$$
$$\left(\sqrt{x}\right)^2 = 2^2$$
$$x = 4$$
Check: $x = 4$
$$3\sqrt{(4)} - 1 \overset{?}{=} 5$$
$5 = 5$ true
The solution is 4.

9.
$$\sqrt{x-1} = 2$$
$$\left(\sqrt{x-1}\right)^2 = 2^2$$
$$x - 1 = 4$$
$$x = 5$$
Check: $x = 5$
$$\sqrt{(5)-1} \overset{?}{=} 2$$
$2 = 2$ true
The solution is 5.

11.
$$\sqrt[4]{r+2} = 2$$
$$\left(\sqrt[4]{r+2}\right)^4 = (2)^4$$
$$r + 2 = 16$$
$$r = 14$$
Check: $r = 14$
$$\sqrt[4]{14+2} \overset{?}{=} 2$$
$2 \overset{?}{=} 2$ true
The solution is 14.

13.
$$\sqrt{5x-7} + 7 = 3$$
$$\sqrt{5x-7} = -4$$
$$\left(\sqrt{5x-7}\right)^2 = (-4)^2$$
$$5x - 7 = 16$$
$$5x = 23$$
$$x = \frac{23}{5}$$
Check: $x = \frac{23}{5}$
$$\sqrt{5\left(\frac{23}{5}\right)-7} + 7 \overset{?}{=} 3$$
$11 \overset{?}{=} 3$ false
There are no real solutions.

15.
$$\sqrt[3]{2x-5} + 3 = 7$$
$$\sqrt[3]{2x-5} = 4$$
$$\left(\sqrt[3]{2x-5}\right)^3 = (4)^3$$
$$2x - 5 = 64$$
$$2x = 69$$
$$x = \frac{69}{2}$$

Check: $x = \dfrac{69}{2}$

$\sqrt[3]{2\left(\dfrac{69}{2}\right) - 5} + 3 \overset{?}{=} 7$

$7 \overset{?}{=} 7$ true

The solution is $\dfrac{69}{2}$.

17.
$2 - 10\sqrt{6x+3} = -98$

$-10\sqrt{6x+3} = -100$

$\sqrt{6x+3} = 10$

$\left(\sqrt{6x+3}\right)^2 = (10)^2$

$6x+3 = 100$

$6x = 97$

$x = \dfrac{97}{6}$

Check: $x = \dfrac{97}{6}$

$2 - 10\sqrt{6\left(\dfrac{97}{6}\right) + 3} + 3 \overset{?}{=} -98$

$-98 \overset{?}{=} -98$ true

The solution is $\dfrac{97}{6}$.

19.
$\sqrt{3k+1} = \sqrt{2k+6}$

$\left(\sqrt{3k+1}\right)^2 = \left(\sqrt{2k+6}\right)^2$

$3k+1 = 2k+6$

$k = 5$

Check: $k = 5$

$\sqrt{3(5)+1} \overset{?}{=} \sqrt{2(5+6}$

$4 \overset{?}{=} 4$ true

The solution is 5.

21.
$\sqrt[4]{6x-3} = \sqrt[4]{2x+17}$

$\left(\sqrt[4]{6x-3}\right)^4 = \left(\sqrt[4]{2x+17}\right)^4$

$6x-3 = 2x+17$

$4x = 20$

$x = 5$

Check: $x = 5$

$\sqrt[4]{6(5)-3} \overset{?}{=} \sqrt[4]{2(5)+17}$

$\sqrt[4]{27} \overset{?}{=} \sqrt[4]{27}$ true

The solution is 5.

23.
$2\sqrt{1-x} - \sqrt{2x+5} = 0$

$2\sqrt{1-x} = \sqrt{2x+5}$

$\left(2\sqrt{1-x}\right)^2 = \left(\sqrt{2x+5}\right)^2$

$4(1-x) = 2x+5$

$4 - 4x = 2x+5$

$-6x = 1$

$x = -\dfrac{1}{6}$

Check: $x = -\dfrac{1}{6}$

$2\sqrt{1-\left(-\dfrac{1}{6}\right)} - \sqrt{2\left(-\dfrac{1}{6}\right)+5} \overset{?}{=} 0$

$2\sqrt{\dfrac{7}{6}} - \sqrt{\dfrac{28}{6}} \overset{?}{=} 0$

$\sqrt{\dfrac{28}{6}} - \sqrt{\dfrac{28}{6}} \overset{?}{=} 0$

$0 \overset{?}{=} 0$ true

The solution is $-\dfrac{1}{6}$.

25.
$\sqrt{3w+3} = w-5$

$\left(\sqrt{3w+3}\right)^2 = (w-5)^2$

$3w+3 = w^2 - 10w + 25$

$w^2 - 13w + 22 = 0$

$(w-11)(w-2) = 0$

$w-11 = 0$ or $w-2 = 0$

$w = 11$ or $w = 2$

Check: $w = 11$

$\sqrt{3(11)+3} \overset{?}{=} (11) - 5$

$6 = 6$ true

Check: $w = 2$

$\sqrt{3(2)+3} \overset{?}{=} (2) - 5$

$3 \overset{?}{=} -3$ false

The solution is 11.

27.
$$\sqrt{12x+13}+2=3x$$
$$\sqrt{12x+13}=3x-2$$
$$\left(\sqrt{12x+13}\right)^2=(3x-2)^2$$
$$12x+13=9x^2-12x+4$$
$$9x^2-24x-9=0$$
$$3\left(3x^2-8x-3\right)=0$$
$$3(3x+1)(x-3)=0$$
$$3x+1=0 \text{ or } x-3=0$$
$$x=-\frac{1}{3} \text{ or } x=3$$

Check: $x=-\dfrac{1}{3}$
$$\sqrt{12\left(-\frac{1}{3}\right)+13}+2\overset{?}{=}3\left(-\frac{1}{3}\right)$$
$$5\overset{?}{=}-1 \text{ false}$$

Check: $x=3$
$$\sqrt{12(3)+13}+2\overset{?}{=}3(3)$$
$$9=9 \text{ true}$$
The solution is 3.

29.
$$\sqrt{3x+4}-x=3$$
$$\sqrt{3x+4}=x+3$$
$$\left(\sqrt{3x+4}\right)^2=(x+3)^2$$
$$3x+4=x^2+6x+9$$
$$x^2+3x+5=0$$
$$x=\frac{-3\pm\sqrt{(3)^2-4(1)(5)}}{2(1)}$$
$$=\frac{-3\pm\sqrt{-11}}{2}$$
There are no real solutions.

31.
$$\sqrt{r^2-5r+1}=r-3$$
$$\left(\sqrt{r^2-5r+1}\right)^2=(r-3)^2$$
$$r^2-5r+1=r^2-6r+9$$
$$r=8$$
Check: $r=8$

$$\sqrt{(8)^2-5(8)+1}\overset{?}{=}(8)-3$$
$$5=5 \text{ true}$$
The solution is 8.

33.
$$\sqrt{x}-1=\sqrt{5-x}$$
$$\left(\sqrt{x}-1\right)^2=\left(\sqrt{5-x}\right)^2$$
$$x-2\sqrt{x}+1=5-x$$
$$2x-4=2\sqrt{x}$$
$$x-2=\sqrt{x}$$
$$(x-2)^2=\left(\sqrt{x}\right)^2$$
$$x^2-4x+4=x$$
$$x^2-5x+4=0$$
$$(x-4)(x-1)=0$$
$$x-4=0 \text{ or } x-1=0$$
$$x=4 \text{ or } x=1$$
Check: $x=4$
$$\sqrt{(4)}-1\overset{?}{=}\sqrt{5-(4)}$$
$$1=1 \text{ true}$$
Check: $x=1$
$$\sqrt{(1)}-1\overset{?}{=}\sqrt{5-(1)}$$
$$0\overset{?}{=}2 \text{ false}$$
The solution is 4.

35.
$$\sqrt{x}-\sqrt{2x}=-1$$
$$\sqrt{2x}=\sqrt{x}+1$$
$$\left(\sqrt{2x}\right)^2=\left(\sqrt{x}+1\right)^2$$
$$2x=x+2\sqrt{x}+1$$
$$x-1=2\sqrt{x}$$
$$(x-1)^2=\left(2\sqrt{x}\right)^2$$
$$x^2-2x+1=4x$$
$$x^2-6x+1=0$$
$$x=\frac{-(-6)\pm\sqrt{(-6)^2-4(1)(1)}}{2(1)}$$
$$=\frac{6\pm\sqrt{32}}{2}$$
$$=3\pm2\sqrt{2}$$
Check: $3+2\sqrt{2}$ $(x\approx5.83)$

$$\sqrt{(5.83)} - \sqrt{2(5.83)} \overset{?}{=} -1$$

$$-1.00 \overset{?}{=} -1 \text{ true}$$

Check: $3 - 2\sqrt{2}$ $(x \approx 0.172)$

$$\sqrt{(0.172)} - \sqrt{2(0.172)} \overset{?}{=} -1$$

$$-0.172 \overset{?}{=} -1 \text{ false}$$

The solution is $3 + 2\sqrt{2}$.

37.
$$\sqrt{x-3} + \sqrt{x+5} = 4$$
$$\sqrt{x-3} = 4 - \sqrt{x+5}$$
$$\left(\sqrt{x-3}\right)^2 = \left(4 - \sqrt{x+5}\right)^2$$
$$x - 3 = 16 - 8\sqrt{x+5} + x + 5$$
$$8\sqrt{x+5} = 24$$
$$\sqrt{x+5} = 3$$
$$\left(\sqrt{x+5}\right)^2 = 3^2$$
$$x + 5 = 9$$
$$x = 4$$

Check: $x = 4$
$$\sqrt{(4)-3} + \sqrt{(4)+5} \overset{?}{=} 4$$
$$4 = 4 \text{ true}$$

The solution is 4.

39.
$$\sqrt{2p-1} + \sqrt{3p-2} = 2$$
$$\sqrt{2p-1} = 2 - \sqrt{3p-2}$$
$$\left(\sqrt{2p-1}\right)^2 = \left(2 - \sqrt{3p-2}\right)^2$$
$$2p - 1 = 4 - 4\sqrt{3p-2} + 3p - 2$$
$$4\sqrt{3p-2} = p + 3$$
$$\left(4\sqrt{3p-2}\right)^2 = (p+3)^2$$
$$16(3p-2) = p^2 + 6p + 9$$
$$48p - 32 = p^2 + 6p + 9$$
$$p^2 - 42p + 41 = 0$$
$$(p-41)(p-1) = 0$$
$$p - 41 = 0 \text{ or } p - 1 = 0$$
$$p = 41 \text{ or } p = 1$$

Check: $p = 41$

$$\sqrt{2(41)-1} + \sqrt{3(41)-2} \overset{?}{=} 2$$
$$20 \overset{?}{=} 2 \text{ false}$$

Check: $p = 1$
$$\sqrt{2(1)-1} + \sqrt{3(1)-2} \overset{?}{=} 2$$
$$2 = 2 \text{ true}$$

The solution is 1.

41.
$$\sqrt{\sqrt{x}-2} = 3$$
$$\left(\sqrt{\sqrt{x}-2}\right)^2 = 3^2$$
$$\sqrt{x} - 2 = 9$$
$$\sqrt{x} = 11$$
$$\left(\sqrt{x}\right)^2 = 11^2$$
$$x = 121$$

Check: $x = 121$
$$\sqrt{\sqrt{(121)}-2} \overset{?}{=} 3$$
$$3 = 3 \text{ true}$$

The solution is 121.

43.
$$\frac{1}{\sqrt{x+2}} = 3 - \sqrt{x+2}$$
$$\sqrt{x+2} \cdot \frac{1}{\sqrt{x+2}} = \sqrt{x+2}\left(3 - \sqrt{x+2}\right)$$
$$1 = 3\sqrt{x+2} - x - 2$$
$$3\sqrt{x+2} = x + 3$$
$$\left(3\sqrt{x+2}\right)^2 = (x+3)^2$$
$$9(x+2) = x^2 + 6x + 9$$
$$9x + 18 = x^2 + 6x + 9$$
$$x^2 - 3x - 9 = 0$$
$$x = \frac{-(-3) \pm \sqrt{(-3)^2 - 4(1)(-9)}}{2(1)}$$
$$= \frac{3 \pm 3\sqrt{5}}{2}$$

Check: $\dfrac{3 + 3\sqrt{5}}{2}$ $(x \approx 4.85)$

$$\frac{1}{\sqrt{(4.85)+2}} \overset{?}{=} 3 - \sqrt{(4.85)+2}$$
$$0.382 = 0.382 \text{ true}$$

Check: $\dfrac{3-3\sqrt{5}}{2}$ $\quad (x \approx -1.8541)$

$$\dfrac{1}{\sqrt{(-1.8541)+2}} \overset{?}{=} 3 - \sqrt{(-1.8541)+2}$$

$$2.62 = 2.62 \text{ true}$$

The solutions are $\dfrac{3 \pm 3\sqrt{5}}{2}$.

45.
$$5.2\sqrt{x} - 2.8 = 13.9$$
$$5.2\sqrt{x} = 16.7$$
$$\sqrt{x} = \dfrac{16.7}{5.2}$$
$$\left(\sqrt{x}\right)^2 = \left(\dfrac{16.7}{5.2}\right)^2$$
$$x \approx 10.31$$

47.
$$1.52 - 4.91\sqrt{3.18x - 7.14} = -0.69$$
$$-4.91\sqrt{3.18x - 7.14} = -2.21$$
$$\sqrt{3.18x - 7.14} \approx 0.45$$
$$\left(\sqrt{3.18x - 7.14}\right)^2 \approx (0.45)^2$$
$$3.18x - 7.14 \approx 0.20$$
$$3.18x \approx 7.34$$
$$x \approx 2.31$$

49.

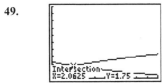

The solution is $x \approx 2.06$.

51.

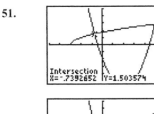

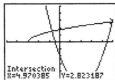

The solutions are $x \approx -0.74$ and $x \approx 4.97$.

53. The solutions are $x \approx -1.6$ and $x \approx 3.8$.

55. The solution is $x = -4$.

57. The solution is $(-3.2, 1.4)$.

59.
$$h(x) = 3\sqrt{-3x + 4} - 15$$
$$3\sqrt{-3x + 4} - 15 = 0$$
$$3\sqrt{-3x + 4} = 15$$
$$\sqrt{-3x + 4} = 5$$
$$\left(\sqrt{-3x + 4}\right)^2 = 5^2$$
$$-3x + 4 = 25$$
$$-3x = 21$$
$$x = -7$$
Check: $x = -7$
$$3\sqrt{-3(-7) + 4} - 15 \overset{?}{=} 0$$
$$0 = 0 \text{ true}$$
The x-intercept is $(-7, 0)$.

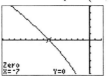

61.
$$f(x) = \sqrt{3x - 2} - \sqrt{x + 8}$$
$$\sqrt{3x - 2} - \sqrt{x + 8} = 0$$
$$\sqrt{3x - 2} = \sqrt{x + 8}$$
$$\left(\sqrt{3x - 2}\right)^2 = \left(\sqrt{x + 8}\right)^2$$
$$3x - 2 = x + 8$$
$$2x = 10$$
$$x = 5$$
Check: $x = 5$
$$\sqrt{3(5) - 2} - \sqrt{(5) + 8} \overset{?}{=} 0$$
$$0 = 0 \text{ true}$$
The x-intercept is $(5, 0)$.

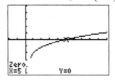

63.
$$h(x) = 2\sqrt{x+4} + 3\sqrt{x-5}$$
$$2\sqrt{x+4} + 3\sqrt{x-5} = 0$$
$$2\sqrt{x+4} = -3\sqrt{x-5}$$
$$\left(2\sqrt{x+4}\right)^2 = \left(-3\sqrt{x-5}\right)^2$$
$$4(x+4) = 9(x-5)$$
$$4x+16 = 9x-45$$
$$-5x = -61$$
$$x = \frac{61}{5}$$

Check: $x = \dfrac{61}{5}$

$$2\sqrt{\left(\frac{61}{5}\right)+4} + 3\sqrt{\left(\frac{61}{5}\right)-5} \overset{?}{=} 0$$

$$2\sqrt{\left(\frac{81}{5}\right)} + 3\sqrt{\left(\frac{36}{5}\right)} \overset{?}{=} 0$$

$$\frac{36}{\sqrt{5}} \overset{?}{=} 0 \ \text{ false}$$

No real number solution. There are no x-intercepts.

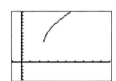

65.
$$f(x) = 3\sqrt{x} - 7$$
$$3\sqrt{x} - 7 = -1$$
$$3\sqrt{x} = 6$$
$$\sqrt{x} = 2$$
$$\left(\sqrt{x}\right)^2 = 2^2$$
$$x = 4$$
Check: $x = 4$
$$3\sqrt{(4)} - 7 \overset{?}{=} -1$$
$$-1 = -1 \ \text{ true}$$
When $x = 4$, $f(x) = -1$.

67.
$$f(x) = -2\sqrt{x-4} + 5$$
$$-2\sqrt{x-4} + 5 = 7$$
$$-2\sqrt{x-4} = 2$$
$$\sqrt{x-4} = -1$$
$$\left(\sqrt{x-4}\right)^2 = (-1)^2$$
$$x - 4 = 1$$
$$x = 5$$
Check: $x = 5$
$$-2\sqrt{(5)-4} - 5 \overset{?}{=} 7$$
$$-7 \overset{?}{=} 7 \ \text{ false}$$
No real number solutions. There is no value of x that would make $f(x) = 7$.

69. a.
$$f(t) = 21.4\sqrt{t} + 21$$
$$f(10) = 21.4\sqrt{10} + 21$$
$$f(10) \approx 88.7$$
In 2009, about 89% of e-mails will be spam.

b.
$$f(t) = 21.4\sqrt{t} + 21$$
$$95 = 21.4\sqrt{t} + 21$$
$$74 = 21.4\sqrt{t}$$
$$\frac{74}{21.4} = \sqrt{t}$$
$$11.96 \approx t$$
In 2011, 95% of e-mails will be spam.

c.
$$f(t) = 21.4\sqrt{t} + 21$$
$$100 = 21.4\sqrt{t} + 21$$
$$79 = 21.4\sqrt{t}$$
$$\frac{79}{21.4} = \sqrt{t}$$
$$13.63 \approx t$$
In 2013, 100% of e-mails will be spam. Model breakdown has likely occurred.

71. a.

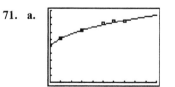

The model fits the data well.

b. $f(2) = 257\sqrt[4]{2+1} = 338.23$

The estimated charge is about $338. It is an underestimate.

c. $385 = 257\sqrt[4]{n+1}$

$\dfrac{385}{257} = \sqrt[4]{n+1}$

$5.03 \approx n+1$

$n \approx 4.03$

Grade 4 students will pay this charge.

d. This charge is higher than what all other students pay, including those in higher grades.

73. In the third line, the student did not properly square $(x+3)$.

$\sqrt{x^2+4x+5} = x+3$

$\left(\sqrt{x^2+4x+5}\right)^2 = (x+3)^2$

$x^2+4x+5 = x^2+6x+9$

$-2x = 4$

$x = -2$

75. $S = \sqrt{gd}$

$(S)^2 = \left(\sqrt{gd}\right)^2$

$S^2 = gd$

$\dfrac{S^2}{g} = d$

77. $d = \sqrt{\dfrac{3h}{2}}$

$(d)^2 = \left(\sqrt{\dfrac{3h}{2}}\right)^2$

$d^2 = \dfrac{3h}{2}$

$2d^2 = 3h$

$\dfrac{2d^2}{3} = h$

79. $v = \sqrt{\dfrac{2GM}{R}}$

$(v)^2 = \left(\sqrt{\dfrac{2GM}{R}}\right)^2$

$v^2 = \dfrac{2GM}{R}$

$Rv^2 = 2GM$

$R = \dfrac{2GM}{v^2}$

81. $y = 3\sqrt{x} - 4$

$y = -2\sqrt{x} + 6$

Since the left hand sides are equal, set the right hand sides equal to each other and solve the resulting equation.

$3\sqrt{x} - 4 = -2\sqrt{x} + 6$

$5\sqrt{x} = 10$

$\sqrt{x} = 2$

$\left(\sqrt{x}\right)^2 = 2^2$

$x = 4$

Substitute this value into either original equation and solve for y.

$y = 3\sqrt{(4)} - 4 = 2$

The solution is $(4, 2)$.

 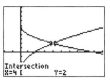

83. The left hand side was not squared properly in the second line. It should be:

$(2x)^2 - 2(2x)(x) + (-x)^2$

85. $3\sqrt{x} + 4 - 7\sqrt{x} + 1 = (3-7)\sqrt{x} + 5$

$= -4\sqrt{x} + 5$

87.
$$3\sqrt{x}+4-7\sqrt{x}+1=-7$$
$$(3-7)\sqrt{x}+5=-7$$
$$-4\sqrt{x}+5=-7$$
$$-4\sqrt{x}=-12$$
$$\sqrt{x}=3$$
$$\left(\sqrt{x}\right)^2=(3)^2$$
$$x=9$$

89.
$$\left(\sqrt{p}+3\right)\left(\sqrt{p}+1\right)=3$$
$$\sqrt{p}\cdot\sqrt{p}+3\cdot\sqrt{p}+\sqrt{p}\cdot1+3\cdot1=3$$
$$p+4\sqrt{p}+3=3$$
$$p+4\sqrt{p}=0$$
$$p=0$$

91.
$$\left(\sqrt{p}+3\right)\left(\sqrt{p}+1\right)$$
$$=\sqrt{p}\cdot\sqrt{p}+3\cdot\sqrt{p}+\sqrt{p}\cdot1+3\cdot1$$
$$=p+4\sqrt{p}+3$$

93.
$$50-4(2)^x=-83$$
$$-4(2)^x=-133$$
$$2^x=33.25$$
$$x\approx5.0553$$

95.
$$\sqrt{x+3}-\sqrt{x-2}=1$$
$$\sqrt{x+3}=1+\sqrt{x-2}$$
$$\left(\sqrt{x+3}\right)^2=\left(1+\sqrt{x-2}\right)^2$$
$$x+3=1+2\sqrt{x-2}+x-2$$
$$x+3=-1+2\sqrt{x-2}+x$$
$$4=2\sqrt{x-2}$$
$$2=\sqrt{x-2}$$
$$(2)^2=\left(\sqrt{x-2}\right)^2$$
$$4=x-2$$
$$6=x$$

97.
$$-3(2k-5)+1=2(4k+3)$$
$$-6k+15+1=8k+6$$
$$-6k+16=8k+6$$
$$-14k=-10$$
$$k=\frac{5}{7}$$

99.
$$\log_2\left(5t-1\right)=5$$
$$5t-1=2^5$$
$$5t-1=32$$
$$5t=33$$
$$t=\frac{33}{5}$$

101.
$$\frac{3x^2-x-10}{x^3-x^2-x+1}\div\frac{3x^2-12}{2x^2+x-2}$$
$$=\frac{(3x+5)(x-2)}{(x-1)(x-1)(x+1)}\div\frac{3(x-2)(x+2)}{(2x+3)(x-1)}$$
$$=\frac{(3x+5)(x-2)}{(x-1)(x-1)(x+1)}\cdot\frac{(2x+3)(x-1)}{3(x-2)(x+2)}$$
$$=\frac{(3x+5)(2x+3)}{3(x+1)(x-1)(x+2)}$$
It is a rational expression in one variable.

103.
$$\frac{6}{b-2}+\frac{3b}{b^2-7b+10}$$
$$=\frac{6(b-5)}{(b-2)(b-5)}+\frac{3b}{(b-2)(b-5)}$$
$$=\frac{3(3b-10)}{(b-2)(b-5)}$$
It is a rational expression in one variable.

105.
$$\frac{6}{x-2}+\frac{3x}{x^2-7x+10}=\frac{x}{x-5}$$
$$6x-30+3x=x^2-2x$$
$$x^2-11x-30=0$$
$$(x-5)(x-6)=0$$
$x=5$ is not in the domain of the equation, so the only solution is $x=6$.
It is a rational equation in one variable.

Homework 9.6

1. $(0,3)$ and $(4,5)$

   Substitute the point $(0,3)$ into the equation $y = a\sqrt{x} + b$.

   $3 = a\sqrt{0} + b$

   $b = 3$

   Substitute the point $(4,5)$ into the equation $y = a\sqrt{x} + 3$ and solve for a.

   $5 = a\sqrt{4} + 3$

   $2a = 2$

   $a = 1$

   The equation is $y = \sqrt{x} + 3$.

3. $(0,2)$ and $(9,6)$

   Substitute the point $(0,2)$ into the equation $y = a\sqrt{x} + b$.

   $2 = a\sqrt{0} + b$

   $b = 2$

   Substitute the point $(9,6)$ into the equation $y = a\sqrt{x} + 2$ and solve for a.

   $6 = a\sqrt{9} + 2$

   $3a = 4$

   $a = \dfrac{4}{3}$

   The equation is $y = \dfrac{4}{3}\sqrt{x} + 2$.

5. $(0, 4)$ and $(5, 7)$

   Substitute the point $(0, 4)$ into the equation $y = a\sqrt{x} + b$.

   $4 = a\sqrt{0} + b$

   $b = 4$

   Substitute the point $(5, 7)$ into the equation $y = a\sqrt{x} + 4$ and solve for a.

   $7 = a\sqrt{5} + 4$

   $3 = a\sqrt{5}$

   $a \approx 1.34$

   The equation is $y = 1.34\sqrt{x} + 4$.

7. $(0, 9)$ and $(3, 2)$

   Substitute the point $(0, 9)$ into the equation

   $y = a\sqrt{x} + b$.

   $9 = a\sqrt{0} + b$

   $b = 9$

   Substitute the point $(3, 2)$ into the equation $y = a\sqrt{x} + 9$ and solve for a.

   $2 = a\sqrt{3} + 9$

   $-7 = a\sqrt{3}$

   $a \approx -4.04$

   The equation is $y = -4.04\sqrt{x} + 9$.

9. $(1, 2)$ and $(4, 3)$

   Substitute the points into the equation $y = a\sqrt{x} + b$.

   $2 = a\sqrt{1} + b$

   $3 = a\sqrt{4} + b$

   Rewrite as:

   $a + b = 2$

   $2a + b = 3$

   Substitute $b = 2 - a$ into the second equation.

   $2a + (2 - a) = 3$

   $a = 1$

   Solve for b.

   $b = 2 - 1 = 1$

   The equation is $y = \sqrt{x} + 1$.

11. $(2,4)$ and $(3,5)$

    Substitute the points into the equation $y = a\sqrt{x} + b$.

    $4 = a\sqrt{2} + b$

    $5 = a\sqrt{3} + b$

    Rewrite as:

    $1.4142a + b = 4$

    $1.7321a + b = 5$

    Solve the resulting system. Multiply the first equation by -1 and add to the second equation.

    $-1.4142a - b = -4$

    $\underline{1.7321a + b = 5}$

    $0.3179a = 1$

    $a \approx 3.15$

    Substitute the point $(2,4)$ into the equation $y = 3.15\sqrt{x} + b$ and solve for b.

$4 = 3.15\sqrt{2} + b$

$b \approx -0.45$

The equation is roughly $y = 3.15\sqrt{x} - 0.45$.

13. $(2,6)$ and $(5,4)$

Substitute the points into the equation $y = a\sqrt{x} + b$.

$6 = a\sqrt{2} + b$

$4 = a\sqrt{5} + b$

Rewrite as:

$1.4142a + b = 6$

$2.2361a + b = 4$

Solve the resulting system. Multiply the first equation by -1 and add to the second equation.

$-1.4142a - b = -6$

$\underline{2.2361a + b = 4}$

$0.8129a = -2$

$a \approx -2.43$

Substitute the point $(2,6)$ into the equation

$y = -2.43\sqrt{x} + b$ and solve for b.

$6 = -2.43\sqrt{2} + b$

$b \approx 9.44$

The equation is roughly

$y = -2.43\sqrt{x} + 9.44$.

15. $(5, 7)$ and $(13, 21)$

Substitute the points into the equation $y = a\sqrt{x} + b$.

$7 = a\sqrt{5} + b$

$21 = a\sqrt{13} + b$

Rewrite as:

$2.2361a + b = 7$

$3.6056a + b = 21$

Solve the resulting system. Multiply the first equation by -1 and add to the second equation.

$-2.2361a - b = -7$

$\underline{3.6056a + b = 21}$

$1.3695a = 14$

$a \approx 10.22$

Substitute the point $(5, 7)$ into the equation $y = 10.22\sqrt{x} + b$ and solve for b.

$7 = 10.22\sqrt{5} + b$

$b \approx -15.85$

The equation is roughly

$y = 10.22\sqrt{x} - 15.85$.

17. $(7, 31)$ and $(10, 6)$

Substitute the points into the equation $y = a\sqrt{x} + b$.

$31 = a\sqrt{7} + b$

$6 = a\sqrt{10} + b$

Rewrite as:

$2.6458a + b = 31$

$3.1623a + b = 6$

Solve the resulting system. Multiply the first equation by -1 and add to the second equation.

$-2.6458a - b = -31$

$\underline{3.1623a + b = 6}$

$0.5165a = 25$

$a \approx -48.40$

Substitute the point $(7, 31)$ into the equation

$y = -48.40\sqrt{x} + b$ and solve for b.

$31 = -48.40\sqrt{7} + b$

$b \approx 159.06$

The equation is roughly

$y = -48.40\sqrt{x} + 159.06$.

19. $(15, 3)$ and $(35, 18)$

Substitute the points into the equation $y = a\sqrt{x} + b$.

$3 = a\sqrt{15} + b$

$18 = a\sqrt{35} + b$

Rewrite as:

$3.873a + b = 3$

$5.9161a + b = 18$

Solve the resulting system. Multiply the first equation by -1 and add to the second equation.

$-3.873a - b = -3$

$\underline{5.9161a + b = 18}$

$2.0431a = 15$

$a \approx 7.34$

Substitute the point $(15, 3)$ into the equation

$y = 7.34\sqrt{x} + b$ and solve for b.

$3 = 7.34\sqrt{15} + b$

$b \approx -25.43$

The equation is roughly

$y = 7.34\sqrt{x} - 25.43$.

21. Increase the value of b to shift the graph up.

23. a. Start by plotting the data.

Answers may vary. A square root model may be reasonable. Use the points $(0, 12)$ and $(4, 30.3)$.
Substitute the point $(0, 12)$ into the equation $y = a\sqrt{x} + b$.

$12 = a\sqrt{0} + b$

$b = 12$

Substitute the point $(4, 30.3)$ into the equation $y = a\sqrt{x} + 12$ and solve for a.

$30.3 = a\sqrt{4} + 12$

$a = \dfrac{18.3}{2} = 9.15$

$f(t) = 9.15\sqrt{t} + 12$

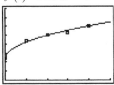

Your equation may differ according to the points you chose.

b. The n-intercept is 12, which means that in 2002 *American Idol* was watched by an average of 12.0 million viewers per episode.

c. $38 = 9.15\sqrt{t} + 12$

$t \approx 8.07$

In 2010, the average number of viewers per episode will reach 38 million people.

d. $f(9) = 9.15\sqrt{9} + 12 = 39.45$

In 2011, the average number of viewers will be about 39.5 million.

25. a. Start by plotting the data.

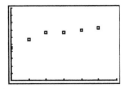

A square root model may be reasonable. Use the points $(0, 9.1)$ and $(5, 14.4)$.
Substitute the point $(0, 9.1)$ into the equation $y = a\sqrt{x} + b$.

$9.1 = a\sqrt{0} + b$

$b = 9.1$

Substitute the point $(5, 14.4)$ into the equation $y = a\sqrt{x} + 9.1$ and solve for a.

$14.4 = a\sqrt{5} + 9.1$

$a = \dfrac{5.3}{2.236} \approx 2.37$

$f(t) = 2.37\sqrt{t} + 9.1$

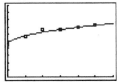

Your equation may differ according to the points you chose.

b. The n-intercept is 9.1, which means that 9.1 million households had webcams in 2000.

c. $f(11) = 2.37\sqrt{11} + 9.1 \approx 16.96$

In 2011, about 17 million households will have webcams.

d. $18 = 2.37\sqrt{t} + 9.1$

$t = 14.1$

In 2014, 18 million households will have webcams.

27. a. $f(18000) = \sqrt{9.8(18000)} = 420$

The average speed would be 420 meters per second.

b. No, this would suggest that the depth is much less because the speed is half of what it should be.

c.
$$203 = \sqrt{9.8t}$$
$$t = 4205$$
$$210 = \sqrt{9.8t}$$
$$t = 4500$$
The average depth would be 4205 to 4500 meters.

d. Yes.

29. a. Start by plotting the data.

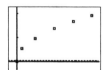

Answers may vary. A square root model seems to be appropriate. Use the points $(0,0)$ and $(52.5,1.94)$.

Substitute the point $(0,0)$ into the equation $y = a\sqrt{x} + b$.
$$0 = a\sqrt{0} + b$$
$$b = 0$$
Substitute the point $(52.5,1.94)$ into the equation $y = a\sqrt{x}$ and solve for a.
$$1.94 = a\sqrt{52.5}$$
$$a \approx 0.27$$
$$S(h) = 0.27\sqrt{h}$$

Your equation may differ according to the points you chose.

b. i. Graph all three functions.

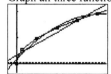

The model $S(h)$ appears to fit the best.

ii. $S(0) = 0; L(0) = 0.327; Q(0) = 0.165$
S models the situation best near 0

since it is the only model that passes through the origin.

iii. Zoom out.

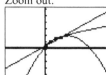

Q is not possible since it indicates that the falling time will reach 0 for larger drop heights.

iv. S models the situation the best and has no problems with larger h.

v.
$$T = \sqrt{\frac{2h}{32.2}}$$
$$= \sqrt{\frac{2}{32.2}}\sqrt{h}$$
$$\approx 0.249\sqrt{h}$$
This is close to the model $S(h) = 0.27\sqrt{h}$.

c.
$$0.27\sqrt{h} = 3$$
$$\sqrt{h} = \frac{3}{0.27}$$
$$\left(\sqrt{h}\right)^2 = \left(\frac{3}{0.27}\right)^2$$
$$h \approx 123.46$$
According to the model, the height of the cliff is roughly 123.46 feet.

d. $S(1250) = 0.27\sqrt{1250} \approx 9.55$

It would take about 9.55 seconds for the baseball to reach the ground if it were dropped from the top of New York City's Empire State Building.

31. a. Start by plotting the data.

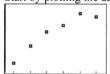

A square root model may fit reasonably well.
Use the points $(2,54.3)$ and $(4,73)$.

Substitute the points into the equation

$y = a\sqrt{x} + b$.

$54.3 = a\sqrt{2} + b$

$73 = a\sqrt{4} + b$

Rewrite as:

$1.4142a + b = 54.3$

$2a + b = 73$

Solve the system of equations. Multiply the first equation by -1 and add to the second equation.

$-1.4142a - b = -54.3$

$\underline{2a + b = 73}$

$0.5858a = 18.7$

$a \approx 31.92$

Substitute the point $(2, 54.3)$ into the equation $y = 31.92\sqrt{x} + b$ and solve for b.

$54.3 = 31.92\sqrt{2} + b$

$b = 54.3 - 31.92\sqrt{2}$

$b \approx 9.16$

$f(n) = 31.92\sqrt{n} + 9.16$

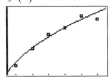

b. $f(7) = 31.92\sqrt{(7)} + 9.16 \approx 93.61$

About 93.6% of 7th births occurred despite the use of contraception.

c. $100 = 31.92\sqrt{n} + 9.16$

$31.92\sqrt{n} = 90.84$

$\sqrt{n} = \dfrac{90.84}{31.92}$

$\left(\sqrt{n}\right)^2 = \left(\dfrac{90.84}{31.92}\right)^2$

$n \approx 8.1$

All 8th births occurred despite the use of contraception. Model breakdown has likely occurred.

d. The higher the birth order, the higher the percent of births that happened despite the use of contraception. Answers may vary. Perhaps couples without children are more careful in their use of contraception.

33. a.

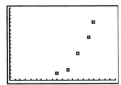

Answers may vary.
Either an exponential or square root function may fit the data well.

b. Exponential: $f(t) = 1.1(1.37)^t$

Square root:
Use the points (9, 20) and (16, 160).
Substitute the points into the equation

$y = a\sqrt{x} + b$.

$20 = a\sqrt{9} + b$

$160 = a\sqrt{16} + b$

Rewrite as:

$3a + b = 20$

$4a + b = 160$

Solve the system of equations. Multiply the first equation by -1 and add to the second equation.

$-3a - b = -20$

$\underline{4a + b = 160}$

$a = 140$

Substitute the point (9, 20) into the equation $y = 140\sqrt{x} + b$ and solve for b.

$20 = 140\sqrt{9} + b$

$b = -400$

$f(t) = 140\sqrt{t} - 400$

Your equation may differ according to the points you chose.

c.

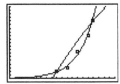

The exponential function fits the data better.

d. The exponential function fits the data better before 1999.

e.
$$1200 = 1.1(1.37)^t$$
$$t = 22.2$$
$$1200 = 140\sqrt{t} - 400$$
$$t = 130.6$$

According to the exponential model, there will be 1200 U.S. communities with red-light cameras in 2012. According to the square root model, this will occur in 2121. The exponential model increases at a much faster rate than the square root model.

f. Answers may vary. Using the exponential model, Redflex will reach $260 million in revenue in 2012. Using the square root model, Redflex will reach $260 million in revenue in 2121.

35. Answers may vary.
$$\frac{4x-1}{2} = \frac{5x+3}{3}$$
$$12x - 3 = 10x + 6$$
$$2x = 9$$
$$x = \frac{9}{2}$$

37. Answers may vary.
$$\frac{4x-1}{2} - \frac{5x+3}{3} = \frac{12x-3}{6} - \frac{10x+6}{6}$$
$$= \frac{2x-9}{6}$$

39. Answers may vary.
$$2\sqrt{x} - 5 = 4$$
$$2\sqrt{x} = 9$$
$$\sqrt{x} = \frac{9}{2}$$
$$x = \frac{81}{4}$$

41. Answers may vary.
$$f(x) = 2(3)^x - 2.5$$

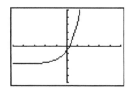

Chapter 9 Review Exercises

1. $x^{3/7} = \sqrt[7]{x^3}$

2. $\sqrt[5]{(3k+4)^7} = (3k+4)^{7/5}$

3.
$$\sqrt{8x^6} = \sqrt{4x^6 \cdot 2}$$
$$= \sqrt{4x^6}\sqrt{2}$$
$$= 2x^3\sqrt{2}$$

4.
$$\sqrt{18x^7 y^{10}} = \sqrt{9x^6 y^{10} \cdot 2x}$$
$$= \sqrt{9x^6 y^{10}}\sqrt{2x}$$
$$= 3x^3 y^5 \sqrt{2x}$$

5.
$$\sqrt[8]{x^6} = x^{6/8}$$
$$= x^{3/4}$$
$$= \sqrt[4]{x^3}$$

6.
$$\sqrt[3]{24x^{10} y^{24}} = \sqrt[3]{8x^9 y^{24} \cdot 3x}$$
$$= \sqrt[3]{8x^9 y^{24}}\sqrt[3]{3x}$$
$$= 2x^3 y^8 \sqrt[3]{3x}$$

7.
$$\sqrt[5]{(6x+11)^{27}} = \sqrt[5]{(6x+11)^{25} \cdot (6x+11)^2}$$
$$= \sqrt[5]{(6x+11)^{25}}\sqrt[5]{(6x+11)^2}$$
$$= (6x+11)^5 \sqrt[5]{(6x+11)^2}$$

8.
$$5\sqrt{20x} - 2\sqrt{45x} + 7\sqrt{5x}$$
$$= 5\sqrt{4 \cdot 5x} - 2\sqrt{9 \cdot 5x} + 7\sqrt{5x}$$
$$= 5\sqrt{4}\sqrt{5x} - 2\sqrt{9}\sqrt{5x} + 7\sqrt{5x}$$
$$= 10\sqrt{5x} - 6\sqrt{5x} + 7\sqrt{x}$$
$$= 11\sqrt{5x}$$

9.
$$b\sqrt[3]{16a^5b} + a\sqrt[3]{2a^2b^4}$$
$$= b\sqrt[3]{8a^3 \cdot 2a^2b} + a\sqrt[3]{b^3 \cdot 2a^2b}$$
$$= b\sqrt[3]{8a^3}\sqrt[3]{2a^2b} + a\sqrt[3]{b^3}\sqrt[3]{2a^2b}$$
$$= 2ab\sqrt[3]{2a^2b} + ab\sqrt[3]{2a^2b}$$
$$= 3ab\sqrt[3]{2a^2b}$$

10.
$$5\left(4\sqrt{x} - \sqrt[3]{x}\right) - 2\sqrt[3]{x} + 8\sqrt{x}$$
$$= 20\sqrt{x} - 5\sqrt[3]{x} - 2\sqrt[3]{x} + 8\sqrt{x}$$
$$= 28\sqrt{x} - 7\sqrt[3]{x}$$

11.
$$3\sqrt{x}\left(\sqrt{x} - 7\right) = 3\sqrt{x} \cdot \sqrt{x} - 3\sqrt{x} \cdot 7$$
$$= 3\sqrt{x \cdot x} - 21\sqrt{x}$$
$$= 3\sqrt{x^2} - 21\sqrt{x}$$
$$= 3x - 21\sqrt{x}$$

12.
$$\left(4\sqrt{x} - 3\right)\left(2\sqrt{x} + 1\right)$$
$$= 4\sqrt{x} \cdot 2\sqrt{x} - 3 \cdot 2\sqrt{x} + 4\sqrt{x} \cdot 1 - 3 \cdot 1$$
$$= 8\sqrt{x \cdot x} - 6\sqrt{x} + 4\sqrt{x} - 3$$
$$= 8\sqrt{x^2} - 2\sqrt{x} - 3$$
$$= 8x - 2\sqrt{x} - 3$$

13.
$$\left(2\sqrt{a} - \sqrt{b}\right)\left(5\sqrt{a} + \sqrt{b}\right)$$
$$= 2\sqrt{a} \cdot 5\sqrt{a} - \sqrt{b} \cdot 5\sqrt{a} + 2\sqrt{a} \cdot \sqrt{b} - \sqrt{b} \cdot \sqrt{b}$$
$$= 10\sqrt{a \cdot a} - 5\sqrt{a \cdot b} + 2\sqrt{a \cdot b} - \sqrt{b \cdot b}$$
$$= 10\sqrt{a^2} - 3\sqrt{ab} - \sqrt{b^2}$$
$$= 10a - 3\sqrt{ab} - b$$

14.
$$\left(5\sqrt{a} - 7\sqrt{b}\right)\left(5\sqrt{a} + 7\sqrt{b}\right)$$
$$= 5\sqrt{a} \cdot 5\sqrt{a} - 7\sqrt{b} \cdot 5\sqrt{a} + 5\sqrt{a} \cdot 7\sqrt{b} - 7\sqrt{b} \cdot 7\sqrt{b}$$
$$= 25\sqrt{a \cdot a} - 35\sqrt{a \cdot b} + 35\sqrt{a \cdot b} - 49\sqrt{b \cdot b}$$
$$= 25\sqrt{a^2} - 35\sqrt{ab} + 35\sqrt{ab} - 49\sqrt{b^2}$$
$$= 25a - 49b$$

15.
$$\left(4\sqrt{x} + 3\right)^2 = \left(4\sqrt{x}\right)^2 + 2\left(4\sqrt{x}\right)(3) + (3)^2$$
$$= 16x + 24\sqrt{x} + 9$$

16.
$$\left(2\sqrt[3]{x} + 5\right)^2 = \left(2\sqrt[3]{x}\right)^2 + 2\left(2\sqrt[3]{x}\right)(5) + (5)^2$$
$$= 4\sqrt[3]{x^2} + 20\sqrt[3]{x} + 25$$

17.
$$\sqrt[4]{x}\sqrt[5]{x} = x^{1/4} \cdot x^{1/5}$$
$$= x^{\frac{1}{4} + \frac{1}{5}}$$
$$= x^{\frac{5}{20} + \frac{4}{20}}$$
$$= x^{9/20}$$
$$= \sqrt[20]{x^9}$$

18.
$$\frac{\sqrt[4]{x}}{\sqrt[6]{x}} = \frac{x^{1/4}}{x^{1/6}}$$
$$= x^{\frac{1}{4} - \frac{1}{6}}$$
$$= x^{\frac{3}{12} - \frac{2}{12}}$$
$$= x^{1/12}$$
$$= \sqrt[12]{x}$$

19.
$$\sqrt{\frac{3}{x}} = \frac{\sqrt{3}}{\sqrt{x}}$$
$$= \frac{\sqrt{3}}{\sqrt{x}} \cdot \frac{\sqrt{x}}{\sqrt{x}}$$
$$= \frac{\sqrt{3 \cdot x}}{\sqrt{x \cdot x}}$$
$$= \frac{\sqrt{3x}}{x}$$

20.
$$\frac{5t}{\sqrt[3]{t}} = \frac{5t}{\sqrt[3]{t}} \cdot \frac{\sqrt[3]{t^2}}{\sqrt[3]{t^2}}$$
$$= \frac{5t\sqrt[3]{t^2}}{\sqrt[3]{t \cdot t^2}}$$
$$= \frac{5\sqrt[3]{t^2}}{\sqrt[3]{t^3}}$$
$$= \frac{5t\sqrt[3]{t^2}}{t}$$
$$= 5\sqrt[3]{t^2}$$

21.

$$\sqrt[5]{\frac{7y}{27x^2}} = \frac{\sqrt[5]{7y}}{\sqrt[5]{27x^2}}$$

$$= \frac{\sqrt[5]{7y}}{\sqrt[5]{27x^2}} \cdot \frac{\sqrt[5]{9x^3}}{\sqrt[5]{9x^3}}$$

$$= \frac{\sqrt[5]{7y \cdot 9x^3}}{\sqrt[5]{27x^2 \cdot 9x^3}}$$

$$= \frac{\sqrt[5]{63x^3 y}}{\sqrt[5]{243x^5}}$$

$$= \frac{\sqrt[5]{63x^3 y}}{3x}$$

22.

$$\frac{\sqrt{a}}{\sqrt{a} - 2\sqrt{b}} = \frac{\sqrt{a}}{\sqrt{a} - 2\sqrt{b}} \cdot \frac{\sqrt{a} + 2\sqrt{b}}{\sqrt{a} + 2\sqrt{b}}$$

$$= \frac{\sqrt{a}\left(\sqrt{a} + 2\sqrt{b}\right)}{\left(\sqrt{a}\right)^2 - \left(2\sqrt{b}\right)^2}$$

$$= \frac{a + 2\sqrt{ab}}{a - 4b}$$

23.

$$\frac{5\sqrt{x} - 4}{2\sqrt{x} + 3} = \frac{5\sqrt{x} - 4}{2\sqrt{x} + 3} \cdot \frac{2\sqrt{x} - 3}{2\sqrt{x} - 3}$$

$$= \frac{5\sqrt{x} \cdot 2\sqrt{x} - 4 \cdot 2\sqrt{x} - 5\sqrt{x} \cdot 3 + 4 \cdot 3}{\left(2\sqrt{x}\right)^2 - (3)^2}$$

$$= \frac{10\sqrt{x \cdot x} - 8\sqrt{x} - 15\sqrt{x} + 12}{4x - 9}$$

$$= \frac{10x - 23\sqrt{x} + 12}{4x - 9}$$

24. $y = -\sqrt{x-5} + 3$

x	y
5	3
6	2
9	1
14	0
21	−1

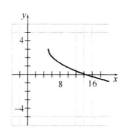

25. $y = 2\sqrt{x+4} - 1$

x	y
−4	−1
−3	1
0	3
5	5
12	7

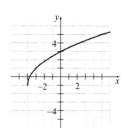

26.

$$f + g = \left(3\sqrt{x} + 5\right) + \left(2 - 4\sqrt{x}\right)$$

$$= 3\sqrt{x} + 5 + 2 - 4\sqrt{x}$$

$$= -\sqrt{x} + 7$$

27.

$$f - g = \left(3\sqrt{x} + 5\right) - \left(2 - 4\sqrt{x}\right)$$

$$= 3\sqrt{x} + 5 - 2 + 4\sqrt{x}$$

$$= 7\sqrt{x} + 3$$

28.

$$f \cdot g = \left(3\sqrt{x} + 5\right)\left(2 - 4\sqrt{x}\right)$$

$$= 3\sqrt{x} \cdot 2 + 5 \cdot 2 - 3\sqrt{x} \cdot 4\sqrt{x} - 5 \cdot 4\sqrt{x}$$

$$= 6\sqrt{x} + 10 - 12x - 20\sqrt{x}$$

$$= -12x - 14\sqrt{x} + 10$$

29.

$$\frac{f}{g} = \frac{3\sqrt{x} + 5}{2 - 4\sqrt{x}}$$

$$= \frac{3\sqrt{x} + 5}{2 - 4\sqrt{x}} \cdot \frac{2 + 4\sqrt{x}}{2 + 4\sqrt{x}}$$

$$= \frac{3\sqrt{x} \cdot 2 + 5 \cdot 2 + 3\sqrt{x} \cdot 4\sqrt{x} + 5 \cdot 4\sqrt{x}}{(2)^2 - \left(4\sqrt{x}\right)^2}$$

$$= \frac{6\sqrt{x} + 10 + 12x + 20\sqrt{x}}{4 - 16x}$$

$$= \frac{12x + 26\sqrt{x} + 10}{4 - 16x}$$

$$= \frac{2\left(6x + 13\sqrt{x} + 5\right)}{2\left(2 - 8x\right)}$$

$$= \frac{6x + 13\sqrt{x} + 5}{2 - 8x}$$

30.
$$\sqrt{2x+1}+4=7$$
$$\sqrt{2x+1}=3$$
$$\left(\sqrt{2x+1}\right)^2=3^2$$
$$2x+1=9$$
$$2x=8$$
$$x=4$$
Check: $x=4$
$$\sqrt{2(4)+1}+4\overset{?}{=}7$$
$$7=7 \text{ true}$$

The solution is 4.

31.
$$\sqrt{2x-4}-x=-2$$
$$\sqrt{2x-4}=x-2$$
$$\left(\sqrt{2x-4}\right)^2=(x-2)^2$$
$$2x-4=x^2-4x+4$$
$$x^2-6x+8=0$$
$$(x-4)(x-2)=0$$
$$x-4=0 \text{ or } x-2=0$$
$$x=4 \text{ or } x=2$$
Check: $x=4$
$$\sqrt{2(4)-4}-4\overset{?}{=}-2$$
$$-2=2 \text{ true}$$
Check: $x=2$
$$\sqrt{2(2)-4}-2\overset{?}{=}-2$$
$$-2=-2 \text{ true}$$
The solutions are 4 and 2.

32.
$$\sqrt{x}+6=x$$
$$\sqrt{x}=x-6$$
$$\left(\sqrt{x}\right)^2=(x-6)^2$$
$$x=x^2-12x+36$$
$$x^2-13x+36=0$$
$$(x-9)(x-4)=0$$
$$x-9=0 \text{ or } x-4=0$$
$$x=9 \text{ or } x=4$$
Check: $x=9$
$$\sqrt{(9)}+6\overset{?}{=}(9)$$
$$9=9 \text{ true}$$

Check: $x=4$
$$\sqrt{(4)}+6\overset{?}{=}(4)$$
$$8\overset{?}{=}4 \text{ false}$$
The solution is 9.

33.
$$\sqrt{13x+4}=\sqrt{5x-20}$$
$$\left(\sqrt{13x+4}\right)^2=\left(\sqrt{5x-20}\right)^2$$
$$13x+4=5x-20$$
$$8x=-24$$
$$x=-3$$
Check: $x=-3$
$$\sqrt{13(-3)+4}\overset{?}{=}\sqrt{5(-3)-20}$$
$$\sqrt{-35}\overset{?}{=}\sqrt{-35}$$
There is no real solution.

34.
$$\sqrt{x+2}+\sqrt{x+9}=7$$
$$\sqrt{x+2}=7-\sqrt{x+9}$$
$$\left(\sqrt{x+2}\right)^2=\left(7-\sqrt{x+9}\right)^2$$
$$x+2=49-14\sqrt{x+9}+x+9$$
$$14\sqrt{x+9}=56$$
$$\sqrt{x+9}=4$$
$$\left(\sqrt{x+9}\right)^2=4^2$$
$$x+9=16$$
$$x=7$$
Check: $x=7$
$$\sqrt{(7)+2}+\sqrt{(7)+9}\overset{?}{=}7$$
$$7=7 \text{ true}$$
The solution is 7.

35.
$$3.57+2.99\sqrt{8.06x-6.83}=14.55$$
$$2.99\sqrt{8.06x-6.83}=10.98$$
$$\sqrt{8.06x-6.83}\approx3.67$$
$$8.06x-6.83\approx13.47$$
$$8.06x\approx20.3$$
$$x\approx2.52$$

36.

$x = -1.36$

$x = 4.56$

37. $f(x) = \sqrt{4x-7} - \sqrt{2x+1}$

$\sqrt{4x-7} - \sqrt{2x+1} = 0$

$\sqrt{4x-7} = \sqrt{2x+1}$

$\left(\sqrt{4x-7}\right)^2 = \left(\sqrt{2x+1}\right)^2$

$4x - 7 = 2x + 1$

$2x = 8$

$x = 4$

Check: $x = 4$

$\sqrt{4(4)-7} - \sqrt{2(4)+1} \overset{?}{=} 0$

$0 = 0$ true

The x-intercept is $(4,0)$.

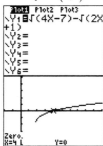

38. Increase b to raise the y-intercept and decrease a to lower the rate of increase. Sketches may vary.

39. The equation is of the form $y = a\sqrt{x} + b$.

The y-intercept is $(0,3)$ so $b = 3$.

Substitute the point $(4,8)$ into the equation

$y = a\sqrt{x} + 3$ and solve for a.

$8 = a\sqrt{4} + 3$

$2a = 5$

$a = \dfrac{5}{2}$

The equation is $y = \dfrac{5}{2}\sqrt{x} + 3$.

40. $(3,7)$ and $(5,4)$

Substitute the points into the equation

$y = a\sqrt{x} + b$.

$7 = a\sqrt{3} + b$

$4 = a\sqrt{5} + b$

Rewrite as:

$1.7321a + b = 7$

$2.2361a + b = 4$

Solve the system of equations. Multiply the first equation by -1 and add to the second equation.

$-1.7321a - b = -7$

$\underline{2.2361a + b = 4}$

$0.504a = -3$

$a \approx -5.95$

Substitute the point $(3,7)$ into the equation

$y = -5.95\sqrt{x} + b$ and solve for b.

$7 = -5.95\sqrt{3} + b$

$b = 7 + 5.95\sqrt{3}$

$b \approx 17.31$

The equation is roughly $y = -5.95\sqrt{x} + 17.31$.

41. **a.** Start by plotting the data.

A square root model, $y = a\sqrt{x} + b$, seems reasonable.

Use the points $(0,16)$ and $(4,28.8)$.

The y-intercept is $(0,16)$ so $b = 16$.

Substitute the point $(4,28.8)$ into the

equation $y = a\sqrt{x} + 16$ and solve for b.

$28.8 = a\sqrt{4} + 16$

$2a = 12.8$

$a = 6.4$

$f(t) = 6.4\sqrt{t} + 16$

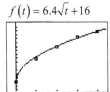

Your equation may differ according to the points you chose.

b. $(0,16)$; In 1998 there were 16 million U.S. households with a Sony PlayStation.

c. $f(14) = 6.4\sqrt{14} + 16 = 39.95$

This means that, in 2012, there will be about 40 million households that have a Sony PlayStation.

d. $6.4\sqrt{t} + 16 = 38$

$6.4\sqrt{t} = 22$

$\sqrt{t} = 3.4375$

$t \approx 11.82$

In 2010, 38 million households in the United States will have a Sony PlayStation.

Chapter 9 Test

1. $\sqrt{32x^9 y^{12}} = \sqrt{16x^8 y^{12} \cdot 2x}$

$= \sqrt{16x^8 y^{12}} \sqrt{2x}$

$= 4x^4 y^6 \sqrt{2x}$

2. $\sqrt[3]{64x^{22} y^{14}} = \sqrt[3]{64x^{21} y^{12} \cdot xy^2}$

$= \sqrt[3]{64x^{21} y^{12}} \sqrt[3]{xy^2}$

$= 4x^7 y^4 \sqrt[3]{xy^2}$

3. $\sqrt[4]{(2x+8)^{27}} = \sqrt[4]{(2x+8)^{24} \cdot (2x+8)^3}$

$= \sqrt[4]{(2x+8)^{24}} \sqrt[4]{(2x+8)^3}$

$= (2x+8)^6 \sqrt[4]{(2x+8)^3}$

4. $\dfrac{4\sqrt[3]{x}}{6\sqrt[5]{x}} = \dfrac{2x^{1/3}}{3x^{1/5}}$

$= \dfrac{2}{3} x^{\frac{1}{3} - \frac{1}{5}}$

$= \dfrac{2}{3} x^{\frac{5}{15} - \frac{3}{15}}$

$= \dfrac{2}{3} x^{2/15}$

$= \dfrac{2\sqrt[15]{x^2}}{3}$

5. $\dfrac{\sqrt{x}+1}{2\sqrt{x}-3} = \dfrac{\sqrt{x}+1}{2\sqrt{x}-3} \cdot \dfrac{2\sqrt{x}+3}{2\sqrt{x}+3}$

$= \dfrac{\sqrt{x} \cdot 2\sqrt{x} + 1 \cdot 2\sqrt{x} + \sqrt{x} \cdot 3 + 1 \cdot 3}{\left(2\sqrt{x}\right)^2 - (3)^2}$

$= \dfrac{2x + 2\sqrt{x} + 3\sqrt{x} + 3}{4x - 9}$

$= \dfrac{2x + 5\sqrt{x} + 3}{4x - 9}$

6. $4\sqrt{12x^3} - 2x\sqrt{75x} + \sqrt{3x^3}$

$= 4\sqrt{4x^2 \cdot 3x} - 2x\sqrt{25 \cdot 3x} + \sqrt{x^2 \cdot 3x}$

$= 4 \cdot 2x\sqrt{3x} - 2x \cdot 5\sqrt{3x} + x\sqrt{3x}$

$= 8x\sqrt{3x} - 10x\sqrt{3x} + x\sqrt{3x}$

$= -x\sqrt{3x}$

7. $3\sqrt{x}\left(6\sqrt{x} - 5\right) = 3\sqrt{x} \cdot 6\sqrt{x} - 3\sqrt{x} \cdot 5$

$= 18\sqrt{x^2} - 15\sqrt{x}$

$= 18x - 15\sqrt{x}$

8. $\left(2 + 4\sqrt{x}\right)\left(3 - 5\sqrt{x}\right)$

$= 2 \cdot 3 + 4\sqrt{x} \cdot 3 - 2 \cdot 5\sqrt{x} - 4\sqrt{x} \cdot 5\sqrt{x}$

$= 6 + 12\sqrt{x} - 10\sqrt{x} - 20\sqrt{x^2}$

$= -20x + 2\sqrt{x} + 6$

9. $\left(3\sqrt{a} - 5\sqrt{b}\right)\left(3\sqrt{a} + 5\sqrt{b}\right) = \left(3\sqrt{a}\right)^2 - \left(5\sqrt{b}\right)^2$

$= 9a - 25b$

10.
$$\left(4\sqrt[5]{x}-3\right)^2 = \left(4\sqrt[5]{x}\right)^2 - 2\left(4\sqrt[5]{x}\right)(3)+(3)^2$$
$$= 16\sqrt[5]{x^2} - 24\sqrt[5]{x} + 9$$

11.
$$\frac{\sqrt[n]{x}}{\sqrt[k]{x}} = \frac{x^{1/n}}{x^{1/k}}$$
$$= x^{\frac{1}{n}-\frac{1}{k}}$$
$$= x^{\frac{k}{kn}-\frac{n}{kn}}$$
$$= x^{\frac{k-n}{kn}}$$
$$= \sqrt[kn]{x^{k-n}}$$

12. $y = -2\sqrt{x+3}+1$

x	y
-3	1
-2	-1
1	-3
6	-5
13	-7

13. **a.** We need $a < 0$ and $k \geq 0$, or we need $a > 0$ and $k \leq 0$. In either case, h can be any real number.

b. $f(x) = a\sqrt{x-h}+k$

$$a\sqrt{x-h}+k = 0$$
$$a\sqrt{x-h} = -k$$
$$\sqrt{x-h} = -\frac{k}{a}$$
$$\left(\sqrt{x-h}\right)^2 = \left(-\frac{k}{a}\right)^2$$
$$x-h = \frac{k^2}{a^2}$$
$$x = h + \frac{k^2}{a^2}$$

The *x*-intercept is $\left(h+\dfrac{k^2}{a^2},0\right)$.

14.
$$f + g = \left(7-3\sqrt{x}\right)+\left(4+5\sqrt{x}\right)$$
$$= 7-3\sqrt{x}+4+5\sqrt{x}$$
$$= 2\sqrt{x}+11$$

15.
$$f - g = \left(7-3\sqrt{x}\right)-\left(4+5\sqrt{x}\right)$$
$$= 7-3\sqrt{x}-4-5\sqrt{x}$$
$$= 3-8\sqrt{x}$$

16.
$$f \cdot g = \left(7-3\sqrt{x}\right)\left(4+5\sqrt{x}\right)$$
$$= 7\cdot 4 - 3\sqrt{x}\cdot 4 + 7\cdot 5\sqrt{x} - 3\sqrt{x}\cdot 5\sqrt{x}$$
$$= 28 - 12\sqrt{x} + 35\sqrt{x} - 15x$$
$$= -15x + 23\sqrt{x} + 28$$

17.
$$\frac{f}{g} = \frac{7-3\sqrt{x}}{4+5\sqrt{x}}$$
$$= \frac{7-3\sqrt{x}}{4+5\sqrt{x}}\cdot\frac{4-5\sqrt{x}}{4-5\sqrt{x}}$$
$$= \frac{7\cdot 4 - 3\sqrt{x}\cdot 4 - 7\cdot 5\sqrt{x} + 3\sqrt{x}\cdot 5\sqrt{x}}{(4)^2 - \left(5\sqrt{x}\right)^2}$$
$$= \frac{28 - 12\sqrt{x} - 35\sqrt{x} + 15x}{16 - 25x}$$
$$= \frac{15x - 47\sqrt{x} + 28}{16 - 25x}$$

18.
$$2\sqrt{x}+3 = 13$$
$$2\sqrt{x} = 10$$
$$\sqrt{x} = 5$$
$$\left(\sqrt{x}\right)^2 = 5^2$$
$$x = 25$$
Check: $x = 25$
$$2\sqrt{(25)}+3 \overset{?}{=} 13$$
$$13 = 13 \text{ true}$$
The solution is 25.

19.
$$3\sqrt{5x-4} = 27$$
$$\sqrt{5x-4} = 9$$
$$\left(\sqrt{5x-4}\right)^2 = 9^2$$
$$5x-4 = 81$$
$$5x = 85$$
$$x = 17$$

Check: $x = 17$
$$3\sqrt{5(17)-4} \overset{?}{=} 27$$
$$27 = 27 \text{ true}$$
The solution is 17.

20.
$$3 - 2\sqrt{x} + \sqrt{9-x} = 0$$
$$\sqrt{9-x} = 2\sqrt{x} - 3$$
$$\left(\sqrt{9-x}\right)^2 = \left(2\sqrt{x}-3\right)^2$$
$$9 - x = 4x - 12\sqrt{x} + 9$$
$$12\sqrt{x} = 5x$$
$$\left(12\sqrt{x}\right)^2 = \left(5x\right)^2$$
$$144x = 25x^2$$
$$25x^2 - 144x = 0$$
$$x(25x - 144) = 0$$
$$x = 0 \text{ or } 25x - 144 = 0$$
$$x = 0 \text{ or } x = \frac{144}{25}$$

Check: $x = 0$
$$3 - 2\sqrt{(0)} + \sqrt{9-(0)} \overset{?}{=} 0$$
$$6 \overset{?}{=} 0 \text{ false}$$

Check: $x = \frac{144}{25}$
$$3 - 2\sqrt{\left(\frac{144}{25}\right)} + \sqrt{9-\left(\frac{144}{25}\right)} \overset{?}{=} 0$$
$$0 = 0 \text{ true}$$
The solution is $\frac{144}{25}$.

21.
$$f(8) = 6 - 4\sqrt{(8)+1}$$
$$= 6 - 4\sqrt{9}$$
$$= 6 - 4(3)$$
$$= 6 - 12$$
$$= -6$$

22.
$$-2 = 6 - 4\sqrt{x+1}$$
$$-8 = -4\sqrt{x+1}$$
$$2 = \sqrt{x+1}$$
$$4 = x+1$$
$$3 = x$$

23.
$$f(x) = 3\sqrt{2x-4} - 2\sqrt{2x+1}$$
$$3\sqrt{2x-4} - 2\sqrt{2x+1} = 0$$
$$3\sqrt{2x-4} = 2\sqrt{2x+1}$$
$$\left(3\sqrt{2x-4}\right)^2 = \left(2\sqrt{2x+1}\right)^2$$
$$9(2x-4) = 4(2x+1)$$
$$18x - 36 = 8x + 4$$
$$10x = 40$$
$$x = 4$$

Check: $x = 4$
$$3\sqrt{2(4)-4} - 2\sqrt{2(4)+1} \overset{?}{=} 0$$
$$0 = 0 \text{ true}$$
The x-intercept is $(4,0)$.

24.
$$\sqrt{x+4} = x^2 - 4x + 5$$
$$x = 0.9 \text{ and } x = 3.3$$

25.
$$\sqrt{x+4} = 1$$
$$x = -3$$

26. Decrease b to lower the y-intercept and increase a to increase the rate of increase. Graphs may vary.

27. Substitute the points $(2,4)$ and $(5,6)$ into the equation $y = a\sqrt{x} + b$.
$$4 = a\sqrt{2} + b$$
$$6 = a\sqrt{5} + b$$
Rewrite as:
$$1.4142a + b = 4$$
$$2.2361a + b = 6$$

Solve the system of equations. Multiply the first equation by -1 and add to the second equation.

$$-1.4142a - b = -4$$
$$\underline{2.2361a + b = 6}$$
$$0.8219a = 2$$
$$a \approx 2.43$$

Substitute the point $(2,4)$ into the equation $y = 2.43\sqrt{x} + b$ and solve for b.

$$4 = 2.43\sqrt{2} + b$$
$$b = 4 - 2.43\sqrt{2}$$
$$b \approx 0.56$$

The equation is $y = 2.43\sqrt{x} + 0.56$.

28.   **a.**   Start by plotting the data.

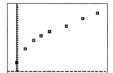

Answers may vary. A square root model seems reasonable.

Use the points $(0, 20.5)$ and $(60, 43.4)$.

The y-intercept is $(0, 20.5)$ so $b = 20.5$.

Substitute the point $(60, 43.4)$ into the equation $y = a\sqrt{x} + 20.5$ and solve for a.

$$43.4 = a\sqrt{60} + 20.5$$
$$a\sqrt{60} = 22.9$$
$$a \approx 2.96$$
$$f(t) = 2.96\sqrt{t} + 20.5$$

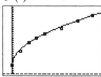

Your equation may differ according to the points you chose.

b. $f(72) = 2.96\sqrt{72} + 20.5 \approx 45.62$

According to the model, the median height of 6-year-old boys is about 45.6 inches.

c.
$$36 = 2.96\sqrt{t} + 20.5$$
$$2.96\sqrt{t} = 15.5$$
$$\sqrt{t} = \frac{15.5}{2.96}$$
$$\left(\sqrt{t}\right)^2 = \left(\frac{15.5}{2.96}\right)^2$$
$$t \approx 27.42$$

The median height of 27-month-old boys is 3 feet.

d.   The h-intercept is $(0, 20.5)$. The median height of boys at birth is 20.5 inches.

Chapter 10
Series and Sequences

1. $11-3=8, 19-11=8, 27-19=8,$
$35-27=8$
The sequence has a common difference of 8.
It is arithmetic.

3. $5-1=4, 7-5=2$
The sequence does not have a common difference. It is not arithmetic.

5. $-13-(-20)=7, -6-(-13)=7,$
$1-(-6)=7, 8-1=7$
The sequence has a common difference of 7.
It is arithmetic.

7. $44-4=40, 444-44=400$
The sequence does not have a common difference. It is not arithmetic.

9. The sequence has a common difference of 6.
$a_n = 5+(n-1)\cdot 6$
$\quad = 5+6n-6$
$a_n = 6n-1$

11. The sequence has a common difference of -11.

$a_n = -4+(n-1)\cdot(-11)$
$\quad = -4+(-11n)+11$
$a_n = -11n+7$

13. The sequence has a common difference of -6.
$a_n = 100+(n-1)\cdot(-6)$
$\quad = 100-6n+6$
$a_n = -6n+106$

15. The sequence has a common difference of 2.
$a_n = 1+(n-1)\cdot 2$
$\quad = 1+2n-2$
$a_n = 2n-1$

17. The sequence has a common difference of 3.

$a_{37} = 5+(37-1)\cdot 3$
$\quad = 5+36\cdot 3$
$\quad = 5+108$
$\quad = 113$

19. The sequence has a common difference of -9.
$a_{45} = 200+(45-1)\cdot(-9)$
$\quad = 200+44\cdot(-9)$
$\quad = 200+(-396)$
$\quad = -196$

21. The sequence has a common difference of 1.6.
$a_{96} = 4.1+(96-1)\cdot 1.6$
$\quad = 4.1+95\cdot 1.6$
$\quad = 4.1+152$
$\quad = 156.1$

23. The sequence has a common difference of 1.
$a_{400} = 1+(400-1)\cdot 1$
$\quad = 400$

25. The sequence has a common difference of 5.
$533 = 3+(n-1)\cdot 5$
$533 = 3+5n-5$
$533 = 5n-2$
$535 = 5n$
$107 = n$

533 is the 107th term.

27. The sequence has a common difference of 8.
$695 = 7+(n-1)\cdot 8$
$695 = 7+8n-8$
$695 = 8n-1$
$696 = 8n$
$87 = n$

695 is the 87th term.

29. The sequence has a common difference of 8.

$$2469 = -27 + (n-1) \cdot 8$$
$$2469 = -27 + 8n - 8$$
$$2469 = 8n - 35$$
$$2504 = 8n$$
$$313 = n$$

2469 is the 313th term.

31. The sequence has a common difference of -4.

$$-14251 = 29 + (n-1) \cdot (-4)$$
$$-14251 = 29 - 4n + 4$$
$$-14251 = 33 - 4n$$
$$-14284 = -4n$$
$$3571 = n$$

-14251 is the 3571st term.

33.   **EQ 1**

$$24 = a_1 + (7-1)d$$
$$24 = a_1 + 6d$$
$$24 - 6d = a_1$$

EQ 2

$$66 = a_1 + (13-1)d$$
$$66 = a_1 + 12d$$
$$66 - 12d = a_1$$

Solve the system of linear equations by setting the left side of each equation equal to each other.

$$24 - 6d = 66 - 12d$$
$$6d = 42$$
$$d = 7$$

Use EQ 1 and $d = 7$ to find a_1.

$$24 - 6(7) = a_1$$
$$-18 = a_1$$

$$a_{40} = -18 + (40-1) \cdot 7$$
$$= -18 + 39 \cdot 7$$
$$= 255$$

35.

EQ 1	**EQ 2**
$500 = a_1 + (41-1)d$	$500 = a_1 + (81-1)d$
$500 = a_1 + 40d$	$500 = a_1 + 80d$
$500 - 40d = a_1$	$500 - 80d = a_1$

$$500 = a_1 + (81-1)d$$
$$500 = a_1 + 80d$$
$$500 - 80d = a_1$$

Solve the system of linear equations by setting the left side of each equation equal to each other.

$$500 - 40d = 500 - 80d$$
$$40d = 0$$
$$d = 0$$

Use EQ 1 and $d = 0$ to find a_1.

$$500 - 40 \cdot 0 = a_1$$
$$500 = a_1$$

$$a_{990} = 500 + (990-1) \cdot 0$$
$$= 500$$

37.
$$f(1) = 4(1) - 2 = 2$$
$$f(2) = 4(2) - 2 = 6$$
$$f(3) = 4(3) - 2 = 10$$

Yes, this sequence is arithmetic with a common difference equal to the slope, 4.

39.
$$f(1) = 1^2 = 1$$
$$f(2) = 2^2 = 4$$
$$f(3) = 3^2 = 9$$

No, this sequence is not arithmetic. There is no common difference.

41. The student's work is not correct. The sequence is not arithmetic because there is no common difference.

43. $15 - 8 = 7, 22 - 15 = 7, 29 - 22 = 7,$
$36 - 29 = 7$
The sequence has a common difference of 7. It is arithmetic.

$2537 = 8 + (n-1) \cdot 7$

$2537 = 8 + 7n - 7$

$2537 = 7n + 1$

$2536 = 7n$

$\quad n \approx 362.3$

Since n is not a counting number, 2537 is not a term in the sequence.

45.   Since $d = 9$ and $a_1 = 8$,

$f(n) = 8 + (n-1) \cdot 9$

$\quad = 8 + 9n - 9$

$\quad = 9n - 1$

47. a. $a_n = 27,500 + (n-1) \cdot 800$

$\quad = 27,500 + 800n - 800$

$a_n = 26,700 + 800n$

b. $a_{22} = 26,700 + 800 \cdot 22$

$\quad = \$44,300$

The salary for the 22nd year will be \$44,300.

c. $50,000 = 26,700 + 800n$

$23,300 = 800n$

$29.125 = n$

The salary will first be above \$50,000 in the 30th year.

49. a.

$a_n = 35 + \dfrac{1}{6}n$

b.

$a_1 = 35 + \dfrac{1}{6} \cdot 1 \approx 35.17$

$a_2 = 35 + \dfrac{1}{6} \cdot 2 \approx 35.33$

$a_3 = 35 + \dfrac{1}{6} \cdot 3 = 35.5$

$a_4 = 35 + \dfrac{1}{6} \cdot 4 \approx 35.67$

These values represent the number of hours the instructor would work if she had 1, 2, 3, or 4 students, respectively.

c.

$a_{130} = 35 + \dfrac{1}{6} \cdot 130$

$\quad \approx 56.67$

56.7 hours per week

d.

$60 = 35 + \dfrac{1}{6}n$

$25 = \dfrac{1}{6}n$

$150 = n$

The greatest number is 150 students.

51. a.   The band collects $0.3(6) = \$1.80$ per cover charge, so the common difference is 1.8.

$a_n = -50 + 0.3(6)n$

$\quad = -50 + 1.8n$

b. $256 = -50 + 1.8n$

$306 = 1.8n$

$170 = n$

170 people paid the cover charge.

c.   Total number of people who pay is $200 - 18 - 11 - 6 = 165$.

$a_{165} = -50 + 1.8(165)$

$\quad = 247$

Their maximum profit is \$247.00.

d. $0 = -50 + 0.3(6)n$

$0 = -50 + 1.8n$

$50 = 1.8n$

$n \approx 27.8$

Little Muddy will lose money for values of n less than or equal to 27.

53. a.

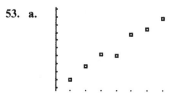

b. $f(t) = 12.61t + 44.07$

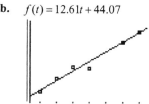

c. $f(5) = 107.12$

$f(6) = 119.73$

$f(7) = 132.34$

$f(8) = 144.95$

$f(9) = 157.56$

X	Y₁
3	81.893
4	94.5
5	107.11
6	119.71
7	132.32
8	144.93
9	157.54

X=3

These values represent the pharmaceutical industry's spending on government and politics (in millions of dollars) in 2000, 2001, 2002, 2003, and 2004 respectively.

d. $f(16) = 12.61(16) + 44.07$

$f(16) = 245.83$

55. a. $a_n = 0.39 + (n-1) \cdot 0.24$

$= 0.39 + 0.24n - 0.24$

$a_n = 0.15 + 0.24n$

b. $a_{13} = 0.15 + 0.24(13)$

$= 3.27$

a_{13} is equal to $3.27.

c. $a_{16} = 0.15 + 0.24(16)$

$= 3.99$

No, $4.05 is not a better deal.

d. $a_{80} = 0.15 + 0.24(80) =$

19.35

a_{80} is equal to $19.35.

57. a. $7-5 = 2, 9-7 = 2, 11-9 = 2,$

$13 - 11 = 2$

The arithmetic sequence has a common difference of 2.

b. $m = \dfrac{7-5}{2-1} = \dfrac{2}{1} = 2$

$m = \dfrac{9-7}{3-2} = \dfrac{2}{1} = 2$

$m = \dfrac{11-9}{4-3} = \dfrac{2}{1} = 2$

$m = \dfrac{13-11}{5-4} = \dfrac{2}{1} = 2$

The slope of the line containing the points given is $m = 2$.

c. The common difference of the arithmetic sequence is equal to the slope of the function. Answers may vary. The form of the equation of an arithmetic sequence is the same as the form of a line in slope-intercept form, where m takes the place of d.

59.

$2\sqrt{x+3} - 1 = 5$

$2\sqrt{x+3} = 6$

$\sqrt{x+3} = 3$

$x + 3 = 9$

$x = 6$

check :

$2\sqrt{(6)+3} - 1 = 5$

$2\sqrt{9} - 1 = 5$

$2(3) - 1 = 5$

$6 - 1 = 5$

$5 = 5$

$2\sqrt{x+3} - 1 = 5$ is a radical equation in one variable.

61.

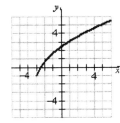

$f(x) = 2\sqrt{x+3} - 1$ is a radical function.

63. $\left(4\sqrt{x}-5\right)\left(3\sqrt{x}-2\right)$

$= 12 \cdot x - 8\sqrt{x} - 15\sqrt{x} + 10$

$= 12x - 23\sqrt{x} + 10$

It is a radical expression in one variable.

Homework 10.2

1. $\dfrac{28}{4} = 7, \dfrac{196}{28} = 7, \dfrac{1372}{196} = 7, \dfrac{9604}{1372} = 7...$

The sequence has a common ratio of 7. It is geometric.

3. $6 - 13 = -7, -1 - 6 = -7, -8 - (-1) = -7,$

$-15 - (-8) = -7...$

The sequence has a common difference of -7. It is arithmetic.

5. $\dfrac{4}{3} \approx 1.33, \dfrac{6}{4} = 1.5$

The sequence has no common ratio.
$4 - 3 = 1, 6 - 4 = 2$

The sequence has no common difference.
The sequence is neither arithmetic nor geometric.

7. $\dfrac{40}{200} = \dfrac{1}{5}, \dfrac{8}{40} = \dfrac{1}{5}, \dfrac{\frac{8}{5}}{8} = \dfrac{1}{5}, \dfrac{\frac{8}{25}}{\frac{8}{5}} = \dfrac{1}{5}$

The sequence has a common ratio of $\dfrac{1}{5}$. It is geometric.

9. The sequence has a common ratio of 2.

$a_n = 3(2)^{n-1}$

$= 3(2)^n (2)^{-1}$

$a_n = \dfrac{3(2)^n}{2} = \dfrac{3}{2}(2)^n$

Solution: $a_n = 3(2)^{n-1}$ or $a_n = \dfrac{3}{2}(2)^n$

11. The sequence has a common ratio of $\dfrac{1}{4}$.

$a_n = 800\left(\dfrac{1}{4}\right)^{n-1}$

$= 800\left(\dfrac{1}{4}\right)^n \left(\dfrac{1}{4}\right)^{-1}$

$= 800\left(\dfrac{1}{4}\right)^n (4)$

$a_n = 3200\left(\dfrac{1}{4}\right)^n$

Solution: $a_n = 800\left(\dfrac{1}{4}\right)^{n-1}$ or $a_n = 3200\left(\dfrac{1}{4}\right)^n$

13. The sequence has a common ratio of $\dfrac{1}{2}$.

$a_n = 100\left(\dfrac{1}{2}\right)^{n-1}$

$= 100\left(\dfrac{1}{2}\right)^n \left(\dfrac{1}{2}\right)^{-1}$

$= 100\left(\dfrac{1}{2}\right)^n (2)$

$a_n = 200\left(\dfrac{1}{2}\right)^n$

Solution: $a_n = 100\left(\dfrac{1}{2}\right)^{n-1}$ or $a_n = 200\left(\dfrac{1}{2}\right)^n$

15. The sequence has a common ratio of 4.

$a_n = 1(4)^{n-1}$

$= 4^n (4)^{-1}$

$= 4^n \left(\dfrac{1}{4}\right)$

$a_n = \dfrac{1}{4}(4)^n$

Solution: $a_n = 1(4)^{n-1}$ or $a_n = \dfrac{1}{4}(4)^n$

17. The sequence has a common ratio of 5.

$a_{34} = 4(5)^{34-1}$

$= 4(5)^{33}$

$\approx 4.6566 \times 10^{23}$

19. The sequence has a common ratio of $\dfrac{1}{2}$.

$$a_{27} = 80\left(\frac{1}{2}\right)^{27-1}$$

$$= 80\left(\frac{1}{2}\right)^{26}$$

$$\approx 1.1921 \times 10^{-6}$$

21. The sequence has a common ratio of 2.

$$a_{23} = 8(2)^{23-1}$$

$$= 8(2)^{22}$$

$$= 33,554,432$$

$$\approx 3.3554 \times 10^{7}$$

23.

The sequence has a common ratio of $\frac{1}{2}$.

$$0.46875 = 240\left(\frac{1}{2}\right)^{n-1}$$

$$0.001953125 = \left(\frac{1}{2}\right)^{n-1}$$

$$\log(0.001953125) = \log\left(\frac{1}{2}\right)^{n-1}$$

$$\log(0.001953125) = (n-1)\log\left(\frac{1}{2}\right)$$

$$\frac{\log(0.001953125)}{\log\left(\frac{1}{2}\right)} = n-1$$

$$\frac{\log(0.001953125)}{\log\left(\frac{1}{2}\right)} + 1 = n$$

$$10 = n$$

25. Use the sequence 0.00224, 0.0112, 0.056, 0.28, 1.4,…,109,375. This sequence has a common ratio of 5.

$$109,375 = 0.00224(5)^{n-1}$$

$$48,828,125 = 5^{n-1}$$

$$\log(48,828,125) = \log(5^{n-1})$$

$$\log(48,828,125) = (n-1)\log 5$$

$$\frac{\log(48,828,125)}{\log 5} = n-1$$

$$\frac{\log(48,828,125)}{\log 5} + 1 = n$$

$$12 = n$$

27. The sequence has a common ratio of 2.

$$3,407,872 = 13(2^{n-1})$$

$$262,144 = 2^{n-1}$$

$$\log(262,144) = \log(2^{n-1})$$

$$\log(262,144) = (n-1)\log 2$$

$$\frac{\log(262,144)}{\log 2} = n-1$$

$$\frac{\log(262,144)}{\log 2} + 1 = n$$

$$19 = n$$

29. The sequence has a common ratio of 3.

$$28,697,814 = 2(3)^{n-1}$$

$$14,348,907 = 3^{n-1}$$

$$\log(14,348,907) = \log(3^{n-1})$$

$$\log(14,348,907) = (n-1)\log 3$$

$$\frac{\log(14,348,907)}{\log 3} = n-1$$

$$\frac{\log(14,348,907)}{\log 3} + 1 = n$$

$$16 = n$$

31. The sequence is geometric. The common ratio is 5.

33. The sequence is arithmetic. The common difference is the slope which is 7.

35. The sequence has a common ratio of 3.

$$f(n) = 8(3)^{n-1}$$

37. Answers may vary. The sequence is geometric with a common ratio of 2 and $a_1 = 13$. Therefore, all terms must be divisible by 13. 9,238,946 is not divisible by 13, so it is not a term in the geometric sequence.

39. The student's work is not correct. The student is using the formula for a geometric sequence but the sequence is arithmetic. The arithmetic sequence has a common difference of 4.

$$a_{17} = 2 + (17-1) \cdot 4$$
$$= 66$$

41. a. $a_n = 27,000(1.04)^{n-1}$

b. $a_{10} = 27,000(1.04)^{10-1}$
$$= 27,000(1.04)^9$$
$$\approx \$38,429.42$$
The person's salary will be $38,429.42 for the 10th year.

c.
$$50,000 = 27,000(1.04)^{n-1}$$
$$\frac{50}{27} = 1.04^{n-1}$$
$$\log\left(\frac{50}{27}\right) = \log\left(1.04^{n-1}\right)$$
$$\log\left(\frac{50}{27}\right) = (n-1)\log 1.04$$
$$\frac{\log\left(\frac{50}{27}\right)}{\log 1.04} = n-1$$
$$\frac{\log\left(\frac{50}{27}\right)}{\log 1.04} + 1 = n$$
$$16.7 \approx n$$
The salary will first exceed $50,000 in the 17th year.

43. a. $2, 4, 8, 16, 32$

b. The sequence has a common ratio of 2.
$$a_n = 2(2)^{n-1}$$
$$= 2^1 \cdot 2^{n-1}$$
$$= 2^{1+n-1}$$
$$= 2^n$$

c. $a_8 = 2^8 = 256$ ancestors

d. $a_{35} = 2^{35}$
$$\approx 3.436 \times 10^{10}$$
$$\approx 34.36 \text{ billion ancestors}$$
Model breakdown has occurred. Answers may vary. The number of ancestors is much higher than the world's current population. One assumption is that no ancestor is related to any other ancestor, and this assumption is likely false.

45. a.

b.

$$f(t) = 865.47(1.39)^t$$

c. $f(1) = 865.47(1.39)^1$
$$\approx 1203$$
$$f(2) = 865.47(1.39)^2$$
$$\approx 1672$$
$$f(3) = 865.47(1.39)^3$$
$$\approx 2324$$
$$f(4) = 865.47(1.39)^4 \quad f(5) = 865.47(1.39)^5$$
$$\approx 3231 \qquad\qquad \approx 4491$$
This means that in 2001, 1203 girls named Nevaeh were born; in 2002, 1672 girls named Nevaeh were born; in 2003, 2324 girls named Nevaeh were born; in 2004, 3231 girls named Nevaeh were born; in 2005, 4491 girls named Nevaeh were born.

d. $f(t) = 865.47(1.39)^t$
$$f(10) = 865.47(1.39)^{10}$$
$$\approx 23,302$$
23,302 is about 1.17% of 2,000,000. 1.25% of 2,000,000 indicates 25,000 girls will be named Emily. Emily will be a more popular name than Neveah.

47. a. $a_n = 5(3)^{n-1}$

b. $a_5 = 5(3)^{5-1}$
$$= 5(3)^4$$
$$= 405$$
a_5 is equal to 405 students.

c. $a_{11} = 5(3)^{11-1}$

$\phantom{a_{11}} = 5(3)^{10}$

$\phantom{a_{11}} = 295,245$

Answers may vary. Model breakdown has occurred. No campus has 295, 245 students.

d. Answers may vary. One of the assumptions was that a student would tell the rumor to 3 other students who have not heard the rumor yet. This assumption is reasonable for the first several days. However, as the number of students who heard the rumor grows larger, it is unlikely that those students would each know 3 other students who had not heard the rumor yet.

49. a. $\dfrac{14}{7} = 2, \dfrac{28}{14} = 2, \dfrac{56}{28} = 2, \dfrac{112}{56} = 2$

The series is geometric with a common ratio of 2.

b. $y = ab^x$

$7 = a \cdot b^1$

$7 = ab$

$a = \dfrac{7}{b}$

Substituting $a = \dfrac{7}{b}$ into $14 = ab^2$

$14 = \left(\dfrac{7}{b}\right)b^2$

$14 = 7b$

$2 = b$

So the base is 2.

c. The common ratio for the sequence and the base of the function are the same. Answers may vary. The form of the equation of an geometric sequence is the same as the form of an exponential function, where the common ratio of the sequence is the base of the function.

51. The sequence has a common difference of 5.

$a_n = 14 + (n-1) \cdot 5$

$ = 14 + 5n - 5$

$ = 5n + 9$

53. The sequence has a common ratio of $\dfrac{1}{2}$.

$a_n = 448\left(\dfrac{1}{2}\right)^{n-1}$

$ = 448\left(\dfrac{1}{2}\right)^{n}\left(\dfrac{1}{2}\right)^{-1}$

$ = 448\left(\dfrac{1}{2}\right)^{n}(2)$

$a_n = 896\left(\dfrac{1}{2}\right)^{n}$

Solution: $a_n = 448\left(\dfrac{1}{2}\right)^{n-1}$ or $a_n = 896\left(\dfrac{1}{2}\right)^{n}$

55. The sequence has a common ratio of 5.

$a_9 = 2(5)^{9-1}$

$ = 2(5)^{8}$

$ = 781,250$

57. The sequence has a common difference of -5.

$a_{99} = 17 + (99-1) \cdot (-5)$

$\phantom{a_{99}} = -473$

59. The sequence has a common difference of 3.

$367 = 4 + (n-1) \cdot 3$

$367 = 4 + 3n - 3$

$367 = 1 + 3n$

$366 = 3n$

$122 = n$

61. The sequence is geometric with a common ratio of $\dfrac{1}{4}$ and $a_1 = 8192$.

$0.0078125 = 8192\left(\dfrac{1}{4}\right)^{n-1}$

$9.536743164 \times 10^{-7} = \left(\dfrac{1}{4}\right)^{n-1}$

$\log 9.536743164 \times 10^{-7} = \log\left(\dfrac{1}{4}\right)^{n-1}$

$$\log 9.536743164 \times 10^{-7} = (n-1)\log\left(\frac{1}{4}\right)$$

$$\frac{\log 9.536743164 \times 10^{-7}}{\log\left(\dfrac{1}{4}\right)} = n-1$$

$$n = \frac{\log 9.536743164 \times 10^{-7}}{\log\left(\dfrac{1}{4}\right)} + 1 = 11$$

0.0078125 is the 11th term of the geometric sequence.

63.
$$-3(4)^x = -44$$

$$4^x = \frac{44}{3}$$

$$\log 4^x = \log\left(\frac{44}{3}\right)$$

$$x\log 4 = \log\left(\frac{44}{3}\right)$$

$$x = \frac{\log\left(\dfrac{44}{3}\right)}{\log 4} \approx 1.9372$$

Check:
$$-3(4)^{1.937234559} = -44$$

$$-3\left(\frac{44}{3}\right) = -44$$

$$-44 = -44 \text{ True}$$

$-3(4)^x = -44$ is an exponential equation in one variable

65.

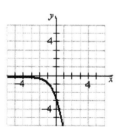

$f(x) = -3(4)^x$ is an exponential function.

67.
$$2\log_b\left(5x^3\right) - 3\log\left(2x^7\right)$$

$$= \log_b\left(5x^3\right)^2 - \log\left(2x^7\right)^3$$

$$= \log_b\left(25x^6\right) - \log\left(8x^{21}\right)$$

$$= \log_b\left(\frac{25x^6}{8x^{21}}\right)$$

$$= \log_b\left(\frac{25}{8x^{15}}\right)$$

It is a logarithmic expression in one variable.

Homework 10.3

1.
$$S_{90} = \frac{90(2+447)}{2}$$
$$= 20,205$$

3.
$$S_{108} = \frac{108(13+548)}{2}$$
$$= 30,294$$

5.
$$S_{72} = \frac{72\left(37+(-1099)\right)}{2}$$
$$= -38,232$$

7. The series is arithmetic with a common difference of 8.

$$S_{74} = \frac{74(5+589)}{2}$$
$$= 21,978$$

9. The series is arithmetic with a common difference of –4.

$$S_{101} = \frac{101\left(93+(-307)\right)}{2}$$
$$= -10,807$$

11. The series is arithmetic with a common difference of 0.

$$S_{117} = \frac{117(4+4)}{2}$$
$$= 468$$

13. The series is arithmetic with a common difference of 10.

$$a_{125} = 3 + (125 - 1) \cdot 10$$
$$= 3 + 124 \cdot 10$$
$$= 1243$$
$$S_{125} = \frac{125(3 + 1243)}{2}$$
$$= 77,875$$

15. The series is arithmetic with a common difference of 11.
$$a_{81} = 8 + (81 - 1) \cdot 11$$
$$= 8 + 80 \cdot 11$$
$$= 888$$
$$S_{81} = \frac{81(8 + 888)}{2}$$
$$= 36,288$$

17. The series is arithmetic with a common difference of −13.
$$a_{152} = -15 + (152 - 1) \cdot (-13)$$
$$= -1978$$
$$S_{152} = \frac{152(-15 + (-1978))}{2}$$
$$= -151,468$$

19. The series is arithmetic with a common difference of 3.
$$a_{137} = -40 + (137 - 1) \cdot 3$$
$$= 368$$
$$S_{137} = \frac{137(-40 + 368)}{2}$$
$$= 22,468$$

21. The series is arithmetic with a common difference of 6.
$$247 = 19 + (n - 1) \cdot 6$$
$$247 = 19 + 6n - 6$$
$$247 = 13 + 6n$$
$$234 = 6n$$
$$39 = n$$
So $247 = a_{39}$
$$S_{39} = \frac{39(19 + 247)}{2}$$
$$= 5187$$

23. The series is arithmetic with a common difference of −8.
$$-900 = 900 + (n - 1) \cdot (-8)$$
$$-900 = 900 - 8n + 8$$
$$-900 = 908 - 8n$$
$$-1808 - -8n$$
$$226 = n$$
So $-900 = a_{226}$
$$S_{226} = \frac{226(900 + (-900))}{2}$$
$$= 0$$

25. The series is arithmetic with a common difference of 3.
$$340 = 4 + (n - 1) \cdot 3$$
$$340 = 4 + 3n - 3$$
$$340 = 3n + 1$$
$$339 = 3n$$
$$113 = n$$
So $340 = a_{113}$
$$S_{113} = \frac{113(4 + 340)}{2}$$
$$= 19,436$$

27. The series is arithmetic with a common difference of 1.
$$10,000 = 1 + (n - 1) \cdot 1$$
$$10,000 = 1 + n - 1$$
$$10,000 = n$$
So $10,000 = a_{10000}$
$$S_{10,000} = \frac{10,000(1 + 10,000)}{2}$$
$$= 50,005,000$$

29. S_n is positive it will be the sum of n positive numbers.

31. S_n is positive because it will be the sum of three relatively small negative numbers and many larger positive numbers.

33. Yes, the series is arithmetic. The common difference is the slope, 7.

35. a.
$$a_{28} = 28,500 + (28-1) \cdot 1100$$
$$= 28,500 + 27 \cdot 1100$$
$$= \$58,200$$

b.
$$S_{28} = \frac{28(28,500 + 58,200)}{2}$$
$$= \$1,213,800$$

37.
Company A
$$a_{20} = 35,000 + (20-1) \cdot 700$$
$$= \$48,300$$
$$S_{20} = \frac{20(35,000 + 48,300)}{2}$$
$$= \$833,000$$

Company B
$$a_{20} = 27,000 + (20-1) \cdot 1500$$
$$= \$55,500$$
$$S_{20} = \frac{20(27,000 + 55,500)}{2}$$
$$= \$825,000$$
Your total earnings for 20 years would be greater at Company A by $8000.

39. a.
$$a_{30} = 20 + (30-1) \cdot 4$$
$$= 136$$
There are 136 seats in the 30th row, the back row.

b.
$$S_{30} = \frac{30(20 + 136)}{2}$$
$$= 2340$$
There are 2340 seats in the auditorium.

41. a. Since $t = 3$ corresponds to the year 1998, according to the model,
$$f(3) = 12.61(3) + 44.07$$
$$\approx 82$$
The model estimates that the pharmaceutical industry spent approximately 82 million dollars on government and politics in 1998.

b. Since $t = 15$ corresponds to the year 2010, according to the model,
$$f(15) = 12.61(15) + 44.07$$
$$\approx 233$$

So in 2010, the pharmaceutical industry will spend approximately 233 million dollars on government and politics.

c.
$$S_{13} = \frac{13(82 + 233)}{2}$$
$$= 2047.5$$
From 1998 through 2010 (including 2010), the pharmaceutical industry will spend a total of approximately 2048 million dollars, or 2.05 billion, on government and politics.

43. a.
$$a_{26} = 24,800 + (26-1) \cdot 1200$$
$$= \$54,800$$
$$S_{26} = \frac{26(24,800 + 54,800)}{2}$$
$$= \$1,034,800$$

b.
$$a_1 = 0$$
$$a_{26} = 54,800 - 24,800$$
$$= 30,000$$
$$n = 26$$
$$S_{26} = \frac{26(0 + 30,000)}{2}$$
$$= 390,000$$
The total amount of money earned from raises in 26 years is $390,000.

c.
$$\text{mean} = \frac{1,034,800}{26}$$
$$= \$39,800$$
The mean salary over the 26 years is $39,800. For the first 13 years this mean will be greater than the yearly salary. For the last 13 years, the mean will be less than the yearly salary.

d. The taxable income for the first 5 years is $20,550, $21,750, $22,950, $24,150, and $25,350. The taxable income does not exceed $25,000 until the 5th year. Therefore, the total income taxed at the lower rate will be
$$20,550 + 21,750 + 22,950 + 24,150$$
$$+ 22(25,000)$$
$$= \$639,400.$$
The taxable income at the higher rate is an arithmetic sequence whose first term is $350

$(25,350 - 25,000)$ and whose common difference is $1200. The number of terms in this sequence is 22 because taxable income did not exceed $25,000 until the 5th year.

$$a_{22} = 350 + (22-1) \cdot 1200$$
$$= \$25,550$$
$$S_{22} = \frac{22(350 + 25,550)}{2}$$
$$= \$284,900$$

The estimated income tax will be
$$\$639,400(0.15016) + \$284,900(0.1704)$$
$$\approx \$144,559.26$$

45. The arithmetic sequence has a common difference of 16.
$$a_{15} = 8 + (15-1) \cdot 16$$
$$= 232$$

47. The arithmetic series has a common difference of 16.
$$a_{15} = 8 + (15-1) \cdot 16$$
$$= 232$$
$$S_{15} = \frac{15(8 + 232)}{2}$$
$$= 1800$$

49.
$$\frac{x-5}{x^2-9} + \frac{x+3}{x^2-8x+15}$$
$$= \frac{x-5}{(x-3)(x+3)} + \frac{x+3}{(x-3)(x-5)}$$
$$= \frac{(x-5)}{(x-3)(x+3)} \cdot \frac{(x-5)}{(x-5)} + \frac{(x+3)}{(x-3)(x-5)} \cdot \frac{(x+3)}{(x+3)}$$
$$= \frac{(x-5)(x-5)}{(x-3)(x+3)(x-5)} + \frac{(x+3)(x+3)}{(x-3)(x-5)(x+3)}$$
$$= \frac{(x-5)(x-5) + (x+3)(x+3)}{(x-3)(x+3)(x-5)}$$
$$= \frac{x^2 - 5x - 5x + 25 + x^2 + 3x + 3x + 9}{(x-3)(x+3)(x-5)}$$
$$= \frac{2x^2 - 4x + 34}{(x-3)(x+3)(x-5)}$$
$$= \frac{2(x^2 - 2x + 17)}{(x-3)(x+3)(x-5)}$$

It is a rational expression in one variable.

51.
$$\frac{x-5}{x^2-9} \cdot \frac{x+3}{x^2-8x+15}$$
$$= \frac{x-5}{(x-3)(x+3)} \cdot \frac{x+3}{(x-3)(x-5)}$$
$$= \frac{(x-5)}{(x-3)(x+3)} \cdot \frac{(x+3)}{(x-3)(x-5)}$$
$$= \frac{(x-5)}{(x-3)} \cdot \frac{1}{(x-3)(x-5)}$$
$$= \frac{1}{(x-3)^2}$$

It is a rational expression in one variable.

53.
$$\frac{x-5}{x^2-9} + \frac{x+3}{x^2-8x+15} = \frac{2}{x-5}$$
$$\frac{x-5}{(x-3)(x+3)} + \frac{x+3}{(x-3)(x-5)} = \frac{2}{x-5}$$
$$(x-5)(x-5) + (x+3)(x+3) = 2(x-3)(x+3)$$
$$x^2 - 10x + 25 + x^2 + 6x + 9 = 2x^2 - 18$$
$$2x^2 - 4x + 34 = 2x^2 - 18$$
$$-4x + 34 = -18$$
$$-4x = -52$$
$$x = 13$$

Check:
$$\frac{(13)-5}{(13)^2-9} + \frac{(13)+3}{(13)^2 - 8(13) + 15} = \frac{2}{(13)-5}$$
$$0.25 = 0.25 \quad \text{True}$$
It is a rational equation in one variable.

Homework 10.4

1.
$$S_{13} = \frac{5(1 - 2^{13})}{1-2}$$
$$= 40,955$$

3.
$$S_{12} = \frac{6(1 - 1.3^{12})}{1 - 1.3}$$
$$\approx 445.9617$$

5.
$$S_{13} = \frac{13(1 - 0.8^{13})}{1 - 0.8}$$
$$\approx 61.4266$$

7.
$$S_{10} = \frac{2.3(1-0.9^{10})}{1-0.9}$$
$$\approx 14.9804$$

9. The series is geometric with a common ratio of 5.
$$S_{13} = \frac{2(1-5^{13})}{1-5}$$
$$= 610,351,562$$

11. The series is geometric with a common ratio of 0.3.
$$S_{11} = \frac{600(1-0.3^{11})}{1-0.3}$$
$$\approx 857.1413$$

13. The series is geometric with a common ratio of $\frac{2}{3}$.
$$S_{10} = \frac{3\left(1-\left(\frac{2}{3}\right)^{10}\right)}{1-\frac{2}{3}}$$
$$\approx 8.8439$$

15. The series is geometric with a common ratio of 4.
$$67,108,864 = 1(4)^{n-1}$$
$$\log 67,108,864 = \log 4^{n-1}$$
$$\log 67,108,864 = (n-1)\log 4$$
$$\frac{\log 67,108,864}{\log 4} = n-1$$
$$\frac{\log 67,108,864}{\log 4}+1 = n$$
$$14 = n$$
$$S_{14} = \frac{1(1-4^{14})}{1-4}$$
$$= 89,478,485$$

17. The series is geometric with a common ratio of 1.2.

$$21.4990848 = 5(1.2)^{n-1}$$
$$4.29981696 = 1.2^{n-1}$$
$$\log 4.29981696 = \log 1.2^{n-1}$$
$$\log 4.29981696 = (n-1)\log 1.2$$
$$\frac{\log 4.29981696}{\log 1.2} = n-1$$
$$\frac{\log 4.29981696}{\log 1.2}+1 = n$$
$$9 = n$$
$$S_9 = \frac{5(1-1.2^9)}{1-1.2}$$
$$\approx 103.9945$$

19. The series is geometric with common ratio of $\frac{1}{2}$.

$$4.8828125 = 10,000\left(\frac{1}{2}\right)^{n-1}$$
$$0.00048828125 = \left(\frac{1}{2}\right)^{n-1}$$
$$\log 0.00048828125 = \log\left(\frac{1}{2}\right)^{n-1}$$
$$\log 0.00048828125 = (n-1)\log\left(\frac{1}{2}\right)$$
$$\frac{\log 0.00048828125}{\log\left(\frac{1}{2}\right)} = n-1$$
$$\frac{\log 0.00048828125}{\log\left(\frac{1}{2}\right)}+1 = n$$
$$12 = n$$
$$S_{12} = \frac{10,000\left(1-\left(\frac{1}{2}\right)^{12}\right)}{1-\frac{1}{2}}$$
$$\approx 19,995.1172$$

21. The series is arithmetic with a common difference of 0.
$$S_{100} = \frac{100(1+1)}{2}$$
$$= 100$$

23. The series is geometric with a common ratio of $\frac{1}{3}$.

$$\frac{4}{729} = 324\left(\frac{1}{3}\right)^{n-1}$$

$$\frac{4}{729} = 324\left(\frac{1}{3}\right)^{n-1}$$

$$1.693508781 \times 10^{-5} = \left(\frac{1}{3}\right)^{n-1}$$

$$\log\left(1.693508781 \times 10^{-5}\right) = \log\left(\frac{1}{3}\right)^{n-1}$$

$$\log\left(1.693508781 \times 10^{-5}\right) = (n-1)\log\left(\frac{1}{3}\right)$$

$$\frac{\log\left(1.693508781 \times 10^{-5}\right)}{\log\left(\frac{1}{3}\right)} = n-1$$

$$\frac{\log\left(1.693508781 \times 10^{-5}\right)}{\log\left(\frac{1}{3}\right)} + 1 = n$$

$$11 = n$$

$$S_{11} = \frac{324\left(1 - \left(\frac{1}{3}\right)^{11}\right)}{1 - \left(\frac{1}{3}\right)}$$

$$\approx 485.9973$$

25. S_n must be positive because it is the sum of all positive values.

27. The series is arithmetic because $f(x)$ is linear. The common difference of the series is the slope of $f(x)$ which is -1.

29. $$S_{20} = \frac{23500(1 - 1.04^{20})}{1 - 1.04}$$
$$\approx \$699,784.85$$

The person's total earnings after 20 years of work will be $699,784.85.

31. **Company A**
$$S_{30} = \frac{26000(1 - 1.05^{30})}{1 - 1.05} \approx \$1,727,410.04$$

Company B
$$S_{30} = \frac{31000(1 - 1.03^{30})}{1 - 1.03} \approx \$1,474,837.89$$

The earnings at Company A after 30 years will be $252,572.15 more than Company B.

33. Recall, the number of ancestors n generations back is a geometric series with a common ratio of 2.

$$S_n = \frac{2(1 - 2^{10})}{1 - 2} \text{ ancestors}$$
$$= 2046$$

35. a. The entrepreneur's name would be taken off the list in the 11th round. The amount of money sent to the entrepreneur each round is a geometric series with common ratio 8.

$$S_{10} = \frac{40(1 - 8^{10})}{1 - 8}$$
$$= 6,135,667,560$$

The entrepreneur could receive as much as approximately $6.14 billion.

b.
$$6,500,000,000 = \frac{8(1 - 8^n)}{1 - 8}$$
$$6,500,000,000 = -\frac{8}{7}(1 - 8^n)$$
$$5,687,500,000 = 8^n - 1$$
$$8^n = 5,687,500,001$$
$$\log 8^n = \log 5,687,500,001$$
$$n\log 8 = \log 5,687,500,001$$
$$n = \frac{\log 5,687,500,001}{\log 8}$$
$$n \approx 10.80$$

There will be ten full rounds and part of an 11th round.

c. The money from the first 10 rounds will go to the entrepreneur. The chain letter runs out of people (and money!) to complete the 11th round. All the money from the 11th round would go to the first 8 people besides the entrepreneur. This amount is (in billions):

$$\frac{32.5 - 6.136}{8} \approx 3.3$$

So, 9 people will receive money from the chain letters. The entrepreneur will receive

374

approximately \$6.14 billion. The 8 people besides the entrepreneur will receive an average of \$3.30 billion.

37. a. $f(t) = 865.47(1.39)^t$

$f(1) = 865.47(1.39)^1$

≈ 1203.00

This means that in 2001, 1203 girls named Nevaeh were born.

b. $f(11) = 865.47(1.39)^{11}$

$\approx 32,390.29$

This means that in 2011, 32,390 girls named Nevaeh will be born.

c. Find the sum of

$f(1), f(2), f(3), f(4), f(5), f(6),$

$f(7), f(8), f(9), f(10), f(11)$

$S_{11} = \dfrac{1203(1 - 1.39^{11})}{1 - 1.39}$

$\approx 112,357$

This means that from 2001 through 2011 (including 2011), a total of 112,357 girls named Nevaeh will be born.

39. a. The series is geometric with a common ratio of 2.

$2560 = 5(2)^{n-1}$

$512 = (2)^{n-1}$

$\log 512 = \log(2)^{n-1}$

$\log 512 = (n-1)\log(2)$

$\dfrac{\log 512}{\log 2} = n - 1$

$\dfrac{\log 512}{\log 2} + 1 = n$

$10 = n$

$S_{10} = \dfrac{5(1 - 2^{10})}{1 - 2}$

$= 5115$

b.

$a_n = a_1 r^{n-1}$

$\dfrac{a_n}{a_1} = r^{n-1}$

$\log \dfrac{a_n}{a_1} = \log r^{n-1}$

$\log \dfrac{a_n}{a_1} = (n-1)\log r$

$\dfrac{\log\left(\dfrac{a_n}{a_1}\right)}{\log r} = (n-1)$

$n = \dfrac{\log\left(\dfrac{a_n}{a_1}\right)}{\log r} + 1$

$n = \dfrac{\log\left(\dfrac{a_n}{a_1}\right)}{\log r} + \dfrac{\log r}{\log r}$

$n = \dfrac{\log\left(\dfrac{a_n}{a_1}\right) + \log r}{\log r}$

$n = \dfrac{\log\left(\dfrac{a_n r}{a_1}\right)}{\log r}$

c.

$S_n = \dfrac{a_1\left(1 - r^n\right)}{1 - r}$

$S_n = \dfrac{a_1\left(1 - r^{\log(a_n r / a_1)/\log r}\right)}{1 - r}$

d.

$S_{10} = \dfrac{5\left(1 - 2^{\log(2560 \cdot 2/5)/\log 2}\right)}{1 - 2}$

$S_{10} = \dfrac{5\left(1 - 2^{10}\right)}{1 - 2}$

$S_{10} = 5115$

e. Answers may vary.

41. The series is arithmetic with a common difference of 6.

$$351 = 3 + (n-1) \cdot 6$$
$$351 = 3 + 6n - 6$$
$$351 = 6n - 3$$
$$354 = 6n$$
$$59 = n$$
$$S_{59} = \frac{59(3 + 351)}{2}$$
$$= 10,443$$

43. The series is geometric with a common ratio of 0.9.

$$3.486784401 = 10(0.9)^{n-1}$$
$$0.3486784401 = (0.9)^{n-1}$$
$$\log 0.3486784401 = \log(0.9)^{n-1}$$
$$\log 0.3486784401 = (n-1)\log 0.9$$
$$\frac{\log 0.3486784401}{\log 0.9} = n - 1$$
$$\frac{\log 0.3486784401}{\log 0.9} + 1 = n$$
$$11 = n$$
$$S_{11} = \frac{10(1 - 0.9^{11})}{1 - 0.9}$$
$$\approx 68.6189$$

45. Answers may vary.
$$y = 4x^2 - 8x + 6$$

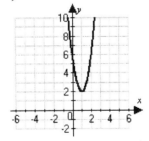

47. Answers may vary.
$$\frac{x^2 - 6x + 9}{x^2 + 7x + 10} \div \frac{x - 3}{x + 2} = \frac{(x-3)(x-3)}{(x+5)(x+2)} \cdot \frac{x+2}{x-3}$$
$$= \frac{x - 3}{x + 5}$$

49. Answers may vary.

$$x^2 - 9x + 14 = 0$$
$$(x - 2)(x - 7) = 0$$
$$x - 2 = 0 \quad \text{or} \quad x - 7 = 0$$
$$x = 2 \qquad\qquad x = 7$$

51. Answers may vary.
$$y = 3(2)^x$$

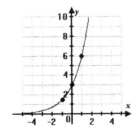

53. Answers may vary.
$$y = x + 3$$
$$4x + 2y = 15$$
Solve by substitution:
$$4x + 2(x + 3) = 15$$
$$4x + 2x + 6 = 15$$
$$6x = 9$$
$$x = \frac{3}{2}$$

Substitute $x = \frac{3}{2}$ into $y = x + 3$:
$$y = x + 3$$
$$y = \frac{3}{2} + 3$$
$$y = \frac{9}{2}$$
The solution is $\left(\frac{3}{2}, \frac{9}{2} \right)$.

53. Answers may vary.

Chapter 10 Review Exercises

1. $\frac{40}{160} = \frac{1}{4}, \frac{10}{40} = \frac{1}{4}, \frac{2.5}{10} = \frac{1}{4}, \frac{0.625}{2.5} = \frac{1}{4}$

The sequence is geometric with a common ratio of $\frac{1}{4}$.

2. $24 - 13 = 11, 35 - 24 = 11, 46 - 35 = 11,$
$57 - 46 = 11$
The series is arithmetic with a common difference of 11.

3. $95 - 101 = -6, 89 - 95 = -6,$
$83 - 89 = -6, 77 - 83 = -6$
The sequence is arithmetic with a common difference of -6.

4. $\dfrac{\frac{7}{5}}{7} = \dfrac{1}{5}, \dfrac{\frac{7}{25}}{\frac{7}{5}} = \dfrac{1}{5}, \dfrac{\frac{7}{125}}{\frac{7}{25}} = \dfrac{1}{5}, \dfrac{\frac{7}{625}}{\frac{7}{125}} = \dfrac{1}{5}$
The series is geometric with a common ratio of $\dfrac{1}{5}$.

5. The sequence is geometric with a common ratio of 3.
$a_n = 2(3)^{n-1}$
$\quad = 2(3)^n (3)^{-1}$
$\quad = 2(3)^n \left(\dfrac{1}{3}\right)$
$a_n = \dfrac{2}{3}(3)^n$
Solution: $a_n = 2(3)^{n-1}$ or $a_n = \dfrac{2}{3}(3)^n$

6. The sequence is arithmetic with a common difference of -5.
$a_n = 9 + (n-1) \cdot (-5)$
$\quad = 9 - 5n + 5$
$a_n = 14 - 5n$

7. The sequence is geometric with a common ratio of $\dfrac{1}{2}$.
$a_n = 200 \left(\dfrac{1}{2}\right)^{n-1}$
$\quad = 200 \left(\dfrac{1}{2}\right)^n \left(\dfrac{1}{2}\right)^{-1}$
$\quad = 200 \left(\dfrac{1}{2}\right)^n (2)$
$a_n = 400 \left(\dfrac{1}{2}\right)^n$

Solution: $a_n = 200 \left(\dfrac{1}{2}\right)^{n-1}$ or $a_n = 400 \left(\dfrac{1}{2}\right)^n$

8. The sequence is arithmetic with a common difference of 2.7.
$a_n = 3.2 + (n-1) \cdot 2.7$
$\quad = 3.2 + 2.7n - 2.7$
$a_n = 2.7n + 0.5$

9. The sequence is geometric with a common ratio 2.
$a_{47} = 6(2)^{47-1}$
$\quad = 6(2)^{46}$
$\quad \approx 4.2221 \times 10^{14}$

10. The sequence is geometric with a common ratio $\dfrac{1}{4}$.
$a_9 = 768 \left(\dfrac{1}{4}\right)^{9-1}$
$\quad = 768 \left(\dfrac{1}{4}\right)^8$
$\quad \approx 0.01172$

11. The sequence is arithmetic with a common difference of -3.
$a_{98} = 87 + (98 - 1) \cdot (-3)$
$\quad = -204$

12. The sequence is arithmetic with a common difference of 2.6.
$a_{87} = 2.3 + (87 - 1) \cdot 2.6$
$\quad = 225.9$

13. The sequence is arithmetic with a common difference 4.
$2023 = 7 + (n-1) \cdot 4$
$2023 = 7 + 4n - 4$
$2023 = 3 + 4n$
$2020 = 4n$
$505 = n$
2023 is the 505th term.

14. The sequence is arithmetic with a common difference -8.

$-107 = 501 + (n-1) \cdot (-8)$

$-107 = 501 - 8n + 8$

$-107 = 509 - 8n$

$-616 = -8n$

$77 = n$

-107 is the 77th term.

15. The sequence is geometric with a common ratio 3.

$$470,715,894,135 = 5(3)^{n-1}$$

$$94,143,178,827 = 3^{n-1}$$

$$\log 94,143,178,827 = \log 3^{n-1}$$

$$\log 94,143,178,827 = (n-1)\log 3$$

$$\frac{\log 94,143,178,827}{\log 3} = n-1$$

$$\frac{\log 94,143,178,827}{\log 3} + 1 = n$$

$$24 = n$$

$470,715,894,135$ is the 24th term.

16. **EQ 1**

$$52 = a_1 + (5-1)d$$

$$52 = a_1 + 4d$$

$$52 - 4d = a_1$$

EQ 2

$$36 = a_1 + (9-1)d$$

$$36 = a_1 + 8d$$

$$36 - 8d = a_1$$

Solve the system of linear equations by setting the left side of each equation equal to each other.

$$52 - 4d = 36 - 8d$$

$$4d = -16$$

$$d = -4$$

Use EQ 1 and $d = -4$ to find a_1.

$$52 - 4 \cdot (-4) = a_1$$

$$68 = a_1$$

$$a_{69} = 68 + (69-1) \cdot (-4) = -204$$

17.
$$S_{43} = \frac{43(52 + -200)}{2}$$
$$= -3182$$

18.
$$S_{22} = \frac{4(1-1.7^{22})}{1-1.7}$$
$$\approx 671,173.0723$$

19. The series is geometric with a common ratio of 2.

$$1,610,612,736 = 3(2)^{n-1}$$

$$536,870,912 = 2^{n-1}$$

$$\log 536,870,912 = \log 2^{n-1}$$

$$\log 536,870,912 = (n-1)\log 2$$

$$\frac{\log 536,870,912}{\log 2} = n-1$$

$$\frac{\log 536,870,912}{\log 2} + 1 = n$$

$$30 = n$$

$$S_{30} = \frac{3(1-2^{30})}{1-2}$$
$$= 3,221,225,469$$

20. The series is arithmetic with a common difference of 6.

$$1200 = 30 + (n-1) \cdot 6$$

$$1200 = 30 + 6n - 6$$

$$1200 = 24 + 6n$$

$$1176 = 6n$$

$$196 = n$$

$$S_{196} = \frac{196(30+1200)}{2}$$
$$= 120,540$$

21. The series is arithmetic with a common difference of -4.

$$a_{33} = 11 + (33-1) \cdot (-4)$$
$$= -117$$

$$S_{33} = \frac{33(11 + (-117))}{2}$$
$$= -1749$$

22. The series is geometric with a common ratio of

$\dfrac{1}{3}.$

$a_n = a_1 r^{n-1}$

$a_{13} = 531,441\left(\dfrac{1}{3}\right)^{13-1}$

$= 1$

$S_{13} = \dfrac{531,441\left(1-\left(\frac{1}{3}\right)^{13}\right)}{1-\frac{1}{3}}$

$= 797,161$

23. A geometric sequence with a common ratio of 5, since the ratio of any two consecutive terms is 5.

$\dfrac{4(5)^x}{4(5)^{x-1}}$

$= \dfrac{4(5)^x}{4(5)^x(5)^{-1}}$

$= \dfrac{1}{(5)^{-1}}$

$= 5.$

24. An arithmetic series with a common difference of -9, since the difference between two of consecutive terms is -9.

$= \big(-9(x)+40\big) - \big(-9(x-1)+40\big)$

$= (-9x+40) - (-9x+9+40)$

$= (-9x+40) - (-9x+49)$

$= -9x+40+9x-49$

$= -9$

25. a. **Company A**

$a_{25} = 28,000(1.04)^{25-1}$

$\approx \$71,772.52$

Company B

$a_{25} = 34,000 + (25-1)\cdot 1500$

$= \$70,000$

b. **Company A**

$S_{25} = \dfrac{28,000(1-1.04^{25})}{1-1.04}$

$\approx \$1,166,085.43$

Company B

$S_{25} = \dfrac{25(34000+70000)}{2}$

$= \$1,300,000$

c. You could earn more money in the early years at Company A, but receive smaller raises. Answers may vary.

26. a. Using linear regression, we get $f(t)$.

$f(t) = 0.28t + 5.64$

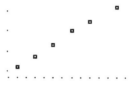

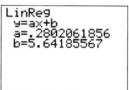

```
LinReg
 y=ax+b
 a=.2802061856
 b=5.64185567
```

b. $f(20) = 0.28(20) + 5.64$

$= 11.24$

In 2010, there will be about 11,240 deaths.

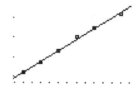

c. Since f is linear we can treat the sum of all the terms as an arithmetic series with a common difference of 0.28. Since

$f(1) = 0.28(1) + 5.64$

$= 5.92$

$a_1 = 5.92.$

$S_{20} = \dfrac{20(5.92+11.25)}{2}$

$= 171.7$

From 1990 through 2010 (including 2010) there will be about 169,860 deaths.

d. Answers may vary.

Chapter 10 Test

1. $\frac{6}{3} = 2, \frac{12}{6} = 2, \frac{24}{12} = 2, \frac{48}{24} = 2$

   It is a geometric sequence with a common ratio of 2.

2. $19 - 20 = -1, 17 - 19 = -2$

   $\frac{19}{20} = 0.95, \frac{17}{19} \approx 0.89474$

   The sequence has neither a common difference nor a common ratio, so it is none of these.

3. $\frac{35}{7} = 5, \frac{175}{35} = 5, \frac{875}{175} = 5, = \frac{4375}{875} = 5$

   It is a geometric sequence with a common ratio of 5.

4. It is an arithmetic series with a common difference of -8.

5. The sequence is arithmetic with a common difference of -6.
   $$a_n = 31 + (n-1) \cdot (-6)$$
   $$= 31 - 6n + 6$$
   $$a_n = 37 - 6n$$

6. The sequence is geometric with a common ratio of 4.
   $$a_n = 6(4)^{n-1}$$
   $$= 6(4)^n (4)^{-1}$$
   $$= 6(4)^n \left(\frac{1}{4}\right)$$
   $$a_n = \frac{3}{2}(4)^n$$

   Solution: $a_n = 6(4)^{n-1}$ or $a_n = \frac{3}{2}(4)^n$

7. The sequence is arithmetic with a common difference of 3.
   $$a_{87} = 4 + (87-1) \cdot 3$$
   $$= 262$$

8. The series is geometric with a common ratio of $\frac{1}{2}$.

9. $a_{16} = 6144 \left(\frac{1}{2}\right)^{16-1} = \frac{3}{16}$ or 0.1875

10. The sequence is arithmetic with a common difference of 4.
    $$1789 = -27 + (n-1) \cdot 4$$
    $$1789 = -27 + 4n - 4$$
    $$1789 = -31 + 4n$$
    $$1820 = 4n$$
    $$455 = n$$
    1789 is the 455th term in the sequence.

11. The series is geometric with a common ratio of 1.1.
    $$428.717762 = 200(1.1)^{n-1}$$
    $$2.14358881 = (1.1)^{n-1}$$
    $$\log 2.14358881 = \log 1.1^{n-1}$$
    $$\log 2.14358881 = (n-1)\log 1.1$$
    $$\frac{\log 2.14358881}{\log 1.1} = n - 1$$
    $$\frac{\log 2.14358881}{\log 1.1} + 1 = n$$
    $$9 = n$$
    428.717762 is the 9th term in the sequence.

12. The series is geometric with a common ratio of $\frac{1}{3}$.
    $$S_{20} = \frac{27 \left(1 - \left(\frac{1}{3}\right)^{20}\right)}{1 - \frac{1}{3}}$$
    $$\approx 40.5000$$

13. The series is geometric with a common ratio of 2.
    $$2,147,483,648 = 4(2)^{n-1}$$
    $$536,870,912 = 2^{n-1}$$
    $$\log 536,870,912 = \log 2^{n-1}$$
    $$\log 536,870,912 = (n-1)\log 2$$
    $$\frac{\log 536,870,912}{\log 2} = n - 1$$
    $$\frac{\log 536,870,912}{\log 2} + 1 = n$$
    $$30 = n$$

$$S_{30} = \frac{4(1-2^{30})}{1-2}$$
$$= 4,294,967,292$$
$$\approx 4.295 \times 10^9$$

13. The series is arithmetic with a common difference of –4.
$$-78 = 50 + (n-1) \cdot (-4)$$
$$-78 = 50 - 4n + 4$$
$$-78 = 54 - 4n$$
$$-132 = -4n$$
$$33 = n$$
$$S_{33} = \frac{33(50 + (-78))}{2}$$
$$= -462$$

14. The series is arithmetic with a common difference of 14.
$$a_{400} = 19 + (400-1) \cdot 14$$
$$= 5605$$
$$S_{400} = \frac{400(19 + 5605)}{2}$$
$$= 1,124,800$$
$$= 1.1248 \times 10^6$$

15.
$$(7+2) + (7 \cdot 2 + 2^2) + (7 \cdot 3 + 2^3) + (7 \cdot 4 + 2^4)$$
$$+ (7 \cdot 5 + 2^5) + \dots + (7 \cdot 20 + 2^{20})$$
$$= (7 + 7 \cdot 2 + 7 \cdot 3 + 7 \cdot 4 + 7 \cdot 5 + \dots + 7 \cdot 20)$$
$$+ (2 + 2^2 + 2^3 + 2^4 + 2^5 + \dots + 2^{20})$$
$$= \frac{20(7 + 140)}{2} + \frac{2(1 - 2^{20})}{1-2}$$
$$= 1470 + 2,097,150$$
$$= 2,098,620$$

16.
$$f(1) = 3(1)^2 + 1 = 4$$
$$f(2) = 3(2)^2 + 1 = 13$$
$$f(3) = 3(3)^2 + 1 = 28$$
The series has neither a common difference nor a common ratio, so it is neither geometric nor arithmetic.

17. S_n is negative because most of the terms of the series will be negative. The sum of negative numbers is negative.

18. **a.**

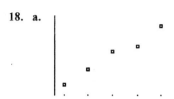

b. Use a linear regression to find $f(t)$.
$$f(t) = 35t + 7.2$$

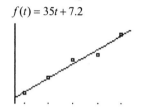

c. $f(1) = 35(1) + 7.2$
$$= 42.2$$
This value estimates the dollars of retail sales (in billions) in 2001.

d. $f(15) = 35(15) + 7.2$
$$= 532.2$$
This value estimates the dollars of retail sales (in billions) in 2015.

e. Since f is linear we can treat the sum of all the terms as an arithmetic series with a common difference of 35 and $a_1 = 42.2$.

$$S_{15} = \frac{15(42.2 + 532.2)}{2}$$
$$= 4308$$
From 2000 through 2015 (including 2015) there will be about 4308 billion dollars of retail sales, or about 4.3 trillion dollars ($4,308,000,000,000).

19. **a.** $a_n = 32(1.03)^{n-1}$

b.
$$40 = 32(1.03)^{n-1}$$
$$1.25 = 1.03^{n-1}$$
$$\log 1.25 = \log 1.03^{n-1}$$
$$\log 1.25 = (n-1)\log 1.03$$
$$\frac{\log 1.25}{\log 1.03} = n-1$$
$$\frac{\log 1.25}{\log 1.03} + 1 = n$$
$$8.5 \approx n$$

The salary will first be above $40,000 in the 9th year.

c.
$$a_{25} = 32(1.03)^{24}$$
$$\approx 65.04941$$

The salary in the 25th year will be $65,049.41$.

d.
$$S_{25} = \frac{32(1-1.03^{25})}{1-1.03} \text{ (in thousands)}$$
$$\approx 1,166.69646$$

The salary for the sum of the 1st through 25th years will be $1,166,696.46$.

Cumulative Review of Chapters 1 - 10

1.
$$6x^2 + 13x = 5$$
$$6x^2 + 13x - 5 = 0$$
$$(3x-1)(2x+5) = 0$$
$$3x-1 = 0 \text{ or } 2x+5 = 0$$
$$x = \frac{1}{3} \text{ or } x = -\frac{5}{2}$$

2.
$$\log_3(4x-7) = 4$$
$$4x-7 = 3^4$$
$$4x-7 = 81$$
$$4x = 88$$
$$x = 22$$

3.
$$(t+3)(t-4) = 5$$
$$t^2 + 3t - 4t - 12 = 5$$
$$t^2 - t - 17 = 0$$

$$t = \frac{-(-1) \pm \sqrt{(-1)^2 - 4(1)(-17)}}{2(1)}$$
$$= \frac{1 \pm \sqrt{69}}{2}$$

4.
$$\frac{1}{w^2 - w - 6} - \frac{w}{w+2} = \frac{w-2}{w-3}$$
$$\frac{1}{(w-3)(w+2)} - \frac{w}{w+2} = \frac{w-2}{w-3}$$
$$\frac{1 - w^2 + 3w}{(w-3)(w+2)} = \frac{w^2 - 4}{(w-3)(w+2)}$$
$$\frac{w^2 - 4 - 1 + w^2 - 3w}{(w-3)(w+2)} = 0$$
$$\frac{2w^2 - 3w - 5}{(w-3)(w+2)} = 0$$
$$2w^2 - 3w - 5 = 0 \qquad w \neq 3, -2$$
$$(2w-5)(w+1) = 0$$
$$2x-5 = 0 \text{ or } x+1 = 0$$
$$x = \frac{5}{2} \text{ or } x = -1$$

5.
$$5(3x-2)^2 + 7 = 17$$
$$5(3x-2)^2 = 10$$
$$(3x-2)^2 = 2$$
$$3x-2 = \pm\sqrt{2}$$
$$3x = 2 \pm \sqrt{2}$$
$$x = \frac{2 \pm \sqrt{2}}{3}$$

6.
$$\log_6(3x) + \log_6(x-1) = 1$$
$$\log_6(3x(x-1)) = 1$$
$$\log_6(3x^2 - 3x) = 1$$
$$6^1 = 3x^2 - 3x$$
$$6 = 3x^2 - 3x$$
$$0 = 3x^2 - 3x - 6$$
$$0 = 3(x^2 - x - 2)$$

$$0 = 3(x-2)(x+1)$$
$$0 = (x-2)(x+1)$$
$$0 = x-2 \text{ or } 0 = x+1$$
$$x = 2 \quad \text{ or } \quad x = -1$$
Check:
$$\log_6(3(2)) + \log_6((2)-1) = 1$$
$$\log_6 6 + \log_6 1 = 1$$
$$1 + 0 = 1$$
$$1 = 1$$
$$\log_6(3(-1)) + \log_6((-1)-1) = 1$$
$$\log_6(-3) + \log_6(-2) \neq 1$$
Cannot take the logarithm of a negative number. Solution: $x = 2$.

7. $$20 - 4x = 7(2x+9)$$
$$20 - 4x = 14x + 63$$
$$-4x = 14x + 43$$
$$-18x = 43$$
$$x = -\frac{43}{18}$$
$$x = -2\frac{7}{18}$$

8. $$\sqrt{x+1} - \sqrt{2x-5} = 1$$
$$\sqrt{x+1} = 1 + \sqrt{2x-5}$$
Square both sides.
$$\left(\sqrt{x+1}\right)^2 = \left(1+\sqrt{2x-5}\right)^2$$
$$x+1 = 1 + \sqrt{2x-5} + \sqrt{2x-5} + (2x-5)$$
$$x+1 = 1 + 2\sqrt{2x-5} + 2x - 5$$
$$x+1 = 2\sqrt{2x-5} + 2x - 4$$
$$-x+5 = 2\sqrt{2x-5}$$
$$\frac{-x+5}{2} = \sqrt{2x-5}$$
Square both sides again.
$$\left(\frac{-x+5}{2}\right)^2 = \left(\sqrt{2x-5}\right)^2$$

$$\frac{x^2 - 5x - 5x + 25}{4} = 2x - 5$$
$$\frac{x^2 - 10x + 25}{4} = 2x - 5$$
$$x^2 - 10x + 25 = 8x - 20$$
$$x^2 - 18x + 45 = 0$$
$$(x-3)(x-15) = 0$$
$$(x-3) = 0 \text{ or } (x-15) = 0$$
$$x = 3 \text{ or } x = 15$$
Check:
$$\sqrt{(3)+1} - \sqrt{2(3)-5} = 1$$
$$\sqrt{4} - \sqrt{1} = 1$$
$$2 - 1 = 1$$
$$1 = 1$$
$$\sqrt{(15)+1} - \sqrt{2(15)-5} = 1$$
$$\sqrt{16} - \sqrt{25} = 1$$
$$4 - 5 = 1$$
$$-1 \neq 1$$

9. $$2b^7 - 3 = 51$$
$$2b^7 = 54$$
$$b^7 = 27$$
$$b = 27^{1/7}$$
$$b = \sqrt[7]{27}$$
$$\approx 1.6013$$

10. $$6(3)^x - 5 = 52$$
$$6(3)^x = 57$$
$$3^x = \frac{19}{2}$$
$$x = \log_3 \frac{19}{2}$$
$$= \frac{\ln(19/2)}{\ln 3}$$
$$\approx 2.0492$$

11.
$$5e^x = 98$$
$$e^x = \frac{98}{5}$$
$$\ln(e^x) = \ln\left(\frac{98}{5}\right)$$
$$x = \ln\left(\frac{98}{5}\right)$$
$$\approx 2.9755$$

12.
$$3x^2 - 5x + 1 = 0$$
$$3x^2 - 5x = -1$$
$$3\left(x^2 - \frac{5}{3}x\right) = -1$$
$$3\left(x^2 - \frac{5}{3}x + \frac{25}{36}\right) = -1 + 3 \cdot \frac{25}{36}$$
$$3\left(x - \frac{5}{6}\right)^2 = -1 + \frac{75}{36}$$
$$3\left(x - \frac{5}{6}\right)^2 = \frac{39}{36}$$
$$\left(x - \frac{5}{6}\right)^2 = \frac{13}{36}$$
$$x - \frac{5}{6} = \pm\sqrt{\frac{13}{36}}$$
$$x = \frac{5}{6} \pm \frac{\sqrt{13}}{6}$$
$$x = \frac{5 \pm \sqrt{13}}{6}$$

13.
$$2x^2 = 4x - 3$$
$$2x^2 - 4x + 3 = 0$$
$$x = \frac{-(-4) \pm \sqrt{(-4)^2 - 4(2)(3)}}{2(2)}$$
$$= \frac{4 \pm \sqrt{-8}}{4}$$
$$= \frac{4 \pm i\sqrt{8}}{4}$$
$$= \frac{4 \pm 2i\sqrt{2}}{4}$$
$$= \frac{2 \pm i\sqrt{2}}{2}$$

14.
$$2x + 4y = 0$$
$$5x + 3y = 7$$
Multiply the first equation by –3 and the second equation by 4.
$$-6x - 12y = 0$$
$$20x + 12y = 28$$
Add the two equations and solve the result for *x*.
$$14x = 28$$
$$x = 2$$
Substitute this result for *x* in the first equation.
$$2(2) + 4y = 0$$
$$4 + 4y = 0$$
$$4y = -4$$
$$y = -1$$
The solution to the system is $(2, -1)$.

15.
$$y = 3x + 9$$
$$4x + 2y = -2$$
Substitute the first equation for *y* in the second equation.
$$4x + 2(3x + 9) = -2$$
$$4x + 6x + 18 = -2$$
$$10x = -20$$
$$x = -2$$
Substitute this value for *x* into the first equation.
$$y = 3x + 9$$
$$= 3(-2) + 9$$
$$= -6 + 9$$
$$= 3$$
The solution to the system is $(-2, 3)$.

16.
$$2x - 3y + 4z = 19$$
$$5x + y - 5z = -6$$
$$3x - y + 2z = 13$$
Multiply the second equation by 3 and add to first equation.
$$2x - 3y + 4z = 19$$
$$\underline{15x + 3y - 15z = -18}$$
$$17x - 11z = 1$$
Add the second and third equations.

$$5x + y - 5z = -6$$

$$\underline{3x - y + 2z = 13}$$

$$8x - 3z = 7$$

$$8x - 3z - 7 \quad \rightarrow \quad -88x + 33z = -77$$

$$\underline{17x - 11z = 1 \quad \rightarrow \quad 51x - 33z = 3}$$

$$-37x = -74$$

$$x = 2$$

Substitute $x = 2$ into $8x - 3z = 7$ and solve for z.

$$8(2) - 3z = 7$$

$$16 - 3z = 7$$

$$-3z = -9$$

$$z = 3$$

Substitute $x = 2$ and $z = 3$ into $2x - 3y + 4z = 19$ and solve for y.

$$2(2) - 3y + 4(3) = 19$$

$$4 - 3y + 12 = 19$$

$$-3y + 16 = 19$$

$$-3y = 3$$

$$y = -1$$

The solution is $(2, -1, 3)$.

17.

$$5 - 2(3x - 5) + 1 \ge 2 - 4x$$

$$5 - 6x + 10 + 1 \ge 2 - 4x$$

$$16 - 6x \ge 2 - 4x$$

$$-2x \ge -14$$

$$x \le 7$$

Interval: $(-\infty, 7]$

18.

$$\left(3b^{-2}c^{-3}\right)^4 \left(6b^{-5}c^2\right)^2 = 81b^{-8}c^{-12} \cdot 36b^{-10}c^4$$

$$= 2916b^{-8+(-10)}c^{-12+4}$$

$$= 2916b^{-18}c^{-8}$$

$$= \frac{2916}{b^{18}c^8}$$

19.

$$\frac{8b^{1/2}c^{-4/3}}{10b^{3/4}c^{-7/3}} = \frac{4}{5}b^{1/2-3/4}c^{-4/3-(-7/3)}$$

$$= \frac{4}{5}b^{2/4-3/4}c^{-4/3+7/3}$$

$$= \frac{4}{5}b^{-1/4}c^{3/3}$$

$$= \frac{4c}{5b^{1/4}}$$

20.

$$3y\sqrt{8x^3} - 2x\sqrt{18xy^2}$$

$$= 3y\sqrt{4x^2 \cdot 2x} - 2x\sqrt{9 \cdot 2x \cdot y^2}$$

$$= 3y\sqrt{4x^2}\sqrt{2x} - 2x\sqrt{9}\sqrt{2x}\sqrt{y^2}$$

$$= 3y \cdot 2x\sqrt{2x} - 2x \cdot 3y\sqrt{2x}$$

$$= 6xy\sqrt{2x} - 6xy\sqrt{2x}$$

$$= 0$$

21.

$$\sqrt{12x^7y^{14}} = \sqrt{4x^6 \cdot 3x \cdot y^{14}}$$

$$= \sqrt{4x^6}\sqrt{3x}\sqrt{y^{14}}$$

$$= 2x^3y^7\sqrt{3x}$$

22.

$$\sqrt[3]{\frac{4}{x}} = \frac{\sqrt[3]{4}}{\sqrt[3]{x}}$$

$$= \frac{\sqrt[3]{4}}{\sqrt[3]{x}} \cdot \frac{\sqrt[3]{x^2}}{\sqrt[3]{x^2}}$$

$$= \frac{\sqrt[3]{4 \cdot x^2}}{\sqrt[3]{x \cdot x^2}}$$

$$= \frac{\sqrt[3]{4x^2}}{x}$$

23.

$$\frac{3\sqrt{x} - \sqrt{y}}{2\sqrt{x} + \sqrt{y}}$$

$$= \frac{3\sqrt{x} - \sqrt{y}}{2\sqrt{x} + \sqrt{y}} \cdot \frac{2\sqrt{x} - \sqrt{y}}{2\sqrt{x} - \sqrt{y}}$$

$$= \frac{3\sqrt{x} \cdot 2\sqrt{x} - 3\sqrt{x} \cdot \sqrt{y} - 2\sqrt{x} \cdot \sqrt{y} + \sqrt{y} \cdot \sqrt{y}}{\left(2\sqrt{x}\right)^2 - \left(\sqrt{y}\right)^2}$$

$$= \frac{6x - 3\sqrt{xy} - 2\sqrt{xy} + y}{4x - y}$$

$$= \frac{6x - 5\sqrt{xy} + y}{4x - y}$$

24.

$$2\ln\left(x^4\right)+3\ln\left(x^9\right)=\ln\left(\left(x^4\right)^2\right)+\ln\left(\left(x^9\right)^3\right)$$
$$=\ln\left(x^8\right)+\ln\left(x^{27}\right)$$
$$=\ln\left(x^8 x^{27}\right)$$
$$=\ln\left(x^{8+27}\right)$$
$$=\ln\left(x^{35}\right)$$

25.

$$4\log_b\left(x^5\right)-5\log_b\left(2x\right)$$
$$=\log_b\left(\left(x^5\right)^4\right)-\log_b\left(\left(2x\right)^5\right)$$
$$=\log_b\left(x^{20}\right)-\log_b\left(32x^5\right)$$
$$=\log_b\left(\frac{x^{20}}{32x^5}\right)$$
$$=\log_b\left(\frac{x^{20-5}}{32}\right)$$
$$=\log_b\left(\frac{x^{15}}{32}\right)$$

26.

$$\left(3a-5b\right)^2=\left(3a\right)^2-2\left(3a\right)\left(5b\right)+\left(5b\right)^2$$
$$=9a^2-30ab+25b^2$$

27.

$$\left(3\sqrt{k}-4\right)\left(2\sqrt{k}+7\right)$$
$$=3\sqrt{k}\cdot 2\sqrt{k}-4\cdot 2\sqrt{k}+3\sqrt{k}\cdot 7-4\cdot 7$$
$$=6k-8\sqrt{k}+21\sqrt{k}-28$$
$$=6k+13\sqrt{k}-28$$

28.

$$\left(2x^2-x+3\right)\left(x^2+2x-1\right)$$
$$=2x^2\left(x^2+2x-1\right)-x\left(x^2+2x-1\right)$$
$$\quad +3\left(x^2+2x-1\right)$$
$$=2x^4+4x^3-2x^2-x^3-2x^2+x+3x^2+6x-3$$
$$=2x^4+3x^3-x^2+7x-3$$

29.

$$\frac{x^3-27}{2x^2-3x+1}\div\frac{2x^3+6x^2+18x}{4x^2-1}$$
$$=\frac{x^3-27}{2x^2-3x+1}\cdot\frac{4x^2-1}{2x^3+6x^2+18x}$$
$$=\frac{\left(x-3\right)\left(x^2+3x+9\right)}{\left(2x-1\right)\left(x-1\right)}\cdot\frac{\left(2x-1\right)\left(2x+1\right)}{2x\left(x^2+3x+9\right)}$$
$$=\frac{\left(x-3\right)\cancel{\left(x^2+3x+9\right)}}{\cancel{\left(2x-1\right)}\left(x-1\right)}\cdot\frac{\cancel{\left(2x-1\right)}\left(2x+1\right)}{2x\cancel{\left(x^2+3x+9\right)}}$$
$$=\frac{\left(x-3\right)\left(2x+1\right)}{2x\left(x-1\right)}$$

30.

$$\frac{3x}{x^2-10x+25}-\frac{x+2}{x^2-7x+10}$$
$$=\frac{3x}{\left(x-5\right)\left(x-5\right)}-\frac{x+2}{\left(x-5\right)\left(x-2\right)}$$
$$=\frac{3x\left(x-2\right)}{\left(x-5\right)\left(x-5\right)\left(x-2\right)}-\frac{\left(x+2\right)\left(x-5\right)}{\left(x-5\right)\left(x-5\right)\left(x-2\right)}$$
$$=\frac{3x^2-6x}{\left(x-5\right)^2\left(x-2\right)}-\frac{x^2-3x-10}{\left(x-5\right)^2\left(x-2\right)}$$
$$=\frac{3x^2-6x-x^2+3x+10}{\left(x-5\right)^2\left(x-2\right)}$$
$$=\frac{2x^2-3x+10}{\left(x-5\right)^2\left(x-2\right)}$$

31.

$$\frac{4x-x^2}{6x^2+10x-4}\cdot\frac{7-21x}{x^2-8x+16}$$
$$=\frac{-x\left(x-4\right)}{2\left(3x-1\right)\left(x+2\right)}\cdot\frac{-7\left(3x-1\right)}{\left(x-4\right)\left(x-4\right)}$$
$$=\frac{-x\cancel{\left(x-4\right)}}{2\cancel{\left(3x-1\right)}\left(x+2\right)}\cdot\frac{-7\cancel{\left(3x-1\right)}}{\left(x-4\right)\cancel{\left(x-4\right)}}$$
$$=\frac{7x}{2\left(x+2\right)\left(x-4\right)}$$

32.

$$\frac{1}{x^2+12x+27}+\frac{x+2}{x^3+x^2-9x-9}$$

$$=\frac{1}{(x+9)(x+3)}+\frac{x+2}{x^2(x+1)-9(x+1)}$$

$$=\frac{1}{(x+9)(x+3)}+\frac{x+2}{(x+1)(x^2-9)}$$

$$=\frac{1}{(x+9)(x+3)}+\frac{x+2}{(x+1)(x+3)(x-3)}$$

$$=\frac{(x-3)(x+1)+(x+2)(x+9)}{(x+9)(x+3)(x-3)(x+1)}$$

$$=\frac{x^2-3x+x-3+x^2+2x+9x+18}{(x+9)(x+3)(x-3)(x+1)}$$

$$=\frac{2x^2+9x+15}{(x+9)(x+3)(x-3)(x+1)}$$

33.

$$\frac{\dfrac{x+2}{x^2-64}}{\dfrac{x^2+4x+4}{3x+24}}=\frac{x+2}{x^2-64}\cdot\frac{3x+24}{x^2+4x+4}$$

$$=\frac{(x+2)}{(x-8)(x+8)}\cdot\frac{3(x+8)}{(x+2)(x+2)}$$

$$=\frac{\cancel{(x+2)}}{(x-8)(x+8)}\cdot\frac{3(x+8)}{(x+2)\cancel{(x+2)}}$$

$$=\frac{1}{(x-8)\cancel{(x+8)}}\cdot\frac{3\cancel{(x+8)}}{(x+2)}$$

$$=\frac{3}{(x-8)(x+2)}$$

34.

$$f(x)=-3(x+3)^2-7$$

$$=-3(x^2+6x+9)-7$$

$$=-3x^2-18x-27-7$$

$$=-3x^2-18x-34$$

$$f(x)=-3x^2-18x-34$$

35.

$$4x^3-8x^2-25x+50$$

$$=4x^2(x-2)-25(x-2)$$

$$=(x-2)(4x^2-25)$$

$$=(x-2)(2x-5)(2x+5)$$

36.

$$2x^3-4x^2-30x=2x(x^2-2x-15)$$

$$=2x(x-5)(x+3)$$

37.

$$6w^2+2wy-20y^2=2(3w^2+wy-10y^2)$$

$$=2(3w-5y)(w+2y)$$

38. $100p^2-1=(10p-1)(10p+1)$

39. $f(2)=3$

40. When $f(x)=3$, $x=0$ or $x=2$.

41. The graph is quadratic so the function is of the form $f(x)=a(x-h)^2+k$. The vertex is $(h,k)=(1,4)$ so we have

$f(x)=a(x-1)^2+4$.

Choosing another point on the graph, $(0,3)$, we can find the value of a.

$$3=a(0-1)^2+4$$

$$3=a+4$$

$$-1=a$$

Thus, the function is

$$f(x)=-(x-1)^2+4$$

$$=-x^2+2x+3$$

42. Domain of f:
the set of all real numbers or $(-\infty,\infty)$

43. Range of f: $\{y\mid y\le 4\}$ or $(-\infty,4]$

44. $y=-3(x-4)^2+3$

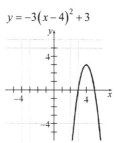

45. $y=2\sqrt{x+5}-4$

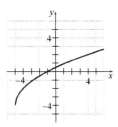

46. $y = 15\left(\dfrac{1}{3}\right)^x$

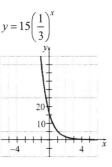

47. $y = 2x^2 + 5x - 1$

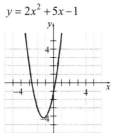

48. $2x(x-3) + y = 5(x+1)$

$2x^2 - 6x + y = 5x + 5$

$y = -2x^2 + 11x + 5$

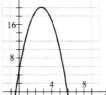

49. $(-3, 2)$ and $(2, -5)$

$m = \dfrac{-5 - 2}{2 - (-3)} = -\dfrac{7}{5}$

Using the slope m and the point $(-3, 2)$, we get:

$y = mx + b$

$2 = -\dfrac{7}{5}(-3) + b$

$b = -\dfrac{11}{5}$

The equation of the line is $y = -\dfrac{7}{5}x - \dfrac{11}{5}$ or

$7x + 5y = -11$.

50. Using the points $(3, 95)$ and $(6, 12)$, we want to fit the model $y = a(b)^x$. Plug both points into the equation.

$95 = a(b)^3$

$12 = a(b)^6$

Divide the second equation by the first.

$\dfrac{12}{95} = \dfrac{ab^6}{ab^3}$

$\dfrac{12}{95} = b^3$

$b = \sqrt[3]{\dfrac{12}{95}}$

$b \approx 0.50$

Substitute the point $(3, 95)$ into the equation $y = a(0.50)^x$.

$95 = a(0.50)^3$

$a = \dfrac{95}{0.50^3} = 760$

The equation is $y = 760(0.502)^x$.

51. $(2, 1), (3, 6),$ and $(4, 15)$

Substitute the points into the equation $y = ax^2 + bx + c$.

$1 = a(2)^2 + b(2) + c$

$6 = a(3)^2 + b(3) + c$

$15 = a(4)^2 + b(4) + c$

Rewrite as:

$4a + 2b + c = 1$

$9a + 3b + c = 6$

$16a + 4b + c = 15$

Multiply the first equation by -1 and add to both the second and third equations.

$$4a + 2b + c = 1$$
$$5a + b = 5$$
$$12a + 2b = 14$$

Multiply the second equation by -2 and add to the third equation.

$$4a + 2b + c = 1$$
$$5a + b = 5$$
$$2a = 4$$

Solve the third equation for a.

$$2a = 4$$
$$a = 2$$

Substitute this value into the second equation and solve for b.

$$5(2) + b = 5$$
$$10 + b = 5$$
$$b = -5$$

Substitute the values for a and b into the first equation and solve for c.

$$4(2) + 2(-5) + c = 1$$
$$8 - 10 + c = 1$$
$$c = 3$$

The equation is $y = 2x^2 - 5x + 3$.

52. $(2, 5)$ and $(6, 17)$

Substitute the points into the equation $y = a\sqrt{x} + b$.

$$5 = a\sqrt{2} + b$$
$$17 = a\sqrt{6} + b$$

Rewrite as:

$$1.4142a + b = 5$$
$$2.4495a + b = 17$$

Multiply the first equation by -1 and add to the second equation.

$$1.4142a + b = 5$$
$$1.0353a = 12$$

Solve the second equation for a.

$$1.0353a = 12$$
$$a \approx 11.59$$

Substitute this value into the first equation and solve for b.

$$1.4142(11.59) + b = 5$$
$$b \approx -11.39$$

The equation is roughly
$y = 11.59\sqrt{x} - 11.39$.

53. a. Linear: $f(x) = mx + b$

The y-intercept is $(0, 2)$ so $b = 2$.

$$m = \frac{4 - 2}{1 - 0} = 2$$
$$f(x) = 2x + 2$$

Exponential:

$$g(x) = a \cdot b^x$$

The y-intercept is $(0, 2)$ so $a = 2$.

Now plug in the point $(1, 4)$.

$$4 = 2(b)^1$$
$$4 = 2b$$
$$2 = b$$
$$g(x) = 2(2)^x$$

Quadratic:

$$h(x) = ax^2 + bx + c$$

Answers may vary. One possibility:

Let $a = 2$ so we have $h(x) = 2x^2 + bx + c$.

Plug in the point $(0, 2)$.

$$2 = 2(0)^2 + b(0) + c$$
$$2 = c$$
$$h(x) = 2x^2 + bx + 2$$

Plug in the point $(1, 4)$.

$$4 = 2(1)^2 + b(1) + 2$$
$$4 = 2 + b + 2$$
$$4 = b + 4$$
$$0 = b$$
$$h(x) = 2x^2 + 2$$

b.

```
Plot1 Plot2 Plot3      WINDOW
\Y1=2X+2               Xmin=-3
\Y2=2(2)^X             Xmax=3
\Y3=2X²+2■             Xscl=1
\Y4=                   Ymin=-2
\Y5=                   Ymax=10
\Y6=                   Yscl=1
\Y7=                   Xres=1
```

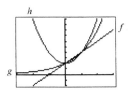

54.

$$\log_3(81) = \log_3(3^4)$$
$$= 4\log_3 3$$
$$= 4 \cdot 1$$
$$= 4$$

55.

$$\log_b(\sqrt{b}) = \log_b(b^{1/2})$$
$$= \frac{1}{2}\log_b b$$
$$= \frac{1}{2} \cdot 1$$
$$= \frac{1}{2}$$

56.

$$y = g(x) = \log_2 x$$
Switch x and y, and solve for y.
$$x = \log_2 y$$
$$y = 2^x$$
$$g^{-1}(x) = 2^x$$

57.

$$y = f(x) = -4x - 7$$
Switch x and y, and solve for y.
$$x = -4y - 7$$
$$4y = -x - 7$$
$$y = -\frac{1}{4}x - \frac{7}{4}$$
$$f^{-1}(x) = -\frac{1}{4}x - \frac{7}{4}$$

58.

$$f(x) = \frac{x-3}{x^2 - 2x - 35}$$
$$= \frac{x-3}{(x-7)(x+5)}$$

The domain is the set of all real numbers except 7 and -5 since these values make the denominator equal zero.

59. The series is geometric with a common ratio of 4.

$$a_n = a_1 r^{n-1}$$
$$a_{10} = 2(4)^{10-1}$$
$$= 524,288$$

60. This is an arithmetic sequence with a common difference of $d = 4$. Since $a_1 = -86$ and $a_n = 170$, we have

$$a_n = a_1 + d(n-1)$$
$$170 = -86 + 4(n-1)$$
$$256 = 4(n-1)$$
$$64 = n-1$$
$$65 = n$$

The last term in the sequence is term 65.

61. This is a geometric series with $r = \dfrac{1}{2}$ and $a_1 = 98,304$.

$$a_n = a_1 r^{n-1}$$
$$3 = 98304\left(\frac{1}{2}\right)^{n-1}$$
$$\frac{3}{98304} = \left(\frac{1}{2}\right)^{n-1}$$
$$\ln\left(\frac{3}{98304}\right) = (n-1)\ln\left(\frac{1}{2}\right)$$
$$\frac{\ln\left(\dfrac{3}{98304}\right)}{\ln\left(\dfrac{1}{2}\right)} = n-1$$
$$15 = n-1$$
$$16 = n$$

There are 16 terms in the series.

$$S_{16} = \frac{a_1\left(1 - r^{16}\right)}{1 - r}$$
$$= \frac{98304\left(1 - \left(\dfrac{1}{2}\right)^{16}\right)}{1 - \dfrac{1}{2}}$$
$$= 196,605$$

The sum of the series is 196,605.

62. This is an arithmetic sequence with $d = 3$

and $a_1 = 11$.

$$a_n = a_1 + (n-1)d$$
$$182 = 11 + (n-1)3$$
$$171 = 3(n-1)$$
$$57 = n-1$$
$$58 = n$$

There are 58 terms in the series.

$$S_n = \frac{n(a_1 + a_n)}{2}$$
$$S_{58} = \frac{58(11+182)}{2}$$
$$= 29(11+182)$$
$$= 29(193)$$
$$= 5597$$

63. Let x = number of liters of 15% acid solution
Let y = number of liters of 30% acid solution
EQ 1: $x + y = 6$

EQ 2: $0.15x + 0.30y = (0.25)6$

Multiply both sides of equation 2 by 100.
$$15x + 30y = 150$$

To use elimination, multiply both sides of equation 1 by -15 to eliminate x when added to equation 2.
$$x + y = 6 \quad \rightarrow \quad -15x - 15y = -90$$
$$15x + 30y = 150$$

$$\begin{array}{r} 15x + 30y = 150 \\ -15x - 15y = -90 \\ \hline 15y = 60 \\ y = 4 \end{array}$$

Plug $y = 4$ into $x + y = 6$ to find x.
$$x + 4 = 6$$
$$x = 2$$

The chemist needs to mix 2 liters of the 15% acid solution with 4 liters of the 30% acid solution to create 6 liters of the 25% acid solution.

64. a. $f(t) = 1.46t + 34.8$

b. $p = f(t) = 1.46t + 34.8$
Switch t and p, and solve for p.

$$t = 1.46p + 34.8$$
$$t - 34.8 = 1.46p$$
$$p = \frac{t - 34.8}{1.46}$$
$$p = 0.68t - 23.84$$
$$f^{-1}(p) = 0.68p - 23.84$$

c. $f(20) = 1.46(20) + 34.8$
$$= 64$$
This means in 2010, 20 years after 1990, we predict that 64% of passenger vehicles sold in the U.S. will be light trucks.

d. $f^{-1}(60) \approx \dfrac{60 - 34.8}{1.46}$
$$\approx 17$$
This indicates that the year in which this data would predict that 60% of passenger vehicles sold in the U.S. will be light trucks will be 2007, about 17 years after 1990.

e. A scattergram of the data:

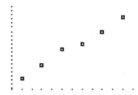

The linear regression data.

```
LinReg
 y=ax+b
 a=1.461428571
 b=34.79714286
```

The linear regression equation graphed.

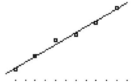

The slope of $f(t) = 1.46t + 34.8$ is 1.46, this is the approximate rate of change of the percentage of passenger vehicles sold in the U.S. will be light trucks. It increases about 1.46% each year.

65. a. We are given two data points for India's population: $(0, 0.687)$ and $(25, 1.003)$

The y-intercept is $(0, 0.687)$ so $b = 0.687$.

The slope of the line can be found by using the two given points.

$$m = \frac{1.003 - 0.687}{25 - 0}$$
$$= 0.0126$$

The linear model is $L(t) = 0.0126t + 0.687$.

b. We now fit the model $y = a(b)^x$. Since the y-intercept is $(0, 0.687)$, we have $a = 0.687$.

Substitute the point $(25, 1.003)$ into the equation $y = 0.687(b)^x$ and solve for b.

$$1.003 = 0.687(b)^{25}$$
$$b^{25} = \frac{1.003}{0.687}$$
$$b = \sqrt[25]{\frac{1.003}{0.687}} \approx 1.0153$$

The model is $E(t) = 0.687(1.0153)^t$.

c. $L(70) = 0.0126(70) + 0.687$
$$= 1.569$$

$E(70) = 0.687(1.0153)^{70}$
$$= 1.989$$

According to the linear model, India's population will be 1.5769 billion in 2050. According to the exponential model, India's population will be 1.989 billion in 2050.

d. $E(70) - L(70) = 1.989 - 1.569$
$$= 0.42$$

The exponential model's predicted population exceeds that of the linear model by 420 million. This is equal to the size of the predicted U.S. population for 2050.

e. $L(t) = 0.0126t + 0.687$
$$1.424 = 0.0126t + 0.687$$
$$0.737 = 0.0126t$$
$$t \approx 58$$
$$E(t) = 0.687(1.0153)^t$$

$$1.424 = 0.687(1.0153)^t$$
$$2.07 = (1.0153)^t$$
$$\log 2.07 = \log(1.0153)^t$$
$$\log 2.07 = t \log 1.0153$$
$$t = \frac{\log 2.07}{\log 1.0153}$$
$$\approx 48$$

According to the linear model, India's population will reach 1.424 billion about 58 years after 1980 in 2038.
According to the exponential model, India's population will reach 1.424 billion about 48 years after 1980 in 2028.

66. a.

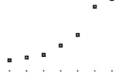

QuadReg
y=ax²+bx+c
a=1.714285714
b=-31.21428571
c=152.8571429

$$Q(t) = 1.71t^2 - 31.21t + 152.86$$

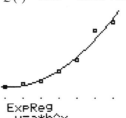

ExpReg
y=a*b^x
a=.4982949132
b=1.388949711

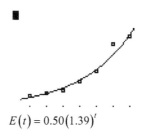

$$E(t) = 0.50(1.39)^t$$

Each fits most of the data well.
Answers may vary.

b. The exponential model. Answers may vary.

c.
$$E(t) = 0.50(1.39)^t$$
$$300 = 0.50(1.39)^t$$
$$600 = (1.39)^t$$
$$\log 600 = \log(1.39)^t$$
$$\log 600 = t \log 1.39$$
$$t = \frac{\log 600}{\log 1.39}$$
$$\approx 19$$

Solution: 19, or about 19 years after 1990.
According to the exponential model, by 2009 there will be 300 thousand complaints about consumer debt collection.

d.
$$Q(t) = 1.71t^2 - 31.21t + 152.86$$
$$300 = 1.71t^2 - 31.21t + 152.86$$
Graph $Y_1 = 1.71t^2 - 31.21t + 152.86$
$$Y_2 = 300$$
Use the intersection function (on the Calculate menu).

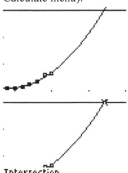

Intersection
X=22.093362 Y=300

Window shown: x: [8.4,35] y: [1.48,310]
Solution: $x = 22.093362$, or about 22 years after 1990.
According to the quadratic model, by 2012 there will be 300 thousand complaints about consumer debt collection.

e. Exponential growth functions tend to grow much more rapidly than quadratic ones. Answers may vary.

67. a. Start by plotting the data.

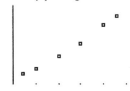

Use a quadratic regression to find $B(t)$.

The model is
$$B(t) = y = 0.02t^2 + 0.82t + 8.08.$$

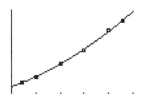

b. Start by plotting the data.

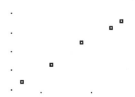

A linear model may be reasonable. Use a linear regression to find $R(t)$.

LinReg
y=ax+b
a=32.37312139
b=-81.1800578

The model is $R(t) = y = 32.37t - 81.18.$

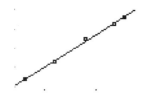

c.
$$P(t) = \frac{B(t)}{R(t)}$$
$$= \frac{32.37t - 81.18}{0.02t^2 + 0.82t + 8.08}$$

d. The ratio $P(t) = \dfrac{B(t)}{R(t)}$.

Minimum
X=30 . . . . . Y=17.55959 .
Window: x: [13,30] y: [1,25]

That point means that the lowest percentage of recreation expenditures predicted to be spent on books from 1993 to 2010 is about 18% in 2010. The percentage is expected to drop.

e.
$$6 = \frac{32.37t - 81.18}{0.02t^2 + 0.82t + 8.08}$$
$$6(0.02t^2 + 0.82t + 8.08) = 32.37t - 81.18$$
$$0.12t^2 + 4.92t + 48.48 = 32.37t - 81.18$$
$$0.12t^2 - 27.45t + 129.66 = 0$$
$$t = \frac{-(-27.45) \pm \sqrt{(-27.45)^2 - 4(0.12)(129.66)}}{2(0.12)}$$
$$= \frac{27.45 \pm 691.2657}{0.24}$$
$$t = 2995 \text{ or } t = -2765.90$$

6% of recreational expenditures will consist of book sales in 4975.

Chapter 11
Additional Topics

1. $|x| = 7$

$x = 7$ or $x = -7$

3. $|x| = -3$

Since $|x|$ is always nonnegative, the solution set for $|x| = -3$ is the empty set.

5. $5|p| - 3 = 15$

$5|p| = 18$

$|p| = \dfrac{18}{5}$

$p = -\dfrac{18}{5}$ or $p = \dfrac{18}{5}$

7. $|x + 2| = 5$

$x + 2 = -5$ or $x + 2 = 5$

$x = -7$ or $x = 3$

9. $|x - 5| = 0$

$x - 5 = 0$

$x = 5$

11. $|3t - 1| = 11$

$3t - 1 = -11$ or $3t - 1 = 11$

$3t = -10$ or $3t = 12$

$t = -\dfrac{10}{3}$ or $t = 4$

13. $|2x + 9| = -6$

Since $|2x + 9|$ is always nonnegative, the solution set for $|2x + 9| = -6$ is the empty set.

15. $|4x| + 1 = 9$

$|4x| = 8$

$4x = -8$ or $4x = 8$

$x = -2$ or $x = 2$

17. $2|a + 5| = 8$

$|a + 5| = 4$

$a + 5 = -4$ or $a + 5 = 4$

$a = -9$ or $a = -1$

19. $|2x - 5| - 4 = -3$

$|2x - 5| = 1$

$2x - 5 = -1$ or $2x - 5 = 1$

$2x = 4$ or $2x = 6$

$x = 2$ or $x = 3$

21. $|4x - 5| = |3x + 2|$

$4x - 5 = -(3x + 2)$ or $4x - 5 = 3x + 2$

$4x - 5 = -3x - 2$ or $4x = 3x + 7$

$7x = 3$ or $x = 7$

$x = \dfrac{3}{7}$ or $x = 7$

23. $|5w + 1| = |3 - w|$

$5w + 1 = -(3 - w)$ or $5w + 1 = 3 - w$

$5w + 1 = -3 + w$ or $5w = 2 - w$

$4w = -4$ or $6w = 2$

$w = -1$ or $w = \dfrac{1}{3}$

25. $\left|\dfrac{4x + 3}{2}\right| = 5$

$\dfrac{4x + 3}{2} = -5$ or $\dfrac{4x + 3}{2} = 5$

$4x + 3 = -10$ or $4x + 3 = 10$

$4x = -13$ or $4x = 7$

$x = -\dfrac{13}{4}$ or $x = \dfrac{7}{4}$

27. $\left|\dfrac{1}{2}x - \dfrac{5}{3}\right| = \dfrac{7}{6}$

$$\frac{1}{2}x - \frac{5}{3} = -\frac{7}{6} \quad \text{or} \quad \frac{1}{2}x - \frac{5}{3} = \frac{7}{6}$$

$$\frac{1}{2}x = -\frac{7}{6} + \frac{5}{3} \quad \text{or} \quad \frac{1}{2}x = \frac{7}{6} + \frac{5}{3}$$

$$\frac{1}{2}x = \frac{1}{2} \quad \text{or} \quad \frac{1}{2}x = \frac{17}{6}$$

$$x = 1 \quad \text{or} \quad x = \frac{17}{3}$$

29. $\left|\frac{2}{3}k + \frac{4}{9}\right| = \left|\frac{5}{6}k - \frac{1}{3}\right|$

$$\frac{2}{3}k + \frac{4}{9} = -\left(\frac{5}{6}k - \frac{1}{3}\right) \quad \text{or} \quad \frac{2}{3}k + \frac{4}{9} = \frac{5}{6}k - \frac{1}{3}$$

$$\frac{2}{3}k + \frac{5}{6}k = \frac{1}{3} - \frac{4}{9} \quad \text{or} \quad \frac{2}{3}k - \frac{5}{6}k = -\frac{1}{3} - \frac{4}{9}$$

$$\frac{3}{2}k = -\frac{1}{9} \quad \text{or} \quad -\frac{1}{6}k = -\frac{7}{9}$$

$$k = -\frac{2}{27} \quad \text{or} \quad k = \frac{14}{3}$$

31. $4.7|x| - 3.9 = 8.8$

$$4.7|x| = 12.7$$

$$|x| \approx 2.70$$

$$x \approx -2.70 \text{ or } x \approx 2.70$$

33. $|2.1x + 5.8| - 9.7 = 10.2$

$$|2.1x + 5.8| = 19.9$$

$$2.1x + 5.8 = -19.9 \quad \text{or} \quad 2.1x + 5.8 = 19.9$$

$$2.1x = -25.7 \quad \text{or} \quad 2.1x = 14.1$$

$$x \approx -12.24 \text{ or } x \approx 6.71$$

35.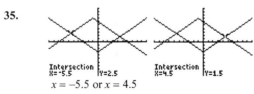

$x = -5.5$ or $x = 4.5$

37.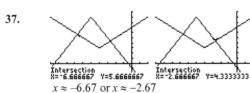

$x \approx -6.67$ or $x \approx -2.67$

39. $x = \pm 4$

41. $x = 2$ or $x = -3$

43. $f(x) = 2|x| - 11$

$$f(-5) = 2|-5| - 11$$

$$f(-5) = 2(5) - 11$$

$$f(-5) = -1$$

45. $f(x) = 2|x| - 11$

$$-5 = 2|x| - 11$$

$$6 = 2|x|$$

$$3 = |x|$$

$$x = -3 \text{ or } x = 3$$

47. $f(x) = |4x + 7| - 9$

$$f(-3) = |4(-3) + 7| - 9$$

$$f(-3) = |-12 + 7| - 9$$

$$f(-3) = |-5| - 9$$

$$f(-3) = 5 - 9$$

$$f(-3) = -4$$

49. $f(x) = |4x + 7| - 9$

$$-3 = |4x + 7| - 9$$

$$6 = |4x + 7|$$

$$4x + 7 = -6 \quad \text{or} \quad 4x + 7 = 6$$

$$4x = -13 \quad \text{or} \quad 4x = -1$$

$$x = -\frac{13}{4} \text{ or } x = -\frac{1}{4}$$

51. $|x| < 4$

$$-4 < x < 4$$

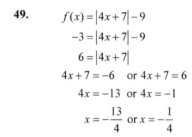

Interval: $(-4, 4)$

53. $|x| \geq 3$

$$x \leq -3 \text{ or } x \geq 3$$

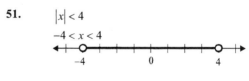

Interval: $(-\infty, -3] \cup [3, \infty)$

55. $|r| < -3$

Since $|r|$ is nonnegative, the inequality

$|r| < -3$ has an empty set solution.

57. $|x| > 0$

$x < 0$ or $x > 0$

Interval: $(-\infty, 0) \cup (0, \infty)$

59. $2|x| - 5 > 3$

$2|x| > 8$

$|x| > 4$

$x < -4$ or $x > 4$

Interval: $(-\infty, -4) \cup (4, \infty)$

61. $2 - 5|p| \le -8$

$-5|p| \le -10$

$|p| \ge 2$

$p \le -2$ or $p \ge 2$

Interval: $(-\infty, -2] \cup [2, \infty)$

63. $|x - 6| \ge 7$

$x - 6 \le -7$ or $x - 6 \ge 7$

$x \le -1$ or $x \ge 13$

Interval: $(-\infty, -1] \cup [13, \infty)$

65. $|2x + 5| < 15$

$-15 < 2x + 5 < 15$

$-20 < 2x < 10$

$-10 < x < 5$

Interval: $[-10, 5]$

67. $|7x + 15| > -4$

Since $|7x + 15|$ is always nonnegative, the solution set for the inequality $|7x + 15| > -4$ is the set of all real numbers.

Interval: $(-\infty, \infty)$

69. $|0.25t - 1.3| \ge 1.1$

$0.25t - 1.3 \le -1.1$ or $0.25t - 1.3 \ge 1.1$

$0.25t \le 0.2$ or $0.25t \ge 2.4$

$t \le 0.8$ or $t \ge 9.6$

Interval: $(-\infty, -0.8] \cup [9.6, \infty)$

71. $7 - |x + 3| \le 2$

$-|x + 3| \le -5$

$|x + 3| \ge 5$

$x + 3 \le -5$ or $x + 3 \ge 5$

$x \le -8$ or $x \ge 2$

Interval: $(-\infty, -8] \cup [2, \infty)$

73. $\left| \dfrac{x + 4}{3} \right| \ge 2$

$\dfrac{x + 4}{3} \le -2$ or $\dfrac{x + 4}{3} \ge 2$

$x + 4 \le -6$ or $x + 4 \ge 6$

$x \le -10$ or $x \ge 2$

Interval: $(-\infty, -10] \cup [2, \infty)$

75. $\left| \dfrac{2x}{5} + \dfrac{3}{2} \right| \le \dfrac{9}{20}$

$-\dfrac{9}{20} \le \dfrac{2x}{5} + \dfrac{3}{2} \le \dfrac{9}{20}$

$-\dfrac{39}{20} \le \dfrac{2x}{5} \le -\dfrac{21}{20}$

$-\dfrac{39}{4} \le 2x \le -\dfrac{21}{4}$

$-\dfrac{39}{8} \le x \le -\dfrac{21}{8}$

Interval: $\left[-\dfrac{39}{8}, -\dfrac{21}{8} \right]$

77. $|mx + b| + c = k$

$|mx + b| = k - c$

$$mx + b = -(k - c) \quad \text{or } mx + b = k - c$$
$$mx = -b - (k - c) \text{ or } mx = -b + (k - c)$$
$$x = \frac{-b \pm (k - c)}{m}$$

79. Answers may vary. The student failed to use the Absolute Value Property for Equations. Instead, the student tried to take the absolute value of $x - 5$ directly, but this leads to the wrong answer. Also the student interchanges $x - 5$ with $x + 5$, in line two, which is also incorrect.
$$|x - 5| = 7$$
$$x - 5 = -7 \text{ or } x - 5 = 7$$
$$x = -2 \text{ or } x = 12$$

81. Answers may vary. The student attempted to use the Absolute Value Property for Equations, but he or she should have used the Absolute Value Property for Inequalities.
$$|x + 3| < 10$$
$$-10 < x + 3 < 10$$
$$-13 < x < 7$$

83. a. $|2x + 3| = 13$
$$2x + 3 = -13 \text{ or } 2x + 3 = 13$$
$$2x = -16 \text{ or } 2x = 10$$
$$x = -8 \text{ or } x = 5$$

b. $|2x + 3| < 13$
$$-13 < 2x + 3 < 13$$
$$-16 < 2x < 10$$
$$-8 < x < 5$$

c. $|2x + 3| > 13$
$$2x + 3 < -13 \text{ or } 2x + 3 > 13$$
$$2x < -16 \text{ or } 2x > 10$$
$$x < -8 \text{ or } x > 5$$

d.
Answers may vary. The three different graphs each use –8 and 5, either as included points or as non-included endpoints. Between the three graphs, every part of the number line is covered.

85. Answers may vary. The statement "$|a + b| = |a| + |b|$ for all real numbers a and b" is false. For a counterexample, let $a = -1$ and $b = 3$.
$$|-1 + 3| \neq |-1| + |3|$$
$$|2| \neq 1 + 3$$
$$2 \neq 4$$

87. $|x - 5| = 4$
$$x - 5 = -4 \text{ or } x - 5 = 4$$
$$x = 1 \quad \text{or } x = 9$$

89. $|2^y - 5| = 4$
$$2^y - 5 = -4 \text{ or } 2^y - 5 = 4$$
$$2^y = 1 \text{ or } 2^y = 9$$
$$y = 0 \text{ or } y \approx 3.1699$$

91. $\left| \dfrac{2x + 3}{x - 2} - 5 \right| = 4$
$$\frac{2x + 3}{x - 2} - 5 = -4 \quad \text{or} \quad \frac{2x + 3}{x - 2} - 5 = 4$$
$$\frac{2x + 3}{x - 2} = 1 \quad \text{or} \quad \frac{2x + 3}{x - 2} = 9$$
$$2x + 3 = x - 2 \text{ or } 2x + 3 = 9x - 18$$
$$x = -5 \quad \text{or } -7x = -21$$
$$x = -5 \quad \text{or } x = 3$$

93. $3(2x) - 5 \leq 7$
$$6x \leq 12$$
$$x \leq 2$$
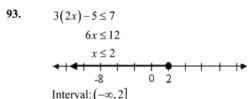
Interval: $(-\infty, 2]$

95. $3|2x| - 5 \leq 7$
$$3|2x| \leq 12$$
$$|2x| \leq 4$$
$$-4 \leq 2x \leq 4$$
$$-2 \leq x \leq 2$$
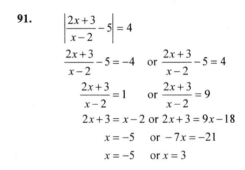
Interval: $[-2, 2]$

97.

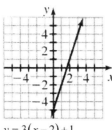

$$y = 3(x-2)+1$$
$$= 3x - 6$$

This is a linear function.

99.
$$3|x-2|+1 = 7$$
$$3|x-2| = 6$$
$$|x-2| = 2$$
$$x - 2 = -2 \text{ or } x - 2 = 2$$
$$x = 0 \quad \text{or } x = 4$$

$3|x-2|+1 = 7$ is an absolute value equation in one variable.

101. If the line contains the points $(-4, 2)$ and

$(5, -3)$, the slope is $\dfrac{-3-2}{5-(-4)} = -\dfrac{5}{9}$.

$$y = mx + b$$
$$2 = -\frac{5}{9}(-4) + b$$
$$2 = \frac{20}{9} + b$$
$$-\frac{2}{9} = b$$

The equation is $y = -\dfrac{5}{9}x - \dfrac{2}{9}$, which is a

linear equation in two variables.

Quiz 11.1

1.
$$3|t| - 4 = 11$$
$$3|t| = 15$$
$$|t| = 5$$
$$t = 5 \text{ or } t = -5$$

2.
$$5|6r-5| = 15$$
$$|6r-5| = 3$$

$$6r - 5 = -3 \quad \text{or} \quad 6r - 5 = 3$$
$$6r = 2 \quad \text{or} \quad 6r = 8$$
$$r = \frac{1}{3} \quad \text{or} \quad r = \frac{4}{3}$$

3.
$$|7x+1| = -3$$

Since $|7x+1|$ is always nonnegative, the solution set for $|7x+1| = -3$ is the empty set.

4.
$$|5x-2| = |3x+6|$$
$$5x - 2 = -(3x+6) \text{ or } 5x - 2 = 3x + 6$$
$$5x = -3x - 4 \quad \text{or } 5x = 3x + 8$$
$$8x = -4 \qquad \text{or } 2x = 8$$
$$x = -\frac{1}{2} \qquad \text{or } x = 4$$

5.
$$\left|\frac{3}{4}x - \frac{1}{2}\right| = \frac{7}{8}$$
$$\frac{3}{4}x - \frac{1}{2} = -\frac{7}{8} \text{ or } \frac{3}{4}x - \frac{1}{2} = \frac{7}{8}$$
$$\frac{3}{4}x = -\frac{3}{8} \text{ or } \frac{3}{4}x = \frac{11}{8}$$
$$x = -\frac{1}{2} \text{ or } x = \frac{11}{6}$$

6. Answers may vary. The statement
"$|a-b| = |a| - |b|$ for all real numbers a and
b" is false. For a counterexample, let $a = -1$
and $b = 3$.
$$|-1-3| \neq |-1| - |3|$$
$$|-4| \neq 1 - 3$$
$$4 \neq -2$$

7.
$$3|k| - 4 \geq 2$$
$$3|k| \geq 6$$
$$|k| \geq 2$$
$$k \leq -2 \text{ or } k \geq 2$$

Interval: $(-\infty, -2] \cup [2, \infty)$

8. $|4c - 8| > 12$

$4c - 8 < -12$ or $4c - 8 > 12$

$4c < -4$ or $4c > 20$

$c < -1$ or $c > 5$

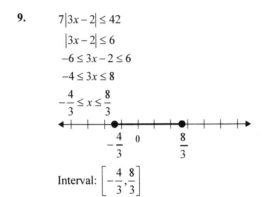

Interval: $(-\infty, -1) \cup (5, \infty)$

9. $7|3x - 2| \le 42$

$|3x - 2| \le 6$

$-6 \le 3x - 2 \le 6$

$-4 \le 3x \le 8$

$-\dfrac{4}{3} \le x \le \dfrac{8}{3}$

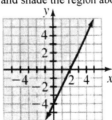

Interval: $\left[-\dfrac{4}{3}, \dfrac{8}{3} \right]$

10. $|x - 5| < -7$

Since $|x - 5|$ is always nonnegative, the solution set for $|x - 5| < -7$ is the empty set.

Homework 11.2

1. $y \ge 2x - 4$

Graph the line $y = 2x - 4$ with a solid line and shade the region above it.

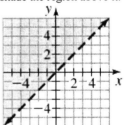

3. $y < -\dfrac{1}{2}x + 3$

Graph the line with a dashed line and shade the region below it.

5. $y \le -2x + 6$

Graph the line $y = -2x + 6$ with a solid line and shade the region below it.

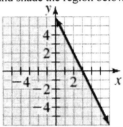

7. $y > x$

Graph the line $y = x$ with a dashed line and shade the region above it.

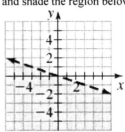

9. $y < -\dfrac{1}{3}x$

Graph the line $y = -\dfrac{1}{3}x$ with a dashed line and shade the region below it.

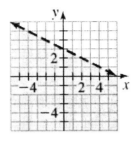

11. $2x + 5y < 10$

$$5y < -2x + 10$$

$$y < -\frac{2}{5}x + 2$$

Graph the line $y = -\frac{2}{5}x + 2$ with a dashed

line and shade the region below it.

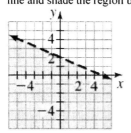

13. $4x - 6y - 6 \ge 0$

$$-6y \ge -4x + 6$$

$$y \le \frac{2}{3}x - 1$$

Graph the line $y = \frac{2}{3}x - 1$ with a solid line

and shade the region below it.

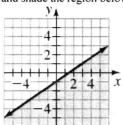

15. $3(x - 2) + y \le -2$

$$3x - 6 + y \le -2$$

$$y \le -3x + 4$$

Graph the line $y = -3x + 4$ with a solid line

and shade the region below it.

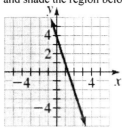

17. $y \le 2$

Graph the line $y = 2$ with a solid line and
shade the region below it.

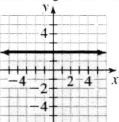

19. $x > -3$

Graph the line $x = -3$ with a dashed line and
shade the region above it.

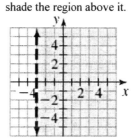

21.

$$y \ge \frac{1}{3}x - 2$$

$$y > -x + 3$$

Graph the line $y = \frac{1}{3}x - 2$ with a solid line

and the line $y = -x + 3$ with a dashed line.
The solution region of the system is the
intersection of the solution regions of

$y \ge \frac{1}{3}x - 2$ and $y > -x + 3$.

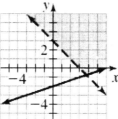

23.

$$y \le x - 4$$

$$y \ge -3x$$

Graph the line $y = x - 4$ with a solid line
and the line $y = -3x$ with a solid line. The
solution region of the system is the

intersection of the solution regions of
$y \le x - 4$ and $y \ge -3x$.

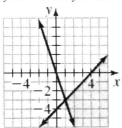

25. $y \le -3x + 9$
$y \ge 2x - 3$
$x \ge 0$
$y \ge 0$
Graph the lines $y = -3x + 9$, $y = 2x - 3$,
$x = 0$, and $y = 0$ with solid lines. The
solution region of the system is the
intersection of the solution regions of
$y \le -3x + 9$, $y \ge 2x - 3$, $x \ge 0$ and $y \ge 0$.

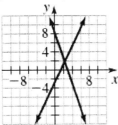

27. $y < -x + 5$
$y \le x + 5$
$y > \frac{1}{2}x + 1$

Graph the lines $y = -x + 5$ and $y = \frac{1}{2}x + 1$
with dashed lines, and the line $y = x + 5$
with a solid line. The solution region of the
system is the intersection of the solution
regions of $y < -x + 5$, $y \le x + 5$ and
$y > \frac{1}{2}x + 1$.

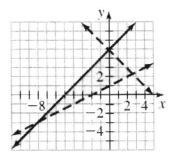

29. $y \le -3$
$y \ge -5$
Graph the lines $y = -3$ and $y = -5$ with
solid lines. The solution region of the system
is the intersection of the solution regions of
$y \le -3$ and $y \ge -5$.

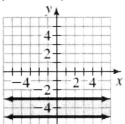

31. $2x - 4y \le 8$ $3x + 5y \le 10$
$-4y \le -2x + 8$ $5y \le -3x + 10$
$y \ge \frac{1}{2}x - 2$ $y \le -\frac{3}{5}x + 2$

Graph the lines $y = \frac{1}{2}x - 2$ and $y = -\frac{3}{5}x + 2$
with solid lines. The solution region of the
system is the intersection of the solution
regions of $y \ge \frac{1}{2}x - 2$ and $y \le -\frac{3}{5}x + 2$.

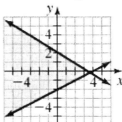

33.

$$x - 2y > 6 \qquad x + 3y \le 3$$

$$-2y > -x + 6 \qquad 3y \le -x + 3$$

$$y < \frac{1}{2}x - 3 \qquad y \le -\frac{1}{3}x + 1$$

Graph the line $y = \frac{1}{2}x - 3$ with a dashed line

and the line $y = -\frac{1}{3}x + 1$ with a solid line.

The solution region of the system is the intersection of the solution regions of

$y < \frac{1}{2}x - 3$ and $y \le -\frac{1}{3}x + 1$.

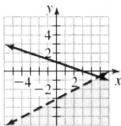

35.

$$1 + y \ge \frac{1}{2}(x - 4) \quad 3 - y > 2(x - 1)$$

$$\qquad\qquad\qquad -y > 2x - 2 - 3$$

$$y \ge \frac{1}{2}x - 2 - 1 \quad -y > 2x - 5$$

$$y \ge \frac{1}{2}x - 3 \qquad\quad y < -2x + 5$$

Graph the line $y = \frac{1}{2}x - 3$ with a solid line

and the line $y = -2x + 5$ with a dashed line.

The solution region of the system is the intersection of the solution regions of

$y \ge \frac{1}{2}x - 3$ and $y < -2x + 5$.

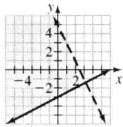

37.

$$5y \le 2x + 20$$

$$y \le \frac{2}{5}x + 4$$

$$5y \ge 2x + 5$$

$$y \ge \frac{2}{5}x + 1$$

$$x \ge 3$$

$$x \le 5$$

Graph the lines $y = \frac{2}{5}x + 4$, $y = \frac{2}{5}x + 1$,

$x = 3$, and $x = 5$ with solid lines. The solution region of the system is the intersection of the solution regions of

$y \le \frac{2}{5}x + 4$, $y \ge \frac{2}{5}x + 1$, $x \ge 3$, and $x \le 5$.

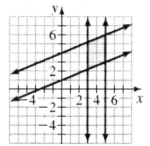

39. a. Answers may vary. By entering the sets of data into a graphing calculator, using the linear regression feature, and rounding to the second decimal place, we find the following equations.

$$B(t) = 0.20t + 69.97$$

$$T(t) = 0.17t + 51.73$$

b. The life expectancies of U.S. males from 0 years to 20 years must be less than or equal to *T(t)* and greater than or equal to *B(t)*. Also, limiting the years to 1980 to 2015 means that *t* must be greater than or equal to 0 and less than or equal to 35. Therefore, the system of equations is:

$$L \le 0.20t + 69.97$$

$$L \ge 0.17t + 51.73$$

$$t \ge 0$$

$$t \le 35$$

c.

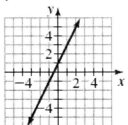

d.
$$T(30) \leq L \leq B(30)$$
$$0.17(30) + 51.73 \leq L \leq 0.20(30) + 69.97$$
$$5.1 + 51.73 \leq L \leq 6 + 69.97$$
$$56.83 \leq L \leq 75.97$$

41. a. Answers may vary. By entering the sets of data into a graphing calculator, using the linear regression feature, and rounding to the second decimal place, we find the following equations.
$$B(w) = 0.44w + 84.21$$
$$I(w) = 0.44w + 89.21$$

b. The ski lengths for beginning to intermediate skiers must be greater than or equal to *B(w)* and less than or equal to *I(w)*. Also, *w* must be greater than or equal to 130 and less than or equal to 150. Therefore, the system of equations is:
$$L \geq 0.44w + 84.21$$
$$L \leq 0.44w + 89.21$$
$$w \geq 130$$
$$w \leq 150$$

c.

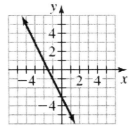

d.
$$B(140) \leq L \leq I(140)$$
$$0.44(140) + 84.21 \leq L \leq 0.44(140) + 89.21$$
$$61.6 + 84.21 \leq L \leq 61.6 + 89.21$$
$$145.81 \leq L \leq 150.81$$

43. Answers may vary. I would remind the student that, since the coefficient of the *y* variable is negative, the direction of the inequality will need to be switched. Therefore, the graph of $2x - 3y < 6$ will actually be above the line $2x - 3y = 6$.

45. Answers may vary. One possible answer: $y > x$

$(3,4)$ is a solution but $(4,3)$ is not a solution.

47. The intersection of the solution regions of $y \geq 2x + 1$ and $y \leq 2x + 1$ is the solid line $y = 2x + 1$.

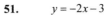

49. Answers may vary. To graph an inequality in two variables, first isolate the *y* variable on the left side of the inequality. If you multiply or divide both sides of the equation by a negative number during this process, reverse the direction of the inequality symbol. Then, substitute an equal sign for the inequality symbol, and graph the line given by this equation. If the inequality symbol is < or >, use a dotted line; if it is ≤ or ≥, use a solid line. Finally, if the inequality symbol is < or ≤, shade below the line; if the symbol is > or ≥, shade above the line.

51. $y = -2x - 3$

53. $y < -2x - 3$
Graph the line $y = -2x - 3$ with a dashed line and shade the region below it.

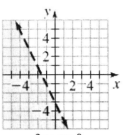

55.
$$2x + y = 8$$
$$y = 8 - 2x$$
$$3x - 2y = -2$$
$$3x - 2(8 - 2x) = -2$$
$$3x - 16 + 4x = -2$$
$$7x = 14$$
$$x = 2$$
$$2(2) + y = 8$$
$$y = 4$$

The solution is $(2, 4)$.

57.

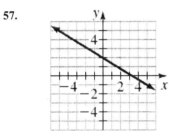

$f(x) = -\dfrac{3}{5}x + 2$ is a linear function.

59.
$$f(x) = -\frac{3}{5}x + 2$$
$$f(2) = -\frac{3}{5}(2) + 2$$
$$f(2) = \frac{4}{5}$$

$f(x) = -\dfrac{3}{5}x + 2$ is a linear function.

61.
$$f(x) = -\frac{3}{5}x + 2$$
$$5 = -\frac{3}{5}x + 2$$
$$3 = -\frac{3}{5}x$$
$$-5 = x$$

$f(x) = -\dfrac{3}{5}x + 2$ is a linear function.

Quiz 11.2

1. $y \le 2x - 6$

Graph the line $y = 2x - 6$ with a solid line and shade the region below it.

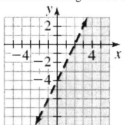

2.
$$4x - 2y > 8$$
$$-2y > 8 - 4x$$
$$y < 2x - 4$$

Graph the line $y = 2x - 4$ with a dashed line and shade the region below it.

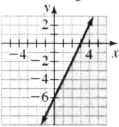

3.
$$-2(y + 3) + 4x \ge -8$$
$$-2y - 6 + 4x \ge -8$$
$$-2y \ge -4x - 2$$
$$y \le 2x + 1$$

Graph the line $y = 2x + 1$ with a solid line and shade the region below it.

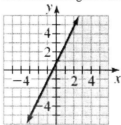

4. $y < -2$

Graph the line $y = 2$ with a dashed line and shade the region below it.

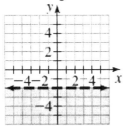

5.

$y \le \dfrac{2}{5}x + 1$

$y < -\dfrac{1}{4}x + 2$

Graph the line $y = \dfrac{2}{5}x + 1$ with a solid line

and the line $y = -\dfrac{1}{4}x + 2$ with a dashed line.

The solution region of the system is the intersection of the solution regions for

$y \le \dfrac{2}{5}x + 1$ and $y < -\dfrac{1}{4}x + 2$.

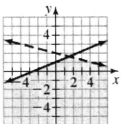

6. $3x - 4y \ge 12$ $6y - 2x \le 12$

$\quad -4y \ge -3x + 12$ $6y \le 2x + 12$

$\quad y \le \dfrac{3}{4}x - 3$ $y \le \dfrac{1}{3}x + 2$

Graph the lines $y = \dfrac{3}{4}x - 3$ and $y = \dfrac{1}{3}x + 2$

with solid lines. The solution region of the system is the intersection of the solution

regions for $y \le \dfrac{3}{4}x - 3$ and $y \le \dfrac{1}{3}x + 2$.

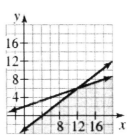

7. $x - y < 3, so$

$\quad y > x - 3$

$\quad x + y < 5, so$

$\quad y < -x + 5$

$\quad x > 0$

$\quad y > 0$

Graph the lines $y = x - 3$, $y = -x + 5$, $x = 0$, and $y = 0$ with dashed lines. The solution region of the system is the intersection of the solution regions of $y > x - 3$, $y < -x + 5$, $x > 0$, and $y > 0$.

8. $2x - 5y > 10$

$\quad -5y > -2x + 10$

$\quad y < \dfrac{2}{5}x - 2$

Answers may vary.
Three possible solutions:
$(-5, -5), (0, -4),$ and $(5, -2)$

$-5 < \dfrac{2}{5}(-5) - 2$ $-4 < \dfrac{2}{5}(0) - 2$ $-2 < \dfrac{2}{5}(5) - 2$

$-5 < -2 - 2$ $-4 < 0 - 2$ $-2 < 2 - 2$

$-5 < -4$ $-4 < -2$ $-2 < 0$

  true   true   true

Three possible non-solutions:
$(-5, 0), (0, 1),$ and $(5, 2)$

$0 < \dfrac{2}{5}(-5) - 2$ $1 < \dfrac{2}{5}(0) - 2$ $2 < \dfrac{2}{5}(5) - 2$

$0 < -2 - 2$ $1 < 0 - 2$ $2 < 2 - 2$

$0 < -4$ $1 < -2$ $2 < 0$

  false   false   false

Homework 11.3

1. $(4 - 7i) + (3 + 10i) = 4 - 7i + 3 + 10i$

$= 4 + 3 - 7i + 10i$

$= 7 + 3i$

3.
$$\left(5-\sqrt{-9}\right)+\left(2-\sqrt{-25}\right)=5-3i+2-5i$$
$$=5+2-3i-5i$$
$$=7-8i$$

5.
$$\left(6-5i\right)-\left(2-13i\right)=6-5i-2+13i$$
$$=6-2-5i+13i$$
$$=4+8i$$

7.
$$\left(6-\sqrt{-49}\right)-\left(1+\sqrt{-81}\right)=6-7i-1-9i$$
$$=6-1-7i-9i$$
$$=5-16i$$

9.
$$2i\cdot9i=18i^2$$
$$=18(-1)$$
$$=-18$$

11.
$$-10i\left(-5i\right)=50i^2$$
$$=50(-1)$$
$$=-50$$

13.
$$\sqrt{-4}\sqrt{-25}=2i\cdot5i$$
$$=10i^2$$
$$=10(-1)$$
$$=-10$$

15.
$$\sqrt{-3}\sqrt{-5}=i\sqrt{3}\cdot i\sqrt{5}$$
$$=i^2\sqrt{15}$$
$$=(-1)\sqrt{15}$$
$$=-\sqrt{15}$$

17.
$$(8i)^2=64i^2$$
$$=64(-1)$$
$$=-64$$

19.
$$5i\left(3-2i\right)=5i\cdot3-5i\cdot2i$$
$$=15i-10i^2$$
$$=15i-10(-1)$$
$$=15i+10$$
$$=10+15i$$

21.
$$20-3i\left(2-7i\right)=20-3i\cdot2+3i\cdot7i$$
$$=20-6i+21i^2$$
$$=20-6i+21(-1)$$
$$=20-6i-21$$
$$=-1-6i$$

23.
$$\left(2+5i\right)\left(3+4i\right)=2\cdot3+2\cdot4i+5i\cdot3+5i\cdot4i$$
$$=6+8i+15i+20i^2$$
$$=6+23i+20(-1)$$
$$=6+23i-20$$
$$=-14+23i$$

25.
$$\left(3-6i\right)\left(5+2i\right)=3\cdot5+3\cdot2i-6i\cdot5-6i\cdot2i$$
$$=15+6i-30i-12i^2$$
$$=15-24i-12(-1)$$
$$=15-24i+12$$
$$=27-24i$$

27.
$$\left(-6+4i\right)\left(-2+7i\right)=12-42i-8i+28i^2$$
$$=12-28-42i-8i$$
$$=-16-50i$$

29.
$$\left(5+4i\right)\left(5-4i\right)=5^2-\left(4i\right)^2$$
$$=25-16i^2$$
$$=25-16(-1)$$
$$=25+16$$
$$=41$$

31.
$$\left(2-9i\right)\left(2+9i\right)=2^2-\left(9i\right)^2$$
$$=4-81i^2$$
$$=4-81(-1)$$
$$=4+81$$
$$=85$$

33.
$$\left(1+i\right)\left(1-i\right)=1^2-i^2$$
$$=1-(-1)$$
$$=1+1$$
$$=2$$

35.
$$(2+7i)^2 = 2^2 + 2(2)(7i) + (7i)^2$$
$$= 4 + 28i + 49i^2$$
$$= 4 - 49 + 28i$$
$$= -45 + 28i$$

37.
$$(4-5i)^2 = 4^2 - 2(4)(5i) + (5i)^2$$
$$= 16 - 40i + 25i^2$$
$$= 16 - 25 - 40i$$
$$= -9 - 40i$$

39.
$$(-4+3i)^2 = (-4)^2 + 2(-4)(3i) + (3i)^2$$
$$= 16 - 24i + 9i^2$$
$$= 16 - 9 - 24i$$
$$= 7 - 24i$$

41.
$$\frac{3}{2+5i} = \frac{3}{2+5i} \cdot \frac{2-5i}{2-5i}$$
$$= \frac{6-15i}{4-25i^2}$$
$$= \frac{6-15i}{4-25(-1)}$$
$$= \frac{6-15i}{4+25}$$
$$= \frac{6-15i}{29}$$
$$= \frac{6}{29} - \frac{15}{29}i$$

43.
$$\frac{3i}{7-2i} = \frac{3i}{7-2i} \cdot \frac{7+2i}{7+2i}$$
$$= \frac{21i+6i^2}{49-4i^2}$$
$$= \frac{-6+21i}{53}$$
$$= -\frac{6}{53} + \frac{21}{53}i$$

45.
$$\frac{2+3i}{7+i} = \frac{2+3i}{7+i} \cdot \frac{7-i}{7-i}$$
$$= \frac{14+21i-2i-3i^2}{49-i^2}$$
$$= \frac{17+19i}{50}$$
$$= \frac{17}{50} + \frac{19}{50}i$$

47.
$$\frac{3+4i}{3-4i} = \frac{3+4i}{3-4i} \cdot \frac{3+4i}{3+4i}$$
$$= \frac{9+12i+12i+16i^2}{9-16i^2}$$
$$= \frac{9+24i+16(-1)}{9-16(-1)}$$
$$= \frac{-7+24i}{25}$$
$$= -\frac{7}{25} + \frac{24}{25}i$$

49.
$$\frac{3-5i}{2-9i} = \frac{3-5i}{2-9i} \cdot \frac{2+9i}{2+9i}$$
$$= \frac{6+27i-10i-45i^2}{4-81i^2}$$
$$= \frac{51+17i}{85}$$
$$= \frac{51}{85} + \frac{17}{85}i$$

51.
$$\frac{5+7i}{4i} = \frac{5+7i}{4i} \cdot \frac{i}{i}$$
$$= \frac{5i+7i^2}{4i^2}$$
$$= \frac{-7+5i}{-4}$$
$$= \frac{7}{4} - \frac{5}{4}i$$

53.
$$\frac{7}{5i} = \frac{7}{5i} \cdot \frac{i}{i}$$
$$= \frac{7i}{5i^2}$$
$$= -\frac{7}{5}i$$

55. Answers may vary. Student 2's work is correct, and Student 1's work is incorrect. If a radical has a negative radicand, you must rewrite the radical using *i* before performing any operations. Student 1 did not perform this step, and therefore got the wrong answer.

57. a. Answers may vary. A possible answer is $a = 3$, $b = -2$, $c = -8$, and $d = 5$.

$$(a+bi)+(c+di) = (3-2i)+(-8+5i)$$
$$= 3-8-2i+5i$$
$$= -5+3i$$

b. Answers may vary. A possible answer is $a = -2$, $b = 5$, $c = -3$, and $d = -5$.

$$(a+bi)+(c+di) = (-2+5i)+(-3-5i)$$
$$= -2-3+5i-5i$$
$$= -5$$

c. Answers may vary. A possible answer is $a = 7$, $b = -4$, $c = -7$, and $d = -2$.

$$(a+bi)+(c+di) = (7-4i)+(-7-2i)$$
$$= 7-7-4i-2i$$
$$= -6i$$

59. The square of a pure imaginary number will always be a negative real number. A pure imaginary number has two parts: the coefficient and *i*. When the coefficient is squared, it always becomes a positive real number. When *i* is squared, it always becomes −1. Multiplying a positive real number by −1 always gives a negative real product.

61.
$$\frac{4}{3+2\sqrt{x}} = \frac{4}{3+2\sqrt{x}} \cdot \frac{3-2\sqrt{x}}{3-2\sqrt{x}}$$
$$= \frac{12-8\sqrt{x}}{9-\left(2\sqrt{x}\right)^2}$$
$$= \frac{12-8\sqrt{x}}{9-4x}$$

63.
$$\frac{4}{3+2i} = \frac{4}{3+2i} \cdot \frac{3-2i}{3-2i}$$
$$= \frac{12-8i}{9-4i^2}$$
$$= \frac{12-8i}{13}$$
$$= \frac{12}{13} - \frac{8}{13}i$$

65.
$$3x^2 - 2x + 3 = 0$$
$$\frac{-b \pm \sqrt{b^2-4ac}}{2a} = \frac{2 \pm \sqrt{(-2)^2 - 4(3)(3)}}{2(3)}$$
$$= \frac{2 \pm \sqrt{-32}}{6}$$
$$= \frac{2 \pm 4i\sqrt{2}}{6}$$
$$= \frac{1 \pm 2i\sqrt{2}}{3}$$

67.
$$5x^2 - 4x = -1$$
$$5x^2 - 4x + 1 = 0$$
$$\frac{-b \pm \sqrt{b^2-4ac}}{2a} = \frac{4 \pm \sqrt{(-4)^2 - 4(5)(1)}}{2(5)}$$
$$= \frac{4 \pm \sqrt{-4}}{10}$$
$$= \frac{4 \pm 2i}{10}$$
$$= \frac{2 \pm i}{5}$$

69.
$$(x-3)(2x+1) = -10$$
$$x \cdot 2x + x \cdot 1 - 3 \cdot 2x - 3 \cdot 1 = -10$$
$$2x^2 + x - 6x - 3 + 10 = 0$$
$$2x^2 - 5x + 7 = 0$$
$$\frac{-b \pm \sqrt{b^2-4ac}}{2a} = \frac{5 \pm \sqrt{(-5)^2 - 4(2)(7)}}{2(2)}$$
$$= \frac{5 \pm \sqrt{-31}}{4}$$
$$= \frac{5 \pm i\sqrt{31}}{4}$$

71.
$$x(3x-2) = 2+2(x-3)$$
$$3x^2 - 2x = 2 + 2x - 6$$
$$3x^2 - 2x - 2x - 2 + 6 = 0$$
$$3x^2 - 4x + 4 = 0$$

$$\frac{-b \pm \sqrt{b^2-4ac}}{2a} = \frac{4 \pm \sqrt{(-4)^2 - 4(3)(4)}}{2(3)}$$
$$= \frac{4 \pm \sqrt{-32}}{6}$$
$$= \frac{4 \pm 4i\sqrt{2}}{6}$$
$$= \frac{2 \pm 2i\sqrt{2}}{3}$$

73.
$$(5x+3)^2 = -20$$
$$25x^2 + 2(5x)(3) + 9 + 20 = 0$$
$$25x^2 + 30x + 29 = 0$$
$$\frac{-b \pm \sqrt{b^2-4ac}}{2a} = \frac{-30 \pm \sqrt{30^2 - 4(25)(29)}}{2(25)}$$
$$= \frac{-30 \pm \sqrt{900 - 2900}}{50}$$
$$= \frac{-30 \pm \sqrt{-2000}}{50}$$
$$= \frac{-30 \pm 20i\sqrt{5}}{50}$$
$$= \frac{-3 \pm 2i\sqrt{5}}{5}$$

75.
$$4x^2 - 2x + 3 = 0$$
$$\frac{-b \pm \sqrt{b^2-4ac}}{2a} = \frac{2 \pm \sqrt{(-2)^2 - 4(4)(3)}}{2(4)}$$
$$= \frac{2 \pm \sqrt{-44}}{8}$$
$$= \frac{2 \pm 2i\sqrt{11}}{8}$$
$$= \frac{1 \pm i\sqrt{11}}{4}$$

$4x^2 - 2x + 3 = 0$ is a quadratic equation in one variable.

77.
$$10x^2 - 19x + 6$$
$$(5x-2)(2x-3)$$
$10x^2 - 19x + 6$ is a quadratic expression in one variable.

79.
$$(3i-7)(4i+6) = 12i^2 + 18i - 28i - 42$$
$$= -12 - 42 + 18i - 28i$$
$$= -54 - 10i$$
$(3i-7)(4i+6)$ is an imaginary number.

Quiz 11.3

1.
$$(6-2i)+(3-4i) = 6 - 2i + 3 - 4i$$
$$= 6 + 3 - 2i - 4i$$
$$= 9 - 6i$$

2.
$$(3+7i)-(8-2i) = 3 + 7i - 8 + 2i$$
$$= 3 - 8 + 7i + 2i$$
$$= -5 + 9i$$

3.
$$-4i \cdot 3i = -12i^2$$
$$= -12(-1)$$
$$= 12$$

4.
$$\sqrt{-2}\sqrt{-7} = i\sqrt{2} \cdot i\sqrt{7}$$
$$= i^2\sqrt{14}$$
$$= -\sqrt{14}$$

5.
$$(5-3i)(7+i) = 5 \cdot 7 + 5 \cdot i - 3i \cdot 7 - 3i \cdot i$$
$$= 35 + 5i - 21i - 3i^2$$
$$= 35 - 16i - 3(-1)$$
$$= 35 - 16i + 3$$
$$= 38 - 16i$$

6.
$$(4-3i)^2 = (4)^2 - 2(4)(3i) + (3i)^2$$
$$= 16 - 24i + 9i^2$$
$$= 16 - 24i + 9(-1)$$
$$= 16 - 24i - 9$$
$$= 7 - 24i$$

7.

$$(8+5i)(8-5i) = (8)^2 \quad (5i)^2$$
$$= 64 - 25i^2$$
$$= 64 - 25(-1)$$
$$= 64 + 25$$
$$= 89$$

8.

$$\frac{3+2i}{5-4i} = \frac{3+2i}{5-4i} \cdot \frac{5+4i}{5+4i}$$
$$= \frac{15+12i+10i+8i^2}{25-16i^2}$$
$$= \frac{15+22i+8(-1)}{25-16(-1)}$$
$$= \frac{7+22i}{41}$$
$$= \frac{7}{41} + \frac{22}{41}i$$

9.

$$\frac{5-7i}{6i} = \frac{5-7i}{6i} \cdot \frac{i}{i}$$
$$= \frac{5i-7i^2}{6i^2}$$
$$= \frac{7+5i}{-6}$$
$$= -\frac{7}{6} - \frac{5}{6}i$$

10. False. Answers may vary.
The number $3i$ (or $0 + 3i$) is a complex number and i is a pure imaginary number. Then $(i)(3i) = 3i^2 = -3$. Since -3 is not an imaginary number, the statement is false.

Homework 11.4

1.

$$c^2 = a^2 + b^2$$
$$c^2 = 5^2 + 12^2$$
$$c^2 = 25 + 144$$
$$c^2 = 169$$
$$c = 13$$

3.

$$c^2 = a^2 + b^2$$
$$c^2 = 4^2 + 5^2$$
$$c^2 = 16 + 25$$
$$c^2 = 41$$
$$c = \sqrt{41}$$

5.

$$a^2 + b^2 = c^2$$
$$3^2 + b^2 = 8^2$$
$$9 + b^2 = 64$$
$$b^2 = 55$$
$$b = \sqrt{55}$$

7.

$$a^2 + b^2 = c^2$$
$$a^2 + 5^2 = 7^2$$
$$a^2 + 25 = 49$$
$$a^2 = 24$$
$$a = \sqrt{24}$$
$$a = 2\sqrt{6}$$

9.

$$c^2 = a^2 + b^2$$
$$c^2 = \left(\sqrt{2}\right)^2 + \left(\sqrt{5}\right)^2$$
$$c^2 = 2 + 5$$
$$c^2 = 7$$
$$c = \sqrt{7}$$

11. The lengths of the two legs are given, so let $a = 11$ and $b = 7$.

$$c^2 = a^2 + b^2$$
$$c^2 = 11^2 + 7^2$$
$$c^2 = 121 + 49$$
$$c^2 = 170$$
$$c = \sqrt{170}$$

13. The lengths of a leg and the hypotenuse are given, so let $a = 10$ and $c = 12$.

$$a^2 + b^2 = c^2$$
$$10^2 + b^2 = 12^2$$
$$100 + b^2 = 144$$
$$b^2 = 44$$
$$b = 2\sqrt{11}$$

15. $a = 5, b = 20, c = $ length of ladder
$$c^2 = a^2 + b^2$$
$$c^2 = 5^2 + 20^2$$
$$c^2 = 25 + 400$$
$$c^2 = 425$$
$$c = \sqrt{425}$$
$$c = 5\sqrt{17}$$
$$c \approx 20.6$$
The ladder must be approximately 20.6 feet long.

17. $a = 13, b = $ width of screen, $c = 20$
$$a^2 + b^2 = c^2$$
$$13^2 + b^2 = 20^2$$
$$169 + b^2 = 400$$
$$b^2 = 231$$
$$b = \sqrt{231}$$
$$b \approx 15.2$$
The screen must be approximately 15.2 inches wide.

19. $a = 2.8, \ b = $ distance across lake, $c = 3.4$
$$a^2 + b^2 = c^2$$
$$2.8^2 + b^2 = 3.4^2$$
$$7.84 + b^2 = 11.56$$
$$b^2 = 3.72$$
$$b = \sqrt{3.72}$$
$$b \approx 1.9$$
The distance across the lake must be approximately 1.9 miles.

21. $a = 465, c = 964, b = $ distance

$$a^2 + b^2 = c^2$$
$$465^2 + b^2 = 964^2$$
$$b^2 = 713071$$
$$b = \sqrt{713071}$$
$$b \approx 844.4$$
$$a + b + c = 465 + 844.4 + 964$$
$$= 2273.4$$
The total distance of the road trip would be approximately 2273.4 miles.

23. $(2, 9)$ and $(8, 1)$
$$d = \sqrt{(8-2)^2 + (1-9)^2}$$
$$= \sqrt{6^2 + (-8)^2}$$
$$= \sqrt{36 + 64}$$
$$= \sqrt{100}$$
$$= 10$$

25. $(-3, 5)$ and $(4, 2)$
$$d = \sqrt{(4-(-3))^2 + (2-5)^2}$$
$$= \sqrt{7^2 + (-3)^2}$$
$$= \sqrt{49 + 9}$$
$$= \sqrt{58}$$

27. $(-6, -3)$ and $(-4, 1)$

$$d = \sqrt{(-4-(-6))^2 + (1-(-3))^2}$$
$$= \sqrt{2^2 + 4^2}$$
$$= \sqrt{4 + 16}$$
$$= \sqrt{20}$$
$$= 2\sqrt{5}$$

29. $(-4, -5)$ and $(-8, -9)$

$$d = \sqrt{(-8-(-4))^2 + (-9-(-5))^2}$$
$$= \sqrt{(-4)^2 + (-4)^2}$$
$$= \sqrt{16 + 16}$$
$$= \sqrt{32}$$
$$= 4\sqrt{2}$$

31. $(2.1, 8.9)$ and $(5.6, 1.7)$

$d = \sqrt{(5.6 - 2.1)^2 + (1.7 - 8.9)^2}$

$\quad = \sqrt{3.5^2 + (-7.2)^2}$

$\quad = \sqrt{12.25 + 51.84}$

$\quad = \sqrt{64.09}$

$\quad \approx 8.01$

33. $(-2.18, -5.74)$ and $(3.44, 6.29)$

$d = \sqrt{(3.44 - (-2.18))^2 + (6.29 - (-5.74))^2}$

$\quad = \sqrt{5.62^2 + 12.03^2}$

$\quad = \sqrt{31.5844 + 144.7209}$

$\quad = \sqrt{176.3053}$

$\quad \approx 13.28$

35. $C(0,0)$ and $r = 7$

$(x - h)^2 + (y - k)^2 = r^2$

$(x - 0)^2 + (y - 0)^2 = 7^2$

$\quad\quad\quad x^2 + y^2 = 49$

37. $C(0,0)$ and $r = 6.7$

$(x - h)^2 + (y - k)^2 = r^2$

$(x - 0)^2 + (y - 0)^2 = 6.7^2$

$\quad\quad\quad x^2 + y^2 = 44.89$

39. $C(5,3)$ and $r = 2$

$(x - h)^2 + (y - k)^2 = r^2$

$(x - 5)^2 + (y - 3)^2 = 2^2$

$(x - 5)^2 + (y - 3)^2 = 4$

41. $C(-2,1)$ and $r = 4$

$(x - h)^2 + (y - k)^2 = r^2$

$(x - (-2))^2 + (y - 1)^2 = 4^2$

$(x + 2)^2 + (y - 1)^2 = 16$

43. $C(-7, -3)$ and $r = \sqrt{3}$

$(x - h)^2 + (y - k)^2 = r^2$

$(x - (-7))^2 + (y - (-3))^2 = (\sqrt{3})^2$

$(x + 7)^2 + (y + 3)^2 = 3$

45. $x^2 + y^2 = 25$

The equation has the form $x^2 + y^2 = r^2$.

Therefore, $C = (0,0)$ and

$r^2 = 25$

$r = \sqrt{25}$

$r = 5$

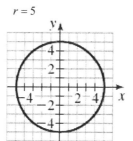

47. $x^2 + y^2 = 8$

The equation has the form $x^2 + y^2 = r^2$.

Therefore, $C = (0,0)$ and

$r^2 = 8$

$r = \sqrt{8}$

$r = 2\sqrt{2}$

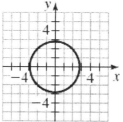

49. $(x - 3)^2 + (y - 5)^2 = 16$

The equation is in the form

$(x - h)^2 + (y - k)^2 = r^2$.

The center is (h, k) or $C(3,5)$ and

$r^2 = 16$

$r = \sqrt{16}$

$r = 4$

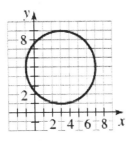

51. $(x+6)^2 + (y-1)^2 = 7$

$(x-(-6))^2 + (y-1)^2 = (\sqrt{7})^2$

The equation is in the form
$(x-h)^2 + (y-k)^2 = r^2$. The center is
$C(-6,1)$ and the radius is $r = \sqrt{7}$.

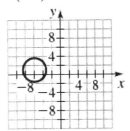

53. $(x+3)^2 + (y+2)^2 = 1$

$(x-(-3))^2 + (y-(-2))^2 = 1^2$

The equation is in the form
$(x-h)^2 + (y-k)^2 = r^2$. The center is
$C(-3,-2)$ and the radius is $r = 1$.

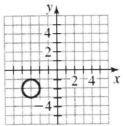

55. $C(0,0)$ and $r = 3$.

$(x-h)^2 + (y-k)^2 = r^2$

$(x-0)^2 + (y-0)^2 = 3^2$

$x^2 + y^2 = 9$

57. $C(-3,2)$ and $r = 2$.

$(x-h)^2 + (y-k)^2 = r^2$

$(x-(-3))^2 + (y-2)^2 = 2^2$

$(x+3)^2 + (y-2)^2 = 4$

59. The radius is the distance from the center to
any point on the circle. The distance between
$C(3,2)$ and $(5,6)$ is given by:

$d = \sqrt{(5-3)^2 + (6-2)^2}$

$= \sqrt{2^2 + 4^2}$

$= \sqrt{4+16}$

$= \sqrt{20}$

The radius is $r = \sqrt{20}$.
The equation of the circle is

$(x-h)^2 + (y-k)^2 = r^2$

$(x-3)^2 + (y-2)^2 = (\sqrt{20})^2$

$(x-3)^2 + (y-2)^2 = 20$

61. Answers may vary. One possible answer:

$(x-2)^2 + (y-3)^2 = 9$

$(x-5)^2 + (y-6)^2 = 9$

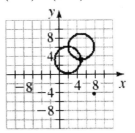

63. a. $x^2 + y^2 = 16$

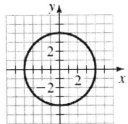

b. Answers may vary.

x	y
-4	0
-2	$2\sqrt{3} \approx 3.46$
-2	$-2\sqrt{3} \approx -3.46$
0	4
0	-4
2	$2\sqrt{3} \approx 3.46$
2	$-2\sqrt{3} \approx -3.46$
4	0

c. For each input-output pair, the sum of the square of the input and the square of the output is 16.

65. Find the equation of the circle that has center $C(3,2)$ and $r = 4$.

$$(x-h)^2 + (y-k)^2 = r^2$$
$$(x-3)^2 + (y-2)^2 = 4^2$$
$$(x-3)^2 + (y-2)^2 = 16$$

Find the coordinates of five points, (x,y), that satisfy this equation. Answers will vary. Five possible answers are: $(3,6)$, $(3,-2)$, $(7,2)$, $(-1,2)$, and $(5,2+\sqrt{12})$.

67. No. Answers may vary. The graph of the relation is a circle with radius 7 and centered at the origin. The graph fails the vertical line test.

69. a. The square root of a nonnegative number is a nonnegative real number and the square root of a negative number is an imaginary number. Therefore, $y \geq 0$ for real number values of y.

b.
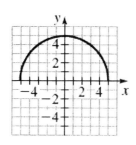

71. a. Sketches may vary. One example:

b. $a = k, b = k$
$$c^2 = a^2 + b^2$$
$$c^2 = k^2 + k^2$$
$$c^2 = 2k^2$$
$$c = \sqrt{2k^2}$$
$$c = \sqrt{2}\sqrt{k^2}$$
$$c = k\sqrt{2}$$

c. $c = k\sqrt{2}$
$$= 3\sqrt{2}$$

d. $c = k\sqrt{2}$
$$5 = k\sqrt{2}$$
$$k = \frac{5}{\sqrt{2}}$$
$$k = \frac{5}{\sqrt{2}} \cdot \frac{\sqrt{2}}{\sqrt{2}}$$
$$k = \frac{5\sqrt{2}}{2}$$

73. $x + y = 4$

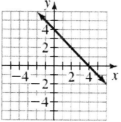

75. $x^2 + y^2 = 4$

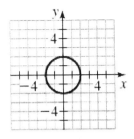

77. $2^x + y = 0$

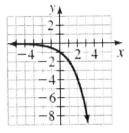

79. $f(x) = 2(x-4)^2 - 3$

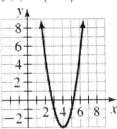

$f(x) = 2(x-4)^2 - 3$ is a quadratic function.

81.
$$6x^2 - 16x + 8 = 2(3x^2 - 8x + 4)$$
$$= 2(3x-2)(x-2)$$

$6x^2 - 16x + 8$ is a quadratic polynomial in one variable.

83.
$$x(5x-3) = 3(x+1)$$
$$5x^2 - 3x = 3x + 3$$
$$5x^2 - 6x - 3 = 0$$

$$\frac{-b \pm \sqrt{b^2 - 4ac}}{2a} = \frac{6 \pm \sqrt{(-6)^2 - 4(5)(-3)}}{2(5)}$$
$$= \frac{6 \pm \sqrt{36 + 60}}{10}$$
$$= \frac{6 \pm 4\sqrt{6}}{10}$$
$$= \frac{3 \pm 2\sqrt{6}}{5}$$

$x(5x-3) = 3(x+1)$ is a quadratic equation in one variable.

Quiz 11.4

1.
$$a = 4, c = 8$$
$$a^2 + b^2 = c^2$$
$$4^2 + b^2 = 8^2$$
$$16 + b^2 = 64$$
$$b^2 = 48$$
$$b = \sqrt{48}$$
$$b = 4\sqrt{3}$$
$$b \approx 6.9$$
The other leg is about 6.9 inches.

2.
$$b = 16, c = 19$$
$$a^2 + b^2 = c^2$$
$$a^2 + 16^2 = 19^2$$
$$a^2 + 256 = 361$$
$$a^2 = 105$$
$$a = \sqrt{105}$$
$$a \approx 10.2$$
The height of the screen is about 10.25 inches.

3.
$$(-2, -5) \text{ and } (3, -1)$$
$$d = \sqrt{(3 - (-2))^2 + (-1 - (-5))^2}$$
$$= \sqrt{5^2 + 4^2}$$
$$= \sqrt{25 + 16}$$
$$= \sqrt{41}$$

4. $(-3,2)$ and $(-7,-2)$

$$d = \sqrt{\left(-7-(-3)\right)^2 + \left(-2-2\right)^2}$$

$$= \sqrt{\left(-4\right)^2 + \left(-4\right)^2}$$

$$= \sqrt{16+16}$$

$$= \sqrt{32}$$

$$= 4\sqrt{2}$$

5. $C(-3,2)$ and $r = 6$

$$\left(x-h\right)^2 + \left(y-k\right)^2 = r^2$$

$$\left(x-(-3)\right)^2 + \left(y-2\right)^2 = 6^2$$

$$\left(x+3\right)^2 + \left(y-2\right)^2 = 36$$

6. $C(0,0)$ and $r = 2.8$

$$\left(x-h\right)^2 + \left(y-k\right)^2 = r^2$$

$$\left(x-0\right)^2 + \left(y-0\right)^2 = 2.8^2$$

$$x^2 + y^2 = 7.84$$

7. $x^2 + y^2 = 12$

The equation is in the form $x^2 + y^2 = r^2$. The center is $C(0,0)$ and

$$r^2 = 12$$

$$r = \sqrt{12}$$

$$r = 2\sqrt{3}$$

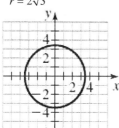

8. $\left(x+4\right)^2 + \left(y-3\right)^2 = 25$

$$\left(x-(-4)\right)^2 + \left(y-3\right)^2 = 5^2$$

The equation is in the form $\left(x-h\right)^2 + \left(y-k\right)^2 = r^2$. The center is $C(-4,3)$ and the radius is $r = 5$.

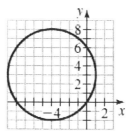

9. $C(2,-1)$

The radius is the distance from the center, $C(2,-1)$, to the point $(4,7)$ that lies on the circle.

$$d = \sqrt{\left(4-2\right)^2 + \left(7-(-1)\right)^2}$$

$$= \sqrt{2^2 + 8^2}$$

$$= \sqrt{4+64}$$

$$= \sqrt{68}$$

The equation of the circle is

$$\left(x-h\right)^2 + \left(y-k\right)^2 = r^2$$

$$\left(x-2\right)^2 + \left(y-(-1)\right)^2 = \left(\sqrt{68}\right)^2$$

$$\left(x-2\right)^2 + \left(y+1\right)^2 = 68$$

10. Answers may vary. One possible answer:

$$\left(x+2\right)^2 + y^2 = 4$$

$$\left(x-3\right)^2 + y^2 = 9$$

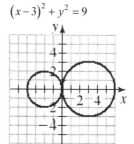

Homework 11.5

1. $\dfrac{x^2}{36} + \dfrac{y^2}{9} = 1$

$a^2 = 36, a = 6$

x-intercepts: $(-6,0),(6,0)$

$b^2 = 9, b = 3$

y-intercepts: $(0,-3),(0,3)$

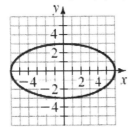

3. $$\frac{x^2}{4}+\frac{y^2}{36}=1$$

$a^2=4, a=2$

x-intercepts: $(-2,0),(2,0)$

$b^2=36, b=6$

y-intercepts: $(0,-6),(0,6)$

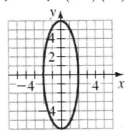

5. $$\frac{x^2}{100}+\frac{y^2}{16}=1$$

$a^2=100, a=10$

x-intercepts: $(-10,0),(10,0)$

$b^2=16, b=4$

y-intercepts: $(0,-4),(0,4)$

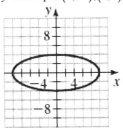

7. $$25x^2+4y^2=100$$

$$\frac{25x^2}{100}+\frac{4y^2}{100}=\frac{100}{100}$$

$$\frac{x^2}{4}+\frac{y^2}{25}=1$$

$a^2=4, a=2$

x-intercepts: $(-2,0),(2,0)$

$b^2=25, b=5$

y-intercepts: $(0,-5),(0,5)$

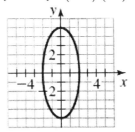

9. $$9x^2+100y^2=900$$

$$\frac{9x^2}{900}+\frac{100y^2}{900}=\frac{900}{900}$$

$$\frac{x^2}{100}+\frac{y^2}{9}=1$$

$a^2=100, a=10$

x-intercepts: $(-10,0),(10,0)$

$b^2=9, b=3$

y-intercepts: $(0,-3),(0,3)$

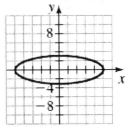

11. $$x^2+y^2=36$$

$$\frac{x^2}{36}+\frac{y^2}{36}=\frac{36}{36}$$

$$\frac{x^2}{36}+\frac{y^2}{36}=1$$

$a^2=36, a=6$

x-intercepts: $(-6,0),(6,0)$

$b^2=36, b=6$

y-intercepts: $(0,-6),(0,6)$

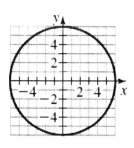

13.

$$x^2 + 25y^2 = 25$$

$$\frac{x^2}{25} + \frac{25y^2}{25} = \frac{25}{25}$$

$$\frac{x^2}{25} + \frac{y^2}{1} = 1$$

$$a^2 = 25, a = 5$$

x-intercepts: $(-5,0), (5,0)$

$$b^2 = 1, b = 1$$

y-intercepts: $(0,-1), (0,1)$

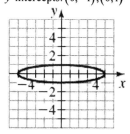

15.

$$5x^2 + 16y^2 = 80$$

$$\frac{5x^2}{80} + \frac{16y^2}{80} = \frac{80}{80}$$

$$\frac{x^2}{16} + \frac{y^2}{5} = 1$$

$$a^2 = 16, a = 4$$

x-intercepts: $(-4,0), (4,0)$

$$b^2 = 5, b = \sqrt{5}$$

y-intercepts: $\left(0,-\sqrt{5}\right), \left(0,\sqrt{5}\right)$

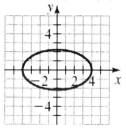

17. The x-intercepts are $(5,0)$ and $(-5,0)$, so $a = 5$. The y-intercepts are $(3,0)$ and $(-3,0)$, so $b = 3$. Therefore:

$$\frac{x^2}{5^2} + \frac{y^2}{3^2} = 1$$

$$\frac{x^2}{25} + \frac{y^2}{9} = 1$$

19.

$$\frac{x^2}{16} - \frac{y^2}{4} = 1$$

$$a^2 = 16, a = 4$$

x-intercepts: $(-4,0), (4,0)$

$$b^2 = 4, b = 2$$

Sketch a dashed rectangle that contains the points $(-4,0), (4,0), (0,-2)$, and $(0,2)$, and then sketch the inclined asymptotes.

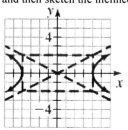

21.

$$\frac{y^2}{16} - \frac{x^2}{25} = 1$$

$$b^2 = 16, b = 4$$

y-intercepts: $(0,-4), (0,4)$

$$a^2 = 25, a = 5$$

Sketch a dashed rectangle that contains the points $(-5,0), (5,0), (0,-4)$, and $(0,4)$, and then sketch the inclined asymptotes.

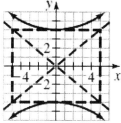

23.

$$\frac{x^2}{25} - \frac{y^2}{81} = 1$$

$a^2 = 25, b = 5$

x-intercepts: $(5,0),(-5,0)$

$b^2 = 81, b = 9$

Sketch a dashed rectangle that contains the points $(-5,0),(5,0),(0,-9)$, and $(0,9)$, and then sketch the inclined asymptotes.

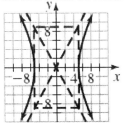

25.

$$16x^2 - 4y^2 = 64$$

$$\frac{16x^2}{64} - \frac{4y^2}{64} = \frac{64}{64}$$

$$\frac{x^2}{4} - \frac{y^2}{16} = 1$$

$a^2 = 4, a = 2$

x-intercepts: $(-2,0),(2,0)$

$b^2 = 16, b = 4$

Sketch a dashed rectangle that contains the points $(-2,0),(2,0),(0,-4)$, and $(0,4)$, and then sketch the inclined asymptotes.

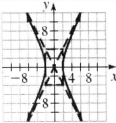

27.

$$x^2 - 9y^2 = 9$$

$$\frac{x^2}{9} - \frac{9y^2}{9} = \frac{9}{9}$$

$$\frac{x^2}{9} - \frac{y^2}{1} = 1$$

$a^2 = 9, a = 3$

x-intercepts: $(-3,0),(3,0)$

$b^2 = 1, b = 1$

Sketch a dashed rectangle that contains the points $(-3,0),(3,0),(0,-1)$, and $(0,1)$, and then sketch the inclined asymptotes.

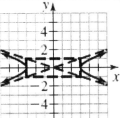

29.

$$y^2 - x^2 = 4$$

$$\frac{y^2}{4} - \frac{x^2}{4} = \frac{4}{4}$$

$$\frac{y^2}{4} - \frac{x^2}{4} = 1$$

$b^2 = 4, b = 2$

y-intercepts: $(0,-2),(0,2)$

$a^2 = 4, a = 2$

Sketch a dashed rectangle that contains the points $(-2,0),(2,0),(0,-2)$, and $(0,2)$, and then sketch the inclined asymptotes.

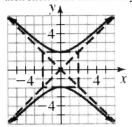

31.

$$16y^2 - x^2 = 16$$

$$\frac{16y^2}{16} - \frac{x^2}{16} = \frac{16}{16}$$

$$\frac{y^2}{1} - \frac{x^2}{16} = 1$$

$b^2 = 1, b = 1$

y-intercepts: $(0,-1),(0,1)$

$a^2 = 16, a = 4$

Sketch a dashed rectangle that contains the points $(-4,0),(4,0),(0,-1)$, and $(0,1)$, and then sketch the inclined asymptotes.

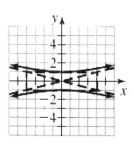

33.
$$25x^2 - 7y^2 = 175$$
$$\frac{25x^2}{175} - \frac{7y^2}{175} = \frac{175}{175}$$
$$\frac{x^2}{7} - \frac{y^2}{25} = 1$$
$$a^2 = 7, a = \sqrt{7}$$
x-intercepts: $\left(-\sqrt{7}, 0\right), \left(\sqrt{7}, 0\right)$

$$b^2 = 25, b = 5$$
Sketch a dashed rectangle that contains the points $\left(-\sqrt{7}, 0\right), \left(\sqrt{7}, 0\right), (0, -5),$ and $(0, 5),$
and then sketch the inclined asymptotes.

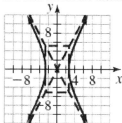

35.
$$\frac{x^2}{64} + \frac{y^2}{4} = 1$$
Ellipse
$$a^2 = 64, a = 8$$
x-intercepts: $(-8, 0), (8, 0)$
$$b^2 = 4, b = 2$$
y-intercepts: $(0, -2), (0, 2)$

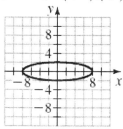

37.
$$x^2 - y^2 = 1$$
$$\frac{x^2}{1} - \frac{y^2}{1} = 1$$
Hyperbola
$$a^2 = 1, a = 1$$
x-intercepts: $(-1, 0), (1, 0)$

$$b^2 = 1, b = 1$$
Sketch a dashed rectangle that contains the points $(-1, 0), (1, 0), (0, -1),$ and $(0, 1),$ and then sketch the inclined asymptotes.

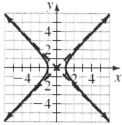

39.
$$81x^2 + 49y^2 = 3969$$
$$\frac{81x^2}{3969} + \frac{49y^2}{3969} = \frac{3969}{3969}$$
$$\frac{x^2}{49} + \frac{y^2}{81} = 1$$
Ellipse
$$a^2 = 49, a = 7$$
x-intercepts: $(-7, 0), (7, 0)$
$$b^2 = 81, b = 9$$
y-intercepts: $(0, -9), (0, 9)$

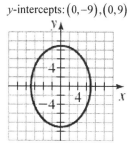

41.
$$x^2 + y^2 = 1$$
$$\frac{x^2}{1} + \frac{y^2}{1} = 1$$
Circle
$$a^2 = 1, a = 1$$
x-intercepts: $(-1, 0), (1, 0)$

$b^2 = 1, b = 1$

y-intercepts: $(0,-1),(0,1)$

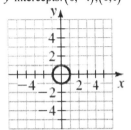

43.

$9y^2 - 4x^2 = 144$

$$\frac{9y^2}{144} - \frac{4x^2}{144} = \frac{144}{144}$$

$$\frac{y^2}{16} - \frac{x^2}{36} = 1$$

Hyperbola

$b^2 = 16, b = 4$

y-intercepts: $(0,-4),(0,4)$

$a^2 = 36, a = 6$

Sketch a dashed rectangle that contains the points $(-6,0),(6,0),(0,-4),$ and $(0,4)$, and then sketch the inclined asymptotes.

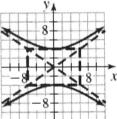

45.

$$\frac{x^2}{25} - \frac{y^2}{25} = 1$$

Hyperbola

$a^2 = 25, a = 5$

x-intercepts: $(-5,0),(5,0)$

$b^2 = 25, b = 5$

Sketch a dashed rectangle that contains the points $(-5,0),(5,0),(0,-5),$ and $(0,5)$, and then sketch the inclined asymptotes.

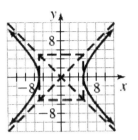

47.

$x^2 + y^2 = 16$

$$\frac{x^2}{16} + \frac{y^2}{16} = 1$$

Circle

$a^2 = 16, a = 4$

x-intercepts: $(-4,0),(4,0)$

$b^2 = 16, b = 4$

y-intercepts: $(0,-4),(0,4)$

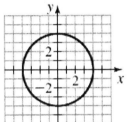

49.

$9x^2 + 16y^2 = 144$

$$\frac{9x^2}{144} + \frac{16y^2}{144} = 1$$

$$\frac{x^2}{16} + \frac{y^2}{9} = 1$$

Ellipse

$a^2 = 16, a = 4$

x-intercepts: $(-4,0),(4,0)$

$b^2 = 9, b = 3$

y-intercepts: $(0,-3),(0,3)$

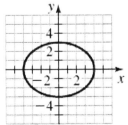

51.

$$\frac{x^2}{16} + \frac{y^2}{16} = 1$$

Circle

$a^2 - 16, a = 4$

x-intercepts: $(-4,0),(4,0)$

$b^2 = 16, b = 4$

y-intercepts: $(0,-4),(0,4)$

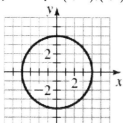

53. a.

i. $\frac{x^2}{c} + \frac{y^2}{d} = 1$

$$\frac{x^2}{4} + \frac{y^2}{16} = 1$$

Ellipse

$a^2 = 4, a = 2$

x-intercepts: $(-2,0),(2,0)$

$b^2 = 16, b = 4$

y-intercepts: $(0,-4),(0,4)$

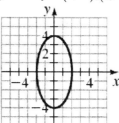

ii. $\frac{x^2}{c} + \frac{y^2}{d} = 1$

$$\frac{x^2}{4} - \frac{y^2}{16} = 1$$

Hyperbola

$a^2 = 4, a = 2$

x-intercepts: $(-2,0),(2,0)$

$b^2 = 16, b = 4$

Sketch a dashed rectangle that contains the points $(-2,0),(2,0),(0,-4),$ and

$(0,4)$, and then sketch the inclined asymptotes.

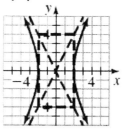

iii. $\frac{x^2}{c} + \frac{y^2}{d} = 1$

$$\frac{y^2}{16} - \frac{x^2}{4} = 1$$

Hyperbola

$b^2 = 16, b = 4$

y-intercepts: $(0,-4),(0,4)$

$a^2 = 4, a = 2$

Sketch a dashed rectangle that contains the points $(-2,0),(2,0),(0,-4),$ and

$(0,4)$, and then sketch the inclined asymptotes.

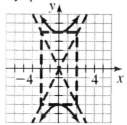

iv. $\frac{x^2}{c} + \frac{y^2}{d} = 1$

$$\frac{x^2}{4} + \frac{y^2}{4} = 1$$

Circle

$a^2 = 4, a = 2$

x-intercepts: $(-2,0),(2,0)$

$b^2 = 4, b = 2$

y-intercepts: $(0,-2),(0,2)$

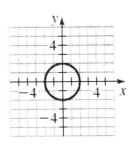

b. If $c > 0$ and $d > 0$ and $c \neq d$, then the graph is an ellipse.
If $c > 0$ and $d < 0$, then the graph is a hyperbola with x-intercepts.
If $c < 0$ and $d > 0$, then the graph is a hyperbola with y-intercepts.
If $c = d$ and $c > 0$, then the graph is a circle.

55. a. $4x^2 + 25y^2 = 100$

$$\frac{4x^2}{100} + \frac{25y^2}{100} = 1$$

$$\frac{x^2}{25} + \frac{y^2}{4} = 1$$

Ellipse
$a^2 = 25, a = 5$
x-intercepts: $(-5, 0), (5, 0)$
$b^2 = 4, b = 2$
y-intercepts: $(0, -2), (0, 2)$

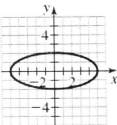

b. Answers may vary.

x	y
-5	0
-2	$\sqrt{3.36} \approx 1.83$
-2	$-\sqrt{3.36} \approx -1.83$
0	2
0	-2
2	$\sqrt{3.36} \approx 1.83$
2	$-\sqrt{3.36} \approx -1.83$
5	0

c. For each input-output pair, the sum of the square of the input divided by 25 and the square of the output divided by 4 is 1.

57. a. $y = \frac{5}{2}\sqrt{4 - x^2}$

Answers may vary. The square root of a nonnegative number is a nonnegative real number and the square root of a negative number is an imaginary number. Since $\frac{5}{2}$ is positive, $\frac{5}{2}\sqrt{4 - x^2}$ is nonnegative for real values of y. Thus, $y \geq 0$ for real number values of y.

b.

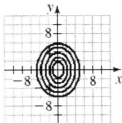

59. Answers may vary. Possible answer:

$$\frac{x^2}{a^2} + \frac{y^2}{b^2} = 1$$

To keep the ellipses from intersecting, we increase the value of a and b for each equation. Some possible equations:

$$\frac{x^2}{1} + \frac{y^2}{4} = 1, \frac{x^2}{4} + \frac{y^2}{9} = 1,$$

$$\frac{x^2}{9} + \frac{y^2}{16} = 1, \frac{x^2}{16} + \frac{y^2}{25} = 1,$$

$$\frac{x^2}{25} + \frac{y^2}{36} = 1$$

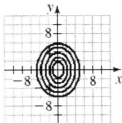

61. $x^2 + y^2 = r^2$

$$\frac{x^2}{r^2} + \frac{y^2}{r^2} = \frac{r^2}{r^2}$$

$$\frac{x^2}{r^2} + \frac{y^2}{r^2} = 1$$

Ellipse

Since $a^2 = b^2 = r^2$, it is also a circle. (Note that all circles are ellipses just as all squares are rectangles.

63. a.

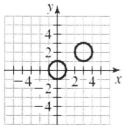

To get the graph of $(x-3)^2 + (y-2)^2 = 1$, translate the graph of $x^2 + y^2 = 1$ rightward by 3 units and upward by 2 units.

b.

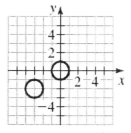

To get the graph of $(x+3)^2 + (y+2)^2 = 1$, translate the graph of $x^2 + y^2 = 1$ leftward by 3 units and downward by 2 units.

c. Translate the graph of $x^2 + y^2 = r^2$ by h units to the right if $h > 0$ or by $|h|$ units to the left if $h < 0$, then by k units up if $k > 0$ or by $|k|$ units down if $k < 0$.

d.

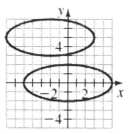

e.

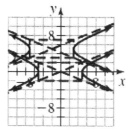

65. $y = \log_2(x)$

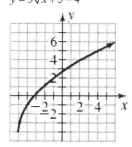

67. $y = 3\sqrt{x+5} - 4$

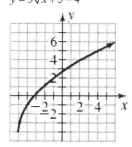

69. No, the relation is not a function. Answers may vary. The graph of $\dfrac{x^2}{4} + \dfrac{y^2}{81} = 1$ is an ellipse, which does not pass the vertical line test.

71.
$$y = 2x^2 - 8x + 3$$
$$y = 2(x^2 - 4x) + 3$$
$$y = 2(x^2 - 4x + 4) + 3 - 8$$
$$y = 2(x-2)^2 - 5$$

$y = 2x^2 - 8x + 3$ is a quadratic function.

73.
$$2x^2 - 8x + 3 = 0$$
$$\frac{-b \pm \sqrt{b^2 - 4ac}}{2a} = \frac{8 \pm \sqrt{(-8)^2 - 4(2)(3)}}{2(2)}$$
$$= \frac{8 \pm \sqrt{64 - 24}}{4}$$
$$= \frac{8 \pm 2\sqrt{10}}{4}$$
$$= \frac{4 \pm \sqrt{10}}{2}$$

$2x^2 - 8x + 3 = 0$ is a quadratic equation in one variable.

75.
$$-5x(2x-1)(3x-1)$$
$$-5x(2x \cdot 3x - 1(2x) - 1(3x) - 1(-1))$$
$$-5x(6x^2 - 5x + 1)$$
$$-30x^3 + 25x^2 - 5x$$
$-5x(2x-1)(3x-1)$ is a cubic polynomial in one variable.

Quiz 11.5

1.
$$\frac{x^2}{9} + \frac{y^2}{25} = 1$$
$$a^2 = 9, a = 3$$
x-intercepts: $(-3,0),(3,0)$
$$b^2 = 25, b = 5$$
y-intercepts: $(0,-5),(0,5)$

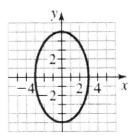

2.
$$\frac{y^2}{49} - \frac{x^2}{9} = 1$$
$$b^2 = 49, b = 7$$
y-intercepts: $(0,-7),(0,7)$
$$a^2 = 9, a = 3$$
Sketch a dashed rectangle that contains the points $(-3,0),(3,0),(0,-7)$, and $(0,7)$, and then sketch the inclined asymptotes.

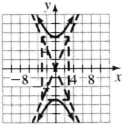

3.
$$4x^2 - y^2 = 16$$
$$\frac{4x^2}{16} - \frac{y^2}{16} = \frac{16}{16}$$
$$\frac{x^2}{4} - \frac{y^2}{16} = 1$$
$$a^2 = 4, a = 2$$
x-intercepts: $(-2,0),(2,0)$
$$b^2 = 16, b = 4$$
Sketch a dashed rectangle that contains the points $(-2,0),(2,0),(0,-4)$, and $(0,4)$, and then sketch the inclined asymptotes.

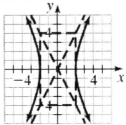

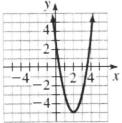

4.
$$16x^2 + 3y^2 = 48$$
$$\frac{16x^2}{48} + \frac{3y^2}{48} = \frac{48}{48}$$
$$\frac{x^2}{3} + \frac{y^2}{16} = 1$$
$$a^2 = 3, a = \sqrt{3}$$
x-intercepts: $\left(-\sqrt{3}, 0\right), \left(\sqrt{3}, 0\right)$
$$b^2 = 16, b = 4$$
y-intercepts: $(0, -4), (0, 4)$

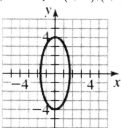

5.
$$x^2 - 9y^2 = 81$$
$$\frac{x^2}{81} - \frac{9y^2}{81} = 1$$
$$\frac{x^2}{81} - \frac{y^2}{9} = 1$$
$$a^2 = 81, a = 9$$
x-intercepts: $(-9, 0), (9, 0)$
$$b^2 = 9, b = 3$$
Sketch a dashed rectangle that contains the points $(-9, 0), (9, 0), (0, -3)$, and $(0, 3)$, and then sketch the inclined asymptotes.

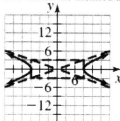

6.
$$4y^2 - 4x^2 = 16$$
$$\frac{4y^2}{16} - \frac{4x^2}{16} = \frac{16}{16}$$
$$\frac{y^2}{4} - \frac{x^2}{4} = 1$$
$$b^2 = 4, b = 2$$

y-intercepts: $(0, -2), (0, 2)$
$$a^2 = 4, a = 2$$
Sketch a dashed rectangle that contains the points $(-2, 0), (2, 0), (0, -2)$, and $(0, 2)$, and then sketch the inclined asymptotes.

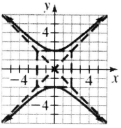

7.
$$\frac{x^2}{5} + \frac{y^2}{14} = 1$$
$$a^2 = 5, a = \sqrt{5}$$
x-intercepts: $\left(-\sqrt{5}, 0\right), \left(\sqrt{5}, 0\right)$
$$b^2 = 14, b = \sqrt{14}$$
y-intercepts: $\left(0, -\sqrt{14}\right), \left(0, \sqrt{14}\right)$

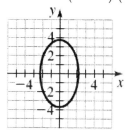

8.
$$\frac{x^2}{8} + \frac{y^2}{3} = 1$$
$$a^2 = 8, a = 2\sqrt{2}$$
x-intercepts: $\left(-2\sqrt{2}, 0\right), \left(2\sqrt{2}, 0\right)$
$$b^2 = 3, b = \sqrt{3}$$
y-intercepts: $\left(0, -\sqrt{3}\right), \left(0, \sqrt{3}\right)$

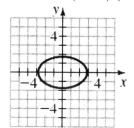

9.
No. The graph of $\dfrac{x^2}{9} - \dfrac{y^2}{4} = 1$ is a hyperbola. The graph fails the vertical line test.

10.
Answers will vary. The points $(0,3)$ and $(0,-3)$ are y-intercepts. An ellipse with these y-intercepts has the form $\dfrac{x^2}{a^2} + \dfrac{y^2}{9} = 1$. Three possibilities: let $a = 1, 2,$ and 4.

$$\dfrac{x^2}{1} + \dfrac{y^2}{9} = 1$$

$$\dfrac{x^2}{4} + \dfrac{y^2}{9} = 1$$

$$\dfrac{x^2}{16} + \dfrac{y^2}{9} = 1$$

Homework 11.6

1.
$$x^2 + y^2 = 25$$
$$4x^2 + 25y^2 = 100$$

The two intersection points $(-5,0)$ and $(5,0)$ are the solutions to the system.
Solve using elimination:
$$-4x^2 - 4y^2 = -100$$
$$\underline{4x^2 + 25y^2 = 100}$$
$$21y^2 = 0$$
$$y^2 = 0$$
$$y = 0$$

Let $y = 0$ in $x^2 + y^2 = 25$ and solve for x.
$$x^2 + 0^2 = 25$$
$$x^2 = 25$$
$$x = \pm 5$$
The solutions are $(-5,0)$ and $(5,0)$.

3.
$$y = x^2 + 1$$
$$y = -x + 3$$

The two intersection points $(-2,5)$ and $(1,2)$ are solutions of the system.
Solve using substitution.
Substitute $x^2 + 1$ for y in the second equation.
$$y = -x + 3$$
$$x^2 + 1 = -x + 3$$
$$x^2 + x - 2 = 0$$
$$(x+2)(x-1) = 0$$
$$x + 2 = 0 \text{ or } x - 1 = 0$$
$$x = -2 \text{ or } x = 1$$
Let $x = -2$ and $x = 1$ in $y = -x + 3$ and solve for y.
$$y = -(-2) + 3 \qquad y = -(1) + 3$$
$$= 2 + 3 \qquad\qquad = -1 + 3$$
$$= 5 \qquad\qquad\quad = 2$$
The solutions are $(-2,5)$ and $(1,2)$.

5.
$$y = x^2 - 2$$
$$y = -x^2 + 6$$
The two intersection points $(2,2)$ and $(-2,2)$ are solutions of the system.
Solve using substitution.
Substitute $x^2 - 2$ for y in the second equation.
$$y = -x^2 + 6$$
$$x^2 - 2 = -x^2 + 6$$
$$2x^2 = 8$$
$$x^2 = 4$$
$$x = \pm 2$$
Let $x = -2$ and $x = 2$ in $y = x^2 - 2$ and solve for y.
$$y = (-2)^2 - 2 \qquad y = (2)^2 - 2$$
$$= 4 - 2 \qquad\qquad = 4 - 2$$
$$= 2 \qquad\qquad\quad = 2$$
The solutions are $(-2,2)$ and $(2,2)$.

7.
$$x^2 + y^2 = 49$$
$$x^2 + y^2 = 16$$
The graphs do not intersect. The solution set is the empty set.
Solve using elimination.
$$x^2 + y^2 = 49$$
$$\underline{-x^2 - y^2 = -16}$$
$$0 = 33 \quad \text{False}$$
There is no solution.

9. $x^2 + y^2 = 25$

$y = -x - 1$

The two intersection points $(-4, 3)$ and $(3, -4)$ are solutions of the system.

Solve using substitution.

Substitute $-x - 1$ for y in the first equation.

$x^2 + y^2 = 25$

$x^2 + (-x - 1)^2 = 25$

$x^2 + x^2 + 2x + 1 = 25$

$2x^2 + 2x - 24 = 0$

$x^2 + x - 12 = 0$

$(x + 4)(x - 3) = 0$

$x + 4 = 0$ or $x - 3 = 0$

$x = -4$ or $x = 3$

Let $x = -4$ and $x = 3$ in $y = -x - 1$ and solve for y.

$y = -(-4) - 1 \qquad y = -(3) - 1$

$\quad = 4 - 1 \qquad\qquad = -3 - 1$

$\quad = 3 \qquad\qquad\quad = -4$

The solutions are $(-4, 3)$ and $(3, -4)$.

11. $y^2 - x^2 = 16$

$y + x^2 = 4$

The three intersection points $(-3, -5)$, $(0, 4)$, and $(3, -5)$ are the solutions to the system.

Solve using elimination.

$y^2 - x^2 = 16$

$\underline{y + x^2 = 4}$

$y^2 + y = 20$

$y^2 + y - 20 = 0$

$(y + 5)(y - 4) = 0$

$y + 5 = 0$ or $y - 4 = 0$

$y = -5$ or $y = 4$

Let $y = -5$ and $y = 4$ in $y + x^2 = 4$ and solve for x.

$-5 + x^2 = 4 \qquad 4 + x^2 = 4$

$\quad x^2 = 9 \qquad\qquad x^2 = 0$

$\quad x = \pm 3 \qquad\qquad x = 0$

The solutions are $(-3, -5)$, $(3, -5)$, and $(0, 4)$.

13. $25x^2 - 9y^2 = 225$

$4x^2 + 9y^2 = 36$

The two intersection points $(-3, 0)$ and $(3, 0)$ are solutions of the system.

Solve using elimination.

$25x^2 - 9y^2 = 225$

$\underline{4x^2 + 9y^2 = 36}$

$29x^2 = 261$

$x^2 = 9$

$x = \pm 3$

Let $x = -3$ and $x = 3$ in $4x^2 + 9y^2 = 36$ and solve for y.

$4(-3)^2 + 9y^2 = 36 \qquad 4(3)^2 + 9y^2 = 36$

$\quad 36 + 9y^2 = 36 \qquad\qquad 36 + 9y^2 = 36$

$\quad\quad 9y^2 = 0 \qquad\qquad\qquad 9y^2 = 0$

$\quad\quad\quad y^2 = 0 \qquad\qquad\qquad\quad y^2 = 0$

$\quad\quad\quad\quad y = 0 \qquad\qquad\qquad\qquad y = 0$

The solutions are $(-3, 0)$ and $(3, 0)$.

15. $9x^2 + y^2 = 9$

$y = 3x + 3$

The two intersection points $(-1, 0)$ and $(0, 3)$ are solutions of the system.

Solve using substitution.

Substitute $3x + 3$ for y in the first equation.

$9x^2 + y^2 = 9$

$9x^2 + (3x + 3)^2 = 9$

$9x^2 + 9x^2 + 18x + 9 = 9$

$18x^2 + 18x = 0$

$18x(x + 1) = 0$

$18x = 0$ or $x + 1 = 0$

$x = 0$ or $x = -1$

Let $x = 0$ and $x = -1$ in $y = 3x + 3$ and solve for y.

$y = 3(0) + 3 \qquad y = 3(-1) + 3$

$\quad = 0 + 3 \qquad\qquad = -3 + 3$

$\quad = 3 \qquad\qquad\quad = 0$

The solutions are $(0,3)$ and $(-1,0)$.

17.
$$4x^2 + 9y^2 = 36$$
$$16x^2 + 25y^2 = 225$$
The graphs do not intersect. The solution set is the empty set.
Solve using elimination.
$$-16x^2 - 36y^2 = -144$$
$$16x^2 + 25y^2 = 225$$
$$-11y^2 = 81$$
$$y^2 = -\frac{81}{11}$$
Since y^2 cannot be negative (in the real number system), there is no solution.

19.
$$y = \sqrt{x} - 3$$
$$y = -x - 1$$
The intersection point $(1,-2)$ is the solution to the system.
Solve using substitution.
Substitute $\sqrt{x} - 3$ for y in the second equation.
$$y = -x - 1$$
$$\sqrt{x} - 3 = -x - 1$$
$$\sqrt{x} = -x + 2$$
$$\left(\sqrt{x}\right)^2 = (-x + 2)^2$$
$$x = x^2 - 4x + 4$$
$$x^2 - 5x + 4 = 0$$
$$(x - 4)(x - 1) = 0$$
$$x - 4 = 0 \text{ or } x - 1 = 0$$
$$x = 4 \text{ or } x = 1$$
Let $x = 4$ and $x = 1$ in $y = \sqrt{x} - 3$ and solve for y.
$$y = \sqrt{4} - 3 \qquad y = \sqrt{1} - 3$$
$$= 2 - 3 \qquad\quad = 1 - 3$$
$$= -1 \qquad\qquad = -2$$
Check each result in $y = -x - 1$.
$$-1 = -(4) - 1 \qquad -2 = -1 - 1$$
$$-1 = -5 \text{ False} \qquad -2 = -2 \text{ True}$$
The only solution is $(1,-2)$.

21.
$$y = 2x^2 - 5$$
$$y = x^2 - 2$$
The two intersection points $\left(-\sqrt{3},1\right)$ and $\left(\sqrt{3},1\right)$ are solutions of the system.
Solve using substitution.
Substitute $2x^2 - 5$ for y in the second equation.
$$y = x^2 - 2$$
$$2x^2 - 5 = x^2 - 2$$
$$x^2 = 3$$
$$x = \pm\sqrt{3}$$
Let $x = -\sqrt{3}$ and $x = \sqrt{3}$ in $y = x^2 - 2$ and solve for y.
$$y = \left(-\sqrt{3}\right)^2 - 2 \qquad y = \left(\sqrt{3}\right)^2 - 2$$
$$= 3 - 2 \qquad\qquad = 3 - 2$$
$$= 1 \qquad\qquad\quad = 1$$
The solutions are $\left(-\sqrt{3},1\right)$ and $\left(\sqrt{3},1\right)$.

23.
$$25y^2 - 4x^2 = 100$$
$$9x^2 + y^2 = 9$$
The four intersection points $(-0.74,-2.02)$, $(-0.74,2.02)$, $(0.74,-2.02)$, and $(0.74,2.02)$ are solutions of the system.
Solve using substitution.
$$9x^2 + y^2 = 9$$
$$y^2 = 9 - 9x^2$$
Substitute $9 - 9x^2$ for y^2 in the first equation.
$$25y^2 - 4x^2 = 100$$
$$25(9 - 9x^2) - 4x^2 = 100$$
$$225 - 225x^2 - 4x^2 = 100$$
$$-229x^2 = -125$$
$$x^2 = \frac{125}{229}$$
$$x = \pm\sqrt{\frac{125}{229}} \approx \pm 0.74$$
Let $x = -0.74$ and $x = 0.74$ in $9x^2 + y^2 = 9$ and solve for y.

$$9(\;0.74)^2 + y^2 - 9$$
$$y^2 = 4.07$$
$$y = \pm\sqrt{4.07} \approx \pm 2.02$$
$$9(0.74)^2 + y^2 = 9$$
$$y^2 = 4.07$$
$$y = \pm\sqrt{4.07} \approx \pm 2.02$$

The solutions are $(-0.74, -2.02)$, $(-0.74, 2.02)$, $(0.74, -2.02)$, and $(0.74, 2.02)$.

25.
$$25x^2 + 9y^2 = 225$$
$$x^2 + y^2 = 16$$

The four intersection points $(-2.25, -3.31)$, $(-2.25, 3.31)$, $(2.25, -3.31)$, and $(2.25, 3.31)$ are solutions of the system.
Solve using elimination.

$$25x^2 + 9y^2 = 225$$
$$\underline{-9x^2 - 9y^2 = -144}$$
$$16x^2 = 81$$
$$x^2 = \frac{81}{16}$$
$$x = \pm\frac{9}{4}$$
$$x = \pm 2.25$$

Let $x = -2.25$ and $x = 2.25$ in $x^2 + y^2 = 16$ and solve for y.
$$(-2.25)^2 + y^2 = 16$$
$$y^2 = 10.9375$$
$$y = \pm 3.31$$
$$(2.25)^2 + y^2 = 16$$
$$y^2 = 10.9375$$
$$y = \pm 3.31$$

The solutions are $(-2.25, -3.31)$, $(-2.25, 3.31)$, $(2.25, -3.31)$, and $(2.25, 3.31)$.

27.
$$9x^2 + y^2 = 85$$
$$2x^2 - 3y^2 = 6$$

Solve using elimination.
$$27x^2 + 3y^2 = 255$$
$$\underline{2x^2 - 3y^2 = 6}$$
$$29x^2 = 261$$
$$x^2 = 9$$
$$x = \pm 3$$

Let $x = -3$ and $x = 3$ in $9x^2 + y^2 = 85$ and solve for y.
$$9(-3)^2 + y^2 = 85 \qquad 9(3)^2 + y^2 = 85$$
$$81 + y^2 = 85 \qquad\quad 81 + y^2 = 85$$
$$y^2 = 4 \qquad\qquad\quad y^2 = 4$$
$$y = \pm 2 \qquad\qquad\quad y = \pm 2$$

The four solutions are $(-3, -2)$, $(-3, 2)$, $(3, -2)$, and $(3, 2)$. Each result satisfies both equations.

29.
$$4y^2 + x^2 = 25$$
$$y = -x + 5$$

Solve using substitution.
Substitute $-x + 5$ for y in the first equation.
$$4y^2 + x^2 = 25$$
$$4(-x + 5)^2 + x^2 = 25$$
$$4(x^2 - 10x + 25) + x^2 = 25$$
$$4x^2 - 40x + 100 + x^2 = 25$$
$$5x^2 - 40x + 75 = 0$$
$$x^2 - 8x + 15 = 0$$
$$(x - 5)(x - 3) = 0$$
$$x - 5 = 0 \text{ or } x - 3 = 0$$
$$x = 5 \text{ or } x = 3$$

Let $x = 5$ and $x = 3$ in $y = -x + 5$ and solve for y.
$$y = -(5) + 5 \qquad y = -(3) + 5$$
$$= -5 + 5 \qquad\quad = -3 + 5$$
$$= 0 \qquad\qquad\quad = 2$$

The solutions are $(3, 2)$ and $(5, 0)$. Each result satisfies both equations.

31.
$$y = x^2 - 3x + 2$$
$$y = 2x - 4$$

Solve using substitution.
Substitute $2x - 4$ for y in the first equation.

$$y = x^2 - 3x + 2$$
$$2x - 4 = x^2 - 3x + 2$$
$$x^2 - 5x + 6 = 0$$
$$(x-3)(x-2) = 0$$
$$x - 3 = 0 \text{ or } x - 2 = 0$$
$$x = 3 \text{ or } x = 2$$

Let $x = 3$ and $x = 2$ in $y = 2x - 4$ and solve for y.

$$\begin{array}{ll} y = 2(3) - 4 & y = 2(2) - 4 \\ \quad = 6 - 4 & \quad = 4 - 4 \\ \quad = 2 & \quad = 0 \end{array}$$

The solutions are $(3, 2)$ and $(2, 0)$. Each result satisfies both equations.

33.
$$x^2 + y^2 = 25$$
$$4x^2 - 25y^2 = 100$$
$$4x^2 + 25y^2 = 100$$

The two intersection points for all three graphs are $(-5, 0)$ and $(5, 0)$. These are the solutions to the system. Each result satisfies all three equations.

35. Answers may vary. One possible answer:
$$x^2 + y^2 = 16$$
$$x^2 - y^2 = 16$$

37.
$$2x^2 + cy^2 = 82$$
$$y = x^2 + dx + 5$$

Substitute $(1, 4)$ into each equation.

$$\begin{array}{ll} 2(1)^2 + c(4)^2 = 82 & 4 = (1)^2 + d(1) + 5 \\ 2 + 16c = 82 & 4 = 1 + d + 5 \\ 16c = 80 & d = -2 \\ c = 5 & \end{array}$$

39. Answers may vary. Graph each of the equations on the same coordinate plane, then find the points of intersection. These points are the solutions to the system.

41.
$$y = 2^x$$
$$y = 4\left(\frac{1}{2}\right)^x$$

Solve by substitution.

Substitute 2^x for y in the second equation.

$$2^x = 4\left(\frac{1}{2}\right)^x$$
$$2^x = 2^2 \left(2^{-1}\right)^x$$
$$2^x = 2^2 \left(2^{-x}\right)$$
$$2^x = 2^{2-x}$$
$$x = 2 - x$$
$$x = 1$$

Let $x = 1$ in $y = 2^x$ and solve for y.

$$y = 2^1$$
$$y = 2$$

The solution is $(1, 2)$

43. Answers may vary.
$$y = -2x + 9$$

45. Answers may vary.
$$\frac{5x - 7}{2x + 2} = 4$$
$$5x - 7 = 4(2x + 2)$$
$$5x - 7 = 8x + 8$$
$$-3x = 15$$
$$x = -5$$

47. Answers may vary.
$$y = 3^x$$

49. Answers may vary.
$$y = x^2 - 6x + 7$$

51. Answers may vary.
$$2x^2 + 8x - 10 = 0$$
$$2\left(x^2 + 4x - 5\right) = 0$$
$$2(x + 5)(x - 1) = 0$$
$$x + 5 = 0$$
$$x = -5$$
$$x - 1 = 0$$
$$x = 1$$

The solutions are -5 and 1.

Quiz 11.6

1. $9x^2 + y^2 = 81$

    $x^2 + y^2 = 9$

    The two intersection points $(-3,0)$ and $(3,0)$ are the solutions to the system.
    Solve using elimination.

    $9x^2 + y^2 = 81$

    $\underline{-9x^2 - 9y^2 = -81}$

    $\qquad -8y^2 = 0$

    $\qquad\quad y^2 = 0$

    $\qquad\quad\; y = 0$

    Let $y = 0$ in $x^2 + y^2 = 9$ and solve for x.

    $x^2 + y^2 = 9$

    $x^2 + 0^2 = 9$

    $\qquad x^2 = 9$

    $\qquad\; x = \pm 3$

    The solutions are $(-3,0)$ and $(3,0)$.

2. $y = x^2 - 2$

    $y = -2x + 1$

    The two intersection points $(1,-1)$ and $(-3,7)$ are the solutions to the system.
    Solve using substitution.
    Substitute $x^2 - 2$ for y in the second equation.

    $y = -2x + 1$

    $x^2 - 2 = -2x + 1$

    $x^2 + 2x - 3 = 0$

    $(x+3)(x-1) = 0$

    $x + 3 = 0$ or $x - 1 = 0$

    $\quad x = -3$ or $\quad x = 1$

    Let $x = -3$ and $x = 1$ in $y = -2x + 1$ and solve for y.

    $y = -2(-3)+1 \qquad y = -2(1)+1$

    $\quad = 6 + 1 \qquad\qquad = -2 + 1$

    $\quad = 7 \qquad\qquad\quad\; = -1$

    The solutions are $(-3,7)$ and $(1,-1)$.

3. $y = x^2 + 3$

    $y = x^2 - 6x + 9$

The intersection point $(1,4)$ is the solution to the system.
Solve using substitution.
Substitute $x^2 + 3$ for y in the second equation.

$y = x^2 - 6x + 9$

$x^2 + 3 = x^2 - 6x + 9$

$6x - 6 = 0$

$x - 1 = 0$

$\quad x = 1$

Let $x = 1$ in $y = x^2 + 3$ and solve for y.

$y = (1)^2 + 3$

$\quad = 1 + 3$

$\quad = 4$

The solution is $(1,4)$.

4. $25x^2 - 4y^2 = 100$

    $9x^2 + y^2 = 9$

    The graphs do not intersect. There are no solutions to the system.
    Solve using elimination.

    $225x^2 - 36y^2 = 900$

    $\underline{-225x^2 - 25y^2 = -225}$

    $\qquad\quad -61y^2 = 675$

    $\qquad\qquad y^2 = -\dfrac{675}{61}$

    Since y^2 must be nonnegative (in the real number system), there are no solutions to the system. The solution set is the empty set.

5. $x^2 - y^2 = 16$

    $x^2 + y^2 = 16$

    $\qquad y = (x+4)^2$

    The intersection point of all three graphs is $(-4,0)$. This is the solution of the system.

6. Answers may vary. One possible answer:

    $x^2 + y^2 = 25$

    $\qquad y = x^2 + 5$

Appendix A

Section A.1

1.

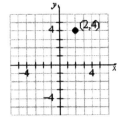

2.

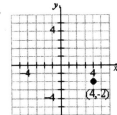

3.

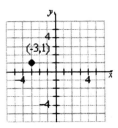

4.

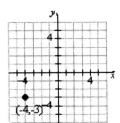

5.

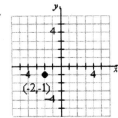

6.

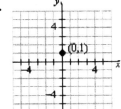

7.

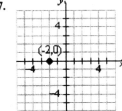

8.

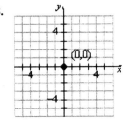

Section A.2

1. 4 and 85 are counting numbers.

2. 4, 0, −2, and 85 are integers.

3. $\frac{2}{9}$, 4, −7.19, 0, −2, and 85 are rational numbers.

4. $\sqrt{17}$ is an irrational number.

5. $\frac{2}{9}$, 4, −7.19, 0, −2, $\sqrt{17}$, and 85 are real numbers.

Section A.3

1. $\left|-3\right| = 3$

2. $|4.69| = 4.69$

3. $|0| = 0$

4. $|-\pi| = \pi$

Section A.4

1. $-3(7) = -21$

2. $5(-6) = -30$

3. $-9(-4) = 36$

4. $-8(-2) = 16$

5. $-(-4) = (-1)(-4)$
$\qquad = 4$

6. $-(-(-9)) = -((-1)(-9))$
$\qquad = (-1)(-1)(-9)$
$\qquad = -9$

7. $\dfrac{8}{-2} = (-1)\left(\dfrac{8}{2}\right)$
$\qquad = -4$

8. $\dfrac{-6}{-2} = \dfrac{6}{2}$
$\qquad = 3$

9. $-3 + (-5) = -8$

10. $-6 + (-7) = -13$

11. $2 + (-8) = -6$

12. $-7 + 3 = -4$

13. $-1 + 6 = 5$

14. $8 + (-3) = 5$

15. $-4 + (-6) = -10$

16. $-2 + (-3) = -5$

17. $3 - 7 = 3 + (-7)$
$\qquad = -4$

18. $2 - 8 = 2 + (-8)$
$\qquad = -6$

19. $5 - (-3) = 5 + (-(-3))$
$\qquad = 5 + 3$
$\qquad = 8$

20. $9 - (-4) = 9 + (-(-4))$
$\qquad = 9 + 4$
$\qquad = 13$

21. $-4 - 9 = -4 + (-9)$
$\qquad = -13$

22. $-2 - 4 = -2 + (-4)$
$\qquad = -6$

23. $-1 - (-1) = -1 + (-(-1))$
$\qquad = -1 + 1$
$\qquad = 0$

24. $-10 - (-6) = -10 + (-(-6))$
$\qquad = -10 + 6$
$\qquad = -4$

Section A.5

1. $7^2 = 7 \cdot 7$
$\qquad = 49$

2. $9^2 = 9 \cdot 9$
$\qquad = 81$

3. $6^3 = 6 \cdot 6 \cdot 6$
$\qquad = 216$

4. $5^4 = 5 \cdot 5 \cdot 5 \cdot 5$
$\qquad = 625$

5. $(-2)^4 = (-2)(-2)(-2)(-2)$
$= 16$

6. $(-3)^3 = (-3)(-3)(-3)$
$= -27$

7. $-2^4 = -(2 \cdot 2 \cdot 2 \cdot 2)$
$= -16$

8. $-3^3 = -(3 \cdot 3 \cdot 3)$
$= -27$

Section A.6

1. $3 + 5 \cdot 2 = 3 + 10$
$= 13$

2. $2(8) - 4 = 16 - 4$
$= 12$

3. $2 + 10 \div (-5) = 2 + (-2)$
$= 0$

4. $14 \div (-2) - 1 = -7 - 1$
$= -8$

5. $2(1-3) + 4 \cdot 2 = 2(-2) + 8$
$= -4 + 8$
$= 4$

6. $10(2-7) + 5 \cdot 4 = 10(-5) + 20$
$= -50 + 20$
$= -30$

7. $(5-9)(4+2) \div 8 + 2 = (-4)(6) \div 8 + 2$
$= -24 \div 8 + 2$
$= -3 + 2$
$= -1$

8. $(3+5)(2-6) \div 4 + 1 = (8)(-4) \div 4 + 1$
$= -32 \div 4 + 1$
$= -8 + 1$
$= -7$

9. $4(3)^2 = 4(9)$
$= 36$

10. $-3(2)^3 = -3(8)$
$= -24$

11. $-3^2 + (-3)^2 - (-3)^2 = -9 + 9 - 9$
$= -9$

12. $2^3 - (-2)^3 + (-2)^3 = 8 - (-8) + (-8)$
$= 8$

13. $5 - 4^2 + (-8) \div (-2) = 5 - 16 + 4$
$= -7$

14. $2^3 - 10 \div (-5) + 1 = 8 - (-2) + 1$
$= 11$

15. $6 - (3-1)^3 + 8 = 6 - (2)^3 + 8$
$= 6 - 8 + 8$
$= 6$

16. $10 - (9-6)^3 + 5 = 10 - (3)^3 + 5$
$= 10 - 27 + 5$
$= -12$

Section A.7

1. $y = mx + b$ is an equation.

2. $3x^2 - 5x + 4 = 8$ is an equation.

3. $2x - 5\pi + 1$ is an expression.

4. $x^3 - 8$ is an expression.

Section A.8

1. $2(x+4) = 2x + 2(4)$
$= 2x + 8$

2. $4(x+7) = 4x + 4(7)$
$= 4x + 28$

3.
$$6(2t \quad 3) = 6(2t) + 6(-3)$$
$$= 12t - 18$$

4.
$$5(4w - 6) = 5(4w) + 5(-6)$$
$$= 20w - 30$$

5.
$$(x + 8)(-3) = -3x + 8(-3)$$
$$= -3x - 24$$

6.
$$(x + 5)(-4) = -4x + 5(-4)$$
$$= -4x - 20$$

7.
$$(2x - 9)(-5) = -10x - 9(-5)$$
$$= -10x + 45$$

8.
$$(3x - 1)(-6) = -18x - 1(-6)$$
$$= -18x + 6$$

9.
$$2.8(p + 4.1) = 2.8p + 2.8(4.1)$$
$$= 2.8p + 11.48$$

10.
$$-5.2(b + 3.9) = -5.2b - 5.2(3.9)$$
$$= -5.2b - 20.28$$

Section A.9

1.
$$4x + 3x = (4 + 3)x$$
$$= 7x$$

2.
$$7x - 2x = (7 - 2)x$$
$$= 5x$$

3.
$$5x - 9y - 3x + 2y = 5x - 3x - 9y + 2y$$
$$= (5 - 3)x + (-9 + 2)y$$
$$= 2x - 7y$$

4.
$$8x - 4y - 6x + 5y = 8x - 6x - 4y + 5y$$
$$= (8 - 6)x + (-4 + 5)y$$
$$= 2x + y$$

5.
$$7a - 4 + b - 9a - 3b + 2$$
$$= 7a - 9a + b - 3b - 4 + 2$$
$$= (7 - 9)a + (1 - 3)b - 2$$
$$= -2a - 2b - 2$$

6.
$$4t - 2w + 5 + t - 1 - 8w$$
$$= 4t + t - 2w - 8w + 5 - 1$$
$$= (4 + 1)t + (-2 - 8)w + 4$$
$$= 5t - 10w + 4$$

7.
$$4(2x + 3) + 5(4x - 1) = 8x + 12 + 20x - 5$$
$$= 8x + 20x + 12 - 5$$
$$= (8 + 20)x + 7$$
$$= 28x + 7$$

8.
$$5(3x + 2) + 2(3x + 6) = 15x + 10 + 6x + 12$$
$$= 15x + 6x + 10 + 12$$
$$= (15 + 6)x + 22$$
$$= 21x + 22$$

9.
$$2(5x - y) - 3(4x + y)$$
$$= 10x - 2y - 12x - 3y$$
$$= 10x - 12x - 2y - 3y$$
$$= (10 - 12)x + (-2 - 3)y$$
$$= -2x - 5y$$

10.
$$3(4x - y) - 5(2x + y)$$
$$= 12x - 3y - 10x - 5y$$
$$= 12x - 10x - 3y - 5y$$
$$= (12 - 10)x + (-3 - 5)y$$
$$= 2x - 8y$$

11.
$$10 - (3m - 2n) + 4m - 7n$$
$$= 10 - 3m + 2n + 4m - 7n$$
$$= 10 - 3m + 4m + 2n - 7n$$
$$= 10 + (-3 + 4)m + (2 - 7)n$$
$$= m - 5n + 10$$

12.
$$6 - (6a - 3b) - 5b + 2a$$
$$= 6 - 6a + 3b - 5b + 2a$$
$$= 6 - 6a + 2a + 3b - 5b$$
$$= 6 + (-6 + 2)a + (3 - 5)b$$
$$= -4a - 2b + 6$$

Section A.10

1.
$$x + 5 = 9$$
$$x + 5 - 5 = 9 - 5$$
$$x = 4$$

2.
$$x - 3 = 4$$
$$x - 3 + 3 = 4 + 3$$
$$x = 7$$

3.
$$4x = 12$$
$$\frac{4x}{4} = \frac{12}{4}$$
$$x = 3$$

4.
$$-3x = 21$$
$$\frac{-3x}{-3} = \frac{21}{-3}$$
$$x = -7$$

5.
$$5(w - 3) = 13$$
$$5w - 15 = 13$$
$$5w - 15 + 15 = 13 + 15$$
$$\frac{5w}{5} = \frac{28}{5}$$
$$w = \frac{28}{5}$$

6.
$$-2(k - 4) = 5$$
$$-2k + 8 = 5$$
$$-2k + 8 - 8 = 5 - 8$$
$$\frac{-2k}{-2} = \frac{-3}{-2}$$
$$k = \frac{3}{2}$$

7.
$$2x + 5 = 6x - 3$$
$$2x + 5 - 5 = 6x - 3 - 5$$
$$2x - 6x = 6x - 6x - 8$$
$$\frac{-4x}{-4} = \frac{-8}{-4}$$
$$x = 2$$

8.
$$4x - 7 = 9x + 3$$
$$4x - 7 + 7 = 9x + 3 + 7$$
$$4x - 9x = 9x - 9x + 10$$
$$\frac{-5x}{-5} = \frac{10}{-5}$$
$$x = -2$$

9.
$$5 - 4(2x - 3) = 13$$
$$5 - 8x + 12 = 13$$
$$-8x + 17 - 17 = 13 - 17$$
$$\frac{-8x}{-8} = \frac{-4}{-8}$$
$$x = \frac{1}{2}$$

10.
$$7 - 2(3x + 5) = 19$$
$$7 - 6x - 10 = 19$$
$$-6x - 3 + 3 = 19 + 3$$
$$\frac{-6x}{-6} = \frac{22}{-6}$$
$$x = -\frac{11}{3}$$

11.
$$\frac{2}{3}t + \frac{1}{4} = \frac{5}{12}$$
$$12\left(\frac{2}{3}t + \frac{1}{4}\right) = 12\left(\frac{5}{12}\right)$$
$$12 \cdot \frac{2}{3}t + 12 \cdot \frac{1}{4} = 12 \cdot \frac{5}{12}$$
$$8t + 3 = 5$$
$$8t + 3 - 3 = 5 - 3$$
$$8t = 2$$
$$\frac{8t}{8} = \frac{2}{8}$$
$$t = \frac{1}{4}$$

12.
$$\frac{5}{9}w + \frac{1}{2} = \frac{7}{6}$$
$$\frac{5}{9}w + \frac{1}{2} - \frac{1}{2} = \frac{7}{6} - \frac{1}{2}$$

$$\frac{5}{9}w = \frac{2}{3}$$

$$\frac{5}{9}w\left(\frac{9}{5}\right) = \frac{2}{3}\left(\frac{9}{5}\right)$$

$$w = \frac{6}{5}$$

13.

$$\frac{5}{2}x - \frac{7}{4} = \frac{3}{8}x$$

$$\frac{5}{2}x - \frac{5}{2}x - \frac{7}{4} = \frac{3}{8}x - \frac{5}{2}x$$

$$-\frac{7}{4} = -\frac{17}{8}x$$

$$-\frac{7}{4}\left(-\frac{8}{17}\right) = -\frac{17}{8}x\left(-\frac{8}{17}\right)$$

$$\frac{14}{17} = x$$

14.

$$\frac{5}{3}x - \frac{7}{2} = \frac{11}{6}x$$

$$\frac{5}{3}x - \frac{5}{3}x - \frac{7}{2} = \frac{11}{6}x - \frac{5}{3}x$$

$$-\frac{7}{2} = \frac{1}{6}x$$

$$-\frac{7}{2}(6) = \frac{1}{6}x(6)$$

$$-21 = x$$

Section A.11

1.
$$2x + y = 8$$
$$y = -2x + 8$$

2.
$$3x - y = 5$$
$$-y = -3x + 5$$
$$y = 3x - 5$$

3.
$$3x - 5y = 15$$
$$3x = 15 + 5y$$
$$x = \frac{5}{3}y + 5$$

4.
$$3x - 5y = 15$$
$$-5y = 15 - 3x$$
$$y = \frac{3}{5}x - 3$$

5.
$$ax - by = c$$
$$-by = c - ax$$
$$y = \frac{ax - c}{b}$$

6.
$$ax - by = c$$
$$ax = by + c$$
$$x = \frac{by + c}{a}$$

7.
$$-4x + 3y = 2x + 9$$
$$-6x + 3y = 9$$
$$-6x = -3y + 9$$
$$\frac{-6x}{-6} = \frac{-3y}{-6} + \frac{9}{-6}$$
$$x = \frac{1}{2}y - \frac{3}{2}$$

8.
$$-4x + 3y = 2x + 9$$
$$3y = 6x + 9$$
$$\frac{3y}{3} = \frac{6x}{3} + \frac{9}{3}$$
$$y = 2x + 3$$

9.
$$\frac{1}{2}x - \frac{3}{4}y = \frac{5}{8}$$
$$8\left(\frac{1}{2}x - \frac{3}{4}y\right) = 8\left(\frac{5}{8}\right)$$
$$8 \cdot \frac{1}{2}x - 8 \cdot \frac{3}{4}y = 8 \cdot \frac{5}{8}$$
$$4x - 6y = 5$$
$$-6y = -4x + 5$$
$$y = \frac{2}{3}x - \frac{5}{6}$$

10.
$$\frac{3}{4}x - \frac{2}{3}y = \frac{1}{4}$$
$$12\left(\frac{3}{4}x - \frac{2}{3}y\right) = 12\left(\frac{1}{4}\right)$$
$$12 \cdot \frac{3}{4}x - 12 \cdot \frac{2}{3}y = 12 \cdot \frac{1}{4}$$
$$9x - 8y = 3$$
$$-8y = -9x + 3$$
$$y = \frac{9}{8}x - \frac{3}{8}$$

11.
$$\frac{x}{a}-\frac{y}{a}=1$$
$$x-y=a$$
$$x=y+a$$

12.
$$\frac{x}{a}-\frac{y}{a}=1$$
$$x-y=a$$
$$-y=a-x$$
$$y=x-a$$

Section A.12

1. Answers may vary.
$$5(x-4)=5\cdot x+5(-4)$$
$$=5x-20$$
The expressions are equivalent.

2. Answers may vary.
$$x+8=0$$
$$x+8-8=0-8$$
$$x=-8$$
The equations are equivalent.

3. Answers may vary.
$$4x-3x+8=x+8$$
$$-12x+8\neq x+8$$
The expressions are not equivalent.

4. Answers may vary.
$$3(x+1)+7=3x+3+7$$
$$=3x+10$$
$$3x+8\neq 3x+10$$
The expressions are not equivalent.

5. Answers may vary. An expression and an equation cannot be equivalent to each other.

6.
$$-3(2x-5)=-3\cdot 2x+(-3)(-5)$$
$$=-6x+15$$
The expressions are equivalent.

7.
$$3x+1=16$$
$$3x+1-1=16-1$$
$$3x=15$$
The equations are equivalent.

8.
$$2(x-3)+5=25$$
$$2x-6+5=25$$
$$2x=26$$
The equations are not equivalent.

9.
$$-3(x-4)=-18$$
$$-3x+12=-18$$
$$-3x=-30$$
$$x=10$$
The equations are not equivalent.

10.
$$3x+4x-2=7x-2$$
$$2x+x-2+5x=8x-2$$
$$7x-2\neq 8x-2$$
The expressions are not equivalent.